IG Macdonald

May 1966

AMERICAN MATHEMATICAL SOCIETY
COLLOQUIUM PUBLICATIONS
VOLUME XXIX

FOUNDATIONS OF ALGEBRAIC GEOMETRY

BY
ANDRÉ WEIL

Revised and Enlarged Edition

PUBLISHED BY THE
AMERICAN MATHEMATICAL SOCIETY
190 HOPE STREET, PROVIDENCE, RHODE ISLAND
1962

Printed in the United States of America

Library of Congress Catalog Number 62–7794

COMPOSED BY THE
WAVERLY PRESS, INC.,
BALTIMORE, MD.

FOREWORD

The mathematician's Δὸς ποῦ στῶ (which perhaps should read Πᾶ βῶ, if the Doric version transmitted by Simplicius is more authentic) has been countered long ago by the poet's "*Où sont les neiges d'antan*?"

Where indeed are the varieties of yesteryear? Fashions in contemporary mathematics change as fast as those for women's clothes, or so it may appear to the casual or superficial observer. Accordingly, when the publishers of this volume, with characteristic forethought and courtesy, gave me to understand that it would soon be out of print, I was confronted with a dilemma. Should I leave the book as it was, with only a few minor changes, as the publishers had at first suggested? Or should I not seek to dress up its contents anew in the style of the current season? I have rather attempted to prolong its period of usefulness, as best I could, without changing its main features, and without inflicting upon myself a heavier task than I felt willing to face. This has been done by reproducing photographically the first six chapters of the first edition and rewriting completely the last ones; an illogical compromise, no doubt, since for instance some of the contents of the new Chapter VII would have found a more suitable place in the old Chapter IV; but not, I hope, an intolerable one. It is not claimed now, any more than it was claimed at first, that the book brings the last word on the topics it deals with; nevertheless, the newly written chapters do include material which was not to be found except in scattered form, if at all, in the literature of the last fifteen years.

The manuscript of the first edition was completed in 1944. In the foreword, I recorded my indebtedness to several friends for their advice, help and encouragement given while the book was being written; I do not wish it to go to the press again without my renewing the expression of my gratitude to those whom I mentioned by name at the time (C. Chevalley, A. Dresden, O. Zariski), to some whom I had then refrained from naming (H. Moe, L. Rapkine, H. Weyl), and also to the Rockefeller Foundation and the J. S. Guggenheim Memorial Foundation.

Rather than tamper with the original introduction, I have left it untouched. The date on it will warn the reader that it has ceased to agree fully with the present state of the literature, and with the text of the book as it now appears.

Princeton, November 21, 1960.

TABLE OF CONTENTS

INTRODUCTION*

Δὸς ποῦ στῶ

Algebraic geometry, in spite of its beauty and importance, has long been held in disrepute by many mathematicians as lacking proper foundations. The mathematician who first explores a promising new field is privileged to take a good deal for granted that a critical investigator would feel bound to justify step by step; at times when vast territories are being opened up, nothing could be more harmful to the progress of mathematics than a literal observance of strict standards of rigor. Nor should one forget, when discussing such subjects as algebraic geometry, and in particular the work of the Italian school, that the so-called "intuition" of earlier mathematicians, reckless as their use of it may sometimes appear to us, often rested on a most painstaking study of numerous special examples, from which they gained an insight not always found among modern exponents of the axiomatic creed. At the same time, it should always be remembered that it is the duty, as it is the business, of the mathematician to prove theorems, and that this duty can never be disregarded for long without fatal effects. The experience of many centuries has shown this to be a matter on which, whatever our tastes or tendencies, whether "creative" or "critical", we mathematicians dare not disagree. As in other kinds of war, so in this bloodless battle with an ever retreating foe which it is our good luck to be waging, it is possible for the advancing army to outrun its services of supply and incur disaster unless it waits for the quartermaster to perform his inglorious but indispensable tasks. Thus for a time the indiscriminate use of divergent series threatened the whole of analysis; and who can say whether Abel and Cauchy acted more as "creative" or as "critical" mathematicians when they hurried to the rescue? One would be lacking in a sense of proportion, should one compare the present situation in algebraic geometry to that which these great men had to face; but there is no doubt that, in this field, the work of consolidation has so long been overdue that the delay is now seriously hampering progress in this and other branches of mathematics. To take only one instance, a personal one, this book has arisen from the necessity of giving a firm basis to Severi's theory of correspondences on algebraic curves, especially in the case of characteristic $p \neq 0$ (in which there is no transcendental method to guarantee the correctness of the results obtained by algebraic means), this being required for the solution of a long outstanding problem, the proof of the Riemann hypothesis in function-fields. The need to remedy such defects has been widely felt for some time; and, during the last twenty years, various authors, among whom it will be enough to mention F. Severi, B. L. van der Waerden, and more recently O. Zariski, have made important contributions towards this end. To them the present book owes of course a great deal; nor is its title intended to suggest that further efforts in the same direction are now superfluous. No treatment of the foundations of algebraic geometry may claim to be exhaustive unless it includes (among other

* Written in 1944 for the first edition.

topics) the definition and elementary properties of differential forms of the first and second kind, the so-called "principle of degeneration", and the method of formal power-series; but, concerning these subjects, nothing more than some cursory remarks in Chap. IX will be found in this book. Therefore some account of its exact scope, and of its relationship to earlier work, must now be given.

The main purpose of the book is to present a detailed and connected treatment of the properties of intersection-multiplicities, which is to include all that is necessary and sufficient to legitimize the use made of these multiplicities in classical algebraic geometry, especially of the Italian school. At the same time, this book seeks to deserve its title by being entirely self-contained, assuming no knowledge whatsoever of algebraic geometry, and no knowledge of modern algebra beyond the simplest facts about abstract fields and their extensions, and the bare rudiments of the theory of ideals. In a treatment of this kind, particular attention must be and has been given to the language and the definitions. Of course every mathematician has a right to his own language — at the risk of not being understood; and the use sometimes made of this right by our contemporaries almost suggests that the same fate is being prepared for mathematics as once befell, at Babel, another of man's great achievements. A choice between equivalent definitions is of small moment, and two theories which consist of the same theorems are to be regarded as identical, whatever their starting points. But in such a subject as algebraic geometry, where earlier authors left many terms incompletely defined, and were wont to make (sometimes implicitly) assumptions from which we wish to be free, all terms have to be defined anew, and to attach precise meanings to them is a task not unworthy of our most solicitous attention. Our chief object here must be to conserve and complete the edifice bequeathed to us by our predecessors. "From the Paradise created for us by Cantor, no one shall drive us forth" was the motto of Hilbert's work on the foundations of mathematics. Similarly, however grateful we algebraic geometers should be to the modern algebraic school for lending us temporary accommodation, makeshift constructions full of rings, ideals and valuations, in which some of us feel in constant danger of getting lost, our wish and aim must be to return at the earliest possible moment to the palaces which are ours by birthright, to consolidate shaky foundations, to provide roofs where they are missing, to finish, in harmony with the portions already existing, what has been left undone. How much the present book contributes to this, our readers, and future algebraic geometers, must judge; at any rate, as has been hinted above, and as will be shown in detail in a forthcoming series of papers, its language and its results have already been applied to the re-statement and extension of the theory of correspondences on algebraic curves, and of the geometry on Abelian varieties, and have successfully stood that test.

Our results include all that is required for a rigorous treatment of so-called "enumerative geometry", thus providing a complete solution of Hilbert's fifteenth problem. They could be said, indeed, to belong to enumerative geometry, had it not become traditional to restrict the use of this phrase to a body of special problems, pertaining to the geometry of the projective spaces and of certain rational varieties (spaces of straight lines, of conics, etc.), whereas we shall emphasize the geometry on an arbitrary variety, or at least on a variety without multiple points. The theory of intersection-multiplicities, however, occupies such a central position among the topics which constitute the foundations of algebraic geometry, that a complete treatment of it necessarily supplies the tools by which many other such topics can be dealt with. In deciding between alternative methods of proof for the theorems in this book, consistency, and the possibility of applying these methods to further problems, have been the main considerations; for instance, one will find here all that is needed for the proof of Bertini's theorems, for a detailed ideal-theoretic study (by geometric means) of the quotient-ring of a simple point, for the elementary part of the theory of linear series, and for a rigorous definition of the various concepts of equivalence. In consequence, the author has deliberately avoided a few short cuts; this is not to say that there may not be many more which he did not notice, and which our readers, it is hoped, may yet discover.

Our method of exposition will be dogmatic and unhistorical throughout, formal proofs, without references, being given at every step. A history of enumerative geometry could be a fascinating chapter in the general history of mathematics during the previous and present centuries, provided it brought to light the connections with related subjects, not merely with projective geometry, but with group-theory, the theory of Abelian functions, topology, etc.; this would require another book and a more competent writer. As for my debt to my immediate predecessors, it will be obvious to any moderately well informed reader that I have greatly profited from van der Waerden's well-known series of papers[1], where, among other results, the intersection-product has for the first time been defined (not locally, however, but only under conditions which ensure its existence "in the large"); from Severi's sketchy but suggestive treatment of the same subject, in his answer to van der Waerden's criticism of the work of the Italian school[2]; and from the topological theory of intersections, as developed by Lefschetz and other contemporary mathematicians. No direct use, however, will be made of their work; at the same time, I believe that whatever, in their results, pertains to the general intersection-theory on algebraic varieties is included in the theorems of the present volume, either as special cases or as immediate consequences. The attentive reader will also detect in many places the influence of O. Zariski's recent work[3]; what he cannot easily imagine is how much benefit I have derived, during the whole period of preparation of this book, from personal contacts both with Zariski and with Chevalley, from their freely given advice and suggestions, and from access to their unpublished manuscripts.

Some brief details of the contents of the various chapters may now be given, more elaborate comments being reserved for Chap. IX. The first three chap-

[1] Published in the Math. Ann. between 1927 and 1938.

[2] In the Hamb. Abh., vol. 9 (1933), p. 335.

[3] In a number of papers published since 1940 in the Amer. J. Math., the Trans. Amer. Math. Soc., and the Ann. of Math. Detailed references need not be given here, especially since these investigations are soon to be published in book-form.

ters are preliminary, and intended to prepare the ground for the geometric theories which follow, by stating and proving all the purely algebraic results on which the latter depend. Chap. I and II are elementary, that is, they make no use of any result in abstract algebra beyond the general theory of abstract fields, and Hilbert's theorem of the existence of a finite basis for ideals of polynomials. The notion of specialization, the properties of which are the main subject of Chap. II, and (in a form adapted to our language and purposes) the theorem on the extension of a specialization (th. 6 of Chap. II, §2) will of course be recognized as coming from van der Waerden. Chap. III is mainly devoted to the proof of the crucial theorem on the multiplicity of a proper specialization (th. 4 of Chap. III, §4), on which our whole theory of intersection-multiplicities will rest. This is the only part of the book where "higher" methods of proof (viz. formal power-series, and the representation of an ideal in a Noetherian ring as intersection of primary ideals) are used; the reader who is willing to take that theorem for granted, or successful in constructing a simpler proof of it, will not require, in all the rest of the book, any knowledge of these methods, or of anything beyond what has been mentioned above. As will be indicated in Chap. IX, it is possible to prove the same theorem, by means of Zariski's results on birational correspondences, without making any use of formal power-series; on the other hand, Chevalley, by giving[4], for some of the main results in the theory of intersections, alternative proofs which begin by establishing the corresponding theorems for algebroid varieties, has shown how the ring of formal power-series can be given the principal role, instead of the subordinate one which it plays in our treatment. Both authors make extensive use of the more technical parts of the abstract theory of ideals; this will be avoided in this book, by following a middle course (which is not, however, a compromise) between these two tendencies. It was not part of our purpose to investigate the connections between these several methods; this is a problem which still remains to be worked out.

The geometric language is then introduced in Chap. IV, which develops the elementary theory of algebraic varieties in affine spaces. The next two chapters contain the definition of intersection-multiplicities, which proceeds step by step, their main properties being stated and proved at every stage in such a way that the next step can then be taken and these properties correspondingly extended. Chap. V deals with the intersections of an arbitrary variety and of a linear variety in an affine space, first (in §1) when these varieties have complementary dimensions, then (in §2) in general; §3 contains some applications of these results to the theory of simple points. The general case is treated in Chap. VI, which includes all those results on intersection-multiplicities which are of a purely local nature.

A somewhat more explicit justification has to be given for the notions introduced in Chap. VII. It is well known that classical algebraic geometry does not usually deal with varieties in affine spaces, but with so-called projective models; the main feature which distinguishes the latter from the former is that they are,

[4] Trans. Amer. Math. Soc., vol. 57 (1945), pp. 1–85.

in a certain sense, "complete", or, in the topological case (when the ground-field is the field of complex numbers), compact. Nevertheless, local properties of varieties in projective spaces are almost always to be studied most conveniently on affine models of such varieties. There is now no reason why affine models, which can thus be pieced together so as to give a complete description of a given variety in a projective space, may not be pieced together differently; and there are problems (e.g. those concerning the Jacobian variety of a curve over a field of characteristic $p \neq 0$, of which it is not known whether it possesses a one-to-one non-singular projective model) which cannot at present be handled otherwise than by such a procedure. cf. p. 318 This idea, inspired by the usual definition of a topological manifold by means of overlapping neighborhoods, leads to the definition of an "abstract variety" in Chap. VII. The main definitions and results of the previous chapters, which are of a "local" nature, can be extended without difficulty to such varieties; and new results "in the large" can be proved about them, because they can be assumed to be complete, while varieties in affine spaces can never be so. In particular, it is then possible to prove the theorem on intersections which provides the keystone for the whole theory; this is th. 8 of Chap. VII, §5, a result closely related to the topological principle known as "Hopf's inverse homomorphism", and of the first importance, not only for the theory itself, but also for all its applications to specific geometric problems, since it enables one to introduce or withdraw at will as many auxiliary elements (points, varieties, etc.) as may be required at any time.

The last § of Chap. VII gives a translation of the main results of intersection-theory into a new language, particularly well adapted to applications, the "calculus of cycles". One main source of ambiguity, in the work of classical algebraic geometers and sometimes even in that of more modern writers, lies in their use of the word "variety", or of the word "curve" when they are dealing merely with the geometry on surfaces. As long as a "curve" or a "variety" is irreducible, there can be no uncertainty about it; but when, in the course of its "continuous variation" (however this may be defined), it splits up into several components, it is not always easy to know whether the resulting geometric entity is meant as a point-set, the union of irreducible varieties which need not even have the same dimension, or as a sum of varieties of the same dimension (a "virtual variety" in the sense of Severi), each multiplied with a well-determined integer which is its multiplicity. In the hope of doing away once for all with the resulting confusion (for those who will adopt our language, or at any rate an equivalent one which may be translated into ours term for term), two separate terms will be used here for these two kinds of entities, instead of the one term "reducible variety" which has previously been applied to both: "bunches of varieties" for the former, and (as in modern topology) "cycles" for the latter, while the word "variety" will be reserved for "absolutely irreducible algebraic varieties", i.e. for those which are irreducible over an algebraically closed ground-field and therefore remain so after an arbitrary extension of that field. An algebraic calculus of cycles can then be developed, closely analogous to the algebra of homology-classes constructed by modern topologists: the main difference between the two is that, while the latter deals with classes, the former operates with the cycles themselves, but is unable, because of this, to have an intersection-product defined without any restrictive assumption. This, as will be seen, entails, in the practical handling of the calculus, a certain amount of inconvenience, which probably could be avoided, as the analogy suggests, by substituting, for the cycles, classes of cycles modulo a suitable concept of equivalence. If a coherent theory of linear equivalence could be built up, it would seem to be the best fitted for this purpose; at the present moment, "continuous" or even "numerical" equivalence would probably offer better prospects of immediate success. This book makes no attempt to proceed in that direction; but all the means for doing so are, it is hoped, provided in Chap. VII and Chap. IX.

Chap. VIII gives, on the basis of the results of the preceding chapters, a detailed treatment of the theory of divisors on a variety, both for its own sake and in order to provide the reader with some examples of the use of our calculus. The divisors which we consider here, and which are defined by means of the intersection-theory, are substantially the same as the "divisors of the first kind" of modern algebraists; they are so at any rate on every normal variety, which, by Zariski's results (partly reproduced and extended in our Appendix II), is enough to make our theory applicable to all cases. The contents of this chapter include all that is needed for the theory of the linear equivalence of divisors (and, in particular, of "virtual curves", i.e., in our language, of cycles of dimension 1, on surfaces), and consequently for the foundation of the theory of linear series on a variety.

A point is thus reached in the systematic development of algebraic geometry, of which this volume may be regarded as the preliminary part, from which one may, with better perspective, look back on the course which has been hitherto followed, and make plans for the continuation of the voyage. This will be done in Chap. IX; it contains such general comments as could not appropriately be made before, formulates problems, some of them of considerable importance, and, in some cases, makes tentative suggestions about what seems to be at present the best approach to their solution; it is hoped that these may be helpful to the reader, to whom the author, having acted as his pilot until this point, heartily wishes Godspeed on his sailing away from the axiomatic shore, further and further into open sea.

ADVICE TO THE READER

It is necessary for the reader to be acquainted with the following topics:

(a) He must have a good elementary knowledge of the theory of abstract fields and their extensions, both algebraic and transcendental, as contained for instance in N. Bourbaki, *Algèbre*, Chapitre V.

(b) He must know the definition of an ideal, at least in a ring of polynomials with coefficients in a field, Hilbert's theorem of the existence of a "finite basis" (or, as one would rather say now, of a finite set of generators) for such an ideal, and Hilbert's *Nullstellensatz*; he should also be familiar with the elementary properties of polynomials in one indeterminate with coefficients in a field, especially their unique decomposition into irreducible factors; the corresponding property for polynomials in several indeterminates is also used at a few places.

(c) If he wishes to study the proofs of Chapter III, he should be acquainted with the representation of ideals in Noetherian rings as intersections of primary ideals, and with the usual characterization of integral elements over such rings.

Some indications will now be given about the logical interdependence of the various parts of this book.

Chapter I, §§1–4 and 6–7, and Chapter II, §§1–2 and 4–5 (with the exception of the second part of §4, consisting of prop. 18, 19 and 20) are fundamental for the rest of the book, and the definitions and main results in them should be thoroughly understood before one proceeds further. The concept of derivation, introduced in §5 of Chapter I, plays no role at all in the book, except as an auxiliary tool in the proof of some algebraic lemmas (specifically, lemmas 3 and 4 of Chapter VIII, §2, and lemma 1 of Chapter IX, §6); except for the latter, all the reader need keep in mind from §5 of Chapter I is the statement of the corollary of th. 1, and that of th. 2, which are basic for the theory of simple points. The contents of §8 of Chapter I are not used until Chapter V, but are of great importance there and in all the ensuing chapters, except that the reader who is interested only in the case of characteristic 0 may disregard them entirely. Chapter II, §3, contains some special results, used at various places throughout the book. Of the results of the latter part of Chapter II, §4, prop. 18 is nowhere used; prop. 20, after being transcribed in geometric terms as prop. 8 of Chapter IV, §2, is used only in one of the two proofs given for th. 7, Chapter IX, §4; in view of the alternative proof given for the latter theorem, it could be dispensed with altogether (as would have been done if Chapter II had been rewritten for this second edition instead of being photographically reproduced from the first one); prop. 19, apart from its use in the proof of the next proposition, appears only in the proof of lemma 2, Chapter VIII, §1, and of prop. 1, App. I. As to the contents of §6 of Chapter II, they are used in Chapter III, §§2–3, and nowhere else.

Chapter III, §§1–3, merely leads up to the proof of prop. 7, §3, which, slightly generalized, becomes th. 4 of §4 of the same Chapter. The proof for these results given in Chapter III is entirely self-contained (except that, as mentioned above, it depends upon the knowledge of the basic facts about ideals in Noetherian rings). An alternative proof for the qualitative part of these results, based on Zariski's "main theorem", is given in full in Chapter X, §5, where the reader will also find the sketch of a simplified proof for the quantitative part, once the qualitative part has been obtained. A reader, willing to take for granted th. 4 of Chapter III, §4, may disregard entirely the contents of §§1–3 of that Chapter, as there will be no reference to them anywhere else.

Chapter IV and §§1–2 of Chapter VII are devoted to the qualitative theory of affine varieties; §§3–6 of Chapter VII deal with the qualitative theory of abstract varieties; the greater part of Chapters V and VI, of §7 of Chapter VII, and of Chapters VIII and IX, is devoted to the quantitative theory, even though it is interspersed with a number of items of more qualitative nature. The quantitative results are entirely based on Chapter III, §4. On the other hand, by giving an ideal-theoretic proof for the first part of th. 7, Chapter IV, §4, one would make the contents of Chapter IV and of §§1–6 of Chapter VII independent of Chapters III, V and VI, except for the second part of th. 7, Chapter IV, §4, prop. 26 of Chapter IV, §7, and prop. 11 and 14 of Chapter VII, §5, which depend upon prop. 13 of Chapter III, §4.

Chapters V, VI, §7 of Chapter VII, and Chapter VIII, are chiefly devoted to the development, step by step, of the theory of intersections; the results of Chapter V, §1, concerning intersections of affine varieties with linear varieties of complementary dimension in the ambient affine space are extended in Chapter V, §§2–3, to intersections of affine varieties with linear varieties of arbitrary dimension, then in Chapter VI and Chapter VII, §7, to the local results for arbitrary intersections, then in Chapter VIII to the corresponding global results. The following table shows how those results correspond to one another:

Chap. V, §1	Chap. V, §§2–3	Chap. VI	Chap. VII, §7	Chap. VIII
Prop. 5	Prop. 12	Th. 3		Th. 4(iii)
Prop. 9	Prop. 13	Th. 4		
	Prop. 15	Th. 5		Th. 4(iv)
Prop. 7	Prop. 16, 21	Th. 6		
Prop. 10	Prop. 17	Th. 7		Th. 5
Prop. 11			Th. 10	Th. 8
	Prop. 18	Th. 8		Th. 8, coroll. 1
Prop. 2, 8 Th. 3	Prop. 14	Th. 11		Th. 6
Th. 2		Th. 12		Th. 7

The reader who does not wish, at least in a first reading, to go systematically through the book in a straightforward manner, may therefore be advised to proceed as follows. Read Chapter I, §§1–7, and Chapter II, §§1–2, §4 (first part) and §5. Read Chapter IV and Chapter VII, §§1–2, following up references to earlier chapters only when necessary; here it should be noted that, if Chapter IV had been rewritten for this second edition, instead of being photographically reproduced from the first one, this would have been done in the language and with the concepts explained in Chapter VII, §§1–2, so that the latter should be understood, not merely to supplement and clarify the former, but also to supersede it to some extent. At this point, if the reader's immediate interests lie more in the direction of the qualitative theory, he can read Chapter VII, §§3–6; he can then get some idea of the main purposes of intersection-theory by reading the definition of a cycle, and of a rational cycle over a field, in Chapter VIII, §1, and then reading the definitions and main theorems of Chapter VIII, §3. Instead of doing this, he may also read the main definitions and results of Chapter VI, in the light of the remarks made in Chapter X, §6. In any case, in order to study the theory of intersections, he will then have to go back to Chapter I, §8, then read at least Chapter III, §4 (and the whole of Chapter III if he does not want to take for granted the final result of Chapter III, §§1–3, viz. prop. 7 of §3), then Chapter V, Chapter VI, and (after reading the rest of Chapter VII) §7 of Chapter VII. In reading Chapter VIII, he may skip the greater part of the contents of §§1–2 (except of course for the definition of chains and cycles and of rational chains and cycles over a field). As to Chapter IX and the Appendices, the reader will be able, to some extent, to pick and choose what may be most to his taste, since the various topics which are treated there are in part independent of one another. The greater part of the comments in Chapter X assume, not only some degree of familiarity with the whole book, but some acquaintance with modern algebraic geometry; nevertheless, it will probably be found helpful, while reading the book, to turn to that chapter from time to time.

Readers acquainted with the first edition of this book should be warned about a few changes in terminology and notations:

(a) Most important among these is that the intersection-product $X \cdot Y$ of two cycles

X, Y on a variety U is now *always* defined, while in the first edition it was defined only for *properly intersecting cycles*; this makes it possible to give slightly more general statements for some of the results of the global theory, and turns out to be technically more convenient. Naturally, every calculation based on the definition of the first edition remains valid according to the new one.

(b) The algebraic projection $\mathrm{pr}_U X$, on a variety U^n, of a cycle X^r on a product $U \times V$, was defined in the first edition only for $0 \leqq r \leqq n$; now it is also defined, and it is 0, if r does not satisfy the latter condition; this is a purely formal change, made only in order to simplify the language in the statements of some results.

(c) In the definition of an abstract variety, what was called "coherent" in the first edition is now called "consistent", while the word "coherent" has been given a new meaning.

(d) The notation $T(V')$, $T^{-1}(W')$, introduced in Chapter IV, §7, to denote geometric images under a birational correspondence, has been kept there, but is not used anywhere else in this edition; as pointed out at the beginning of Chapter VIII, §4, it does not agree with the notations used in this edition in the calculus of cycles, and should be considered as superseded by the latter.

(e) It should also be noted that, in the first edition, the word "projection" was used exclusively in the sense in which it is still used in Chapter IV, to denote the "geometric projection", i.e. the closure of the set-theoretic projection.

In order to enable students of the modern literature in algebraic geometry to locate in this volume the references to the theorems of the first edition, a table of concordance will now be given, which will indicate, for each result in the first edition, the result in the present one which is equivalent to it or which contains it as a special case. As Chapters I–VI of the first edition have been reproduced photographically, nothing is needed for those chapters; we also omit from this table the results in Chapter VII, §§1–3, of the first edition, since these were merely the successive steps in the definitions given there for abstract varieties, and are now subsumed under Chapter VII, §§3 and 5; and we omit a few results, which were given in the first edition merely for purposes of reference.

	First edition	*This edition*
Chap. VII, §4,	prop. 8	Chap. VII, §5, prop. 11
	prop. 9	Chap. VII, §5, corollary of prop. 12
	prop. 10	Chap. VII, §5, th. 7
	prop. 11	Chap. VII, §5, prop. 13
Chap. VII, §5,	th. 8	Chap. VII, §7, th. 10
	prop. 13	Chap. VII, §7, prop. 19
Chap. VII, §6,	th. 10	Chap. VIII, §3, th. 4
	th. 11	Chap. VIII, §3, th. 5
	th. 12	Chap. VIII, §3, th. 6
	th. 13	Chap. VIII, §3, th. 7
	th. 14	Chap. VIII, §3, th. 3
	th. 15	Chap. VIII, §3, corollary of th. 7
	th. 16	Chap. VIII, §3, th. 8
	th. 17 and corollaries	Chap. VIII, §3, th. 3(ii) and corollaries 1–3 of th. 8
	th. 18 and corollary	Chap. VIII, §4, th. 10
	prop. 14	Chap. VIII, §1, prop. 1
	prop. 16	Chap. VIII, §3, prop. 5
	prop. 18	Chap. VIII, §3, prop. 4
Chap. VIII, §1,	prop. 1	Chap. IX, §4, th. 5 and corollary
	prop. 2	Chap. VIII, §3, th. 8, coroll. 3
	prop. 4	Chap. IX, §1, prop. 2
	prop. 5	Chap. VII, §7, th. 9, coroll. 1

	First Edition	*This Edition*
Chap. VIII, §2,	th. 1 and coroll. 1	Chap. IX, §1, prop. 1, coroll. 3, and prop. 2
	th. 1, coroll. 2	Chap. IX, §1, prop. 1, coroll. 4, and prop. 2
	th. 1, coroll. 3	Chap. VIII, §4, prop. 15
	th. 1, coroll. 4	Chap. VIII, §4, corollary of prop. 14
	th. 2	Chap. IX, §1, prop. 1, coroll. 1
	th. 3 and corollaries	Chap. IX, §2, th. 1 and corollaries
	th. 4 and corollaries	Chap. IX, §2, th. 3
	th. 5	Chap. IX, §2, th. 4
	th. 6 and corollaries	Chap. IX, §2, th. 2 and corollaries
	th. 7	Chap. IX, §2, th. 4
Chap. VIII, §3,	th. 8 and corollaries	Chap. IX, §4, th. 5 and corollary
	th. 9	Chap. IX, §4, th. 6
	th. 10 and corollaries	Chap. IX, §4, th. 8 and corollaries
Appendix II,	prop. 1	Appendix I, prop. 1, coroll. 3
	prop. 2	Appendix I, prop. 2
	prop. 3	Chap. IX, §1, prop. 1
	prop. 4	Appendix I, prop. 1
	prop. 5	Appendix I, prop. 1, coroll. 1, and prop. 3, coroll. 2
	prop. 6	Appendix I, prop. 4
Appendix III		Appendix II

We have stated as lemmas those results which do not properly belong to the main trend of ideas in the book. We have stated as corollaries of a theorem or of a proposition those results which seem to group themselves naturally around it, either as more or less immediate consequences or because of the close connection between their respective contents. As a rule, theorems are to be regarded as more important, although not necessarily deeper, than propositions; ordinarily the latter are auxiliary results, while theorems deserve attention for their own sake. The distinction between theorems and propositions, such as it is, is intended to be helpful to the reader, but should not be scrutinized too closely. As to the proofs, we have attempted to bring them all to such a degree of completeness that a moderately attentive reader should find no difficulty in supplying for himself whatever has not been made explicit. To go beyond this point would have been as tedious as it would have been space-consuming. It is well-nigh impossible, however, to achieve complete uniformity in this respect; and we request the reader to accept our apologies for any lack of it, and for any annoyance which we may have given him by saying either too much or too little.

Cross-references have been inserted liberally, perhaps over-generously; trained readers may often find it more convenient to disregard them than to follow them up. Theorems are numbered consecutively from beginning to end of each Chapter; so are propositions, and lemmas. In quoting a result, we indicate, for the convenience of the reader, not only the Chapter, but also the §; examples: th. 6 of Chapter IV, §3; corollary 1 of th. 13, Chapter IV, §6; proposition 5 of Chapter IV, §2. However, in referring to a result within the same Chapter, we do not mention the Chapter; and we do not mention the § in referring to a result within the same §.

Finally, the reader should note that the displaying of formulas has been used merely as a typographical device, whenever a formula did not fit easily into a line of print, and that no special emphasis is intended on displayed formulas.

A table of notations is given on the next page, and a complete index of all definitions will be found at the end of the volume.

TABLE OF NOTATIONS

N.B. We indicate here most of the notations which are used throughout the book or in any important portion of it, and in particular all those which have a definite and invariable meaning. They are listed in the order of their first appearance in the book.

Chapter I.
Characteristic (§1): p (for p^m, $k^{p^{-m}}$, see §4).
Field (§1): k, K, sometimes L.
Algebraic closure of a field k (§1): $\bar{k}$.
Quantity (§1): lower case latin or Greek.
Set of quantities (§1): e.g. $(x) = (x_i) = (x_1, \cdots, x_n)$; $(u) = (u_{ij})$; (ξ); etc.; (x, y) for the set $(x_1, \cdots, x_n, y_1, \cdots, y_m)$ obtained by the juxtaposition of two sets (x), (y); similarly $(x^{(1)}, \cdots, x^{(n)})$ for the set obtained by the juxtaposition of n sets $(x^{(\nu)})$ for $1 \leqq \nu \leqq n$. The same notations are used for sets of generalized quantities (cf. Chap. II, §1). In Chap. IV, sets of n quantities are identified with points in n-space; from then on, one frequently writes x instead of (x) for such a set $(x_1, \cdots, x_n)$.
Extension of a field k, generated by a set of quantities (x) (§1): $k(x)$.
Ring of polynomials over a field k (§1): $k[X] = k[X_1, \cdots, X_n]$, etc.; the indeterminates in polynomials are always denoted by italic capitals, e.g. X, Y, U, T, etc.; the notation for sets of indeterminates is similar to that for sets of quantities.
Polynomials (§1): italic or Greek capitals (e.g. F, G, H, P, Q, sometimes A, B, L, M, Φ, Ψ, etc.), frequently (but not always) followed by the indication of the indeterminates in the polynomial, or of the quantities substituted for these indeterminates, e.g. F, $F(X)$, $F(x)$, G, $G(X, Y)$, $G(x, y)$, etc. Occasionally the same notation is used for rational expressions in some indeterminates, e.g. R, $R(X)$, $R(x)$. The (formally taken) partial derivatives of a polynomial, or of a rational expression, with respect to the indeterminates in it, are indicated in the usual manner, e.g., for the polynomial $F(X)$, by $\partial F/\partial X_i$, or, after the substitution of a set of quantities (x) for the set of indeterminates (X), by $\partial F/\partial x_i$.
Dimension of a set of quantities over a field (§2): $\dim_k(x)$.
Degree of an algebraic extension (§2): $[k':k]$ (for $[k':k]_i$, $[k':k]_s$, see §4; for $[k':k]_\iota$, see §8).
Ideal in a ring of polynomials (§3): German letters, usually capitals (e.g. $\mathfrak{P}$ for a prime ideal, $\mathfrak{Q}$, $\mathfrak{A}$, $\mathfrak{B}$), occasionally lower case, e.g. $\mathfrak{a}$.
Ideal determined by a set of quantities over a field (§3): $\mathfrak{P}_{(x)/k}$.
Isomorphism of a field onto a field (§3): lower case Greek letters, e.g. σ, τ.
Transform of a polynomial by an isomorphism (§3): $F^\sigma(X)$.
Transform of an ideal by an isomorphism (§3): $\mathfrak{P}^\sigma$, $\mathfrak{A}^\sigma$.
p^m, $k^{p^{-m}}$ (§4).
Inseparable and separable factors of the degree of an algebraic extension (§4): $[k':k]_i$, $[k':k]_s$ (for $[k':k]_\iota$, see §8).
Derivation (§5): D.
Formal derivative of a polynomial or of a rational expression (§5): $\partial F/\partial X_i$, $\partial F/\partial x_i$ (cf. above under polynomials). For $\Delta_x P(X)$, see Chap. IV, §6.
Order of inseparability of an extension (§8): $[k(x):k]_\iota$.

Chapter II.
Specialization (§1): $(x) \to (x')$.
Generalized quantity ∞ (§1). For sets of generalized quantities, the notation is the same as for sets of quantities (see above).
Abstract fields (§6): $\mathfrak{K}$, $\mathfrak{L}$; sets of elements of abstract fields: $(\mathfrak{x})$, $(\mathfrak{x}_\iota)$, $(\mathfrak{y})$.

Chapter III.
(N.B. The notations of Chap. III, §§1–3, are not used anywhere else.)
Rings: $\mathfrak{o}$, $\mathfrak{r}$, $\mathfrak{O}$. Ideals in rings: lower case or capital German letters.
Ring of polynomials with coefficients in $\mathfrak{o}$: $\mathfrak{o}[X]$. Ring of power-series in (X) with coefficients in $\mathfrak{o}$: $\mathfrak{o}\{X\}$.
Ring of power-series in (x) with coefficients in k: $\mathfrak{o} = k\{x\}$. Quotient-field (i.e., field of fractions) of $k\{x\}$: Ω. Element of $k\{x\}$: $\varphi(x)$; element of $k\{x\}[Y]$: $\varphi(x, Y)$.

Chapter IV.
Point in n-space (§1): capital or lower case latin letter, e.g. P, Q, M, N, x, y, u, v (same notation occasionally for pseudopoints).
Set of points, or of points and pseudopoints (§1): e.g. $(P_1, \cdots, P_h)$, $(P^{(1)}, \cdots, P^{(h)})$.
Field generated by a point or a set of points over a field (§1): $k(P)$, $k(P, Q)$, $k(P_1, \cdots, P_h)$, etc.
Variety (§1): capital latin (or sometimes Greek) letter, e.g. $U, V, W, X, Y, A, B, \Lambda$.
Point-set attached to a variety (§1): $\{V\}$ (N.B. From Chap. VII on, this is identified with V and denoted simply by V.)
Inclusion relations for varieties (§1): $V \supset W$, $W \subset V$.
n-space (§1): S^n.
Smallest field of definition for a variety (§1): def(V).
Dimension of a variety (§1): dim(V).
Variety of dimension r (§1): V^r.
Transform of a variety by an isomorphism, and in particular conjugate of a variety over a field (§2): V^σ.
Product-variety (§3): $V \times W$, $V_1 \times V_2 \times \cdots \times V_h$, $\prod_\alpha V_\alpha$; in particular, $P \times Q$ for (P, Q), etc.
Bunch of varieties (§4): capital script letter, usually $\mathcal{B}$; point-set attached to a bunch (§4): $\{\mathcal{B}\}$ (N.B. From Chap. VII on, bunches of varieties are identified with the point-sets attached to them in the sense of Chap. IV, i.e. with the closed sets of the Zariski topology, and are usually denoted by latin capitals, e.g. F, X, Y, etc.).
Union and intersection (of varieties, or of bunches of varieties) (§4): $\cup$, $\cap$.
Transform of a bunch by an isomorphism (§4): $\mathcal{B}^\sigma$.
Linear variety (§5): latin capital, usually L, M, N, sometimes R, T, etc. (also Λ in Chap. VI).
Minimal set of linear equations for a linear variety (§5): German capital, with the number of equations as a superscript, e.g. $\mathfrak{S}^r$.
$\Delta_x P(X)$ (§6).
Symbol $[V:V']$ (§7) (V = variety in a product; V' = a projection of V).
Corresponding points or varieties, by a birational correspondence (§7): $T(P)$, $T^{-1}(P)$, $T(V)$, $T^{-1}(V)$ (N.B. From Chap. VII on, this is discarded and replaced by the functional notation).

Chapter V.
Symbol $j(V \cdot L, P)$ (§1); symbol $j(V \cdot L, W)$ (§2).

Chapter VI.
Diagonal on $U \times U$ (§1): Δ_U; the diagonal of $S^N \times S^N$ is denoted by Δ_0. Similarly, in the abstract case, the diagonal of $\boldsymbol{U} \times \boldsymbol{U}$ will be denoted by $\boldsymbol{\Delta_U}$, from Chap. VII on.
Linear variety Λ (§1) (notation used throughout this chapter).
Symbol $i(A \cdot B, C; U)$ (§1).
Varieties ∇_C, Ω_C (§3) (notation used in prop. 6 and in the proof of th. 8 of that §, and again in the proof of th. 10 of Chap. VII, §7).

Chapter VII.
Closed sets (§1): latin capitals, e.g. F, X, Y.
Transform of a closed set by an isomorphism (§1): X^σ.
Open sets (§1): capital latin, Greek or script letter; frequently $\mathfrak{D}$ (particularly for the set of points where a mapping is defined, or where it is biregular).
Functional notation for mappings (§2): imitates the usual functional notation, e.g. $f(P)$, $f(P, Q)$, $f(P_1, \cdots, P_n)$, $g \circ f$, $g(f(P))$, etc.
Geometric image of a variety by a mapping (§2): *in this chapter*, this is denoted by $f(X)$, a notation to be discarded later on since it is then needed for the algebraic image (cf. Chap. VIII, §4).
Graph of a mapping (§2): Γ_f ($\mathbf{\Gamma}_f$ for the graph of a mapping of an abstract variety).
Inverse of a birational mapping (§2): f^{-1}.
Abstract variety (§3): $\mathbf{V} = [V_\alpha, f_{\beta\alpha}]_{\alpha,\beta \in A}$. Abstract varieties are denoted by boldface capitals, e.g. $\mathbf{U}$, $\mathbf{V}$, $\mathbf{W}$, $\mathbf{A}$, $\mathbf{B}$, $\mathbf{C}$, $\mathbf{X}$, $\mathbf{Y}$, $\mathbf{Z}$; the same notation is used for points on abstract varieties (e.g. $\mathbf{M}$, $\mathbf{N}$, $\mathbf{P}$, $\mathbf{Q}$) and for closed sets, chains and cycles on abstract varieties (e.g. $\mathbf{X}$, $\mathbf{Y}$, $\mathbf{R}$, $\mathbf{S}$).
Dimension of an abstract variety (§3): $\dim(\mathbf{V})$.
Pseudopoint (§3): $\infty_{\mathbf{V}}$.
Specialization of points on abstract varieties (§3): $\mathbf{P} \to \mathbf{P}'$.
Projective line (§3): $\mathbf{D}$; the point of $\mathbf{D}$ with the coordinate x is denoted by (x).
Transform of an abstract variety, of a closed set, etc., by an automorphism (§4): $\mathbf{X}^\sigma$.
Product of abstract varieties (§5): $\mathbf{V} \times \mathbf{W}$, $\mathbf{V}_1 \times \cdots \times \mathbf{V}_n$, $\prod_\alpha \mathbf{V}_\alpha$; similarly for points of such products: $\mathbf{P} \times \mathbf{Q}$, $\mathbf{P}_1 \times \cdots \times \mathbf{P}_n$, etc.; the diagonal of $\mathbf{U} \times \mathbf{U}$ is denoted by $\mathbf{\Delta}_{\mathbf{U}}$.
Symbol $[\mathbf{Z}:\mathbf{Z}']$ (§5) ($\mathbf{Z}$ = subvariety of a product of abstract varieties; $\mathbf{Z}'$ = a projection of $\mathbf{Z}$).
Mappings of abstract varieties (§6): same notation as explained above, e.g. $f(\mathbf{P})$, $f(\mathbf{P}, \mathbf{Q})$; $\mathbf{\Gamma}_f$ for the graph of f; $f(\mathbf{X})$ for the geometric image of $\mathbf{X}$ (a notation to be discarded later, cf. Chap. VIII, §4).
Symbol $i(\mathbf{A}\cdot\mathbf{B}, \mathbf{C}; \mathbf{U})$ for abstract varieties (§7).

Chapter VIII.
Coefficient of a variety in a chain or cycle (§1): $\gamma_{\mathbf{A}}(\mathbf{X})$.
Support of a cycle (§1): $|\mathbf{X}|$.
Positive chain or cycle (§1): $\mathbf{X} \succ 0$; also, $\mathbf{X} \succ \mathbf{Y}$ and $\mathbf{Y} \prec \mathbf{X}$ for $\mathbf{X} - \mathbf{Y} \succ 0$.
Transform of a chain or cycle by an automorphism (§1): $\mathbf{X}^\sigma$.
Degree of a chain or cycle of dimension 0 (§2): $\deg(\mathbf{X})$.
Value of a symmetric mapping (§2): $f(\mathbf{X})$, $f(\mathbf{X}_1, \cdots, \mathbf{X}_n)$, where $\mathbf{X}$ and the $\mathbf{X}_i$ are positive 0-cycles.
Operation $\mathbf{X} \times \mathbf{Y}$ on chains or cycles (§3).
Algebraic projection (§3): $\mathrm{pr}_{\mathbf{U}}\mathbf{X}$, $\mathrm{pr}_{\mathbf{U}\times\mathbf{V}}\mathbf{X}$, $\mathrm{pr}_1\mathbf{X}$, etc.
Intersection-product (§3): $\mathbf{X}\cdot\mathbf{Y}$, $\mathbf{X}_1\cdot\mathbf{X}_2\cdot \cdots \cdot\mathbf{X}_n$.
Symbol $\mathbf{X}(\mathbf{P})$ (§3) ($\mathbf{X}$ a cycle on a product, $\mathbf{P}$ a point on the first factor).
Symbol $\mathbf{Z}(\mathbf{X})$ (§4) ($\mathbf{Z}$ a cycle on a product, $\mathbf{X}$ a cycle on the first factor).
Transform of a cycle $\mathbf{Z}$ on a product when the two factors are interchanged (§4): $\mathbf{Z}'$.
Algebraic image, algebraic counterimage (§4): $f(\mathbf{X})$, $f^{-1}(\mathbf{X})$ (the notation $f(\mathbf{X})$ for the algebraic image supersedes the similar earlier notation for the geometric image).

Chapter IX.
Divisor $\mathbf{\Theta} = (0) - (\infty)$ on $\mathbf{D}$ (§2).
Divisor of a function (§2): $\mathrm{div}(f)$.
Symbol $v_{\mathbf{A}}(f)$ (§2).

Vector-space of functions (§2): $\mathfrak{L}$, sometimes $\mathfrak{M}$ (cf. §5).
Vector-space determined by a divisor X (§2): $\mathfrak{L}(X)$ (and $\mathfrak{L}_k(X)$ for the subset consisting of functions rational over k).
Polynomial functions (§4): same notation as for polynomials.
Linear system (§5): usually Λ; Λ_f for the linear system determined by a mapping f into a projective space.
Projective space (§5): P^n.
Canonical morphism of S_*^{n+1} onto P^n (§5): p.
Hyperplanes (§5): usually H.
Degree of a variety or cycle in P^n (§5): deg(V), deg(X).
Frobenius automorphism (§6): π.
Frobenius morphism of V onto V^π (§6): φ, φ_V.

CHAPTER I

ALGEBRAIC PRELIMINARIES

1. Notations. In this book, we shall be dealing with fields, and with the elements of those fields; for convenience, it will be assumed that the fields which will be considered in the greater part of the book are all contained in one and the same field K, which we call "the universal domain", so that their elements can all be combined with each other by the operations of algebra; if then K is of characteristic p, all the fields contained in it contain one and the same field, the "prime field" of characteristic p, isomorphic to the field of rational numbers if p is 0, and to the field of rational integers modulo p if p is not 0. Our basic conventions will therefore be the following.

We adopt once for all, as "universal domain", a field K, of characteristic p, which we assume to be algebraically closed, and of infinite degree of transcendency over the prime field contained in it; the elements of the "universal domain" will be called *quantities*. By *a field* we shall always understand, except when the contrary is specifically stated, a field which is (a) contained in the "universal domain" K, and (b) such that K is of infinite degree of transcendency over it. Because of the latter restriction, K itself may therefore not be referred to as "a field"; we speak of "an abstract field" whenever we have to consider a field which is not subject to the restrictions (a) and (b); such "abstract fields" will occur only in Chap. II, §6, and Chap. III, §§1–3, where they will play merely an auxiliary part, and in Chap. VIII, where they occur as "function-fields".

According to the above conventions, if k is any field (satisfying, therefore, the conditions (a) and (b)), its elements are quantities, and there are infinitely many quantities, not contained in k, which are algebraically independent over k, i.e. which satisfy no algebraic relation with coefficients in k. Furthermore, if k is a field, the set of all quantities which are algebraic over k is an algebraically closed field, which we denote by $\bar{k}$ and call *the* algebraic closure of k. If k is a subfield of a field K, then the set of all the elements of K which are algebraic over k is a field, which will be called *the algebraic closure of* k *in* K; if this is the same as k, then we say that k is *algebraically closed in* K.

When a field k is being used as field of reference, this is indicated by such words as "over k", "with reference to k", "with respect to k", "relatively to k", etc.; occasionally the mention of the field of reference may be omitted when no confusion can occur.

We write (x), or sometimes (x_i), for an indexed set of quantities $(x_1, \cdots, x_n)$ *in finite number*, which need not be distinct, two such sets (x) and (x') being considered as equal if and only if we have $x_i = x'_i$ for every i; whenever we speak of a *set of quantities*, we understand such an indexed set of quantities in finite number, unless the contrary is specifically stated. If $(x) = (x_1, \cdots, x_n)$ and $(y) = (y_1, \cdots, y_m)$ are two such sets, we write (x, y) for the set of $n + m$ quantities $(x_1, \cdots, x_n, y_1, \cdots, y_m)$. If k is any field (subject, of course, to the restrictions which have been stated above), we denote by $k(x)$ the smallest field containing k and all the x_i, and call it *the field generated by* (x) *over* k. Thus $k(x)$ always denotes a finitely generated extension of k, i.e. one which is generated by the adjunction of a finite number of elements; in this book, whenever we shall speak of an *extension* of a field, we shall understand by it a finitely generated extension of that field, even though this may not be explicitly stated.

If k is a field, we denote by $k[X_1, \cdots, X_n]$, or more briefly by $k[X]$, the ring of all polynomials in the indeterminates $X_1, \cdots, X_n$, with coefficients in k; such indeterminates X_i are not to be regarded as quantities, but merely serve the purpose of writing formal polynomials which we accordingly denote by such notations as $F(X)$, $G(X)$, etc. Similarly, the notation $k[X, Y]$ will mean the ring of polynomials in two sets of indeterminates $X_1, \cdots, X_n$ and $Y_1, \cdots, Y_m$, with coefficients in k; and $F(X, Y)$ will denote such a polynomial. If $F(X)$ is in $k[X]$, and if (x) is a set of quantities, we write $F(x)$, as usual, for the result of the substitution of (x) for (X) in $F(X)$; $F(x)$ is then an element of $k(x)$. We shall occasionally have to consider rational expressions in some indeterminates X_i, with coefficients in a field k; for such expressions, we shall use such notations as $R(X)$, etc.

2. Dimension; independence; linear disjointness. By the *dimension* of an extension $k(x)$ of a field k, we understand its degree of transcendency over k, i.e. the greatest number of algebraically independent quantities over k among its elements, or also among the x_i; this is always finite (since we have agreed in §1 that an extension must always be finitely generated). By the *dimension* of a set of quantities (x) over a field k, we understand the dimension of $k(x)$ over k; this will be denoted by $\dim_k (x)$. We have $\dim_k (x) = 0$ if and only if all the x_i are algebraic over k, i.e. if they are elements of $\bar{k}$; in that case, we say that the set (x) is *algebraic over* k. A quantity which is not algebraic over k is said to be *variable* over k.

If (x) is algebraic over k, $k(x)$ is an algebraic extension of k; its *degree* is the greatest number of linearly independent elements in $k(x)$ over k; because our extensions are always finitely generated, the degree of an algebraic extension is always finite. The degree over k of an algebraic extension k' of k will be denoted by $[k':k]$.

If K is an extension of k, and L an extension of K, the dimension of L over k is the sum of the dimension of L over K and of that of K over k; if $K = k(x)$ and $L = K(y) = k(x, y)$, this can be written as $\dim_k (x, y) = \dim_K (y) + \dim_k (x)$. In particular, any algebraic extension of $k(x)$ has the same dimension over k as $k(x)$ itself. There is a corresponding principle for the degrees of algebraic extensions, viz. the following: if k' is an algebraic extension of k, and k'' an algebraic extension of k', then $[k'':k] = [k'':k']\cdot[k':k]$.

If any quantities are algebraically independent over a field k, they are still so over the algebraic closure $\bar{k}$ of k. It follows from this that every set of quantities (x) has the same dimension over $\bar{k}$ as over k.

PROPOSITION 1. *Let k be a common subfield of two fields K and L; and let K and L be such that every set of algebraically independent quantities in K over k is still such over L. Then every set of algebraically independent quantities in L over k is still such over K.*

Let (y) be a set of algebraically independent elements in L over k, and assume that there is a relation between them, with coefficients in K; among the latter coefficients, choose a maximal set (x) of algebraically independent elements over k; then all the coefficients in that relation are algebraic over $k(x)$. The y's, therefore, satisfy a relation with coefficients in the algebraic closure of $k(x)$; hence they cannot be algebraically independent over $k(x)$, so that there is a relation between them with coefficients in $k(x)$. Multiplying the latter relation, if necessary, with a suitable element of $k(x)$, we may assume it to be of the form $F(x, y) = 0$, with $F(X, Y) \in k[X, Y]$. If we consider $F(X, y)$ as a polynomial in (X), with coefficients in $k(y)$, these coefficients must all be 0, since the x's are algebraically independent over k, hence by our assumption over L, hence a fortiori over $k(y)$; but this is impossible unless we have $F(X, Y) = 0$, since the y's are algebraically independent over k.

When the fields k, K and L have the property described in prop. 1, we shall say that K and L are *independent over* k, or *free with respect to each other over* k. We shall use this definition only in the case where at least one of the fields K and L is (in the sense of §1) an extension of k. If a field K, and an extension $k(x)$ of k, are independent over k, we shall also say that K and (x) are *independent*, or *free with respect to each other, over* k; if $k(x)$ and $k(y)$ are independent over k, we say that they are *independent extensions of* k, and that (x) and (y) are *independent*, or *free with respect to each other, over* k.

PROPOSITION 2. *Let (x) be a set of quantities, K a field, and k a subfield of K. Then we have* $\dim_K(x) \leqq \dim_k(x)$; *and the equality* $\dim_K(x) = \dim_k(x)$ *holds if and only if K is free over k with respect to (x).*

Algebraically independent quantities over K are a fortiori such over k; hence the first point. On the other hand, if K is free over k with respect to (x), and if $(u_1, \cdots, u_r)$ is a maximal set of algebraically independent elements in $k(x)$ over k, it is still a set of algebraically independent elements over K, so that we have, in that case, $\dim_K(x) \geqq r = \dim_k(x)$. Finally, if K is not free over k with respect to (x), let $(u_1, \cdots, u_s)$ be a set of algebraically independent elements in $k(x)$ over k, which is not such over K. Then, if $r = \dim_k(x)$, the dimension of $k(x)$ over $k(u)$ is $r - s$, so that, if $(v_1, \cdots, v_{r-s})$ are algebraically independent elements of $k(x)$ over $k(u)$, every x_i is algebraic over $k(u, v)$, hence a fortiori over $K(u, v)$. Then the dimension of $K(x)$ over K is the same as that of $K(u, v)$ over K, i.e. the sum of the dimension of (v) over $K(u)$, which is at most $r - s$, and of the dimension of (u) over K, which is less than s since the u_i are not independent over K. In that case, therefore, we have $\dim_K(x) < r = \dim_k(x)$.

Applying prop. 2 to the case where K is an extension $k(y)$ of k, we see that (x) and (y) are independent over k if and only if we have

$$\dim_k(x, y) = \dim_k(x) + \dim_k(y).$$

More generally, we shall say that sets of quantities in any number, say (x), (y) and (z), are *independent over* a field k if they satisfy the relation

$$\dim_k(x, y, z) = \dim_k(x) + \dim_k(y) + \dim_k(z).$$

This applies in particular to the case where each one of these sets consists of one quantity only; quantities $x_1, \cdots, x_n$ will therefore be called *independent variables over* k when $\dim_k(x_1, \cdots, x_n) = n$, i.e. when the x_i are algebraically independent over k. An extension $k(x)$ of a field k which is generated by a set (x) of independent variables over k will be called a *purely transcendental extension* of k.

We now prove some properties, concerning linear independence, which correspond to the above results on algebraic independence.

PROPOSITION 3. *Let k be a common subfield of two fields K and L; and let K and L be such that every set of linearly independent elements in K over k is still such over L. Then every set of linearly independent elements in L over k is still such over K.*

Let (y) be a set of linearly independent elements in L over k, and assume that there is a linear relation $\sum_\mu u_\mu y_\mu = 0$ between them, with coefficients $u_\mu \in K$. Among the u_μ, choose a maximal set of linearly independent elements v_ρ over k; we can then express all the u_μ in the form $u_\mu = \sum_\rho c_{\mu\rho} v_\rho$, with $c_{\mu\rho} \in k$. Then, putting $z_\rho = \sum_\mu c_{\mu\rho} y_\mu$, we have $\sum_\rho v_\rho z_\rho = 0$; by our assumptions the v_ρ, being linearly independent over k, must still be so over L, so that this relation implies $0 = z_\rho = \sum_\mu c_{\mu\rho} y_\mu$ for all ρ, which is impossible unless all the $c_{\mu\rho}$ and therefore all the u_μ are 0, since the y_μ are linearly independent over k.

When the fields k, K and L have the property described in prop. 3, we shall say that K and L are *linearly disjoint over* k. This is a stronger property than independence over k, as shown by the following proposition:

PROPOSITION 4. *If k is a common subfield of two fields K and L, and if K and L are linearly disjoint over k, then they are independent over k.*

Let (y) be a set of algebraically independent elements in L over k, and assume that there is an algebraic relation, with coefficients in K, between the y's; among the coefficients in that relation, choose a maximal set of linearly independent elements v_ρ over k, and express all those coefficients in the form $u_\mu = \sum_\rho c_{\mu\rho} v_\rho$, with $c_{\mu\rho} \in k$. Then our relation appears in the form $\sum_\rho v_\rho P_\rho(y) = 0$, where the $P_\rho(Y)$ are polynomials in $k[Y]$. By our assumption, this implies that all the $P_\rho(y)$ are 0, which is impossible unless all the $P_\rho(Y)$ are 0, since the y's are independent over k.

PROPOSITION 5. *Let k, K and L be three fields, such that $K \supset k$; and let L_1 be the compositum of k and L. Then, if every set of linearly independent elements in L over k is still such over K, the fields K and L_1 are linearly disjoint over k.*

L_1 is the field of quotients of the ring of all finite sums $\sum_\nu x_\nu y_\nu$, where $x_\nu \in k$ and $y_\nu \in L$; therefore every set of elements of L_1 can, by multiplication with a suitable element of L_1, be transformed into a set of elements $u_\mu = \sum_\nu x_{\mu\nu} y_{\mu\nu}$ of that ring, with $x_{\mu\nu} \in k$, $y_{\mu\nu} \in L$; then we may, among the $y_{\mu\nu}$ which appear in those expressions for the u_μ, choose a maximal set of linearly independent elements z_ρ over k, and express all the $y_{\mu\nu}$ linearly in terms of the z_ρ with coefficients in k; hence the u_μ can be written in the form $u_\mu = \sum_\rho c_{\mu\rho} z_\rho$, where the $c_{\mu\rho}$ are elements of k and the z_ρ are linearly independent elements of L over k. Now, let (w_μ) be a set of linearly independent elements of K over k, and assume that there is a linear relation between them, $\sum_\mu u_\mu' w_\mu = 0$, with coefficients u_μ' in L_1; multiplying this with a suitable element of L_1 as explained above, we can replace it by a relation $\sum_\mu u_\mu w_\mu = 0$ with coefficients u_μ of the form $u_\mu = \sum_\rho c_{\mu\rho} z_\rho$, the $c_{\mu\rho}$ and z_ρ being as before. This gives $\sum_\rho (\sum_\mu c_{\mu\rho} w_\mu) z_\rho = 0$, which, by our assumptions, implies $0 = \sum_\mu c_{\mu\rho} w_\mu$ for all ρ, against the assumption on the w_μ.

We now prove a result on the degrees of algebraic extensions, which corresponds to prop. 2 on the dimensions of arbitrary extensions:

PROPOSITION 6. *Let (ξ) be a set of algebraic elements over a field k, and let K be a field containing k. Then we have $[K(\xi):K] \leqq [k(\xi):k]$; and the equality $[K(\xi):K] = [k(\xi):k]$ holds if and only if K and $k(\xi)$ are linearly disjoint over k.*

It is known that a basis for $K(\xi)$ over K, i.e. a maximal set of linearly independent elements in $K(\xi)$ over K, can be chosen from among the monomials in the ξ_i; the monomials in such a maximal set are still in $k(\xi)$, and, being linearly independent over K, are a fortiori so over k; hence the first point. On the other hand, if K and $k(\xi)$ are linearly disjoint over k, and if $(\alpha_1, \cdots, \alpha_d)$ is a maximal set of linearly independent elements in $k(\xi)$ over k, the α_μ are still linearly independent over K, so that we have, in that case,

$$[K(\xi):K] \geqq d = [k(\xi):k].$$

Finally, if K and $k(\xi)$ are not linearly disjoint, let $\alpha_1, \cdots, \alpha_e$ be a set of linearly independent elements in $k(\xi)$ over k, which is not such over K. Then, if $d = [k(\xi):k]$, we can find $d - e$ elements $\beta_1, \cdots, \beta_{d-e}$ in $k(\xi)$, such that $(\alpha_1, \cdots, \alpha_e, \beta_1, \cdots, \beta_{d-e})$ is a basis of $k(\xi)$ over k. Every monomial in the ξ_i can be expressed linearly in terms of that basis, with coefficients in k, and therefore every element of $K(\xi)$ can be expressed linearly in terms of that basis, with coefficients in K. Since the α_μ are not linearly independent over K, the number of linearly independent elements over K, among the d elements α_μ, β_ν, is less than d; this shows that, in that case, we have $[K(\xi):K] < d$.

PROPOSITION 7. *Let k be a subfield of a field K. Then, if k is algebraically closed in K, and if ξ is any element of $\bar{k}$, K and $k(\xi)$ are linearly disjoint over k.*

By prop. 6, we need only prove that ξ has the same degree over K as over k. Let $F(T)$ and $\Phi(T)$ be the irreducible polynomials with the root ξ, in $k[T]$ and in $K[T]$ respectively, both being normalized by the condition of having their highest coefficient equal to 1. Then $F(T)$ must be a multiple of $\Phi(T)$, so that all the roots of $\Phi(T)$ are roots of $F(T)$ and therefore are algebraic over k; this implies that all the coefficients in $\Phi(T)$ are in $\bar{k}$, and therefore in $\bar{k} \cap K$. As we are assuming that $\bar{k} \cap K = k$, this shows that $\Phi(T)$ is in $k[T]$; it must therefore be the same as $F(T)$.

3. Ideal determined by a set of quantities over a field. If (x) is any set of quantities, and k a field, the set of all polynomials $F(X)$ in $k[X]$, such that $F(x) = 0$, is an ideal in $k[X]$, which we shall call *the ideal determined by (x) over k*, and denote by $\mathfrak{P}_{(x)/k}$. By Hilbert's theorem, it has a finite basis, i.e. there are a finite number of polynomials $F_\mu(X)$ in the ideal, such that every polynomial in the ideal can be expressed in the form $\sum_\mu A_\mu(X) \cdot F_\mu(X)$, where the $A_\mu(X)$ are in $k[X]$. The ideal determined by (x) over k is 0, i.e. contains no polynomial other than 0, if and only if (x) is a set of independent variables over k.

If σ is an isomorphic mapping of a field K on a field K', and $F(X)$ any polynomial in $K[X]$, we denote by $F^\sigma(X)$ the polynomial in $K'[X]$, obtained by applying σ to all the coefficients in $F(X)$; σ is thus extended to an isomorphic mapping of $K[X]$ on $K'[X]$. If $\mathfrak{A}$ is any ideal in $K[X]$, σ transforms $\mathfrak{A}$ into an ideal in $K'[X]$, which we denote by $\mathfrak{A}^\sigma$. If σ is an automorphism of K over some subfield k of K (i.e. if it leaves every element of k invariant), and if an ideal $\mathfrak{A}$ in $K[X]$ has a basis consisting of polynomials in $k[X]$, then we have $\mathfrak{A}^\sigma = \mathfrak{A}$.

PROPOSITION 8. *Let σ be an isomorphism between the fields K and K'; let (x) and (x') be two sets of quantities, in equal number, and let $\mathfrak{P}$, $\mathfrak{P}'$ be the ideals respectively determined by (x) over K and by (x') over K'. Then σ can be extended to an isomorphism between $K(x)$ and $K'(x')$, mapping (x) on (x'), if and only if $\mathfrak{P}^\sigma = \mathfrak{P}'$; and, when that is so, this extension of σ is uniquely determined.*

In fact, if σ can be so extended, and if $F(X)$ is a polynomial in $K[X]$, the equality $F(x) = 0$ implies $F^\sigma(x') = 0$, and conversely, which means that $\mathfrak{P}^\sigma = \mathfrak{P}'$; in that case, moreover, if $z = P(x)/Q(x)$ is any element of $K(x)$, where $P(X)$, $Q(X)$ are two polynomials in $K[X]$, then the corresponding element in $K'(x')$ is uniquely determined by $z^\sigma = P^\sigma(x')/Q^\sigma(x')$. Conversely, if $\mathfrak{P}^\sigma = \mathfrak{P}'$, and if z is any element in $K(x)$, then, expressing z in the form $z = P(x)/Q(x)$ with $P(X)$ and $Q(X)$ in $K[X]$, and writing $z' = P^\sigma(x')/Q^\sigma(x')$, one can easily verify that z' depends only upon z (and not upon the choice of the expression $P(x)/Q(x)$ for z), and that the correspondence between z and z' is an isomorphism between $K(x)$ and $K'(x')$ with the required properties.

As to the possibility of choosing a set of quantities (x') with the properties stated in prop. 8, when K, K', (x) and σ are given, we have the following result:

PROPOSITION 9. *Let σ be an isomorphism between the fields K and K', and let (x) be a set of quantities, of dimension r over K. Then σ can be extended to an isomorphic mapping of $K(x)$ on an extension $K'(x')$ of K', mapping (x) on some set of quantities (x'); moreover, this can be done in such a way that, if L is any given field containing K', the dimension of (x') over L be equal to r.*

By reordering the x_i if necessary, we may assume that $x_1, \cdots, x_r$ are independent variables over K; every x_i must then be algebraic over $K(x_1, \cdots, x_r)$, i.e. must be in the algebraic closure of that field. Let $x_1', \cdots, x_r'$ be r independent variables over the field L, hence a fortiori over K' (the existence of such quantities is a consequence of the conditions (a) and (b) in the definition of a field in §1). Then the ideals determined by $(x_1, \cdots, x_r)$ over K, and by $(x_1', \cdots, x_r')$ over K', are both (0), so that, by prop. 8, σ can be extended to an isomorphism between $K(x_1, \cdots, x_r)$ and $K'(x_1', \cdots, x_r')$, mapping x_j on x_j' for $1 \leqq j \leqq r$; by a well-known theorem of abstract algebra, this can itself be extended to an isomorphism σ_1 between the algebraic closures of those two fields; and σ_1 transforms (x) into a set of quantities (x'), which is algebraic over $K'(x_1', \cdots, x_r')$ and a fortiori over $L(x_1', \cdots, x_r')$, and has therefore the dimension r over L. Moreover, σ_1 induces an isomorphic mapping of $K(x)$ on $K'(x')$; this completes our proof.

We shall also require the following well-known result:

PROPOSITION 10. *Let $(x_0, \cdots, x_r)$ be a set of $r + 1$ quantities, of dimension r over a field k; then the ideal determined by (x) over k has a basis consisting of one polynomial $F(X)$, which is irreducible in $k[X]$ and is uniquely determined except for a constant factor; moreover, if $x_1, \cdots, x_r$ are independent variables over k, and if we put $K = k(x_1, \cdots, x_r)$, the polynomial $G(X_0) = F(X_0, x_1, \cdots, x_r)$ is irreducible in $K[X_0]$. Conversely, if $F(X)$ is an irreducible polynomial in $k[X]$, not of degree 0, there is a set of quantities (x), of dimension r over k, such that $F(X)$ is a basis of the ideal determined by (x) over k.*

We take this for granted for $r = 0$, and reproduce the usual proof for $r > 0$, which proceeds by induction. If $(x_1, \cdots, x_r)$ are independent over k, then $(x_0, \cdots, x_{r-1})$ is a set of r quantities, of dimension $r - 1$ over the field $k' = k(x_r)$, and $x_1, \cdots, x_{r-1}$ are independent over k'; by the induction assumption, the ideal determined by $(x_0, \cdots, x_{r-1})$ over k' has therefore a basis $P(X_0, \cdots, X_{r-1})$, this being a polynomial with coefficients in k', which, after multiplying it, if necessary, with a suitable element in k', we may assume to be of the form $F(X_0, \cdots, X_{r-1}, x_r)$, where $F(X)$ is a polynomial in $k[X]$ which is not a multiple of any non-constant polynomial in $k[X_r]$; it will now be shown that $F(X)$ has the required properties. In fact, let $L(X)$ be in $k[X]$, and such that $L(x) = 0$. Then, by the definition of $F(X)$, there are polynomials $M(X)$ in $k[X]$, and $N(X_r)$ in $k[X_r]$, such that we have

$$L(X_0, \cdots, X_{r-1}, x_r) = F(X_1, \cdots, X_{r-1}, x_r) \cdot M(X_1, \cdots, X_{r-1}, x_r)/N(x_r);$$

after dividing, if necessary, $M(X)$ and $N(X_r)$ by a suitable polynomial in $k[X_r]$, we may assume, moreover, that they have no common non-constant factor. As x_r is variable over k, the above relation implies $N(X_r) \cdot L(X) = F(X) \cdot M(X)$; then $N(X_r)$ must be of degree 0, for otherwise, if $N_1(X_r)$ is any one of its irreducible factors, $N_1(X_r)$ must be a factor either of $F(X)$ or of $M(X)$, which is against the assumptions made about both. This shows that the relation $L(x) = 0$ implies a relation $L(X) = F(X) \cdot M(X)$, i.e. that $F(X)$ is a basis for the ideal determined by (x) over k; moreover, by the definition of $F(X)$ and by the induction assumption, $F(X_0, x_1, \cdots, x_r)$ is irreducible in $K[X_0]$; as to $F(X)$ itself, it is irreducible in $k[X]$, for, if we have $F(X) = F_1(X) \cdot F_2(X)$, then we must have $F_1(x) = 0$ or $F_2(x) = 0$, so that either $F_1(X)$ or $F_2(X)$ must be a multiple of $F(X)$ and must have at least the same degree as $F(X)$, the other one of these two polynomials being then of degree 0. In particular, if $F_1(X)$ is another basis for the ideal determined by (x) over k, we must have $F(X) = F_1(X) \cdot F_2(X)$, and $F_1(X)$ must be the same as $F(X)$ except for a constant factor. Finally, as to our last assertion, let now $F(X)$ be irreducible in $k[X]$; and assume for instance that its degree in X_0 is not 0; let $x_1, \cdots, x_r$ be r independent variables over k; put $K = k(x_1, \cdots, x_r)$, and $G(X_0) = F(X_0, x_1, \cdots, x_r)$; and let x_0 be a root of the equation $G(X_0) = 0$, which is an algebraic quantity over K. Then $(x_0, \cdots, x_r)$ is of dimension r over k, and determines therefore over k an ideal with a basis consisting of a single polynomial $F_1(X)$; as we have $F(x) = 0$, $F(X)$ must then be of the form $F_1(X) \cdot F_2(X)$; and, as $F(X)$ is irreducible in $k[X]$, it follows as above that it differs from $F_1(X)$ only by a constant factor.

Let (x), as in prop. 10, be a set of $r + 1$ quantities, of dimension r over a field k; and let $F(X)$ be a basis for the ideal determined by (x) over k; then the equation $F(X) = 0$, which, by prop. 10, is uniquely determined except for a constant factor, will be called *the irreducible equation for* (x) *over* k.

4. Separability; sets of conjugates. Let ξ be algebraic over a field k; let $F(T)$ be the irreducible polynomial in $k[T]$ with the root ξ. Then ξ is called *separably algebraic*, or more briefly *separable over* k if it is a simple root of $F(T)$, *purely inseparable over* k if $F(T)$ has no other root than ξ; it cannot be both unless it is in k. If the characteristic p is not 0, and if p^m is the highest power of p such that $F(T)$ can be written as $F(T) = G(T^{p^m})$, with $G(T)$ in $k[T]$, then ξ^{p^m} is the lowest power of ξ which is separable over k. If $p = 0$, then every algebraic element over k is separable over k.

Once for all, we shall agree that, if $p = 0$, p^m means 1, and, if $p \neq 0$, p^m means (as usual) the m-th power of p, for $m = 0, 1, 2, \cdots$. That being so, ξ is purely inseparable over k if and only if there is a p^m such that ξ^{p^m} is in k.

A field k' containing k is called separably algebraic, or more briefly separable over k, if all its elements are separable over k; if $p = 0$, this is the case with all fields between k and $\bar{k}$. If all the elements of k' are purely inseparable over k, then we say that k' is purely inseparable over k. If k' is both separable and purely inseparable over k, then $k' = k$. If k' is any field between k and $\bar{k}$, the elements of k' which are separable over k form a field k''; this field k'' is separable over k, while k' is purely inseparable over k'', and k'' is the only field between k and k' which satisfies these two conditions. If k' is separable over k, and k_1' over k', then k_1' is separable over k.

A separably algebraic extension of a field k (in the sense of §1, i.e., as always, one of finite degree) can always be generated over k by the adjunction of a single element; this need not be so when the extension is not separable. If k' is a purely inseparable extension of k, then there is an integer p^m such that k' is contained in the subfield $k^{p^{-m}}$ of $\bar{k}$ which consists of the p^m-th roots of all the elements of k; and the degree of k' over k is of the form p^n, with $n \geqq m$.

An algebraic extension k' of a field k being given, let again k'' be the field consisting of all the elements of k' which are separable over k; then k' is purely inseparable over k'', so that the degree of k' over k'' is of the form p^n; if we put $[k':k] = d$, $[k'':k] = d_1$, this gives $d = p^n \cdot d_1$. That being so, the degrees $p^n = [k':k'']$ and $d_1 = [k'':k]$ will be called, respectively, *the inseparable* and *the separable factor* of the degree of k' over k, and will be denoted by $[k':k]_i$ and $[k':k]_s$.

Two sets (ξ), (ξ_1) of algebraic elements over a field k are called *conjugate over* k if they can be transformed into each other by some automorphism of $\bar{k}$ over k. If the set (ξ) is algebraic over k, and if σ is any isomorphism over k of some field K containing $k(\xi)$ on a field K_1, then the image (ξ_1) of (ξ) by σ is a conjugate of (ξ) over k; for σ can be extended to an isomorphism over k between the algebraic closures of K and K_1, and this induces on $\bar{k}$ an automorphism over k, transforming (ξ) into (ξ_1). If $k' = k(\xi)$ is an algebraic extension of k, and if we call k'' the field consisting of all separable elements of k' over k, then it is known, by the Galois theory, that the automorphisms of $\bar{k}$ over k induce exactly $[k'':k]$ distinct isomorphisms of k'' onto algebraic extensions of k (the conjugates of k'' over k), while every automorphism of $\bar{k}$ over k'' leaves every element of k' invariant; from this it follows that the number of *distinct* conjugates of (ξ) over k is equal to $[k'':k] = [k':k]_s$.

By a *complete set of conjugates* of an algebraic set of elements (ξ) over a field k, we understand a set $(\xi^{(1)}, \cdots, \xi^{(d)})$, where each $(\xi^{(\nu)})$ denotes one of the conjugates of (ξ) over k, and where each such conjugate appears $p^n = [k(\xi):k]_i$ times, so that such a set consists of $p^n \cdot [k(\xi):k]_s$, i.e. of $d = [k(\xi):k]$ sets $(\xi^{(\nu)})$. Any permutation of the $(\xi^{(\nu)})$ in a complete set of conjugates of (ξ) over k, and in particular a permutation induced on them by any automorphism of $\bar{k}$ over k, transforms it into such a complete set again. If the set (ξ) consists of one element ξ only, then a complete set of conjugates of ξ over k is a set consisting of all the roots of the irreducible equation for ξ over k, each root being repeated a number of times equal to its multiplicity.

PROPOSITION 11. *Let* (ξ), (η) *be two sets of algebraic elements over a field* k; *let* $(\xi^{(1)}, \cdots, \xi^{(d)})$ *and* $(\eta^{(1)}, \cdots, \eta^{(\delta)})$ *be complete sets of conjugates of* (ξ) *over* k

and of (η) *over* $k(\xi)$, *respectively. For* $1 \leqq \nu \leqq d$, *let* σ_ν *be some automorphism of* $\bar{k}$ *over* k *which transforms* (ξ) *into* $(\xi^{(\nu)})$, *and let* $(\eta^{(\nu\lambda)})$ *be the transform of* $(\eta^{(\lambda)})$ *by* σ_ν, *for* $1 \leqq \lambda \leqq \delta$. *Then the* $d\delta$ *sets* $(\xi^{(\nu)}, \eta^{(\nu\lambda)})$, *for* $1 \leqq \nu \leqq d$, $1 \leqq \lambda \leqq \delta$, *constitute a complete set of conjugates of* (ξ, η) *over* k. *Moreover, we have* $[k(\xi, \eta):k]_s = [k(\xi, \eta):k(\xi)]_s \cdot [k(\xi):k]_s$, *and* $[k(\xi, \eta):k]_i = [k(\xi, \eta):k(\xi)]_i \cdot [k(\xi):k]_i$.

Let σ be an arbitrary automorphism of $\bar{k}$ over k; it transforms (ξ) into some $(\xi^{(\nu)})$; then $\sigma_\nu^{-1} \cdot \sigma$ transforms (ξ) into itself and therefore is an automorphism of $\bar{k}$ over $k(\xi)$, transforming (η) into some $(\eta^{(\lambda)})$, hence (ξ, η) into $(\xi, \eta^{(\lambda)})$; therefore σ transforms (ξ, η) into $(\xi^{(\nu)}, \eta^{(\nu\lambda)})$. Conversely, if ν, λ are arbitrarily given, and if τ is any automorphism of $\bar{k}$ over $k(\xi)$, transforming (η) into $(\eta^{(\lambda)})$, then $\sigma_\nu \cdot \tau$ is an automorphism of $\bar{k}$ over k which transforms (ξ, η) into $(\xi^{(\nu)}, \eta^{(\nu\lambda)})$. We have thus shown that all the sets $(\xi^{(\nu)}, \eta^{(\nu\lambda)})$ are conjugates of (ξ, η) over k, and that every such conjugate appears among those sets. Now put $D = [k(\xi, \eta):k]$; as we have $d = [k(\xi):k]$, $\delta = [k(\xi, \eta):k(\xi)]$, we have $D = d\delta$. Furthermore, put $D_1 = [k(\xi, \eta):k]_s$, $d_1 = [k(\xi):k]_s$, $\delta_1 = [k(\xi, \eta):k(\xi)]_s$, and $p^M = [k(\xi, \eta):k]_i$, $p^m = [k(\xi):k]_i$, $p^\mu = [k(\xi, \eta):k(\xi)]_i$, so that we have $D = p^M \cdot D_1$, $d = p^m \cdot d_1$, $\delta = p^\mu \cdot \delta_1$. Then d_1 is the number of distinct sets among the $(\xi^{(\nu)})$, and δ_1 is the number of distinct sets among the $(\eta^{(\lambda)})$, hence also among the $(\eta^{(\nu\lambda)})$ for any given value of ν; therefore the number of distinct sets among the $(\xi^{(\nu)}, \eta^{(\nu\lambda)})$ is equal to $d_1 \cdot \delta_1$; since, by what has been proved before, this number is also equal to D_1, we have $D_1 = d_1 \cdot \delta_1$; combining this with the above relations, we get $p^M = p^m \cdot p^\mu$. Finally, each one of the sets $(\xi^{(\nu)}, \eta^{(\nu\lambda)})$ is repeated $p^m \cdot p^\mu$ times when ν, λ run over their ranges of values; as this is equal to p^M, we have thus shown that these D sets constitute a complete set of conjugates of (ξ, η) over k.

PROPOSITION 12. *Let* (ξ) *be a set of algebraic elements over a field* k, *and let* K *be a field containing* k. *Then we have* $[K(\xi):K]_s \leqq [k(\xi):k]_s$, $[K(\xi):K]_i \leqq [k(\xi):k]_i$; *and a complete set* $(\xi^{(1)}, \cdots, \xi^{(d)})$ *of conjugates of* (ξ) *over* k *consists of complete sets of conjugates, over* K, *of the conjugates of* (ξ) *over* k, *each such set of conjugates over* K *being repeated a certain number of times.*

Put $k' = k(\xi)$, and let k'' be the field consisting of all separable elements of k' over k; then we have $k' = k''(\xi)$; moreover, we can write k'' in the form $k'' = k(\zeta)$, where (ζ) is a suitably chosen set of separably algebraic elements over k. Put $K' = K(\xi)$, and $K'' = K(\zeta)$; every ξ_i is purely inseparable over k'' and a fortiori over K'', so that $K' = K''(\xi)$ is purely inseparable over K''; similarly, every ζ_j is separable over k and a fortiori over K, so that $K'' = K(\zeta)$ is separable over K. This shows that K'' is the field consisting of all separable elements of K' over K; it follows that $[K(\xi):K]_s$ is equal to $[K(\zeta):K]$, and similarly that $[K(\xi):K]_i$ is equal to $[K''(\xi):K'']$. Hence we can conclude by use of prop. 6 of §2 that $[K(\xi):K]_s$ is at most equal to $[k(\zeta):k]$, i.e. to $[k(\xi):k]_s$, and that $[K(\xi):K]_i$ is at most equal to $[k''(\xi):k''] = [k(\xi):k]_i$. Now consider the complete set of conjugates $(\xi^{(1)}, \cdots, \xi^{(d)})$; if we put $p^n = [k(\xi):k]_i$, and $p^{N_\nu} = [K(\xi^{(\nu)}):K]_i$ for $1 \leqq \nu \leqq d$, we have, for every ν, $[k(\xi^{(\nu)}):k]_i = p^n$, hence, by what has just been proved, $p^{N_\nu} \leqq p^n$. For any given value of ν, every conjugate of $(\xi^{(\nu)})$ over K is a fortiori a conjugate of $(\xi^{(\nu)})$, hence also of (ξ), over k, and therefore appears p^n times in the complete set $(\xi^{(1)}, \cdots, \xi^{(d)})$; this shows that the latter set contains p^{n-N_ν} times a complete set of conjugates of $(\xi^{(\nu)})$ over K. As this is true for every ν, this completes our proof.

PROPOSITION 13. *Let k be a field, and K a field containing k; let $k(x)$ be an extension of k, such that $k(x)$ and K are linearly disjoint over k; let (y) be a set of elements of $k(x)$, such that $k(x)$ is algebraic over $k(y)$. Then a complete set of conjugates of (x) over $k(y)$ is also such over $K(y)$, and we have $[K(x):K(y)] = [k(x):k(y)]$, $[K(x):K(y)]_i = [k(x):k(y)]_i$, and $[K(x):K(y)]_s = [k(x):k(y)]_s$.*

If some elements of K are linearly independent over $k(y)$, they are a fortiori so over k, hence, by our assumptions, also over $k(x)$; we can therefore apply prop. 5 of §2 to the fields $k(y)$, $k(x)$ and K; this shows that $k(x)$, and the compositum $K(y)$ of K and $k(y)$, are linearly disjoint over $k(y)$. As we have $k(x, y) = k(x)$, $K(x, y) = K(x)$, we can now apply prop. 6 of §2 to (x) and to the fields $k(y)$ and $K(y)$; this shows that, putting $d = [k(x):k(y)]$, we have $[K(x):K(y)] = d$. Now consider a complete set $(x^{(1)}, \cdots, x^{(d)})$ of conjugates of (x) over $k(y)$; by prop. 12, this must contain a complete set of conjugates of (x) over $K(y)$; as we have $[K(x):K(y)] = d$, the latter set must also consist of d conjugates of (x), and therefore exhausts the complete set of conjugates over $k(y)$. This proves our first point. The rest follows from the fact that $[k(x):k(y)]_s$ is the number of distinct conjugates of (x) in a complete set of conjugates of (x) over $k(y)$, and $[k(x):k(y)]_i$ is the number of times that (x) is repeated therein, and from the corresponding fact for $K(x)$ and $K(y)$.

PROPOSITION 14. *Let $k(x)$, $k(y)$ be two linearly disjoint extensions of a field k; let (z) be a set of elements of $k(x)$, and (t) a set of elements of $k(y)$, such that $k(x)$ is algebraic over $k(z)$, and $k(y)$ algebraic over $k(t)$. Let $(x^{(1)}, \cdots, x^{(d)})$ and $(y^{(1)}, \cdots, y^{(e)})$ be complete sets of conjugates of (x) over $k(z)$, and of (y) over $k(t)$, respectively. Then the $d\cdot e$ sets $(x^{(\nu)}, y^{(\lambda)})$, for $1 \leqq \nu \leqq d$, $1 \leqq \lambda \leqq e$, constitute a complete set of conjugates of (x, y) over $k(z, t)$.*

As $k(x)$ and $k(y)$ are linearly disjoint over k, the same is true a fortiori of $k(x)$ and $k(t)$; therefore, by prop. 13, $(x^{(1)}, \cdots, x^{(d)})$ is a complete set of conjugates of (x) over the field $L = k(z, t)$; let, for $1 \leqq \nu \leqq d$, σ_ν be an automorphism of $\bar{L}$ over L which transforms (x) into $(x^{(\nu)})$. Furthermore, as $k(x)$ and $k(y)$, and a fortiori $k(z)$ and $k(y)$, are linearly disjoint over k, it follows from prop. 13 that $(y^{(1)}, \cdots, y^{(e)})$ is a complete set of conjugates of (y) over $k(x, t)$, and also over $k(z, t)$; from the latter fact it follows that the effect of σ_ν on that complete set is merely a permutation. Our conclusion now follows by prop. 11, applied to (x), to (y), and to the field $L = k(z, t)$.

5. Derivations. A *derivation* in a field K is a mapping D of K into itself, such that: a) $D(x + y) = Dx + Dy$; b) $D(xy) = x\cdot Dy + Dx\cdot y$; it is called trivial if $Dx = 0$ for every x in K. A derivation D in K *over* a subfield k of K is one which is such that $Dx = 0$ for every x in k.

From the definition, we deduce the familiar rules for the result of a derivation applied to any rational expression, these rules being those of classical calculus (the part of the "constants" is here played by the elements of the prime field, or by those of k if the derivation is one over the field k). In particular, if D is a derivation over k in $k(x)$, every element z of $k(x)$ can be written, in at least one way, in the form $R(x)$, where $R(X)$ is a rational expression in (X) with coefficients in k; denoting by $R_i(X) = \partial R/\partial X_i$ the (formally taken) partial derivatives of $R(X)$ with respect to the X_i, we have, if $z = R(x)$, $Dz = \sum_i R_i(x) \cdot Dx_i$.

Derivations in K form a vector-space over K, as they can be added and admit of a scalar multiplication by the elements of K. From the formula just given for Dz when $z \in k(x)$, it follows that a derivation D in $K = k(x_1, \cdots, x_n)$ over k is uniquely determined when the Dx_i are given, and that there are no more than n linearly independent such derivations.

Let now D be a derivation in a field K; $K(x)$ being an extension of K, we shall consider whether D can be extended to $K(x)$, i.e. whether there is a derivation $\bar{D}$ in $K(x)$ which coincides with D in K. If $P(X)$ is any polynomial in $K[X]$, we denote by $P^D(X)$ the polynomial obtained by applying D to all the coefficients c_λ in $P(X)$, i.e. by replacing c_λ by Dc_λ for every λ; as already indicated, we denote by $\partial P/\partial X_i$ the (formally taken) partial derivative of $P(X)$ with respect to X_i, and also (when no misunderstanding is likely) by $\partial P/\partial x_i$ the result of the substitution of (x) for (X) in $\partial P/\partial X_i$. With those notations, we have, if $\bar{D}$ is a derivation in $K(x)$ which coincides with D in K, $\bar{D}[P(x)] = P^D(x) + \sum_i \partial P/\partial x_i \cdot \bar{D}x_i$; therefore, if $P(x) = 0$, the right-hand side must be 0.

PROPOSITION 15. *Let D be a derivation in a field K; let (x) be any set of quantities, and let the $F_\mu(X)$ be a basis for the ideal determined by (x) over K. Then, if (u) is any set of elements of $K(x)$, satisfying the set of linear equations*

$$0 = F_\mu^D(x) + \sum_i \partial F_\mu/\partial x_i \cdot u_i,$$

there is one and only one derivation $\bar{D}$ in $K(x)$, coinciding with D on K, and such that $\bar{D}x_i = u_i$ for every i; and every derivation $\bar{D}$ in $K(x)$ which coincides with D on K is such that the $\bar{D}x_i$ satisfy those equations.

The last point follows from the relations

$$0 = \bar{D}[F_\mu(x)] = F_\mu^D(x) + \sum_i \partial F_\mu/\partial x_i \cdot \bar{D}x_i,$$

which must be satisfied if $\bar{D}$ is as stated. Conversely, let the u_i satisfy the above equations. If $F(X)$ is any polynomial in $K[X]$, such that $F(x) = 0$, it can be written in the form $F(X) = \sum_\mu A_\mu(X) \cdot F_\mu(X)$, with $A_\mu(X) \in K[X]$; as we have $F_\mu(x) = 0$ for every μ, this gives

$$F^D(x) = \sum_\mu A_\mu(x) \cdot F_\mu^D(x), \qquad \partial F/\partial x_i = \sum_\mu A_\mu(x) \cdot \partial F_\mu/\partial x_i,$$

hence $0 = F^D(x) + \sum_i \partial F/\partial x_i \cdot u_i$. We now define $\bar{D}$ in $K(x)$ by putting

$$\bar{D}v = P^D(x) + \sum_i \partial P/\partial x_i \cdot u_i$$

if $v = P(x)$, where $P(X)$ is any polynomial in $K[X]$, and $\bar{D}z = w^{-2}(w \cdot \bar{D}v - v \cdot \bar{D}w)$ if $z = v/w$, $v = P(x)$, $w = Q(x)$, where $P(X)$, $Q(X)$ are in $K[X]$. It is easily seen that $\bar{D}z$ depends only upon z, and not upon the way in which it is expressed in the form $z = v/w = P(x)/Q(x)$, and that $\bar{D}$ is a derivation in $K(x)$ which satisfies our requirements.

In particular, if we set $D = 0$ in prop. 15, we get the conditions which must be satisfied by a derivation in $K(x)$ over K.

We now apply prop. 15 to the case where the set (x) consists of a single quantity x. We distinguish three cases:

(a) x is variable over K; then the ideal it determines over K reduces to (0). Every derivation D in K can then be extended to a derivation $\bar{D}$ in $K(x)$; $\bar{D}$ is uniquely determined if D and $\bar{D}x$ are arbitrarily given. In particular, there is one and only one derivation $\bar{D}$ in $K(x)$ over K, such that $\bar{D}x = 1$.

(b) x is separably algebraic over K. Then, if $F(X) = 0$ is the irreducible equation for x over K, x is a simple root of $F(X)$, so that we have $dF/dx \neq 0$. By prop. 15, every derivation D in K can then be extended in one and only one way to a derivation in $K(x)$; the latter will then again be denoted by D.

(c) x is inseparably algebraic over K. Then, $F(X) = 0$ being again the irreducible equation for x over K, we have $dF/dx = 0$. A derivation D in K can then be extended to a derivation $\bar{D}$ in $K(x)$ if and only if $F^D(x) = 0$; when that is so, $\bar{D}x$ can be assigned arbitrarily. Taking $D = 0$, we see that there is one and only one derivation $\bar{D}$ in $K(x)$ over K, such that $\bar{D}x = 1$.

From (b), it follows that every derivation in a field can be extended, in one and only one way, to any separably algebraic extension of that field. From (a) it follows that a derivation D in a field K can be extended, in one and only one way, to a derivation $\bar{D}$ in a purely transcendental extension $K(u)$ of K, generated by a set (u) of independent variables over K, by arbitrarily assigning the $\bar{D}u_i$; this applies in particular to the derivations in $K(u)$ over K, by taking $D = 0$; the n derivations $\partial/\partial u_j$, which can be characterized by $\partial u_i/\partial u_j = \delta_{ij}$, constitute a basis for these derivations.

Theorem 1. *If an extension $k(x)$ of a field k has no non-trivial derivation over k, it is separably algebraic over k, and conversely.*

Let $k(x) = k(x_1, \cdots, x_n)$ be the given extension; put $k_0 = k$, and $k_i = k_{i-1}(x_i)$ for $1 \leqq i \leqq n$. Let h be the smallest integer such that k_n is separably algebraic over k_h; if $h > 0$, then x_h must be either transcendental or inseparably algebraic over k_{h-1} (as otherwise k_n would be separable over k_{h-1}), so that, by what has been proved above, there exists a non-trivial derivation in k_h over k_{h-1}, which can then be extended to a derivation in $k_n = k(x)$. This proves the direct proposition; the converse has been proved already.

Corollary. *Let n quantities x_i satisfy n equations $F_j(X) = 0$, where the $F_j(X)$ are in $k[X]$ and such that the determinant $|\partial F_j/\partial x_i|$ is not 0. Then $k(x)$ is separably algebraic over k.*

In fact, we have the n relations $\sum_i \partial F_j/\partial x_i \cdot Dx_i = 0$, if D is a derivation in $k(x)$ over k, hence $Dx_i = 0$ for all i, hence $D = 0$.

By a *separably generated extension* of a field k, we understand any separably algebraic extension of a purely transcendental extension of k. In other words, $k(x)$ is separably generated over k if there exists in $k(x)$ a set (u) of independent variables over k, such that $k(x)$ is separable over $k(u)$; the number of variables u_i must then obviously be equal to the dimension of $k(x)$ over k. If the characteristic p is 0, every extension is separably generated. Any separably algebraic extension of a separably generated extension of k is itself separably generated over k.

PROPOSITION 16. *If $k(x)$ is a separably generated extension of a field k, of dimension r over k, there are r and no more than r linearly independent derivations in $k(x)$ over k.*

Let $k(x)$ be separable over $k(u)$, where $u_1, \cdots, u_r$ are r independent variables over k; consider the r derivations $\partial/\partial u_i$ in $k(u)$ over k, and their uniquely defined extensions to $k(x)$; they are linearly independent in $k(u)$, hence a fortiori in $k(x)$. If D is any derivation in $k(x)$ over k, put $Du_i = v_i$, and $D' = D - \sum_i v_i \cdot \partial/\partial u_i$; D' is a derivation in $k(x)$. We have $D'u_i = 0$ for every i, so that D' is 0 on $k(u)$; D' is therefore a derivation in $k(x)$ over $k(u)$. By th. 1, this implies that we have $D' = 0$, hence $D = \sum_i v_i \cdot \partial/\partial u_i$.

In the same manner, one can prove that, if there are s linearly independent derivations over k in an arbitrary extension $k(x)$ of k, then s is the smallest number of quantities u_i in $k(x)$ such that $k(x)$ is separably algebraic over $k(u)$; moreover, when p is not 0, p^s is then the degree of $k(x) = k(x_1, \cdots, x_n)$ over $k(x_1^p, \cdots, x_n^p)$. We shall make no use of these results.

THEOREM 2. *Let $F_\mu(X)$ be a basis for the ideal determined over a field k by a set of quantities $(x) = (x_1, \cdots, x_n)$, of dimension r over k. Then the rank of the matrix $||\partial F_\mu/\partial x_i||$ is at most equal to $n - r$; it is equal to $n - r$ if and only if $k(x)$ is separably generated over k; and, when that is so, one can choose, from among the x_i, r independent variables over k, in such a way that $k(x)$ is separable over the extension generated by these over k.*

Let $n - s$ be the rank of the matrix $||\partial F_\mu/\partial x_i||$; after reordering the F_μ and the x_i if necessary, we may assume that the determinant $|\partial F_\mu/\partial x_i|$, for $1 \leqq \mu \leqq n - s$, $s + 1 \leqq i \leqq n$, is not 0. Then, by the coroll. of th. 1, $x_{s+1}, \cdots, x_n$ are separably algebraic over $k(x_1, \cdots, x_s)$; therefore $(x_1, \cdots, x_s)$ must be of dimension r over k; this implies that s is at least equal to r, and, if $s = r$, that $(x_1, \cdots, x_s)$ is a set of independent variables over k, so that $k(x)$ is then separably generated over k and that the last assertion in our theorem holds true. Furthermore, by prop. 15, s is the number of linearly independent derivations in $k(x)$ over k; therefore, by prop. 16, this number must be equal to r if $k(x)$ is separably generated.

6. Extending the field of reference. We shall now consider what happens to the ideal $\mathfrak{P}_{(x)/k}$ determined by a set of quantities (x) over a field k, when k is replaced by a field K containing k, and free over k with respect to (x). This will require a lemma, which we formulate for arbitrary ideals in a ring $K[X]$.

LEMMA 1. *K being a field, and k a subfield of K, let $\mathfrak{A}$ be an ideal in the ring $K[X] = K[X_1, \cdots, X_n]$, with a basis consisting of polynomials $F_\nu(X)$ with coefficients in k. Then every polynomial $\Phi(X)$ in $\mathfrak{A}$ is a linear combination, with coefficients in K, of polynomials in the ideal $\mathfrak{A}_0$ generated in $k[X]$ by the basis $F_\nu(X)$; and, if such a polynomial is written in the form $\Phi(X) = \sum_\lambda \omega_\lambda P_\lambda(X)$, where the $P_\lambda(X)$ are in $k[X]$, the ω_λ in K, and where the ω_λ are linearly independent over k, then every $P_\lambda(X)$ is in $\mathfrak{A}_0$. In particular, $\mathfrak{A} \cap k[X]$ is the same as $\mathfrak{A}_0$.*

If $\Phi(X)$ is in $\mathfrak{A}$, it can be written as a linear combination, with coefficients in K, of polynomials of the form $X_1^{e_1} \cdots X_n^{e_n} \cdot F_\nu(X)$; this proves the first point. Let the $G_\mu(X)$, for $1 \leqq \mu \leqq m$, be a minimal set of polynomials in $\mathfrak{A}_0$, such that $\Phi(X)$ can be expressed in the form $\Phi(X) = \sum_\mu \gamma_\mu G_\mu(X)$, with $\gamma_\mu \in K$; then the $G_\mu(X)$ are linearly independent over k, for otherwise, expressing them in terms of a maximal set of linearly independent polynomials among them, we should get an expression for $\Phi(X)$ in terms of the latter, i.e. in terms of less than m of the $G_\mu(X)$. Now, if $\Phi(X)$ is also expressed as stated in our lemma, we have $\sum_\mu \gamma_\mu G_\mu(X) = \sum_\lambda \omega_\lambda P_\lambda(X)$; equating corresponding coefficients on both sides, we get linear relations between the γ_μ and the ω_λ, of the form $L_\rho(\gamma) = M_\rho(\omega)$, where the $L_\rho(Z)$, $M_\rho(U)$, are linear forms with coefficients in k. There are m linearly independent forms among the $L_\rho(Z)$; for otherwise the set of equations $L_\rho(Z) = 0$ would have a solution (c_μ) in k, and we should have $\sum_\mu c_\mu G_\mu(X) = 0$, against the assumptions on the $G_\mu(X)$. Therefore the relations $L_\rho(\gamma) = M_\rho(\omega)$ can be solved for the γ_μ, so that we can write $\gamma_\mu = \sum_\lambda d_{\mu\lambda}\omega_\lambda$, with $d_{\mu\lambda} \in k$. This gives $\sum_{\mu,\lambda} d_{\mu\lambda}\omega_\lambda G_\mu(X) = \sum_\lambda \omega_\lambda P_\lambda(X)$; as the ω_λ are linearly independent over k, it follows that we have $P_\lambda(X) = \sum_\mu d_{\mu\lambda} G_\mu(X)$, which proves the lemma.

THEOREM 3. *Let (x) be a set of quantities, K a field, and k a subfield of K. Then the ideal determined by (x) over K has a basis in $k[X]$ if and only if K and $k(x)$ are linearly disjoint over k; and, when that is so, every such basis is also a basis for the ideal determined by (x) over k.*

Assume that $\mathfrak{P}_{(x)/K}$ has a basis in $k[X]$; then lemma 1 means that there can be no relation $\sum_\lambda \omega_\lambda P_\lambda(x) = 0$, with $P_\lambda(X) \in k[X]$, between linearly independent elements ω_λ of K over k, unless all the $P_\lambda(x)$ are 0; hence the necessity of our condition. As to the converse, let $\Phi(X)$ be in $K[X]$; choosing among the coefficients in $\Phi(X)$ a maximal set of linearly independent elements ω_λ over k, and expressing all coefficients in $\Phi(X)$ in terms of these, we get for $\Phi(X)$ an expression of the form $\Phi(X) = \sum_\lambda \omega_\lambda P_\lambda(X)$, with $P_\lambda(X) \in k[X]$; then, if we have $\Phi(x) = 0$, this gives $0 = \sum_\lambda \omega_\lambda P_\lambda(x)$, hence $P_\lambda(x) = 0$ for every λ if K and $k(x)$ are linearly disjoint over k; in that case, therefore, every polynomial $\Phi(X)$ in $\mathfrak{P}_{(x)/K}$ is a linear combination of polynomials $P_\lambda(X)$ in $\mathfrak{P}_{(x)/k}$; this shows that our condition is sufficient. As we have $\mathfrak{P}_{(x)/k} = \mathfrak{P}_{(x)/K} \cap k[X]$, the last assertion in our theorem follows now from the last assertion in lemma 1.

Corollary 1. *Let K be a field, k a subfield of K, and (u) a set of independent variables over K. Then K and $k(u)$ are linearly disjoint over k.*

This follows from th. 3 and from the relation $\mathfrak{P}_{(u)/K} = (0)$.

Corollary 2. *Let k be a field, (x) a set of quantities, and (u) a set of independent variables over $k(x)$. Then the ideal determined by (x) over $k(u)$ has a basis in $k[X]$.*

This is clear if one combines th. 3 with coroll. 1.

A further important consequence of lemma 1 is the following:

Theorem 4. *Let (x) and (y) be two sets of quantities such that $k(x)$ and $k(y)$ are linearly disjoint extensions of the field k. Then a basis for the ideal $\mathfrak{P}_{(x)/k}$ in $k[X]$, and a basis for the ideal $\mathfrak{P}_{(y)/k}$ in $k[Y]$, taken jointly, constitute a basis for the ideal $\mathfrak{P}_{(x,y)/k}$ in $k[X, Y]$.*

Let $\Phi(X, Y)$ be any polynomial in $\mathfrak{P}_{(x,y)/k}$. Putting $K = k(y)$, and considering $\Phi(X, y)$ as a polynomial in $K[X]$, we choose, among the coefficients of that polynomial, a maximal set of linearly independent elements over k, which must all be of the form $A_\lambda(y)$, with $A_\lambda(Y) \in k[Y]$. Expressing all coefficients in $\Phi(X, y)$ as linear combinations of the $A_\lambda(y)$, we get for $\Phi(X, y)$ an expression $\Phi(X, y) = \sum_\lambda A_\lambda(y) \cdot P_\lambda(X)$, with $P_\lambda(X) \in k[X]$. But, since we have $\Phi(x, y) = 0$, the polynomial $\Phi(X, y)$ is in the ideal determined by (x) over the field $K = k(y)$; by th. 3, this ideal has a basis in $k[X]$; by lemma 1, therefore, all the $P_\lambda(X)$ must be in $\mathfrak{P}_{(x)/k}$. Now put $\Psi(X, Y) = \Phi(X, Y) - \sum_\lambda A_\lambda(Y) \cdot P_\lambda(X)$; we have $\Psi(X, y) = 0$; therefore, if we write $\Psi(X, Y)$ as a polynomial in (X) with coefficients which are elements of $k[Y]$, these coefficients must all be in $\mathfrak{P}_{(y)/k}$, so that we can write $\Psi(X, Y) = \sum_\mu B_\mu(X) \cdot Q_\mu(Y)$, with $B_\mu(X) \in k[X]$ and $Q_\mu(Y) \in \mathfrak{P}_{(y)/k}$. This gives $\Phi(X, Y) = \sum_\lambda A_\lambda(Y) \cdot P_\lambda(X) + \sum_\mu B_\mu(X) \cdot Q_\mu(Y)$. Expressing the $P_\lambda(X)$, $Q_\mu(Y)$ in terms of the given bases for $\mathfrak{P}_{(x)/k}$, $\mathfrak{P}_{(y)/k}$, we get our result.

Corollary. *Let $F_\mu(X)$ be a basis for the ideal determined by (x) over k; let (u) be a set of independent variables over $k(x)$. Then the $F_\mu(X)$ are a basis for the ideal determined by (x, u) over k.*

This follows from th. 4 and coroll. 1 of th. 3.

7. Regular extensions. The converse of prop. 4 of §2 is not generally true: two fields K and L which are independent over a field k need not be linearly disjoint over k (take e.g. $K = L = \bar{k}$, if k is not algebraically closed). We shall now find additional conditions under which this converse will hold. We first need some auxiliary results.

Proposition 17. *Let k be a subfield of a field K, algebraically closed in K. Then, if a field k', containing k, is separably algebraic over k, K and k' are linearly disjoint over k.*

In fact, consider a set (α) of linearly independent elements in k' over k. Then $k(\alpha)$ is a separably algebraic extension of k, which therefore can be generated over k by the adjunction of a single element ξ; by prop. 7 of §2, K and $k(\xi)$ are linearly disjoint over k, so that the α_i must be linearly independent over K.

PROPOSITION 18. *Let k be a field, and $k(x)$ a separably generated extension of k. Let K be a field containing k, and free over k with respect to (x); and let k' be the field consisting of all those elements of K which are separably algebraic over k. Then K and $k'(x)$ are linearly disjoint over k'.*

Since $k'(x)$ is the compositum of k' and $k(x)$, we can make use of prop. 5 of §2, and therefore need only show that any elements of $k(x)$ which are linearly independent over k' are still such over K. In fact, assume that this is not so; and, of all sets of elements of $k(x)$ which are linearly independent over k' but not over K, choose one, $(y) = (y_1, \cdots, y_m)$, with the smallest number m of elements. Then there is a relation $\sum_{j=1}^{m} w_j y_j = 0$, with coefficients w_j in K, none of which can be 0; multiplying this by an element of K, we may assume that $w_m = 1$. The w_j cannot all be in k'; therefore, by th. 1 of §5, there is a non-trivial derivation D in $k(w)$ over k; then the Dw_j cannot all be 0. Let (u) be a set of independent variables over k in $k(x)$, such that $k(x)$ is separably algebraic over $k(u)$; as K is free over k with respect to (x), (u) is a set of independent variables over K, hence a fortiori over $k(w)$; therefore, by prop. 15 of §5, D can be extended to a derivation in $k(w, u)$, which we also denote by D, by putting $Du_h = 0$ for all h; D is then a derivation in $k(w, u)$ over $k(u)$. Furthermore, as (x) is separable over $k(u)$ and a fortiori over $k(w, u)$, the derivation D in $k(w, u)$ can be extended to a derivation in $k(w, u, x) = k(w, x)$, which we again call D. As $k(x)$ is separable over $k(u)$, and as D is 0 on $k(u)$, we have $Dz = 0$ for every $z \in k(x)$, and in particular $Dy_j = 0$ for $1 \leqq j \leqq m$. Applying D to the relation $\sum_j w_j y_j = 0$, we therefore get $\sum_j Dw_j \cdot y_j = 0$; as we have $w_m = 1$, Dw_m is 0. This shows that $y_1, \cdots, y_{m-1}$ are not linearly independent over K; as they are so over k', this contradicts our definition of the set (y).

PROPOSITION 19. *If $k(x)$ is a separably generated extension of a field k, then, for every p^m, $k^{p^{-m}}$ and $k(x)$ are linearly disjoint over k. Conversely, if, for some $m > 0$, $k^{p^{-m}}$ and $k(x)$ are linearly disjoint over k, then $k(x)$ is separably generated over k.*

The first point follows from prop. 18 by taking $K = k^{p^{-m}}$, hence $k' = k$. We prove the converse by induction on the number n of the x_i; as it is trivial for $p = 0$, we assume $p \neq 0$. If $\mathfrak{P}_{(x)/k} = (0)$, our conclusion holds; if not, let $P(X)$ be a polynomial of smallest degree d in that ideal; put $P_i(X) = \partial P / \partial X_i$. If all the $P_i(X)$ were 0, then $P(X)$ would be of the form $P(X) = Q(X)^p$, $Q(X)$ being a polynomial with coefficients in $k^{1/p}$ and a fortiori in $k^{p^{-m}}$ if $m > 0$; $P(x) = 0$ implies $Q(x) = 0$, so that $Q(X)$ is in the ideal determined by (x) over $k^{p^{-m}}$; by our assumptions and by th. 3 and lemma 1 of §6, this implies that $Q(X)$ is a linear combination of polynomials in $\mathfrak{P}_{(x)/k}$, which is impossible since it is of lower degree than any polynomial in that ideal. We may assume, therefore, that $P_n(X) \neq 0$; as this is a polynomial of degree less than d, we must have $P_n(x) \neq 0$. This means that x_n is separable over k if $n = 1$, which proves our theorem in that case, and that it is separable over $k(x_1, \cdots, x_{n-1})$ if $n > 1$; in the latter case, as $k^{p^{-m}}$ and $k(x)$ are linearly disjoint, the same is a fortiori true of $k^{p^{-m}}$ and $k(x_1, \cdots, x_{n-1})$, so that, by the induction assumption, the latter must be separably generated over k; as we have found that $k(x)$ is separably algebraic over it, this completes the proof.[1]

It follows from prop. 19 that, if $k(x)$ is a separably generated extension of k, and if (y) is any set of elements of $k(x)$, then $k(y)$ also is separably generated over k. Another immediate consequence of prop. 19 is that, if k is such that $k^{1/p} = k$ (i.e. if it is a so-called "perfect" field), then every extension of k is separably generated; in particular, every extension of $\bar{k}$ is separably generated.

We now introduce a definition which will play an essential part in our theory of algebraic varieties (cf. Chap. IV, §1). We say that an extension $k(x)$ of a field k is *regular over* k, or that it is a *regular extension of* k, if $\bar{k}$ and $k(x)$ are linearly disjoint over k. By th. 3 of §6, an extension $k(x)$ of k is regular if and only if the ideal determined by (x) over $\bar{k}$ has a basis in $k[X]$. Every extension $\bar{k}(x)$ of $\bar{k}$ is obviously regular over $\bar{k}$; the next two propositions also are immediate consequences of the definition, and of coroll. 1 of th. 3 of §6, respectively:

PROPOSITION 20. *If $k(x)$ is a regular extension of a field k, and if (y) is a set of elements in $k(x)$, then $k(y)$ also is regular over k.*

PROPOSITION 21. *Every purely transcendental extension of a field k is regular over k.*

PROPOSITION 22. *Let K be a field, and $K(x)$ a regular extension of K. Then, if a subfield k of K is such that K and $k(x)$ are linearly disjoint over k, the extension $k(x)$ of k is regular over k.*

By our assumptions, if any elements of $k(x)$ are linearly independent over k, they are still so over K, therefore also over $\bar{K}$ because $\bar{K}$ and $K(x)$ are linearly disjoint over K, hence a fortiori over $\bar{k}$.

THEOREM 5. *An extension $k(x)$ of a field k is regular over k if and only if k is algebraically closed in $k(x)$, and $k(x)$ separably generated over k. When that is so, then, if K is any free field over k with respect to (x), K and $k(x)$ are linearly disjoint over k, $K(x)$ is regular over K, and the ideal determined by (x) over K has a basis in $k[X]$.*

Assume that $\bar{k}$ and $k(x)$ are linearly disjoint over k; then the same is a fortiori true of $k^{p^{-m}}$ and $k(x)$ for every m, so that, by prop. 19, $k(x)$ is separably generated over k; moreover, if k was not algebraically closed in $k(x)$, there would be some ξ in $k(x)$ which would be in $\bar{k}$ but not in k, and then the elements $(1, \xi)$ of $\bar{k}$ would be linearly independent over k but not over $k(x)$. Now assume, conversely, that k is algebraically closed in $k(x)$, and that $k(x)$ is separably generated over k. Let K be free over k with respect to (x), and call k' the field consisting

[1] Prop. 19 is contained in the results of S. MacLane, *Modular fields* (I), Duke Math. J. vol. 5 (1939), p. 372 (see th. 10, p. 379, and th. 16, p. 385).

of all those elements of K which are separably algebraic over k. If any elements of $k(x)$ are linearly independent over k, then, by prop. 17, applied to k, $k(x)$ and k', they are still so over k', hence, by prop. 18, over K. Therefore K and $k(x)$ are linearly disjoint over k. As $\bar{K}$ also is free over k with respect to (x), it follows that $\bar{K}$ and $k(x)$ are linearly disjoint over k; therefore any elements of $k(x)$ which are linearly independent over K, hence a fortiori over k, are still so over $\bar{K}$; by prop. 5 of §2, applied to the fields K, $\bar{K}$ and $k(x)$, this implies that $\bar{K}$ and $K(x)$ are linearly disjoint over K, i.e. that $K(x)$ is regular over K. Applying this to the special case $K = k$, we see that $k(x)$ is regular over k. The last point follows from th. 3 of §6.

THEOREM 6. *Let $k(x)$ and $k(y)$ be two independent extensions of a field k, both regular over k. Then they are linearly disjoint over k; and their compositum $k(x, y)$ also is regular over k.*

The first point follows from th. 5. Furthermore, by th. 3 of §6, our assumptions imply that the ideal $\mathfrak{P}_{(x)/\bar{k}}$ in $\bar{k}[X]$, and the ideal $\mathfrak{P}_{(y)/\bar{k}}$ in $\bar{k}[Y]$, have bases with coefficients in k. By th. 4 of §6, these bases, taken jointly, constitute a basis for the ideal determined by (x, y) over $\bar{k}$. By th. 3 of §6, this proves our theorem.

We now want to show that, with the assumptions and notations of prop. 22, of all the fields k with the property stated in that proposition, there is a smallest field k_0. This amounts to a result on the ideal $\mathfrak{P}_{(x)/K}$, which we shall state and prove as a lemma on arbitrary ideals in a ring of polynomials $K[X]$.

LEMMA 2. *Let K be a field, and let $\mathfrak{A}$ be an ideal in the ring*

$$K[X] = K[X_1, \cdots, X_n].$$

Then, of all the subfields k of K such that $\mathfrak{A}$ has a basis with coefficients in k, there is a smallest field k_0, contained in all the others. Moreover, if σ is any automorphism of K, then σ transforms $\mathfrak{A}$ into itself if and only if it leaves invariant every element of the field k_0.

We build up a special basis for $\mathfrak{A}$ as follows. We order all monomials $X_1^{e_1} \cdots X_n^{e_n}$ in a sequence $M_i(X)$ $(i = 0, 1, 2, \cdots)$. From this sequence, omit all monomials $M_i(X)$ for which elements c_j of K can be found such that $M_i(X) - \sum_{j=0}^{i-1} c_j M_j(X)$ is in $\mathfrak{A}$; and call $M_{i_\lambda}(X)$ the remaining subsequence (which need not be assumed to be infinite); for every i not in that subsequence, it is then possible to find elements c_λ of K, such that the polynomial

$$P_i(X) = M_i(X) - \sum_{i_\lambda < i} c_\lambda M_{i_\lambda}(X)$$

is in $\mathfrak{A}$, and, for every such i, the c_λ, hence also the polynomial $P_i(X)$, are uniquely determined by that condition. We also put $P_{i_\lambda}(X) = 0$ for every λ, so that the $P_i(X)$ are well-determined for every value of i. Now consider an arbitrary polynomial in $\mathfrak{A}$, and write it in the form $\Phi(X) = \sum_{h=0}^{N} \gamma_h M_h(X)$, where $\gamma_h \in K$, and where we may assume that $\gamma_N \neq 0$; it is easily seen, by induction on N, that this polynomial must be a linear combination, with coefficients in K, of the $P_i(X)$ for $0 \leqq i \leqq N$. Therefore every polynomial in $\mathfrak{A}$ is a linear combination of the $P_i(X)$; from this, and from Hilbert's theorem, it follows that, for a sufficiently large m, the polynomials $P_i(X)$, for $0 \leqq i \leqq m$, constitute a basis for $\mathfrak{A}$; if we take for m the smallest integer for which this is so, we have thus a basis for $\mathfrak{A}$, which is uniquely determined when $\mathfrak{A}$ is given; let k_0 be the field generated, over the prime field in K, by the coefficients in the polynomials of that basis. We shall now show that the field k_0, which we have just defined, has the properties asserted in our lemma. In fact, suppose that $\mathfrak{A}$ has a basis with coefficients in some subfield k of K. For any given i for which $P_i(X)$ is not 0, i.e. for which we have $P_i(X) = M_i(X) - \sum_\lambda c_\lambda M_{i_\lambda}(X)$, choose, among the coefficients of $P_i(X)$, a maximal number of linearly independent elements ω_ρ over k; we may assume that the coefficient 1 of $M_i(X)$ has been chosen as one of these, say as ω_0. Then all the coefficients c_λ can be expressed in the form $c_\lambda = \sum_\rho d_{\lambda\rho}\omega_\rho$, with $d_{\lambda\rho} \in k$; this gives $P_i(X) = \sum_\rho \omega_\rho Q_\rho(X)$ if we put

$$Q_0(X) = M_i(X) - \sum d_{\lambda 0} M_{i_\lambda}(X),$$

and, for $\rho \neq 0$, $Q_\rho(X) = -\sum_\lambda d_{\lambda\rho} M_{i_\lambda}(X)$. By lemma 1 of §6, all the $Q_\rho(X)$ must be in the ideal $\mathfrak{A}_0 = \mathfrak{A} \cap k[X]$, and a fortiori in $\mathfrak{A}$; by the definition of the $M_{i_\lambda}(X)$, this implies that we have $Q_\rho(X) = 0$ for $\rho \neq 0$. Therefore we have $P_i(X) = Q_0(X)$, hence $c_\lambda = d_{\lambda 0}$ for every λ, which shows that the c_λ are in k. As this is true for every i, k must therefore contain k_0, as asserted in our lemma. Furthermore, since the $P_i(X)$ are uniquely determined by the ideal $\mathfrak{A}$, they must be invariant by every automorphism σ of K which transforms $\mathfrak{A}$ into itself; therefore such an automorphism must leave every element of k_0 invariant; conversely, if the latter condition is satisfied, then the $P_i(X)$ are invariant by σ; as they constitute a basis for $\mathfrak{A}$, σ must then transform $\mathfrak{A}$ into itself.

With the same notations and assumptions as in lemma 2, it obviously follows from that lemma that, if k is any subfield of K, then, of all the fields k_1, between k and K, such that $\mathfrak{A}$ has a basis with coefficients in k_1, there is a smallest field k_0', viz. the compositum of k and of k_0; moreover, if we consider any basis for $\mathfrak{A}$ with coefficients in k_0' (for instance the special basis constructed in the proof of lemma 2), then k_0' is the field generated over k by the coefficients in that basis, for otherwise it would not have the minimal property by which we have defined it. This shows that k_0' is then an extension of k (in the sense of §§1–2, i.e. finitely generated over k). In particular, if an ideal $\mathfrak{A}$ in $K[X]$ has a basis with algebraic coefficients over some subfield k of K, then there is a smallest algebraic extension k_0' of k, such that $\mathfrak{A}$ has a basis with coefficients in k_0'; this applies to all ideals in the ring $\bar{k}[X]$.

We now apply lemma 2 to the situation described in prop. 22.

Theorem 7. *Let K be a field, and (x) a set of quantities such that $K(x)$ is regular over K; let $\mathfrak{P}$ be the ideal determined by (x) over K, and let k_0 be the smallest* *field such that $\mathfrak{P}$ has a basis with coefficients in k_0. Then, k being any subfield of K, K and $k(x)$ are linearly disjoint over k if and only if k contains k_0; and, when that is so, $k(x)$ is regular over k.*

If K and $k(x)$ are linearly disjoint over k, then, by th. 3 of §6, $\mathfrak{P}$ has a basis in $k[X]$, so that we have $k \supset k_0$ by the definition of k_0; and $k(x)$ is regular over k by prop. 22. On the other hand, by th. 3 of §6, K and $k_0(x)$ are linearly disjoint over k_0; therefore, if k is any field between k_0 and K, and if any elements of $k_0(x)$ are linearly independent over k, hence a fortiori over k_0, then they are still so over K; by prop. 5 of §2, applied to the fields k, K and $k_0(x)$, this implies that K and $k(x)$ are linearly disjoint over k.

We conclude this § with a result which gives some information about the field k_0, defined in th. 7, in a particularly interesting case.

PROPOSITION 23. *Let k be a field, and (x) any set of quantities; and let k_0' be the smallest field containing k, such that $\mathfrak{P}_{(x)/\bar{k}}$ has a basis in $k_0'[X]$. Then k_0' is a purely inseparable extension of the algebraic closure of k in $k(x)$; moreover, $k(x)$ is separately generated over k if and only if k_0' is separable over k.*

As $\bar{k}(x)$ is regular over $\bar{k}$, th. 7 shows that $k_0'(x)$ is regular over k_0', so that, by th. 5, k_0' must be algebraically closed in $k_0'(x)$; this gives $k_0' = \bar{k} \cap k_0'(x)$, hence a fortiori $k_0' \supset \bar{k} \cap k(x)$. If we put $k_1 = \bar{k} \cap k(x)$, then k_1 is the algebraic closure of k in $k(x)$; we have thus shown that k_0' contains that closure, of which it is therefore an algebraic extension. Now call k_1'' the subfield of $\bar{k}$ consisting of all purely inseparable elements over k_1; then $k_1''(x)$ is purely inseparable over $k_1(x) = k(x)$, so that, if α is in $k_1''(x)$, we have $\alpha^{p^m} \in k(x)$ for some m; if α is at the same time in $\bar{k}$, α^{p^m} is therefore in $\bar{k} \cap k(x) = k_1$, hence α in k_1''; this shows that k_1'' is algebraically closed in $k_1''(x)$. On the other hand, we have $(k_1'')^{p^{-m}} = k_1''$ for every m, so that, by prop. 19, $k_1''(x)$ is separably generated over k_1''. Therefore, by th. 5, $k_1''(x)$ is regular over k_1'', and the ideal determined by (x) over $\bar{k}$ has a basis in k_1''; this shows that k_0' is contained in k_1'', i.e. that it is purely inseparable over k_1. If now $k(x)$ is separably generated over k, then it follows from prop. 18, applied to k, $k(x)$ and $\bar{k}$, and from th. 7, that k_0' is contained in the subfield of $\bar{k}$ which consists of all separably algebraic quantities over k, and that it is therefore separable over k. Conversely, assume that k_0' is separable over k; as $k_0'(x)$ is separably generated over k_0' by th. 7 and th. 5, we can, by th. 2 of §5, select, from among the x_i, a maximal set (u) of independent variables over k_0', such that every x_i is separable over $k_0'(u)$, hence also over $k(u)$ since k_0' is separable over k and therefore $k_0'(u)$ over $k(u)$; this shows that $k(x)$ is then separably generated over k.

8. The order of inseparability. We shall now define, for every extension of a field, an integer, called its order of inseparability, which may be said to measure how far that extension is from being separably generated. The contents of this § are formally true, but trivially so, in the case $p = 0$, provided we interpret, as always, p^m as meaning 1 for $p = 0$, for every m. In our proofs, the case $p = 0$ may be disregarded.

PROPOSITION 24. *Let k be a field, k' an algebraic extension of k, and (x) any set of quantities; let p^m be defined by the relation $[k':k]_i = p^m \cdot [k'(x):k(x)]_i$. Then p^m is an integer; and, if (u) is any maximal set of independent variables over k in $k(x)$, we have the relation $[k(x):k(u)]_i = p^m \cdot [k'(x):k'(u)]_i$.*

That p^m is an integer follows from prop. 12 of §4. Now, (u) being as stated, prop. 11 of §4 gives the two different forms $[k'(x):k(x)]_i \cdot [k(x):k(u)]_i$ and $[k'(x):k'(u)]_i \cdot [k'(u):k(u)]_i$ for $[k'(x):k(u)]_i$. Writing that these two expressions are equal, and observing that we have $[k'(u):k(u)]_i = [k':k]_i$ by prop. 13 of §4 and by coroll. 1 of th. 3, §6, we get the formula of our proposition.

THEOREM 8. *If $k(x)$ is any extension of a field k, there is an integer p^f such that, whenever (u) is a maximal set of independent variables over k in $k(x)$, we have $[k(x):k(u)]_i = p^f \cdot [\bar{k}(x):\bar{k}(u)]_i$; and this integer p^f is equal to 1 if and only if $k(x)$ is separably generated over k.*

Take for k' the algebraic extension of k generated by the coefficients in some basis of the ideal $\mathfrak{P}_{(x)/\bar{k}}$; then, by th. 3 of §6, $\bar{k}$ and $k'(x)$ are linearly disjoint over k', and therefore, if (u) is as stated in our theorem, we have

$$[\bar{k}(x):\bar{k}(u)]_i = [k'(x):k'(u)]_i$$

by prop. 13 of §4. Our first point then follows if we define p^f by the relation $[k':k]_i = p^f \cdot [k'(x):k(x)]_i$ and apply prop. 24. As $\bar{k}(x)$ is separably generated over $\bar{k}$, we can, by th. 2 of §5, choose the set (u) from among the x_i in such a way that $[\bar{k}(x):\bar{k}(u)]_i = 1$; this shows that, if $p^f = 1$, $k(x)$ is then separable over $k(u)$, hence separably generated over k. Conversely, if $k(x)$ is separably generated, we can choose the set (u) so that $[k(x):k(u)]_i = 1$, which implies $p^f = 1$.

An extension $k(x)$ of a field k being given, the integer p^f with the property described in th. 8 will be called *the order of inseparability of $k(x)$ over k*, and denoted by $[k(x):k]_\iota$; by th. 8, it can also be defined as the value of $[k(x):k(u)]_i$ whenever the maximal set (u) of independent variables over k in $k(x)$ is such that $[\bar{k}(x):\bar{k}(u)]_i = 1$, or as the smallest value of $[k(x):k(u)]_i$ for all possible choices of the maximal set (u). In the particular case where $k(x)$ is an algebraic extension of k, then its order of inseparability over k is equal to $[k(x):k]_i$. There is therefore no danger of confusion between the symbols $[k(x):k]_\iota$ and $[k(x):k]_i$, since they coincide whenever they are both defined (i.e. whenever $k(x)$ is algebraic over k).

PROPOSITION 25. *Let (x) be any set of quantities, and k' a separably algebraic extension of a field k. Then $[k'(x):k']_\iota = [k(x):k]_\iota$.*

This is an immediate consequence of prop. 24 and of the definition of the order of inseparability, since the integer p^m, defined as in prop. 24 for k, k' and (x), is here equal to 1.

PROPOSITION 26. *Let k be a field, (x) any set of quantities, and K a free field over k with respect to (x); then $[K(x):K]_\iota \leqq [k(x):k]_\iota$. If, moreover, K and $k(x)$ are linearly disjoint over k, then $[K(x):K]_\iota = [k(x):k]_\iota$.*

Take for (u) a set of independent variables over k in $k(x)$, such that $\bar{k}(x)$ is separable over $\bar{k}(u)$; by th. 2 of §5, such a set (u) can be chosen for instance from among the x_i. Then (x) is separably algebraic over $\bar{k}(u)$ and a fortiori over $\bar{K}(u)$; moreover, K being free over k with respect to (x), (u) is still a set of independent variables over K. Therefore $[k(x):k]_\iota$ and $[K(x):K]_\iota$ are respectively equal to $[k(x):k(u)]_i$ and to $[K(x):K(u)]_i$. Our assertions then follow by prop. 12 and prop. 13 of §4.

PROPOSITION 27. *Let k be a field, (x) any set of quantities, and (y) any set of elements of $k(x)$. Then $[k(x):k]_\iota/[k(y):k]_\iota$ is an integer, equal to*

$$[k(x):k(y)]_\iota/[\bar{k}(x):\bar{k}(y)]_\iota.$$

Take for (v) a maximal set of independent variables over k in $k(y)$, and for (w) a maximal set of independent variables over $k(y)$ in $k(x)$; then (w) is also a maximal set of independent variables over $\bar{k}(y)$ in $\bar{k}(x)$, and (v, w) is a maximal set of independent variables over k in $k(x)$. If, in the equality asserted by our proposition, we express all four orders of inseparability, according to the definition, by means of these maximal sets of independent variables, we find that it is enough to prove the two relations $[k(x):k(v, w)]_i = [k(x):k(y, w)]_i \cdot [k(y):k(v)]_i$ and $[\bar{k}(x):\bar{k}(v, w)]_i = [\bar{k}(x):\bar{k}(y, w)]_i \cdot [\bar{k}(y):\bar{k}(v)]_i$. The first one of those two relations follows from prop. 11 of §4, and from the fact that $[k(y):k(v)]_i$ is equal to $[k(y, w):k(v, w)]_i$ by prop. 13 of §4 and by coroll. 1 of th. 3, §6; the second one holds for similar reasons. This shows that the two ratios in our proposition are equal; moreover, by prop. 26 applied to $k(y)$, to the set (x), and to the field $\bar{k}(y)$, the second one of these ratios must be an integer. This completes our proof.

PROPOSITION 28. *Let k be a field, and (x), (y) two independent sets of quantities over k. Then we have $[k(x, y):k]_\iota \leqq [k(x):k]_\iota \cdot [k(y):k]_\iota$. If, moreover, $k(y)$ is separably generated over k, then we have $[k(x, y):k]_\iota = [k(x):k]_\iota$.*

As to the first assertion, we have $[\bar{k}(y):\bar{k}]_\iota = 1$, hence, by prop. 26,

$$[\bar{k}(x, y):\bar{k}(x)]_\iota = 1.$$

If now we apply prop. 27 to k and to the sets of quantities (x, y) and (x), we get the relation

$$[k(x, y):k]_\iota = [k(x):k]_\iota \cdot [k(x, y):k(x)]_\iota\,;$$

by prop. 26, $[k(x, y):k(x)]_\iota$ is at most equal to $[k(y):k]_\iota$. This proves our first formula. If now we have $[k(y):k]_\iota = 1$, it follows from this that we must have $[k(x, y):k]_\iota \leqq [k(x):k]_\iota$; together with prop. 27, applied to k and to the sets (x, y) and (x), this proves our last assertion.

In the case of an extension of dimension r, generated by $r + 1$ quantities, the order of inseparability has some special properties, which are given in the following proposition:

PROPOSITION 29. *Let* $(x_0, \cdots, x_r)$ *be a set of* $r + 1$ *quantities, of dimension* r *over a field* k; *let* p^f *be the order of inseparability of* $k(x)$ *over* k, *and put* $k_m = k^{p^{-m}}$ *for every* $m \geqq 0$. *Then* $k_m(x)$ *is separably generated over* k_m *for* $m \geqq f$, *and is not so for* $m < f$. *Moreover, if* $F(X) = 0$, $G(X) = 0$, *and* $H(X) = 0$ *are the irreducible equations for* (x) *over* k, *over* k_f, *and over* $\bar{k}$, *respectively, then we have, except for a constant factor,* $F(X) = G(X)^{p^f}$, *and* $G(X) = H(X) \cdot L(X)$, *where* $L(X)$ *is in* $\bar{k}[X]$ *and such that* $L(x) \neq 0$.

By prop. 10 of §3, x_0 is algebraic over the field $K = k(x_1, \cdots, x_r)$ if and only if the degree of $F(X)$ in X_0 is not 0, and, when that is so, then $F(X_0, x_1, \cdots, x_r) = 0$ is the irreducible equation for x_0 over K, and $(x_1, \cdots, x_r)$ is a set of independent variables over k; in that case, by the definition of p^f, the inseparable factor of the degree of x_0 over K must be at least p^f, so that $F(X_0, x_1, \cdots, x_r)$ can be written as a polynomial in $X_0^{p^f}$. Since this applies also to each one of the indeterminates $X_1, \cdots, X_r$, it shows that $F(X)$ can be written as a polynomial in $X_0^{p^f}, \cdots, X_r^{p^f}$, hence also in the form $F(X) = P(X)^{p^f}$, with $P(X) \in k_f[X]$. As we have $F(x) = 0$, we have $P(x) = 0$, so that $P(X)$ must be a multiple of $G(X)$, hence $F(X)$ of $G(X)^{p^f}$; but, as $G(X)$ is in $k_f[X]$, $G(X)^{p^f}$ is in $k[X]$, and therefore cannot divide $F(X)$ without being the same as $F(X)$ except for a constant factor. Therefore, after multiplying, if necessary, $F(X)$, $P(X)$ and $G(X)$ by suitable constants, we may assume that we have $P(X) = G(X)$, and $F(X) = G(X)^{p^f}$. By th. 2 of §5, we may, after reordering the x_i if necessary, assume that x_0 is separably algebraic over $\bar{k}(x_1, \cdots, x_r)$; then, by th. 8, p^f must be the inseparable factor of the degree of x_0 over $k(x_1, \cdots, x_r)$; by prop. 10 of §3, this implies that x_0 is a root of multiplicity p^f of the equation $F(X_0, x_1, \cdots, x_r) = 0$, and therefore a simple root of the equation $G(X_0, x_1, \cdots, x_r) = 0$. Therefore x_0 is then separably algebraic over $k_f(x_1, \cdots, x_r)$, and a fortiori over $k_m(x_1, \cdots, x_r)$ for $m \geqq f$, so that $k_m(x)$ is separably generated over k_m for $m \geqq f$. If $k_m(x)$ was separably generated over k_m for some value of m less than f, then, by th. 8 applied to $k_m(x)$, x_0 would be separably algebraic over $k_m(x_1, \cdots, x_r)$, hence $x_0^{p^m}$ over $k(x_1, \cdots, x_r)$, which would contradict what we have proved above. Finally, $H(X)$ being as stated, $G(X)$ must be a multiple of $H(X)$ in $\bar{k}[X]$, so that we have $G(X) = H(X) \cdot L(X)$, with $L(X) \in \bar{k}[X]$. From this we get

$$G(X_0, x_1, \cdots, x_r) = H(X_0, x_1, \cdots, x_r) \cdot L(X_0, x_1, \cdots, x_r);$$

as x_0 is a simple root of the left-hand side and a root of the first factor in the right-hand side, we must have $L(x) \neq 0$.

From prop. 29, we can deduce some further properties of the order of inseparability of an arbitrary extension.

PROPOSITION 30. *Let* (x) *be a set of quantities, and* k *a field, such that* $k(x)$ *is not separably generated over* k. *Then we have* $[k^{1/p}(x):k^{1/p}]_\iota < [k(x):k]_\iota$.

Take for (u) a set of independent variables over k in $k(x)$, such that $\bar{k}(x)$ is separable over $\bar{k}(u)$; then there is at least one of the x_i, say x_1, which is not separable over $k(u)$, as otherwise $k(x)$ would be separably generated over k. As $\bar{k}(x)$ is separable over $\bar{k}(u)$, $\bar{k}(u, x_1)$ is separable over $\bar{k}(u)$, so that we have $[k(u, x_1):k]_\iota = [k(u, x_1):k(u)]_i$. Let (y) be the set of quantities (u, x_1); if r is the dimension of $k(x)$ over k, this is a set of $r + 1$ quantities, of dimension r over k; therefore, if we call p^f its order of inseparability over k, which is not 1 by what we have just proved, and if we put $k_m = k^{p^{-m}}$, prop. 29 shows that f is the smallest integer such that $k_m(y)$ is separably generated over k_m for $m \geqq f$; by the same prop., applied to k_1 and (y), we find that $[k_1(y):k_1]_\iota = p^{f-1}$. Now we have, by prop. 27,

$$[k_m(x):k_m]_\iota = [k_m(x):k_m(y)]_\iota \cdot [k_m(y):k_m]_\iota / [\bar{k}(x):\bar{k}(y)]_\iota ,$$

for every m; writing this relation for $m = 0$ and for $m = 1$, and using what we have proved above, we get $[k(x):k]_\iota/[k_1(x):k_1]_\iota = p \cdot [k(x):k(y)]_\iota/[k_1(x):k_1(y)]_\iota$; as k_1 is free with respect to (x), the right-hand side, by prop. 26, is at least equal to p, which proves our proposition.

PROPOSITION 31. *Let* (x) *be a set of quantities, and* k *a field; put* $p^f = [k(x):k]_\iota$, *and* $k_m = k^{p^{-m}}$ *for* $m \geqq 0$. *Then* $k_m(x)$ *is separably generated over* k_m *for* $m \geqq f$.

This follows from th. 8 if we have $p^f = 1$. If that is not so, then, by prop. 30, the integers $[k_m(x):k_m]_\iota$, for $m = 0, 1, 2, \cdots$, form a strictly decreasing sequence of powers of p, beginning with p^f, until one of them has the value 1; therefore one of them must have the value 1, and, if the first one to have that value is $[k_g(x):k_g]_\iota$, we have $g \leqq f$; and $k_m(x)$ is separably generated over k_m for $m \geqq g$, hence a fortiori for $m \geqq f$.

CHAPTER II

ALGEBRAIC THEORY OF SPECIALIZATIONS

1. Specializations. Let (x) and (x') be two sets of n quantities, and $\mathfrak{P}$, $\mathfrak{P}'$ the ideals they determine over a field k; if $\mathfrak{P} \subset \mathfrak{P}'$, i.e. if we have $F(x') = 0$ whenever $F(X)$ is in $k[X]$ and such that $F(x) = 0$, then we say that (x') is a *specialization of* (x) *over* k. If three sets of quantities (x), (x'), (x'') are such that (x') is a specialization of (x), and (x'') of (x'), over the field k, then it follows from the definition that (x'') is a specialization of (x) over k.

If the polynomials $F_\mu(X)$ are a basis for the ideal $\mathfrak{P}_{(x)/k}$ determined by a set of quantities (x) over a field k, then it is clear that a set of quantities (x') is a specialization of (x) over k if and only if it satisfies the conditions $F_\mu(x') = 0$ for all μ. In particular, if (x) is a set of independent variables over k, every set of quantities (x') is a specialization of (x) over k; if $(x) = (x_0, \cdots, x_r)$ is a set of $r + 1$ quantities of dimension r over k, and if $F(X) = 0$ is the irreducible equation for (x) over k, then a set of quantities (x') is a specialization of (x) if and only if it satisfies $F(x') = 0$.

In order to ensure the validity of the results to be proved in §2, it is necessary to extend the notions of quantity and of specialization, as follows. By a *generalized quantity* we understand either a quantity (as defined in Chap. I, §1), or a new element, the same once for all, which we denote by ∞. We make the convention that $1/0 = \infty$, $1/\infty = 0$, and that otherwise no symbol of an algebraic operation, applied to ∞, has a meaning. By a *reciprocation*, applied to a set $(x) = (x_1, \cdots, x_n)$ of n generalized quantities, we understand the transformation which replaces some (possibly none, or all) of these quantities, say the x_j for $j = i_1, \cdots, i_m$, by their reciprocals $1/x_j$; to every subset $\{i_1, \cdots, i_m\}$ of the set $\{1, 2, \cdots, n\}$, there belongs in this manner one reciprocation, and these 2^n reciprocations constitute a group of transformations operating on all sets of n generalized quantities. It is clear that, to every set of n generalized quantities, there is at least one reciprocation which transforms it into a set of n quantities.

PROPOSITION 1. *Let (x) and (x') be two sets of n quantities, and assume that a given reciprocation transforms them into two sets of quantities (y), (y'). Then (x') is a specialization of (x) over the field k if and only if (y') is a specialization of (y) over that field.*

After applying to our four sets, if necessary, a suitable permutation, we may assume that the given reciprocation transforms the first m quantities in each set into their reciprocals and leaves the others unchanged. Then none of the x_j, x'_j, y_j, y'_j, for $1 \leqq j \leqq m$, can be 0. Assume that (x') is a specialization of (x) over k. Let $F(Y)$ be in $k[Y]$, and such that $F(y) = 0$. We can find an integer N such that $G(X) = (X_1 \cdots X_m)^N \cdot F(1/X_1, \cdots, 1/X_m, X_{m+1}, \cdots, X_n)$ is a polynomial in (X); we have $G(x) = 0$, hence $G(x') = 0$, hence $F(y') = 0$ since $x'_1 \cdots x'_m$ is not 0. The converse follows by interchanging (x) and (y).

Now, if (x), (x') are two sets of n generalized quantities, and k is a field, we say that (x') is a *specialization of* (x) *over* k if there is a reciprocation which, applied to both sets, transforms them into sets of quantities (y), (y') such that (y') is a specialization of (y) over k. If (x) and (x') are themselves sets of quantities, then, by prop. 1, this definition is equivalent with the earlier one; it is therefore legitimate. Furthermore, if two sets (x), (x') of generalized quantities are such that (x') is a specialization of (x) over k, and if any reciprocation ρ transforms them into sets of quantities (y), (y'), then (y') is a specialization of (y) over k; for, by our definition, there is a reciprocation ρ_1 which transforms (x), (x') into sets of quantities (z), (z') such that (z') is a specialization of (z) over k; then the reciprocation $\rho_1 \cdot \rho^{-1}$ transforms (y), (y') into (z), (z'), and we can apply prop. 1 to these four sets and that reciprocation. Instead of speaking of a specialization (x') of (x) over k, we shall frequently speak of the specialization $(x) \to (x')$ over k.

As the quantity 0 has no other specialization than itself over any field, the generalized quantity ∞ also has no other specialization than itself; conversely, if $(x) \to (x')$ is any specialization over a field k, then $(x, 0) \to (x', 0)$ also is one, hence also $(x, \infty) \to (x', \infty)$. This also shows that, if $(x) \to (x')$ is a specialization over k, and if, for some i, we have $x_i = \infty$, then $x'_i = \infty$; hence, if no x'_i is ∞, no x_i can be ∞. A set (x) of generalized quantities is said to be *finite* if none of the x_i is ∞, i.e. if (x) is a set of quantities; otherwise we say that it is *infinite* or *at infinity*. We thus see that, if $(x) \to (x')$ is a specialization over some field k, and if (x') is finite, then (x) also is finite; if (x) is at infinity, then the same is true of (x'). More generally, if $(x) \to (x')$ is a specialization over k, and if some reciprocation transforms (x') into a set of quantities, then it transforms (x) a fortiori into a set of quantities; this remark is useful whenever one wants to reduce the proof of a statement concerning specializations of generalized quantities to the proof of the corresponding statement about ordinary quantities. For instance, we can thus show that, if $(x) \to (x')$ and $(x') \to (x'')$ are specializations over a field k, then $(x) \to (x'')$ also is one; in fact, applying to all three sets a reciprocation which transforms (x'') into a set of quantities, we see that this must then transform (x'), hence also (x), into finite sets, which brings us back to a previous result.

If two sets of generalized quantities, (x) and (x'), are specializations of each other over a field k, we say that they are *generic specializations* of each other over k. If (x) and (x') are generic specializations of each other over k, then the specializations of (x') over k are the same as those of (x). If (x) and (x') are generic specializations of each other over k, and if one of them is finite, then the other must also be so, and then they determine the same ideal over k; conversely, two sets of n quantities which determine the same ideal over a field k are generic specializations of each other over k.

Let (x) be a set of generalized quantities, and k a field; then, by $k(x)$, we understand the extension of k generated by all those among the x_i which are not ∞; the dimension of $k(x)$ over k will be denoted by $\dim_k(x)$; if this is 0, we say that (x) is algebraic over k. These definitions are obviously in agreement with those of Chap. I, §2. In every isomorphic mapping of a field on a field, the element ∞ should be considered as invariant.

THEOREM 1. *If (x') is a generic specialization of (x) over a field k, there is a uniquely determined isomorphism between $k(x)$ and $k(x')$ over k which transforms (x) into (x'). Conversely, if an isomorphism between two fields over k transforms a set (x) of generalized quantities into a set (x'), then (x') is a generic specialization of (x) over k.*

After applying a suitable reciprocation to (x) and (x'), we may assume that one of them is finite, hence also the other one. Our theorem is then merely a special case of prop. 8 of Chap. I, §3, viz. the case in which $K = K' = k$, σ being the identical automorphism of k.

Just as th. 1 was derived from prop. 8 of Chap. I, §3, we get from prop. 9 of Chap. I, §3, the following result:

THEOREM 2. *If r is the dimension of (x) over a field k, and if K is any field containing k, then there exists a generic specialization of (x) over k which has the dimension r over K.*

THEOREM 3. *Let $(x) \rightarrow (x')$ be a specialization over a field k. Then we have* $\dim_k(x') \leqq \dim_k(x)$; *and the equality* $\dim_k(x') = \dim_k(x)$ *holds if and only if the specialization (x') of (x) over k is generic.*

After applying to (x) and (x') a reciprocation which transforms (x'), hence also (x), into a finite set, we may assume that both are finite. Put $r = \dim_k(x)$, $s = \dim_k(x')$. After reordering the x_i and x'_i if necessary, we may assume that $x'_1, \cdots, x'_s$ are independent variables over k; then the same is true of $x_1, \cdots, x_s$, for any relation between the latter, with coefficients in k, would imply the corresponding relation between the former. Therefore we have $r \geqq s$. If, moreover, we have $r = s$, then $(x_1, \cdots, x_r)$ and $(x'_1, \cdots, x'_r)$ are two sets of independent variables over k, and $k(x)$ is algebraic over $k(x_1, \cdots, x_r)$; that being so, we shall now show that the specialization $(x) \rightarrow (x')$ over k must be generic. In fact, let $F(X)$ be in $k[X]$, and such that $F(x') = 0$. Put $z = F(x)$, so that z is algebraic over $k(x_1, \cdots, x_r)$, and call $P(Z, X_1, \cdots, X_r) = 0$ the irreducible equation for $(z, x_1, \cdots, x_r)$ over k. Then we have $P[F(x), x_1, \cdots, x_r] = 0$, which implies the relation $P[F(x'), x'_1, \cdots, x'_r] = 0$, i.e. $P(0, x'_1, \cdots, x'_r) = 0$. As $x'_1, \cdots, x'_r$ are independent variables over k, this implies

$$P(0, X_1, \cdots, X_r) = 0;$$

therefore 0 is a root of the equation $P(Z, x_1, \cdots, x_r) = 0$, which, by prop. 10 of Chap. I, §3, is the irreducible equation for z over $k(x_1, \cdots, x_r)$; it follows from this that z is 0, i.e. that $F(x) = 0$, which proves our assertion[1]. Finally, if we

[1] This proof is taken from v. d. Waerden, *Einführung in die algebraische Geometrie* (Berlin 1939), pp. 112–113.

assume, conversely, that (x') is a generic specialization of (x), then, by what we have proved, we have $r \geqq s$, and similarly $s \geqq r$, hence $r = s$.

COROLLARY. *Let (ξ) be a set of algebraic quantities over a field k; then every specialization of (ξ) over k is a conjugate of (ξ) over k, and conversely.*

In fact, th. 3 shows that every specialization of (ξ) over k must be generic, hence finite; the rest follows by th. 1.

If $(x) \to (x')$ is a specialization over a field k, then it is such a fortiori over every field contained in k. If $(x, y) \to (x', y')$ is a specialization over k, then (x') is a specialization of (x), and (y') of (y), over k. It is important to find conditions under which the converses of these assertions may hold true; this is the object of the rest of this §. In order to avoid tedious repetitions, the proofs for the following results are given only for finite specializations; the general case can then always trivially be derived from this by means of a suitable reciprocation.

PROPOSITION 2. *Let (x) and (y) be two sets of quantities, and k a field. Then (x') is a specialization of (x) over $k(y)$ if and only if (x', y) is a specialization of (x, y) over k.*

Assume that (x', y) is a specialization of (x, y) over k; put $K = k(y)$, and let $\Phi(X)$ be a polynomial in $K[X]$, such that $\Phi(x) = 0$; we can write it in the form $\Phi(X) = F(X, y)/G(y)$, where $F(X, Y)$ is in $k[X, Y]$, $G(Y)$ in $k[Y]$, and where $G(y) \neq 0$; then we have $F(x, y) = 0$, hence $F(x', y) = 0$, hence $\Phi(x') = 0$. The converse is obvious.

THEOREM 4. *Let k be a field, and (x) a set of quantities such that $k(x)$ is a regular extension of k. Then, if K is any free field over k with respect to (x), every specialization of (x) over k is still such over K.*

This follows at once from th. 3 of Chap. I, §6, and th. 5 of Chap. I, §7.

THEOREM 5. *Let k be a field, and let (x), (y) be two independent sets of quantities over k, such that at least one of the two extensions $k(x)$, $k(y)$ is regular over k. Then, if (x') and (y') are any specializations of (x) and of (y), respectively, over k, (x', y') is a specialization of (x, y) over k.*

This follows from th. 4 of Chap. I, §6, and th. 5 of Chap. I, §7.

COROLLARY. *Let k be a field, (x) a set of quantities, and (u) a set of m independent variables over $k(x)$. Then, if (x') is any specialization of (x) over k, and (u') any set of m quantities, (x', u') is a specialization of (x, u) over k; and (x') is a specialization of (x) over $k(u)$.*

The first point is a special case of th. 5; it shows in particular that (x', u) is a specialization of (x, u) over k; the last point follows from this by prop. 2.

PROPOSITION 3. *Every specialization (x') of a set of quantities (x) over a field k is also such over every purely inseparable extension k' of k.*

Let $F(X)$ be in $k'[X]$ and such that $F(x) = 0$; then there is p^m such that the polynomial $G(X) = F(X)^{p^m}$ is in $k[X]$; we have $G(x) = 0$, which by our assumption implies $G(x') = 0$, hence $F(x') = 0$.

2. Extension of specializations. $(x) \rightarrow (x')$ being a given specialization over a field k, and (y) being arbitrarily given, we now want to know whether there exists a specialization of (x, y) over k, of the form (x', y'). In order to formulate our results conveniently, we shall agree to say, if (x) and (y) are two sets of generalized quantities and (x', y') a specialization of (x, y) over a field k, that $(x, y) \rightarrow (x', y')$ is an *extension of* the specialization $(x) \rightarrow (x')$ over k, or that the latter can be *extended to* the former; we also say, when that is so, that (y') is a specialization of (y) *over* the specialization (x') of (x) with reference to k, or that (y') is a specialization of (y), *compatible with* the specialization $(x) \rightarrow (x')$ over k. Partial results, about the possibility of extending a specialization (x') of (x) to one of (x, y), are contained in th. 5 of §1, and also in the following:

PROPOSITION 4. *Let (x) and (y) be two given sets of quantities, and k a given field. Then any generic specialization (x') of (x) over k can be extended to a generic specialization (x', y') of (x, y) over k.*

By th. 1 of §1, there is an isomorphic mapping σ of $k(x)$ on $k(x')$ over k, which maps (x) on (x'). By prop. 9 of Chap. I, §3, this can be extended to an isomorphic mapping of $k(x, y)$ on some extension of $k(x')$; if this transforms (y) into (y'), the set (y') has the required property, by th. 1 of §1.

Now let (x') be a finite specialization of a set of quantities (x) over a field k; let y be any quantity; we shall discuss the possibility of extending $(x) \rightarrow (x')$ to a specialization $(x, y) \rightarrow (x', y')$ over k. A quantity y' will have the required property if and only if we have $F(x', y') = 0$ whenever $F(X, Y)$ is in the ideal $\mathfrak{P}$ determined by (x, y) over k. Now, if we put $K = k(x')$, it is easy to see that the set of all polynomials in $K[Y]$ which are of the form $w' \cdot F(x', Y)$, with $w' \in K$ and $F(X, Y) \in \mathfrak{P}$, is an ideal $\mathfrak{P}'$ in $K[Y]$. Three cases have then to be considered:

(a) the ideal $\mathfrak{P}'$ is (0). This means that, for every $F(X, Y)$ in $\mathfrak{P}$, we have $F(x', Y) = 0$. Then every quantity y' is such that (x', y') is a specialization of (x, y) over k; in particular, we may take for y' any variable quantity over $k(x')$.

(b) the ideal $\mathfrak{P}'$ is neither (0) nor (1). Then, if we choose in $\mathfrak{P}'$ a polynomial $\Phi(Y)$ of lowest degree d, we have $d > 0$, and all polynomials in $\mathfrak{P}'$ are multiples of $\Phi(Y)$. Multiplying $\Phi(Y)$, if necessary, with a suitable element of K, we may assume that it is of the form $\Phi(Y) = F_0(x', Y)$, with $F_0(X, Y) \in \mathfrak{P}$. Then, to every polynomial $F(X, Y)$ in $\mathfrak{P}$, there is a $G(Y)$ in $K[Y]$, such that

$$F(x', Y) = G(Y) \cdot F_0(x', Y).$$

This shows that (x', y') is a finite specialization of (x, y) over k if and only if y' is a root of $F_0(x', Y) = 0$. The number of distinct roots of that equation is at least one and at most d; taking into account the fact that (x', ∞) may also be a specialization of (x, y) over k, we see that in this case (x, y) has at least one and at most $d + 1$ specializations of the form (x', y') over k, and that these are all algebraic over $k(x')$.

(c) the ideal $\mathfrak{P}'$ is (1). Then there is a polynomial $F(X, Y)$ in $\mathfrak{P}$, such that $F(x', Y)$ reduces to its constant term, and that this term is not 0; we may assume that, of all the polynomials in $\mathfrak{P}$ with that property, $F(X, Y)$ is one of lowest degree m in Y. No choice of the quantity y' can then annul $F(x', y')$, so that $(x) \rightarrow (x')$ cannot be extended to a finite specialization of (x, y) over k. If we write $F(X, Y)$ in the form $F(X, Y) = \sum_{\nu=0}^{m} P_\nu(X) \cdot Y^\nu$, with the $P_\nu(X)$ in $k[X]$, our assumption means that we have $P_0(x') \neq 0$, and $P_\nu(x') = 0$ for $\nu > 0$. We have $y \neq 0$, since otherwise $(x', 0)$ would be a specialization of $(x, y) = (x, 0)$; therefore we may put $z = 1/y$, where z is not ∞. Then, if we write

$$G(X, Z) = \sum_{\nu=0}^{m} P_\nu(X) \cdot Z^{m-\nu},$$

$G(X, Z)$ is such that $G(x, z) = 0$, and that $G(x', Z)$ reduces to its highest term $P_0(x') \cdot Z^m$ which is not 0; moreover, by our assumption on $F(X, Y)$, no polynomial in $k[X, Z]$ with these two properties can be of lower degree in Z than m.

Now,[2] let $H(X, Z)$ be any polynomial in $k[X, Z]$ such that $H(x, z) = 0$. When one carries out the division of $Z^{m-1} \cdot H(X, Z)$ by $G(X, Z)$, both being considered as polynomials in Z with coefficients in $k[X]$, no other denominators are introduced than powers of $P_0(X)$; therefore there is an identity of the form

$$P_0(X)^n \cdot Z^{m-1} \cdot H(X, Z) = A(X, Z) \cdot G(X, Z) + B(X, Z),$$

where n is some integer, $A(X, Z)$ and $B(X, Z)$ are in $k[X, Z]$, and $B(X, Z)$ is of degree $\leqq m - 1$ in Z. Substituting (x, z) for (X, Z), we get $B(x, z) = 0$. Substituting (x', Z) for (X, Z), we get

$$P_0(x')^n \cdot Z^{m-1} \cdot H(x', Z) = A(x', Z) \cdot P_0(x') \cdot Z^m + B(x', Z);$$

if in this we write that the sums of the terms of degree $\leqq m - 1$ in Z on both sides are equal, we get $P_0(x')^n \cdot Z^{m-1} \cdot H(x', 0) = B(x', Z)$. If $H(x', 0)$ were not 0, $B(X, Z)$ would have the same two properties which were stated above for $G(X, Z)$, while being of degree $m - 1$ in Z; as this is not possible, we must have $H(x', 0) = 0$; since this is so for an arbitrary polynomial $H(X, Z)$ in the ideal determined by (x, z) over k, it follows from this that $(x', 0)$ is a specialization of (x, z) over k. As we have $z = 1/y$, this means that (x', ∞) is a specialization of (x, y) over k.

It is now easy to deal with the general case of the extension of a specialization.

THEOREM 6. *Let (x), (y) be two given sets of generalized quantities, and k a given field. Then every specialization (x') of (x) over k can be extended, in at least one way, to a specialization (x', y') of (x, y) over k.*

[2] The device that follows, which, it may be hoped, finally eliminates from algebraic geometry the last traces of elimination-theory, is borrowed from C. Chevalley's Princeton lectures.

By using induction on the number of the y's, we see that it is enough to prove our theorem in the case where there is only one y, which we may assume not to be ∞, as otherwise our conclusion is trivially true. That being so, we may, after applying if necessary a reciprocation to (x) and (x'), assume that these are finite; then we are in the case which has been treated above.

PROPOSITION 5. *Let (x') be a specialization of (x) over a field k; let (y) be such that all the specializations of (y) over $(x) \to (x')$, with reference to k, are algebraic over $k(x')$; then those specializations of (y) are in finite number.*

Put $(y) = (y_1, \cdots, y_m)$. If, for any value of j less than m, there was a specialization of $(y_1, \cdots, y_j)$ over $(x) \to (x')$ which was not algebraic over $k(x')$, this could, by th. 6, be extended to a specialization of (y) over $(x) \to (x')$, which would not be algebraic over $k(x')$, against our assumption. Therefore, for every j, the specializations of $(y_1, \cdots, y_j)$ over $(x) \to (x')$, with reference to k, are all algebraic over $k(x')$. Using induction on j, we need now only show that, under our assumptions, a given specialization of $(y_1, \cdots, y_j)$ over $(x) \to (x')$ can be extended to one of $(y_1, \cdots, y_{j+1})$ over $(x) \to (x')$ only in a finite number of ways. This amounts to proving our proposition in the case $m = 1$, i.e. when the set (y) consists of one y only; it is trivially true for $y = \infty$, so that we may assume that y is not ∞; by applying a reciprocation to (x) and (x') if necessary, we may also assume that both are finite. But then we have only the three possibilities which have been discussed above under (a), (b) and (c); (a) is excluded by our assumption, and our conclusion holds true in cases (b) and (c). This completes our proof.

3. Applications. We shall now derive from the results of §2 a number of consequences which will prove useful in the next chapters. We begin with a new definition and an application of prop. 4.

Let (x', y') be a specialization of (x, y) over a field k; then we say that (y') is an *isolated specialization of (y) over $(x) \to (x')$*, with reference to k, if there does not exist a specialization (x', y'') of (x, y) over k, of higher dimension than (x', y') over k, and having (x', y') as a specialization over k. By prop. 2 and th. 3 of §1, (y') is therefore an isolated specialization of (y) over $(x) \to (x')$, with reference to k, if and only if every specialization (y'') of (y) over $(x) \to (x')$, with reference to k, which has (y') as a specialization over $k(x')$, is a generic specialization of (y') over $k(x')$.

PROPOSITION 6. *Let (x', y', z') be a specialization of (x, y, z) over a field k, such that (y') is an isolated specialization of (y) over $(x) \to (x')$, and (z') an isolated specialization of (z) over $(x, y) \to (x', y')$, with reference to k. Then (y', z') is an isolated specialization of (y, z) over $(x) \to (x')$ with reference to k.*

Suppose that (x', y'', z'') is a specialization of (x, y, z) over k and has (x', y', z') as a specializaton over k. Then, by our assumption on (y'), (x', y'') must have the same dimension as (x', y') over k; therefore, by th. 3 of §1, (x', y') must be a generic specialization of (x', y'') over k; and this, by prop. 4 of §2, can be extended to a generic specialization $(x', y', \bar{z}')$ of (x', y'', z'') over k. Then $(x', y', \bar{z}')$ is a specialization of (x, y, z) and has the specialization (x', y', z') over k, so that, by our assumption on (z'), it must have the same dimension as (x', y', z') over k; as it has the same dimension as (x', y'', z'') over k, this proves our assertion.

The rest of this § will consist of applications of th. 6 of §2.

PROPOSITION 7. *Let (x') be a specialization of (x) over a field k. Then there exists a generic specialization $(\bar{x})$ of (x) over k, such that (x') is a specialization of $(\bar{x})$ over $\bar{k}$.*

By applying a reciprocation to (x) and (x'), we may assume that they are finite. That being so, let $\mathfrak{P}$ be the ideal determined by (x) over $\bar{k}$, and let (ξ) be the set of all coefficients in some basis of $\mathfrak{P}$; then, by th. 3 of Chap. I, §6, and by the definition of a regular extension, $k(\xi, x)$ is a regular extension of $k(\xi)$. By th. 6 of §2, the specialization (x') of (x) can be extended to a specialization (ξ', x') of (ξ, x) over k. Then, by the coroll. of th. 3, §1, (ξ') is a conjugate of (ξ) over k, i.e. a generic specialization of (ξ) over k, which therefore, by prop. 4 of §2, can be extended to a generic specialization $(\xi', \bar{x})$ of (ξ, x) over k; by th. 1 of §1, this implies that there is an isomorphism of $k(\xi, x)$ on $k(\xi', \bar{x})$ which maps (ξ) on (ξ') and (x) on $(\bar{x})$; as $k(\xi, x)$ is regular over $k(\xi)$, it follows from this, e.g. by th. 5 of Chap. I, §7, that $k(\xi', \bar{x})$ is regular over $k(\xi')$. As (ξ', x') is a specialization of (ξ, x) over k, it is also one of $(\xi', \bar{x})$ over k; by prop. 2 of §1, this means that (x') is a specialization of $(\bar{x})$ over $k(\xi')$, and therefore, by th. 4 of §1 (applied to $k(\xi')$, $(\bar{x})$, and $\bar{k}$), also over $\bar{k}$.

PROPOSITION 8. *Let k be a field, and (x) a set of quantities such that $k(x)$ is regular over k. Let (y) be a set of algebraic quantities over $k(x)$; and let $(y^{(1)}, \cdots, y^{(d)})$ be a complete set of conjugates of (y) over $k(x)$. Then every specialization $(x', y'^{(1)}, \cdots, y'^{(d)})$ of $(x, y^{(1)}, \cdots, y^{(d)})$ over k is, except possibly for a permutation of the $(y'^{(\nu)})$, a specialization of $(x, y^{(1)}, \cdots, y^{(d)})$ over $\bar{k}$.*

By prop. 7, it will be enough to prove our assertion for generic specializations of $(x, y^{(1)}, \cdots, y^{(d)})$; therefore we shall assume that $(x', y'^{(1)}, \cdots, y'^{(d)})$ is such. As (x') is a specialization of (x) over k, it is also one over $\bar{k}$ by th. 4 of §1; by th. 3 of §1 it has the same dimension as (x) over k, hence also over $\bar{k}$, and therefore is a generic specialization of (x) over $\bar{k}$; by prop. 4 of §2, this can be extended to a generic specialization $(x', y''^{(1)}, \cdots, y''^{(d)})$ of $(x, y^{(1)}, \cdots, y^{(d)})$ over $\bar{k}$. Then $(x', y'^{(1)}, \cdots, y'^{(d)})$ is a specialization of $(x', y''^{(1)}, \cdots, y''^{(d)})$ over k, so that, by prop. 2 of §1, $(y'^{(1)}, \cdots, y'^{(d)})$ is a specialization of $(y''^{(1)}, \cdots, y''^{(d)})$ over $k(x')$. As the $(y^{(\nu)})$ are algebraic over $k(x)$, th. 1 of §1 shows that the $(y'^{(\nu)})$ and $(y''^{(\nu)})$ are algebraic over $k(x')$; moreover, for the same reason, $(y''^{(1)}, \cdots, y''^{(d)})$ is a complete set of conjugates of any one of the $(y''^{(\nu)})$ over $k(x')$; from this and from the coroll. of th. 3, §1, it follows that every specialization of that set over $k(x')$ can be deduced from it by a permutation of the $(y''^{(\nu)})$; this, applied to $(y'^{(1)}, \cdots, y'^{(d)})$, is what we had to prove.

PROPOSITION 9. *Let k be a field, (x) a set of quantities, and y an algebraic quantity over $k(x)$; let $(y_1, \cdots, y_n)$ be a complete set of conjugates of y over $k(x)$, and let $F(x, Y) = 0$ be an irreducible equation for y over $k(x)$, where $F(X, Y)$ is a polynomial in $k[X, Y]$. Furthermore, let (x') be a finite specialization of (x) over k, such that $F(x', Y)$ is not 0; let m be the degree of $F(x', Y)$ in Y, and let $(y'_1, \cdots, y'_n)$ be a specialization of $(y_1, \cdots, y_n)$ over $(x) \to (x')$, with reference to k. Then the set $(y'_1, \cdots, y'_n)$ consists of all the roots of $F(x', Y)$, each taken with its multiplicity, and of $n - m$ times the element ∞.*

As we have seen in Chap. I, §4, $(y_1, \cdots, y_n)$ is the set consisting of all roots of $F(x, Y) = 0$, so that we have $F(x, Y) = P(x)\cdot\prod_{\nu=1}^{n}(Y - y_\nu)$, where $P(X)$ is in $k[X]$. By reordering the y_ν and y'_ν, we may assume that $y'_\mu \neq \infty$ for $1 \leqq \mu \leqq r$, and $y'_\rho = \infty$ for $r + 1 \leqq \rho \leqq n$; then, if we put $z_\rho = 1/y_\rho$ for $r + 1 \leqq \rho \leqq n$, $(x', y'_1, \cdots, y'_r, 0, \cdots, 0)$ is a finite specialization of $(x, y_1, \cdots, y_r, z_{r+1}, \cdots, z_n)$ over k. Put $v = P(x)\cdot\prod_{\rho=r+1}^{n} y_\rho$, and $w = 1/v$; by th. 6 of §2, there exists a specialization v' of v over

$$(x, y_1, \cdots, y_r, z_{r+1}, \cdots, z_n) \to (x', y'_1, \cdots, y'_r, 0, \cdots, 0);$$

put $w' = 1/v'$. Furthermore, let the polynomials $G(Y)$, $G'(Y)$ be defined by

$$G(Y) = \prod_{\mu=1}^{r}(Y - y_\mu)\cdot\prod_{\rho=r+1}^{n}(z_\rho\cdot Y - 1), \qquad G'(Y) = (-1)^{n-r}\cdot\prod_{\mu=1}^{r}(Y - y'_\mu).$$

Then we have $F(x, Y) = v\cdot G(Y)$ and $G(Y) = w\cdot F(x, Y)$; if v' were 0, the former relation would imply $F(x', Y) = 0$, and, if w' were 0, the latter would imply $G'(Y) = 0$; as neither is the case, this shows that v' can be neither 0 nor ∞. Then the relation $F(x, Y) = v\cdot G(Y)$ implies that we have $F(x', Y) = v'\cdot G'(Y)$; therefore $F(x', Y)$ is of degree r in Y, and has the roots y'_μ for $1 \leqq \mu \leqq r$. This proves our assertion.

PROPOSITION 10. *Let (x') be a specialization of (x) over a field k; let $(y_j) = (y_1, \cdots, y_m)$ be a set of m quantities, not all 0. Then there exists at least one value of the index j, say j_0, such that y_{j_0} is not 0, and that, if we put $z_j = y_j/y_{j_0}$ for $1 \leqq j \leqq m$, the set (z) has a finite specialization (z') over $(x) \to (x')$, with reference to k.*

If this is true for the set $(y_1, \cdots, y_m)$, then it is also true for any set of the form $(y_1, \cdots, y_m, 0, \cdots, 0)$; for, if we choose the same j_0 for the latter as for the former, the set $(z_1, \cdots, z_m, 0, \cdots, 0)$ has then the finite specialization $(z'_1, \cdots, z'_m, 0, \cdots, 0)$ over $(x) \to (x')$. This shows that, conversely, it is enough if we prove our result for the set of all those among the y_j which are not 0. In other words, it is enough to prove our proposition under the additional assumption that none of the y_j is 0. That being assumed, suppose that there is no j_0 with the required property. Then, if we put $u_{jh} = y_j/y_h$ for $1 \leqq j \leqq m$, $1 \leqq h \leqq m$, and if (u') is any specialization of (u) over $(x) \to (x')$, with reference to k, there is, to every j_0, at least one value j_1 of j, such that $u'_{j_1 j_0} = \infty$. As we have

$u_{hj} = 1/u_{jh}$ for all j and h, u'_{hj} must be 0 whenever u'_{jh} is ∞. Therefore there is, to every j_0, some $j_1 = \varphi(j_0)$, such that $u'_{j_0 j_1} = 0$. Take $j_0 = 1$, and $j_{\nu+1} = \varphi(j_\nu)$ for $\nu = 0, 1, 2, 3, \cdots$; some index must then occur twice in the sequence (j_ν), say as $j_\nu = j_{\nu+\rho}$, so that we have $u'_{j_\nu j_{\nu+1}} = \cdots = u'_{j_{\nu+\rho-1} j_\nu} = 0$; but this is impossible since, by the definition of the u_{jh}, the product of the ρ quantities $u_{j_\nu j_{\nu+1}}, \cdots, u_{j_{\nu+\rho-1} j_\nu}$ is equal to 1.

Prop. 10 is of considerable importance for the theory of projective spaces; for the time being, its main use for us lies in the fact that we need it for proving the following:

PROPOSITION 11. *Let k be a field, (x) a set of quantities, and (x') a finite specialization of (x) over k. Let (y) be a set of quantities, not all 0, such that $(x', 0)$ is a specialization of (x, y) over k. Then there exists a set of quantities (z'), not all 0, with the following property: if $F(X, Y)$ is any polynomial in $k[X, Y]$ such that $F(x, y) = 0$ and that $F(X, 0) = 0$, and if we put $F_j(X, Y) = \partial F/\partial Y_j$, then we have $\sum_j F_j(x', 0)\cdot z'_j = 0$.*

We apply prop. 10 to the set (x, y), to its specialization $(x', 0)$, and to the set (y); this shows that, if j_0 is suitably chosen, and if we put $z_j = y_j/y_{j_0}$, then (z) has a finite specialization (z') over $(x, y) \to (x', 0)$, with reference to k; moreover, as we have $z_{j_0} = 1$, we also have $z'_{j_0} = 1$, so that the z'_j are not all 0. Now put $t = y_{j_0}$, so that we have $y_j = t\cdot z_j$ for every j. Since we have $F(X, 0) = 0$, the polynomial $F(X, Y) - \sum_j F_j(X, 0)\cdot Y_j$ consists of terms of degree $\geqq 2$ in (Y); therefore, if we substitute $t\cdot z_j$ for y_j in the relation $F(x, y) = 0$, we get a relation of the form $\sum_j F_j(x, 0)\cdot tz_j + t^2\cdot G(x, z, t) = 0$, where $G(X, Z, T)$ is in $k[X, Z, T]$. Dividing this by t, and substituting $(x', z', 0)$ for (x, z, t), we get our result.

The following result means substantially that every algebraic variety has infinitely many points with algebraic coordinates over the field of reference (cf. Chap. IV, prop. 3).

PROPOSITION 12. *The field k being given, every set of quantities (x) has a finite specialization (x') over k which is algebraic over k; moreover, if k and (x) are given, and if $F(X)$ is any given polynomial in $k[X]$, such that $F(x) \neq 0$, there is a finite specialization (x') of (x) over k, which is algebraic over k, and such that $F(x') \neq 0$.*

We begin by proving the first assertion in the special case where x_1 is a variable quantity over k, and $k(x)$ is algebraic over $k(x_1)$; then we have $\dim_k (x) = 1$, so that, by th.3 of §1, every specialization of (x) over k which is not generic must be algebraic over k. In particular, this is the case for every specialization $(\bar{x})$ of (x) over k which is not finite. Prop. 5 of §2 then shows that, i being given, the specializations $(\bar{x})$ of (x) for which $\bar{x}_i = \infty$ are in finite number; hence there is only a finite number of specializations $(\bar{x}^{(\nu)})$ of (x) over k which are not finite; the elements $\bar{x}_1^{(\nu)}$ in these specializations are therefore also in finite number, and, since $\bar{k}$ contains infinitely many elements, we can choose $x'_1 \in \bar{k}$ so that it will be different from all these $\bar{x}_1^{(\nu)}$. Then, if we extend the specialization $x_1 \rightarrow x'_1$ to a specialization (x') of (x) over k, this will be as required. We now consider the general case, using induction on $r = \dim_k (x)$. Reordering the x_i, we may assume that x_1 is variable over k; then $k(x)$ has the dimension $r - 1$ over $k(x_1)$, so that, by the induction assumption, (x) has a finite specialization $(\bar{x})$ over $k(x_1)$ which is algebraic over $k(x_1)$; then we have $\bar{x}_1 = x_1$. By the special case which has been treated already, $(\bar{x})$ must then have a finite specialization (x') over k, which is algebraic over k; this is as required. Finally, if we want a specialization (x') which will satisfy $F(x') \neq 0$, $F(X)$ being as stated, then, if we have $(x) = (x_1, \cdots, x_n)$, we merely have to write $x_0 = 1/F(x)$ and apply the foregoing result to the set of quantities $(x_0, x_1, \cdots, x_n)$ instead of to (x) itself.

4. Specialization-rings. Let (x') be a finite specialization of a set of quantities (x) over a field k; then the set of all elements z of $k(x)$ which can be written in the form $F(x)/G(x)$, with $F(X)$ and $G(X)$ in $k[X]$ and $G(x') \neq 0$, is a subring of $k(x)$, which will be called[3] *the specialization-ring of (x') in $k(x)$.*

PROPOSITION 13. *Let (x') be a finite specialization of a set of quantities (x) over a field k; let z be an element of $k(x)$, such that either z or $1/z$ is in the specialization-ring of (x') in $k(x)$. Then z has a uniquely determined specialization z' over $(x) \rightarrow (x')$ with reference to k; z' is finite if and only if z itself is in the specialization-ring of (x') in $k(x)$; and, if that is so, and if we have $z = F(x)/G(x)$ with $F(X)$ and $G(X)$ in $k[X]$ and $G(x') \neq 0$, then z' is given by $z' = F(x')/G(x')$, and this is an element of $k(x')$.*

We may assume $z \neq 0$, as our assertions are trivially true if $z = 0$. We know, by th. 6 of §2, that z has at least one specialization z' over $(x) \rightarrow (x')$ with reference to k. Now assume in the first place that z is in the specialization-ring of (x') in $k(x)$, and that we have $z = F(x)/G(x)$, with $F(X)$ and $G(X)$ in $k[X]$ and $G(x') \neq 0$; and put $w = 1/z$. Then we have $G(x) - w \cdot F(x) = 0$; as $G(x')$ is not 0, this shows that $(x', 0)$ is not a specialization of (x, w) over k. Therefore every specialization z' of z over $(x) \rightarrow (x')$ must be finite; as we have

$$F(x) - z \cdot G(x) = 0,$$

we must have, for such a z', $F(x') - z' \cdot G(x') = 0$, hence $z' = F(x')/G(x')$; this shows that z' is then uniquely determined, and that it is as stated in our proposition. On the other hand, if we assume that $w = 1/z$ is in the specialization-ring of (x') in $k(x)$, then we can again write $z = F(x)/G(x)$ with $F(X)$ and $G(X)$ in $k[X]$, but now our assumption is that $F(x')$ is not 0. If $G(x') \neq 0$, the foregoing still applies; if $G(x')$ is 0, then the relation $F(x) - z \cdot G(x) = 0$ shows that z can have no finite specialization over $(x) \rightarrow (x')$ with reference to k. This completes our proof.

[3] Other authors, e.g. O. Zariski, use for this the word "quotient-ring", in agreement with the general theory of ideals.

By prop. 13, and with the same notations as there, the correspondence between z and z' defines a mapping into $k(x')$ of the specialization-ring of (x') in $k(x)$. If now z' is an arbitrarily given element of $k(x')$, we can write it as $z' = F(x')/G(x')$, with $F(X)$ and $G(X)$ in $k[X]$, and $G(x') \neq 0$; as $G(x') \neq 0$ implies $G(x) \neq 0$, we may put $z = F(x)/G(x)$, and this is an element of $k(x)$, with the specialization z' over $(x) \to (x')$, with reference to k. This shows that the correspondence between z and z', defined in prop. 13, is a mapping of the specialization-ring of (x') in $k(x)$ *on* the field $k(x')$; this mapping, moreover, is a ring-homomorphism (i.e. it preserves addition and multiplication). In particular, if the specialization $(x) \to (x')$ is generic, we have the following result, which is an immediate consequence of the definitions, of prop. 13, and of th. 1 of §1:

PROPOSITION 14. *Let (x') be a generic specialization of a set of quantities (x) over a field k. Then the specialization-ring of (x') in $k(x)$ is the field $k(x)$ itself; and the correspondence between an arbitrary element z of $k(x)$, and its uniquely determined specialization z' over $(x) \to (x')$ with reference to k, is the isomorphism between $k(x)$ and $k(x')$ over k in which (x) is transformed into (x').*

PROPOSITION 15. *Let (x) be a set of quantities, (x') a finite specialization of (x) over a field k, and (x'') a finite specialization of (x') over k. Then every element z of the specialization-ring of (x'') in $k(x)$ is also in the specialization-ring of (x') in $k(x)$; and its specialization z' over $(x) \to (x')$, with reference to k, is in the specialization-ring of (x'') in $k(x')$.*

For, putting $z = F(x)/G(x)$, with $F(X)$ and $G(X)$ in $k[X]$ and $G(x'') \neq 0$, we have $G(x') \neq 0$, hence the first point, and $z' = F(x')/G(x')$, hence the second point.

PROPOSITION 16. *Let σ be an isomorphism of a field K on a field K'. Let (x) be a set of quantities, and $(\bar{x})$ a finite specialization of (x) over K. Let (x') and $(\bar{x}')$ be such that σ can be extended to an isomorphism σ of $K(x)$ on $K'(x')$, mapping (x) on (x'), and also to an isomorphism of $K(\bar{x})$ on $K'(\bar{x}')$, mapping $(\bar{x})$ on $(\bar{x}')$. Then $(\bar{x}')$ is a specialization of (x') over K'; and σ maps the specialization-ring of $(\bar{x})$ in $K(x)$ on the specialization-ring of $(\bar{x}')$ in $K'(x')$.*

In fact, this is an immediate consequence of the definitions and of prop. 8 of Chap. I, §3.

PROPOSITION 17. *Let k be a field, (x) a set of quantities such that $k(x)$ is a regular extension of k, and K a free field over k with respect to (x). Let (x') be any finite specialization of (x) over k. Then, if an element z of $k(x)$ is in the specialization-ring of (x') in $K(x)$, it is also in the specialization-ring of (x') in $k(x)$.*

The statement of our proposition depends upon the fact that, under the above assumptions, (x') is a specialization of (x) over K; this was proved as th. 4 of §1. Now, if z is as stated, it can be written as $z = \Phi(x)/\Psi(x)$, with $\Phi(X)$ and $\Psi(X)$ in $K[X]$, and $\Psi(x') \neq 0$. Let the ξ_λ be a maximal set of linearly independent elements over k among the coefficients of $\Phi(X)$ and $\Psi(X)$; expressing all these coefficients in terms of the ξ_λ, we get expressions

$$\Phi(X) = \sum_\lambda \xi_\lambda F_\lambda(X), \qquad \Psi(X) = \sum_\lambda \xi_\lambda G_\lambda(X),$$

where the $F_\lambda(X)$ and $G_\lambda(X)$ are in $k[X]$. This gives the relation

$$\sum_\lambda \xi_\lambda[G_\lambda(x)\cdot z - F_\lambda(x)] = 0.$$

By th. 5 of Chap. I, §7, K and $k(x)$ are linearly disjoint over k, so that the ξ_λ are linearly independent over $k(x)$; therefore the last relation implies that we have $G_\lambda(x)\cdot z = F_\lambda(x)$ for every λ. Since $\Psi(x')$ is not 0, there must be some λ for which $G_\lambda(x')$ is not 0; for that λ, we have a fortiori $G_\lambda(x) \neq 0$; then the relation $z = F_\lambda(x)/G_\lambda(x)$ for that value of λ proves our assertion.

Proposition 18. *Let the $(x'^{(\nu)})$, for $1 \leqq \nu \leqq N$, be finite specializations of a set of quantities (x) over a field k. Then, if an element z of $k(x)$ is, for every ν, in the specialization-ring of $(x'^{(\nu)})$ in $k(x)$, it can be written in the form $z = F(x)/G(x)$, with $F(X)$ and $G(X)$ in $k[X]$, and $G(x'^{(\nu)}) \neq 0$ for $1 \leqq \nu \leqq N$.*

We use induction on N. The polynomials $G(X)$ in $k[X]$ such that we have $G(x)\cdot z = F(x)$ for some $F(X)$ in $k[X]$ obviously form an ideal $\mathfrak{Q}$ in $k[X]$; by the induction assumption, there exists, for every μ, a polynomial $G_\mu(X)$ in $\mathfrak{Q}$, such that we have $G_\mu(x'^{(\nu)}) \neq 0$ for all values of ν except possibly $\nu = \mu$. If, for some μ, we have $G_\mu(x'^{(\mu)}) \neq 0$, then we put $G(X) = G_\mu(X)$ for that value of μ. If, for every μ, we have $G_\mu(x'^{(\mu)}) = 0$, then we put $G(X) = \sum_\nu [\prod_{\mu\neq\nu} G_\mu(X)]$. In both cases, we have thus defined a polynomial $G(X)$ in $\mathfrak{Q}$, such that $G(x'^{(\nu)}) \neq 0$ for $1 \leqq \nu \leqq N$, hence a fortiori $G(x) \neq 0$. Then there is $F(X)$ such that $G(x)\cdot z = F(x)$, hence $z = F(x)/G(x)$. This proves our assertion.

For the proof of prop. 20, we need the following auxiliary result:

Proposition 19. *Let $(\omega) = (\omega_1, \cdots, \omega_m)$ be a set of m quantities, and k a field, such that the ω_λ are linearly independent over $k^{p^{-n}}$ for every $n \geqq 0$. Then there exist m generic specializations $(\omega^{(\rho)})$ of (ω) over k, such that the determinant $|\omega_\lambda^{(\rho)}|$, for $1 \leqq \lambda \leqq m$, $1 \leqq \rho \leqq m$, is not 0.*

In other words, we have to prove that, among all the linear forms $\sum_{\lambda=1}^m \omega'_\lambda U_\lambda$, where we take for (ω') all the generic specializations of (ω) over k, there are m linearly independent forms. If that were not so, then there would exist a set (u) of m quantities, not all 0, which would satisfy the relation $\sum_\lambda \omega'_\lambda u_\lambda = 0$ whenever (ω') is a generic specialization of (ω) over k. Assume that there is such a set (u); let h be the smallest integer such that there exists such a set (u) for which $u_{h+1} = \cdots = u_m = 0$. Such a set (u) being chosen, we have $u_h \neq 0$, because of the definition of h; we may therefore, after replacing the u_λ by u_λ/u_h, assume that we have $u_h = 1$. We have $\sum_{\lambda=1}^h \omega'_\lambda u_\lambda = 0$ whenever (ω') is a generic specialization of (ω) over k, hence in particular $\sum_\lambda \omega_\lambda u_\lambda = 0$; by our assumption on the ω_λ, this implies that the set (u) is not purely inseparable over k, for, if it were so, the u_λ would all be in the field $k^{p^{-n}}$ for some value of n. That being so, either (u) is algebraic over k, and then, since it is not purely inseparable over k, there is some conjugate (u') of (u) over k which is different from (u); or (u) is of dimension $r > 0$ over k, and then, by th. 2 of §1, there is a generic specialization (u') of (u) over k which is of dimension r over $k(u)$ and therefore is different from (u). In view of the coroll. of th. 3, §1, this shows that in either case there is a generic specialization (u') of (u) over k, other than (u). Let now (ω') be any generic specialization of (ω) over k. By prop. 4 of §2, we can extend the generic specialization (u) of (u') to a generic specialization (u, ω'') of (u', ω') over k. Then (ω'') is a generic specialization of (ω'), hence also of (ω), over k, so that we have $\sum_\lambda \omega''_\lambda u_\lambda = 0$; this implies that we have $\sum_\lambda \omega'_\lambda u'_\lambda = 0$. Therefore, for every (ω'), we have both $\sum_{\lambda=1}^{h} \omega'_\lambda u_\lambda = 0$ and $\sum_{\lambda=1}^{h} \omega'_\lambda u'_\lambda = 0$, hence

$$\sum_{\lambda=1}^{h} \omega'_\lambda (u'_\lambda - u_\lambda) = 0;$$

as we have $(u') \neq (u)$, and $u_h = 1$, hence $u'_h = 1$ and $u'_h - u_h = 0$, this contradicts the definition of h.

PROPOSITION 20. *Let k be a field, (x) a set of quantities such that $k(x)$ is regular over k, and (x') a finite specialization of (x) over k. Let K be a free field over k with respect to (x). Let z be an element of $K(x)$ of the form $z = \sum_\lambda \omega_\lambda w_\lambda$, where the w_λ are elements of $k(x)$ and the ω_λ are linearly independent elements of K over k. Then, if all the w_λ are in the specialization-ring of (x') in $k(x)$, z is in the specialization-ring, in $K(x)$, of every generic specialization of (x') over k. Conversely, all the w_λ must be in the specialization-ring of (x') in $k(x)$ whenever z is in the specialization-ring, in $K(x)$, of every generic specialization (x'') of (x') over k such that* $\dim_K (x'') = \dim_k (x')$.

The first part is trivial; one should only observe that its statement depends upon the fact that every specialization of (x') over k is also a specialization of (x) over k, hence also over K by th. 4 of §1. As to the second part, we shall first deal with the case where the ω_λ are linearly independent, not only over k, but also over $k^{p^{-n}}$ for every $n \geqq 0$. Put $K_0 = k(\omega)$; then we have $z \in K_0(x)$; moreover, as we have $k \subset K_0 \subset K$, and as (x) has the same dimension over k and over K, (x) also has that same dimension over K_0, so that K_0 is free over k, and K over K_0, with respect to (x). It follows from this, by th. 5 of Chap. I, §7, that $K_0(x)$ is regular over K_0. Furthermore, it also follows, by prop. 17, that, if (x'') is as stated in our proposition, then z is in the specialization-ring of (x'') in $K_0(x)$. Now apply prop. 19 to the set (ω); if that set consists of m elements, it shows that there are m generic specializations $(\omega^{(\rho)})$ of (ω) over k, such that the determinant $|\omega_\lambda^{(\rho)}|$ is not 0. If that is so for some choice of the $(\omega^{(\rho)})$, then the same is true if we replace the set of m^2 quantities $(\omega^{(1)}, \cdots, \omega^{(m)})$ by any generic specialization of it over k; by th. 2 of §1, we can do that in such a way as to make that set, and the set (x, x'), independent over k; we may assume that this has been done, so that, if we put $K_1 = k(\omega^{(1)}, \cdots, \omega^{(m)})$, the field K_1 is free over k with respect to (x, x'). That being so, $(\omega^{(\rho)})$ and (x) are independent over k for every ρ; since the ω_λ are in K, (ω) and (x) also are independent over k; as $k(x)$ is regular over k, and as (ω) and $(\omega^{(\rho)})$ are specializations of each other over k, it follows from th. 5 of §1 that (ω, x) and $(\omega^{(\rho)}, x)$ are specializations of each other over k, i.e., by prop. 2 of §1, that $(\omega^{(\rho)})$ is a generic specialization of (ω) over $k(x)$; by th. 1 of §1, there is therefore an isomorphism σ_ρ of $k(x, \omega)$ on $k(x, \omega^{(\rho)})$ over $k(x)$, which maps (ω) on $(\omega^{(\rho)})$. The inverse σ_ρ^{-1} of σ_ρ induces an isomorphism of $k(\omega^{(\rho)})$ on $k(\omega)$ over k, in which $(\omega^{(\rho)})$ is mapped on (ω); by prop. 9 of Chap. I, §3, the latter isomorphism can be extended to an isomorphism of $k(\omega^{(\rho)}, x')$ on some extension $k(\omega, x''^{(\rho)})$ of $k(\omega)$, which maps (x') on some set $(x''^{(\rho)})$; moreover, by that same prop., we can assume that this has been done in such a way that the dimension of $(x''^{(\rho)})$ over K is equal to the dimension of (x') over $k(\omega^{(\rho)})$, which is itself equal to $\dim_k(x')$ since (x') and $(\omega^{(\rho)})$ are independent over k. Then $(\omega, x''^{(\rho)})$ is a generic specialization of $(\omega^{(\rho)}, x')$ over k, by th. 1 of §1; and $(x''^{(\rho)})$ is a generic specialization of (x') over k, with a dimension over K equal to $\dim_k(x')$; we can therefore apply to $(x''^{(\rho)})$ what has been proved above of every set (x'') with these properties, viz. the fact that z is in the specialization-ring of every such set in $K_0(x)$. This shows that z can be written as $z = \Phi(x)/\Psi(x)$, with $\Phi(X)$ and $\Psi(X)$ in $K_0[X]$, and $\Psi(x''^{(\rho)}) \neq 0$; multiplying $\Phi(X)$ and $\Psi(X)$ by some suitable element of K_0, we may assume that they are of the form $\Phi(X) = F(\omega, X)$, $\Psi(X) = G(\omega, X)$, with $F(U, X)$ and $G(U, X)$ in $k[U, X]$; then we have $z = F(\omega, x)/G(\omega, x)$, and $G(\omega, x''^{(\rho)}) \neq 0$. By the definition of $(x''^{(\rho)})$, the relation $G(\omega, x''^{(\rho)}) \neq 0$ implies $G(\omega^{(\rho)}, x') \neq 0$. On the other hand, we have $\sum_\lambda \omega_\lambda w_\lambda = F(\omega, x)/G(\omega, x)$; applying to this the above-defined isomorphism σ_ρ, and putting $z_\rho = \sum_\lambda \omega_\lambda^{(\rho)} w_\lambda$, we get

$$z_\rho = F(\omega^{(\rho)}, x)/G(\omega^{(\rho)}, x).$$

As K_1 is free over k with respect to (x), th. 4 of §1 shows that (x') is a specialization of (x) over K_1. Then our expression for z_ρ, together with the relation $G(\omega^{(\rho)}, x') \neq 0$, shows that z_ρ is in the specialization-ring of (x') in $K_1(x)$. As the determinant $|\omega_\lambda^{(\rho)}|$ is not 0, we can solve the relations $z_\rho = \sum_\lambda \omega_\lambda^{(\rho)} w_\lambda$ for the w_λ, which gives $w_\lambda = \sum_\rho \eta_{\lambda\rho} z_\rho$, with $\eta_{\lambda\rho} \in K_1$; this shows that the w_λ also must then be in the specialization-ring of (x') in $K_1(x)$; our conclusion follows from this by prop. 17. Now consider the general case where the ω_λ are no more assumed to be linearly independent over the fields $k^{p^{-n}}$; if m_n is the number of linearly independent elements among them over $k^{p^{-n}}$, the m_n form a non-increasing sequence of integers, and must remain constant from a certain point onwards. In other words, we can find n such that, if (ω') is a maximal set of linearly independent elements among the ω_λ over the field $k' = k^{p^{-n}}$, then the ω'_μ are still linearly independent over $k'^{p^{-\nu}} = k^{p^{-n-\nu}}$ for every $\nu \geqq 0$. Then we can write $\omega_\lambda = \sum_\mu \alpha_{\lambda\mu}\omega'_\mu$, with $\alpha_{\lambda\mu} \in k'$; putting $w'_\mu = \sum_\lambda \alpha_{\lambda\mu} w_\lambda$, we get $z = \sum_\mu \omega'_\mu w'_\mu$, and $w'_\mu \in k'(x)$. If we call K' the compositum of K and k', all the assumptions in the special case which has been treated above are now satisfied by k', (x), (x'), K', z, the ω'_μ, and the w'_μ. Therefore the w'_μ are in the specialization-ring of (x') in $k'(x)$, and we can write them as $w'_\mu = P_\mu(X)/Q(X)$, with $P_\mu(X)$ and $Q(X)$ in $k'[X]$, and $Q(x') \neq 0$. This gives for z an expression $z = \Theta(x)/Q(x)$, with $\Theta(X)$ in $K'[X]$, hence, if we put $\Omega(X) = \Theta(X)\cdot Q(X)^{p^n-1}$, and $G(X) = Q(X)^{p^n}$, $z = \Omega(x)/G(x)$, with $\Omega(X) \in K'[X]$, $G(X) \in k[X]$, and $G(x') \neq 0$. From the set consisting of the ω_λ and all the coefficients in $\Omega(X)$, choose a maximal subset of linearly independent elements over k, in such a way as to include all the ω_λ in that subset; denoting that subset by (ω, ξ), we can express the coefficients in $\Omega(X)$ in terms of these, and thus get for $\Omega(X)$ an expression $\Omega(X) = \sum_\lambda \omega_\lambda F_\lambda(X) + \sum_\alpha \xi_\alpha H_\alpha(X)$, with the $F_\lambda(X)$ and $H_\alpha(X)$ in $k[X]$. This gives

$$\sum_\lambda \omega_\lambda w_\lambda = \sum_\lambda \omega_\lambda F_\lambda(x)/G(x) + \sum_\alpha \xi_\alpha H_\alpha(x)/G(x).$$

By th. 5 of Chap. I, §7, K' and $k(x)$ are linearly disjoint over k, so that the ω_λ and ξ_α, being linearly independent over k, are still such over $k(x)$. The last relation therefore implies $w_\lambda = F_\lambda(x)/G(x)$ for every λ; as $G(x')$ is not 0, this proves our proposition.

5. Finiteness over a specialization. Let (x') be a specialization of (x) over k; then we say that a set of quantities (y) is *finite over* $(x) \to (x')$, with reference to k, if every specialization (y') of (y) over $(x) \to (x')$, with reference to k, is finite.

PROPOSITION 21. *A set of quantities* $(y) = (y_j)$ *is finite over a specialization* $(x) \to (x')$, *with reference to a field* k, *if and only if every one of the* y_j *is finite over* $(x) \to (x')$, *with reference to* k.

The direct proposition is obvious. As to the converse, let us suppose, for instance, that y_1 is not finite over $(x) \to (x')$; this means that (x', ∞) is a specialization of (x, y_1) over k; by th. 6 of §2, this can be extended to a specialization (x', y') of (x, y) over k; as we have $y'_1 = \infty$, (y') is not finite.

PROPOSITION 22. *Let* (x') *be a finite specialization of a set of quantities* (x) *over a field* k. *Then a quantity* y *is finite over* $(x) \to (x')$, *with reference to* k, *if and only if it satisfies a relation of the form* $y^d + z_1\cdot y^{d-1} + \cdots + z_d = 0$, *where the* z_i *are in the specialization-ring of* (x') *in* $k(x)$.

As the case $y = 0$ is trivial, we may assume $y \neq 0$, and put $t = 1/y$; then y is finite over $(x) \to (x')$ if and only if $(x', 0)$ is not a specialization of (x, t) over k. Assume first that there is a relation such as stated in our proposition; then we have $1 + z_1\cdot t + \cdots + z_d\cdot t^d = 0$. If $(x', 0)$ is a specialization of (x, t), it can be extended, by th. 6 of §2, to a specialization $(x', 0, z')$ of (x, t, z); and (z') must be finite by prop. 13 of §4; substituting $(0, z')$ for (t, z) in the above relation, we get a contradiction. Now assume that, conversely, $(x', 0)$ is not a specialization of (x, t); this means that there is a polynomial $F(X, T)$ in $k[X, T]$, such that $F(x, t) = 0$ and that $F(x', 0) \neq 0$. Write $F(X, T) = \sum_{i=0}^{d} P_i(X)\cdot T^i$, with $P_i(X) \in k[X]$; then we have $P_0(x') \neq 0$, so that, if we put $z_i = P_i(x)/P_0(x)$ for $1 \leqq i \leqq d$, the z_i are in the specialization-ring of (x') in $k(x)$. The relation $F(x, t) = 0$ can then be written as $1 + z_1\cdot t + \cdots + z_d\cdot t^d = 0$, hence

$$y^d + z_1\cdot y^{d-1} + \cdots + z_d = 0,$$

which proves our proposition.

PROPOSITION 23. *If a set of quantities (y) is finite over a specialization $(x) \to (x')$ with reference to a field k, then every specialization (y') of (y) over $(x) \to (x')$, with reference to k, is algebraic over $k(x')$.*

By prop. 21, it is enough to consider the case where the set (y) consists of a single quantity y. Assume that (x, y) has a specialization (x', y') with y' variable over $k(x')$; then, by the coroll. of th. 5, $(x', 0)$ is a specialization of $(x', 1/y')$ over k, so that (x', ∞) is a specialization of (x', y'), hence also of (x, y), over k, against the assumption.

The following result is closely allied to E. Noether's well-known "normalization-theorem", and its proof, the geometrical meaning of which becomes clear when it is interpreted in terms of a projective space, is modelled on the usual proof of that theorem.

PROPOSITION 24. *Let $(x) = (x_1, \cdots, x_n)$ be a set of n quantities, of dimension r over a field k. Let the u_{ji}, for $1 \leqq j \leqq r$, $1 \leqq i \leqq n$, be rn independent variables over $k(x)$. Put $K = k(u)$, and $y_j = \sum_{i=1}^{n} u_{ji}x_i$ for $1 \leqq j \leqq r$. Then (y) is a set of independent variables over K; (x) is algebraic over $K(y)$; and (x) is finite over every finite specialization (y') of (y) with reference to K.*

We shall prove the last assertion first. Assume that (x', y') is a specialization of (x, y) over K, that (y') is finite, and that (x') is not so. By prop. 10 of §3, applied to the specialization $(x, y) \to (x', y')$ and to the set (x), we can choose i_0 so that, if we put $w_i = x_i/x_{i_0}$ for $1 \leqq i \leqq n$, the set (w) has a finite specialization (w') over $(x, y) \to (x', y')$, with reference to K. Reordering the x_i if necessary, we may assume that $i_0 = 1$; then we must have $x_1' = \infty$, for otherwise, by prop. 13 of §4, the relations $x_i = x_1 \cdot w_i$ would imply that x_i' is finite, and equal to $x_1' \cdot w_i'$, for every i, so that (x') would be finite. But we have

$$(1/x_1) \cdot y_j = \sum_{i=1}^{n} u_{ji} w_i \, ;$$

substituting, in this, (y', w') for (y, w), and 0 for $1/x_1$, we get $0 = \sum_{i=1}^{n} u_{ji} w_i'$; as we have $w_1 = 1$, w_1' is also 1, so that this can be written

$$u_{j1} = -\sum_{h=2}^{n} u_{jh} w_h' .$$

This shows that, if we call K_1 the field generated over k by the $r(n - 1)$ quantities u_{jh} for $1 \leqq j \leqq r$, $2 \leqq h \leqq n$, the r quantities u_{j1} are in $K_1(w')$. But (x', w') is a specialization of (x, w) over K, and a fortiori over K_1, which is not generic since we have $x_1' = \infty$ while x_1 is not ∞; therefore, by th. 3 of §1, the dimension of (x', w') over K_1, hence a fortiori the dimension of (w') over K_1, must be less than that of (x, w), i.e. less than that of (x), which is r. Hence the r quantities u_{j1}, for $1 \leqq j \leqq r$, cannot be independent variables over K_1, since they are in a field $K_1(w')$ of dimension less than r over K_1. This contradicts our assumption about the u_{ji}. We have thus proved that, if (y') is any finite specialization of (y) over K, (x) is finite over $(y) \to (y')$, with reference to K; hence, by prop. 23, if (x', y') is a specialization of (x, y) over K, and if (y') is finite, (x') must be algebraic over $K(y')$; if we take for (x', y') the set (x, y) itself, this shows that (x) is algebraic over $K(y)$. Therefore the dimension of (y) over K is the same as that of (x, y); as we have $K(x, y) = K(x)$, this is equal to r; therefore the r quantities y_j must be independent variables over K. This completes our proof.

6. Generalizations. For the sake of the proofs in Chap. III, where the conventions and restrictions laid down in Chap. I, §1, will have to be relaxed to some extent, it is necessary to give here some generalizations of the foregoing results. In Chap. III, we shall consider, apart from quantities and fields of quantities, which remain subject to the conventions of Chap. I, §1, other, so-called "abstract" fields, and elements of such fields; every one of our "abstract fields", however, will be assumed to contain some field of quantities, as defined in Chap. I, §1; it is desirable that the distinction between the fields in the sense of Chap. I, §1, and the "abstract fields" should be clearly kept in mind. If $\mathfrak{K}$ is any "abstract field", then one can always construct an algebraic closure $\bar{\mathfrak{K}}$ of $\mathfrak{K}$, which is uniquely determined only up to an isomorphism over $\mathfrak{K}$.

PROPOSITION 25. *Let $\mathfrak{K}$ be an abstract field containing a field k, and generated over k by a finite set $(\mathfrak{x}) = (\mathfrak{x}_1, \cdots, \mathfrak{x}_n)$ of elements. Then there is a set of quantities (x), such that there exists an isomorphic mapping of $\mathfrak{K}$ on $k(x)$ over k, which maps $(\mathfrak{x})$ on (x). Moreover, any set of quantities with that property is a generic specialization of (x) over k, and conversely.*

The proof is similar to that of prop. 9 of Chap. I, §3. Reordering the $\mathfrak{x}_i$ if necessary, we may assume that $\mathfrak{x}_1, \cdots, \mathfrak{x}_r$ are algebraically independent over k, and that $\mathfrak{x}_{r+1}, \cdots, \mathfrak{x}_n$ are algebraic over $\mathfrak{L} = k(\mathfrak{x}_1, \cdots, \mathfrak{x}_r)$. Then, if we construct, as an abstract field, an algebraic closure $\bar{\mathfrak{K}}$ of $\mathfrak{K}$, this is also an algebraic closure of $\mathfrak{L}$. If we take for $x_1, \cdots, x_r$ any r independent variables over k, there is an isomorphism of $\mathfrak{L}$ on the field $L = k(x_1, \cdots, x_r)$ over k which maps $(\mathfrak{x}_1, \cdots, \mathfrak{x}_r)$ on $(x_1, \cdots, x_r)$; this can be extended to an isomorphism of $\bar{\mathfrak{K}}$ on the algebraic closure $\bar{L}$ of L. Then, if we take for (x) the image of $(\mathfrak{x})$ by the latter isomorphism, this satisfies our requirements. The last assertion follows from th. 1, §1.

We use prop. 25 in order to extend the idea of specialization to sets of elements of abstract fields. Let $(\mathfrak{x})$ be a set of elements in an abstract field containing the field k; by prop. 25, there is a set of quantities (x) such that there is an isomorphism of $k(\mathfrak{x})$ on $k(x)$ over k, in which $(\mathfrak{x})$ is mapped on (x); then any specialization of (x) over k, as defined in §1, will be called a *specialization of* $(\mathfrak{x})$ *over* k. By prop. 25, this definition does not depend upon the choice of the set (x) which is used in it. A finite specialization of $(\mathfrak{x})$ is then any set of quantities (x') such that we have $P(x') = 0$ whenever $P(X)$ is a polynomial in $k[X]$ and $P(\mathfrak{x}) = 0$.

We further extend the idea of specialization to infinite sets of elements. Let the $\mathfrak{x}_\iota$ be elements, in finite or infinite number, in some abstract field containing the field k (the case is not excluded that this abstract field may be a field in the sense of Chap. I, §1); let I be the set of values which the index ι may take; and let x_ι, for every $\iota \in I$, be a generalized quantity; then we say that (x_ι) is a *specialization of* $(\mathfrak{x}_\iota)$ *over* k if $(x_{\iota_1}, \cdots, x_{\iota_n})$ is a specialization of $(\mathfrak{x}_{\iota_1}, \cdots, \mathfrak{x}_{\iota_n})$ over k for every finite subset $J = \{\iota_1, \cdots, \iota_n\}$ of I.

THEOREM 7. *Let $(\mathfrak{x}_\iota)$, where ι runs over a finite or infinite set of indices I, be a set of elements in an abstract field $\mathfrak{K}$ containing a field k, and let (x_ι) be a specialization of $(\mathfrak{x}_\iota)$ over k. Then, if $(\mathfrak{y}) = (\mathfrak{y}_1, \cdots, \mathfrak{y}_m)$ is any set of elements of $\mathfrak{K}$ in finite number, the specialization (x_ι) of $(\mathfrak{x}_\iota)$ over k can be extended to a specialization (x_ι, y_j) of $(\mathfrak{x}_\iota, \mathfrak{y}_j)$ over k.*

As in the proof of th. 6 of §2, of which this is a generalization, it is enough to treat the case of one $\mathfrak{y}$ only, as the general case follows from this by induction on m. Let $J = \{\iota_1, \cdots, \iota_n\}$ be any finite subset of I; by prop. 25, we can choose the quantities $(\bar{x}_1, \cdots, \bar{x}_n, \bar{y})$ so that there exists an isomorphism of $k(\mathfrak{x}_{\iota_1}, \cdots, \mathfrak{x}_{\iota_n}, \mathfrak{y})$ on $k(\bar{x}_1, \cdots, \bar{x}_n, \bar{y})$ over k, mapping $(\mathfrak{x}_{\iota_1}, \cdots, \mathfrak{x}_{\iota_n})$ on $(\bar{x}_1, \cdots, \bar{x}_n)$, and $\mathfrak{y}$ on $\bar{y}$. Then, by our definition of a specialization,

$$(x_{\iota_1}, \cdots, x_{\iota_n})$$

must be a specialization of $(\bar{x}_1, \cdots, \bar{x}_n)$ over k, which, by th. 6 of §2, can be extended, in at least one way, to a specialization $(x_{\iota_1}, \cdots, x_{\iota_n}, y)$ of

$$(\bar{x}_1, \cdots, \bar{x}_n, \bar{y}),$$

i.e. of $(\mathfrak{x}_{\iota_1}, \cdots, \mathfrak{x}_{\iota_n}, \mathfrak{y})$, over k. If, in some such specialization, y is variable over $k(x_{\iota_1}, \cdots, x_{\iota_n})$, we put $N(J) = \infty$; when y is such, prop. 2 of §1 shows that $(x_{\iota_1}, \cdots, x_{\iota_n}, 0)$ is a specialization of $(x_{\iota_1}, \cdots, x_{\iota_n}, y)$, hence also of $(\mathfrak{x}_{\iota_1}, \cdots, \mathfrak{x}_{\iota_n}, \mathfrak{y})$, over k. Otherwise, i.e. if the quantity y, subject to the above condition, cannot be variable over $k(x_{\iota_1}, \cdots, x_{\iota_n})$, then, by prop. 5 of §2, there are for y only a finite number of distinct possibilities, and we denote that number by $N(J)$. That being so, if we have $N(J) = \infty$ for every J, then the conclusion in our theorem holds if we take $y = 0$. If not, let N_0 be the smallest value taken by $N(J)$; let J_0 be a finite subset of I such that $N(J_0) = N_0$; and let y_ν, for $1 \leqq \nu \leqq N_0$, be the corresponding possibilities for y. Then, if $J \supset J_0$, the possibilities for y, corresponding to J, are still the same, for otherwise $N(J)$ would be less than N_0. This means that our conclusion holds if we take for y any one of the y_ν.

Theorem 7 can easily be extended to the case where the set $(\mathfrak{y})$ is not assumed to consist of a finite number of elements, and is an arbitrary set (finite or not) of elements of $\mathfrak{K}$; in the proof, one merely has to replace ordinary induction by transfinite induction, or by Zorn's lemma. This generalization will not be needed in this book; it is of importance for those branches of modern algebraic geometry where "valuations" play a part; for a valuation in a field is essentially the same thing as a specialization of the set of all the elements in that field (the "valuation-ring" then being the set of all those elements which are not specialized to ∞).

CHAPTER III

ANALYTIC THEORY OF SPECIALIZATIONS

In this chapter, the §§1–3 are merely preliminary steps to the proof of th. 4 of §4; once this proof will have been achieved, no further use will be made of the results of these §§ in the rest of this book. As pointed out in the Introduction, these §§ are the only ones in the book where we make use of "higher methods of proof", viz. of the general theory of ideals and of power-series rings. Until the end of §3, the restrictions and conventions of Chap. I, §1, should be considered as being no longer in force unless specific reference is made to them. We begin by proving (in §§1–2) a number of well-known results.

1. Ideals in arbitrary rings. Our rings are commutative rings in the usual sense, i.e. sets of elements which can be combined by addition and multiplication, these operations being subject to the usual axioms (including the commutativity of multiplication and the existence of a unit-element, denoted by 1). By a *zero-divisor* in a ring $\mathfrak{o}$ we understand any element ω, other than 0, such that the relation $\omega\cdot\omega' = 0$ is satisfied by some element ω' of $\mathfrak{o}$, other than 0. A ring $\mathfrak{o}$ without zero-divisors being arbitrarily given, one can always construct, by the well-known procedure, its *quotient-field*, i.e. the field consisting of the elements ω/ω', with ω and ω' in $\mathfrak{o}$ and $\omega' \neq 0$, subject to the usual rules for identification, addition and multiplication.

LEMMA 1. *In an arbitrary ring* $\mathfrak{o}$, *let* $\mathfrak{a}$ *be an ideal other than* $\mathfrak{o}$, *and* $\mathfrak{b}$ *an ideal with a finite basis* $\beta_1, \cdots, \beta_n$, *i.e. the ideal* $\mathfrak{b} = \mathfrak{o}\cdot\beta_1 + \cdots + \mathfrak{o}\cdot\beta_n$. *Then, if we have* $\mathfrak{b} \subset \mathfrak{a}\cdot\mathfrak{b}$, *every element of* $\mathfrak{b}$, *other than* 0, *is a zero-divisor in* $\mathfrak{o}$.

Our assumptions imply that we have n relations $\beta_i = \sum_{j=1}^{n} \alpha_{ij}\beta_j$, where the α_{ij} are elements of $\mathfrak{a}$; if δ_{ij} is 1 if $i = j$ and 0 if $i \neq j$, these relations can be written as $\sum_{j=1}^{n}(\delta_{ij} - \alpha_{ij})\beta_j = 0$. If we call Δ the determinant $|\delta_{ij} - \alpha_{ij}|$, and Δ_{ij} its minors, then, multiplying the latter relations with Δ_{hi}, we get, after summation over i, $\Delta\cdot\beta_h = 0$, for $1 \leqq h \leqq n$; if β is any element in $\mathfrak{b}$, it can be written as $\beta = \sum_h \omega_h\beta_h$, with $\omega_h \in \mathfrak{o}$, and therefore we have $\Delta\cdot\beta = 0$. But the definition of Δ shows that we have $\Delta \equiv 1$ mod. $\mathfrak{a}$, which implies that Δ is not 0, as otherwise $\mathfrak{a}$ would contain the element 1 and hence would be $\mathfrak{o}$ itself. The relation $\Delta\cdot\beta = 0$ then shows that β is either 0 or a zero-divisor. It also shows that, if $\mathfrak{b}$ is not (0), Δ is a zero-divisor, so that in that case there is a zero-divisor Δ which satisfies the congruence $\Delta \equiv 1$ mod. $\mathfrak{a}$; this remark is sometimes useful, but we shall make no use of it, as we shall apply lemma 1 only to rings without zero-divisors, in which case our assumptions imply that $\mathfrak{b} = (0)$.

If $\mathfrak{o}$ is any ring, and $\mathfrak{a}$ an ideal in $\mathfrak{o}$, then, identifying all elements of $\mathfrak{o}$ which are congruent to each other modulo $\mathfrak{a}$, we get a ring, called the *residue-ring* of $\mathfrak{o}$

mod. $\mathfrak{a}$, and denoted by $\mathfrak{o}/\mathfrak{a}$; if $\mathfrak{o}/\mathfrak{a}$ is a ring without zero-divisors, then $\mathfrak{a}$ is called a *prime ideal*. Every one of the rings which we shall consider contains a field (in the sense of Chap. I, §1); if a ring $\mathfrak{o}$ contains a field k, and if $\mathfrak{a}$ is any ideal in $\mathfrak{o}$, other than $\mathfrak{o}$ itself, then no element of k can be in $\mathfrak{a}$, so that the elements of k are mapped isomorphically on the corresponding elements of the ring $\mathfrak{o}/\mathfrak{a}$, and may be identified with the latter. Then the elements of $\mathfrak{o}/\mathfrak{a}$ (just as those of $\mathfrak{o}$) admit of multiplication by the elements of k, so that $\mathfrak{o}/\mathfrak{a}$ (as also $\mathfrak{o}$ itself) can be considered as a k-module, or, in geometrical terms, as a "vector-space" over k. The case of interest to us is that in which the k-module $\mathfrak{o}/\mathfrak{a}$ is of finite rank, i.e. has a finite basis over k. If the ω_i are elements of $\mathfrak{o}$, we shall say that they are linearly independent over k modulo $\mathfrak{a}$ if there is no relation $\sum_i c_i\omega_i \equiv 0$ mod. $\mathfrak{a}$, where the c_i are elements of k, not all 0. The ring $\mathfrak{o}/\mathfrak{a}$ is a k-module of finite rank n if and only if n is the greatest number of linearly independent elements over k modulo $\mathfrak{a}$ in $\mathfrak{o}$; then, if $\omega_1, \cdots, \omega_n$ are such elements, there are, for every ω in $\mathfrak{o}$, elements c_i of k such that $\omega \equiv \sum_i c_i\omega_i$ mod. $\mathfrak{a}$, and the c_i are uniquely determined by that condition.

LEMMA 2. *Let $\mathfrak{o}$ be a ring containing a field k; let $\mathfrak{a}$ be an ideal in $\mathfrak{o}$, other than $\mathfrak{o}$, with a finite basis $\alpha_1, \cdots, \alpha_r$, and such that $\mathfrak{o}/\mathfrak{a}$ is a k-module of finite rank; let (ω_i) be a maximal set of linearly independent elements of $\mathfrak{o}$ over k modulo $\mathfrak{a}$. Then, for every ω in $\mathfrak{o}$, there are n sequences of homogeneous polynomials $P_{i\nu}(X)$ in $k[X]$, $P_{i\nu}(X)$ being homogeneous of degree ν in $X_1, \cdots, X_r$, such that, for every N, we have*

$$\omega \equiv \sum_i \sum_{\nu=0}^{N-1} \omega_i P_{i\nu}(\alpha) \text{ mod. } \mathfrak{a}^N.$$

ω being given, there are elements c_i of k, such that $\omega \equiv \sum_i c_i\omega_i$ mod. $\mathfrak{a}$; put $P_{i0}(X) = c_i$. Assume now that polynomials $P_{i\nu}(X)$ have been defined for $0 \leqq \nu \leqq N-1$ in such a way that the element λ_N defined by

$$\lambda_N = \omega - \sum_i \sum_{\nu=0}^{N-1} \omega_i P_{i\nu}(\alpha)$$

is in $\mathfrak{a}^N$. The ideal $\mathfrak{a}^N$ has a basis consisting of all monomials of degree N in $\alpha_1, \cdots, \alpha_r$; if, for the given value of N, we denote by $M_\rho(X)$ all the monomials of degree N in $X_1, \cdots, X_r$, we can therefore write λ_N in the form

$$\lambda_N = \sum_\rho \xi_\rho M_\rho(\alpha),$$

where the ξ_ρ are elements of $\mathfrak{o}$. For every ρ we can determine the $c_{i\rho}$ in k so as to have $\xi_\rho \equiv \sum_i c_{i\rho}\omega_i$ mod. $\mathfrak{a}$; then we have $\lambda_N = \sum_{i,\rho} c_{i\rho}\omega_i M_\rho(\alpha)$ mod. $\mathfrak{a}^{N+1}$. That being so, we put $P_{iN}(X) = \sum_\rho c_{i\rho} M_\rho(X)$. The $P_{i\nu}(X)$ are thus determined by induction on ν so as to satisfy our requirements.

We now introduce E. Noether's famous "chain-condition" (Teilerkettensatz), which, as well known, can be formulated in a ring $\mathfrak{o}$ in the following equivalent manners: (a) in every set of ideals in $\mathfrak{o}$ there is a maximal ideal (not contained in any other ideal of the set); (b) every ideal in $\mathfrak{o}$ has a finite basis. If these conditions are satisfied the ring $\mathfrak{o}$ is called *Noetherian*. If $\mathfrak{o}$ is any Noetherian ring, then the ring $\mathfrak{o}_n = \mathfrak{o}[X_1, \cdots, X_n]$ of all polynomials in the indeterminates X_i with coefficients in $\mathfrak{o}$, and the ring $\mathfrak{o}'_n = \mathfrak{o}\{X_1, \cdots, X_n\}$ of all (formal) power-series in the X_i with coefficients in $\mathfrak{o}$, are both Noetherian; the well-known proof for this, by induction on n, depends upon the fact that $\mathfrak{o}_n$ is isomorphic to $\mathfrak{o}_{n-1}[X_n]$, and $\mathfrak{o}'_n$ to $\mathfrak{o}'_{n-1}\{X_n\}$, and uses the second form (b) of the chain-condition. Furthermore, if $\mathfrak{o}$ is any Noetherian ring, so are the residue-ring $\mathfrak{o}/\mathfrak{a}$ if $\mathfrak{a}$ is any ideal in $\mathfrak{o}$, and, in case $\mathfrak{o}$ is without zero-divisors, the *quotient-ring* derived from $\mathfrak{o}$ and any prime ideal $\mathfrak{p}$ in $\mathfrak{o}$, i.e. the subring of the quotient-field of $\mathfrak{o}$ which consists of all the elements ω/ω' with $\omega \in \mathfrak{o}$, $\omega' \in \mathfrak{o}$, $\omega' \notin \mathfrak{p}$; the proof for this uses the first form (a) of the chain-condition, and rests upon the fact that there is a one-to-one correspondence, preserving inclusion relations, between the ideals in residue-rings and in quotient-rings derived from $\mathfrak{o}$, and certain sets of ideals in $\mathfrak{o}$ itself. Combining these results, we see that, if $\mathfrak{o}$ is a Noetherian ring contained in some abstract field $\mathfrak{K}$, and if $(\xi_1, \cdots, \xi_n)$ is any set of elements of $\mathfrak{K}$, the ring $\mathfrak{o}[\xi_1, \cdots, \xi_n]$, consisting of all the elements of $\mathfrak{K}$ which can be written in the form $\Phi(\xi)$ with $\Phi(X) \in \mathfrak{o}[X]$, is Noetherian; for it is isomorphic to the residue-ring of the ring $\mathfrak{o}[X]$ modulo the ideal of all polynomials $\Phi(X)$ in $\mathfrak{o}[X]$ such that $\Phi(\xi) = 0$. Furthermore, every quotient-ring derived from this ring and a prime ideal in it will be Noetherian.

We shall also make use of the well-known expression of arbitrary ideals in a Noetherian ring by means of primary ideals. A *primary ideal* in a ring $\mathfrak{o}$ is an ideal $\mathfrak{q}$ such that there exists a prime ideal $\mathfrak{p}$ containing $\mathfrak{q}$, with the following properties: (a) if ω, ω' are two elements of $\mathfrak{o}$, such that $\omega \notin \mathfrak{p}$ and $\omega\cdot\omega' \in \mathfrak{q}$, then ω' is in $\mathfrak{q}$; (b) some power of every element of $\mathfrak{p}$ is in $\mathfrak{q}$. The prime ideal $\mathfrak{p}$ is uniquely determined by these properties when $\mathfrak{q}$ is given; $\mathfrak{q}$ is said to *belong to* $\mathfrak{p}$. In a Noetherian ring, if $\mathfrak{q}$ is a primary ideal, belonging to a prime ideal $\mathfrak{p}$, then there is an integer ρ such that $\mathfrak{p} \supset \mathfrak{q} \supset \mathfrak{p}^\rho$. Furthermore, in a Noetherian ring, every ideal can be written as intersection of primary ideals. The intersection of primary ideals belonging to one and the same prime ideal is also primary, and belongs to that prime ideal.

LEMMA 3. *Let $\mathfrak{a}$, $\mathfrak{b}$ be two ideals in a Noetherian ring $\mathfrak{o}$; then there are ideals $\mathfrak{a}'$, $\mathfrak{b}'$, $\mathfrak{c}$ in $\mathfrak{o}$, and an integer ρ, such that $\mathfrak{a}' \supset \mathfrak{a}^\rho$, $\mathfrak{b}' \supset \mathfrak{b}^\rho$, $\mathfrak{c} \supset (\mathfrak{a} + \mathfrak{b})^\rho$, and that $\mathfrak{a}\cdot\mathfrak{b} = \mathfrak{a}' \cap \mathfrak{b} = \mathfrak{a} \cap \mathfrak{b}' = \mathfrak{a} \cap \mathfrak{b} \cap \mathfrak{c}$.*

Write $\mathfrak{a}\cdot\mathfrak{b}$ as intersection of primary ideals, and call $\mathfrak{q}_i$ those among them which belong to prime ideals $\mathfrak{p}_i$ containing $\mathfrak{a}$, and $\mathfrak{q}'_j$ the others. Let $\mathfrak{a}'$ be the intersection of all the $\mathfrak{q}_i$, and $\mathfrak{b}_1$ the intersection of all the $\mathfrak{q}'_j$, so that we have $\mathfrak{a}\cdot\mathfrak{b} = \mathfrak{a}' \cap \mathfrak{b}_1$. There is a ρ such that $\mathfrak{p}_i^\rho \subset \mathfrak{q}_i$ for every i; since every $\mathfrak{p}_i$ contains $\mathfrak{a}$, this implies $\mathfrak{a}^\rho \subset \mathfrak{q}_i$ for every i, hence $\mathfrak{a}^\rho \subset \mathfrak{a}'$. On the other hand, if we consider any one of the ideals $\mathfrak{q}'_j$, there is an α in $\mathfrak{a}$ which is not in the prime ideal to which that $\mathfrak{q}'_j$ belongs; since $\alpha\cdot\mathfrak{b} \subset \mathfrak{a}\cdot\mathfrak{b} \subset \mathfrak{q}'_j$, this implies $\mathfrak{b} \subset \mathfrak{q}'_j$; therefore we have $\mathfrak{b} \subset \mathfrak{b}_1$; this combined with the relation $\mathfrak{a}\cdot\mathfrak{b} = \mathfrak{a}' \cap \mathfrak{b}_1$ and with the obvious relation $\mathfrak{a}\cdot\mathfrak{b} \subset \mathfrak{b}$, gives $\mathfrak{a}\cdot\mathfrak{b} = \mathfrak{a}' \cap \mathfrak{b}$, which proves the first part of our lemma. The second part follows from this by interchanging $\mathfrak{a}$ and $\mathfrak{b}$. The proof of the last part is similar, and, as we shall make no use of it, will be left to the reader.

LEMMA 4 (KRULL'S THEOREM[1]). *If* $\mathfrak{a}$ *is any ideal other than* $\mathfrak{o}$, *in a Noetherian ring* $\mathfrak{o}$ *without zero-divisors, the intersection* $\bigcap_n \mathfrak{a}^n$ *of all powers of* $\mathfrak{a}$ *is* (0).

Put $\mathfrak{b} = \bigcap_n \mathfrak{a}^n$; we have $\mathfrak{b} = \mathfrak{a}^n \cap \mathfrak{b}$ for every n. By lemma 3, we can find $\mathfrak{a}'$ and ρ such that $\mathfrak{a}' \supset \mathfrak{a}^\rho$ and $\mathfrak{a}\cdot\mathfrak{b} = \mathfrak{a}' \cap \mathfrak{b}$, hence $\mathfrak{a}\cdot\mathfrak{b} \supset \mathfrak{a}^\rho \cap \mathfrak{b}$. This gives $\mathfrak{a}\cdot\mathfrak{b} \supset \mathfrak{b}$, hence, by lemma 1, $\mathfrak{b} = (0)$.

2. Ideals in polynomial rings. We now revert to the conventions of Chap. I, §1, as modified in Chap. II, §6. In other words, we shall consider, in this § and the next one, quantities and fields, subject to the conventions of Chap. I, §1, and also "abstract fields" and their elements; every one of our "abstract fields", however, will contain a field in the sense of Chap. I, §1. Thus, if k is a field (in the sense of Chap. I, §1), and if $k[Y]$ is, as before, the ring of polynomials, with coefficients in k, in some indeterminates $Y_1, \cdots, Y_m$, the (abstractly constructed) quotient-field of $k[Y]$, consisting of all rational expressions $R(Y)$ in the Y_j with coefficients in k, is an "abstract field" containing k; it is obviously isomorphic to any purely transcendental extension of k, of dimension m over k.

Let $\mathfrak{A}$ be an ideal in $k[Y]$; by a *zero* of $\mathfrak{A}$, we understand a set of quantities (y) such that we have $P(y) = 0$ for every $P(Y)$ in $\mathfrak{A}$. It is clear that every finite specialization over k of a zero of $\mathfrak{A}$ is a zero of $\mathfrak{A}$. If a zero (y) of $\mathfrak{A}$ is such that there is no zero of $\mathfrak{A}$, of higher dimension than (y) over k, having (y) as a specialization over k, then we say that (y) is an *isolated zero* of $\mathfrak{A}$.

Let (y) be any set of quantities, and $\mathfrak{P}$ the ideal in $k[Y]$, determined by (y) over k; then $\mathfrak{P}$ is a prime ideal, and (y) is a zero of $\mathfrak{P}$; moreover, by the definition of a specialization, every zero of $\mathfrak{P}$ is a specialization of (y) over k; by th. 3 of Chap. II, §1, it follows from this that (y) is an isolated zero of $\mathfrak{P}$. Conversely, let $\mathfrak{P}$ be any prime ideal in $k[Y]$; then the residue-ring of $k[Y]$ modulo $\mathfrak{P}$ is a ring without zero-divisors, which can therefore be imbedded in its quotient-field $\mathfrak{K}$. If, as explained above, every element of k is identified with the corresponding element in the residue-ring of $k[Y]$ modulo $\mathfrak{P}$, then k is contained in this residue-ring, hence also in $\mathfrak{K}$; if the element of the residue-ring which corresponds to Y_j is denoted by $\mathfrak{y}_j$, then the residue-ring can be written as $k[\mathfrak{y}]$, and its quotient-field $\mathfrak{K}$, therefore, as $k(\mathfrak{y})$; a polynomial $P(Y)$ in $k[Y]$ is then in $\mathfrak{P}$ if and only if it satisfies the relation $P(\mathfrak{y}) = 0$. We can now apply prop. 25 of Chap. II, §6; it shows that we can choose a set of quantities (y) in such a way that there will be an isomorphism of $\mathfrak{K} = k(\mathfrak{y})$ on $k(y)$, in which $(\mathfrak{y})$ is mapped on (y). Then, if $P(Y)$ is in $k[Y]$, we have $P(y) = 0$ if and only if we have $P(\mathfrak{y}) = 0$, i.e. if

[1] W. Krull, *Dimensionstheorie in Stellenringen*, Crelles J., 179 (1938), p. 204; cf. also W. Krull, *Idealtheorie* (Berlin 1935), §15. We have substantially followed Krull's proof of his theorem.

and only if $P(Y)$ is in $\mathfrak{P}$. This means that $\mathfrak{P}$ is the ideal determined over k by the set of quantities (y); we have thus shown that every prime ideal in $k[Y]$ can be so defined.

LEMMA 5. *Let $\mathfrak{A}$ be an ideal in the ring $k[Y]$, and (y) an isolated zero of $\mathfrak{A}$. Let $\mathfrak{Q}$ be the set of all those polynomials $P(Y)$ in $k[Y]$, for which there exists a polynomial $L(Y)$ in $k[Y]$ such that $L(y) \neq 0$ and $L(Y) \cdot P(Y) \in \mathfrak{A}$. Then $\mathfrak{Q}$ is a primary ideal in $k[Y]$, belonging to the prime ideal $\mathfrak{P}$ determined by (y) over k.*

Writing $\mathfrak{A}$ as intersection of primary ideals, call $\mathfrak{Q}_0$ the intersection of all those among them which belong to the prime ideal $\mathfrak{P}$; call $\mathfrak{Q}'_i$ all the others, and $\mathfrak{P}'_i$ the prime ideals to which they respectively belong; $\mathfrak{Q}_0$ is then itself a primary ideal belonging to $\mathfrak{P}$, and $\mathfrak{A}$ is the intersection of $\mathfrak{Q}_0$ and of the $\mathfrak{Q}'_i$; we shall prove our lemma by showing that $\mathfrak{Q} = \mathfrak{Q}_0$. In the first place, if $L(y) \neq 0$, i.e. if $L(Y) \notin \mathfrak{P}$, and if $L(Y) \cdot P(Y)$ is in $\mathfrak{A}$, then, since we have $\mathfrak{A} \subset \mathfrak{Q}_0$, $L(Y) \cdot P(Y)$ is in $\mathfrak{Q}_0$, which implies, by the definition of a primary ideal, that $P(Y)$ is in $\mathfrak{Q}_0$; therefore we have $\mathfrak{Q} \subset \mathfrak{Q}_0$. On the other hand, for any given i, let (y') be a set of quantities such that $\mathfrak{P}'_i$ is the ideal determined by (y') over k; since we have $\mathfrak{P}'_i \supset \mathfrak{Q}'_i \supset \mathfrak{A}$, (y') is a zero of $\mathfrak{A}$, and therefore cannot have (y) as a specialization over k unless it has the same dimension as (y) over k, i.e., by th. 3 of Chap. II, §1, unless it is a generic specialization of (y) over k; the latter case, however, cannot occur, since it would imply $\mathfrak{P}'_i = \mathfrak{P}$; therefore (y) is not a specialization of (y') over k, i.e. there is an $L_i(Y)$ in $\mathfrak{P}'_i$, such that $L_i(y) \neq 0$; then there is an integer ρ_i such that $L_i(Y)^{\rho_i}$ is in $\mathfrak{Q}'_i$. That being so, put $L(Y) = \prod_i L_i(Y)^{\rho_i}$; we have $L(y) \neq 0$, and $L(Y) \in \mathfrak{Q}'_i$ for every i; therefore, if $P(Y)$ is any polynomial in $\mathfrak{Q}_0$, $L(Y) \cdot P(Y)$ is in the intersection of $\mathfrak{Q}_0$ and of all the $\mathfrak{Q}'_i$, i.e. in $\mathfrak{A}$, hence $P(Y)$ in $\mathfrak{Q}$. This shows that we have $\mathfrak{Q}_0 \subset \mathfrak{Q}$, which completes our proof.

LEMMA 6. *Let $\mathfrak{A}$ be an ideal in $k[Y]$, and (α) an isolated zero of $\mathfrak{A}$, (α) being algebraic over k. Let $\mathfrak{O}'$ be the subring of the quotient-field of $k[Y]$, consisting of all the elements in that field which can be written in the form $P(Y)/Q(Y)$ with $P(Y)$ and $Q(Y)$ in $k[Y]$, and $Q(\alpha) \neq 0$. Then the elements of $\mathfrak{O}'$ which can be written in the form $P(Y)/Q(Y)$ with $P(Y) \in \mathfrak{A}$, $Q(Y) \in k[Y]$, and $Q(\alpha) \neq 0$, form an ideal $\mathfrak{Q}'$ in $\mathfrak{O}'$; the residue-ring $\mathfrak{O}'/\mathfrak{Q}'$ is a k-module of finite rank, and this rank is a multiple of $[k(\alpha):k]$.*

The first point is clear. Furthermore, the mapping of $\mathfrak{O}'$ into $k(\alpha)$, in which, to every element $P(Y)/Q(Y)$ of $\mathfrak{O}'$, there corresponds the element $P(\alpha)/Q(\alpha)$ of $k(\alpha)$, is obviously a ring-homomorphism, i.e. preserves addition and multiplication, and it maps $\mathfrak{O}'$ on $k(\alpha)$; in this homomorphism, an element $P(Y)/Q(Y)$ of $\mathfrak{O}'$ is mapped on 0 if and only if $P(\alpha)$ is 0. As is well-known (and as can easily be verified) this implies that the set of elements of $\mathfrak{O}'$ which can be written as $P(Y)/Q(Y)$ with $P(Y)$ and $Q(Y)$ in $k[Y]$, $P(\alpha) = 0$, and $Q(\alpha) \neq 0$, is a prime ideal $\mathfrak{P}'$ in $\mathfrak{O}'$, and that the residue-ring $\mathfrak{O}'/\mathfrak{P}'$ is isomorphic to $k(\alpha)$ and therefore is a k-module of rank $[k(\alpha):k]$. The ring $\mathfrak{O}'$ is Noetherian, being the quotient-ring derived from $k[Y]$ and from the prime ideal $\mathfrak{P}$ in $k[Y]$ which is determined by (α) over k. We now show that the ideal $\mathfrak{Q}'$ of our lemma is a primary ideal in $\mathfrak{O}'$, belonging to the prime ideal $\mathfrak{P}'$. In the first place, it is clear that we have $\mathfrak{P}' \supset \mathfrak{Q}'$. Furthermore, if an element $R(Y)$ of $\mathfrak{O}'$ is not in $\mathfrak{P}'$, then it is of the form $P(Y)/Q(Y)$ with $P(\alpha) \neq 0$ and $Q(\alpha) \neq 0$, so that its reciprocal $1/R(Y)$ is also in $\mathfrak{O}'$; therefore, if $R(Y)$ is such, and if $R_1(Y)$ is an element of $\mathfrak{O}'$ such that the element $S(Y) = R(Y) \cdot R_1(Y)$ is in $\mathfrak{Q}'$, then the relation

$$R_1(Y) = 1/R(Y) \cdot S(Y)$$

implies that $R_1(Y)$ is in $\mathfrak{Q}'$. Now let $\mathfrak{Q}$ be the ideal in $k[Y]$, consisting of all polynomials $P(Y)$ for which there exists an $L(Y) \in k[Y]$ such that $L(\alpha) \neq 0$ and $L(Y) \cdot P(Y) \in \mathfrak{A}$; by lemma 5, $\mathfrak{Q}$ is a primary ideal belonging to the prime ideal $\mathfrak{P}$. Let $P(Y)/Q(Y)$ be any element of $\mathfrak{P}'$, so that we have $P(\alpha) = 0$ and $Q(\alpha) \neq 0$; as $P(Y)$ is in $\mathfrak{P}$, some power $P(Y)^\rho$ of $P(Y)$ is in $\mathfrak{Q}$, and therefore satisfies a relation of the form $L(Y) \cdot P(Y)^\rho = M(Y)$ with $L(\alpha) \neq 0$ and $M(Y) \in \mathfrak{A}$. This gives $[P(Y)/Q(Y)]^\rho = M(Y)/L(Y)Q(Y)^\rho$, which, since $M(Y)$ is in $\mathfrak{A}$ and $L(\alpha)$ and $Q(\alpha)$ are not 0, shows that the left-hand side is in $\mathfrak{Q}'$. This completes the proof of our statement that $\mathfrak{Q}'$ is primary and belongs to the prime $\mathfrak{P}'$; there is therefore an integer ρ such that we have $\mathfrak{P}' \supset \mathfrak{Q}' \supset \mathfrak{P}'^\rho$. That being so, there cannot be more linearly independent elements of $\mathfrak{O}'$ over k modulo $\mathfrak{Q}'$ than modulo $\mathfrak{P}'^\rho$; since, by lemma 2, applied to $\mathfrak{O}'$ and $\mathfrak{P}'$, the ring $\mathfrak{O}'/\mathfrak{P}'^\rho$ is a k-module of finite rank, it follows from this that $\mathfrak{O}'/\mathfrak{Q}'$ also is a k-module of finite rank. In order to prove the last point, we use a well-known device[2] by introducing the ideals $\mathfrak{Q}'_\nu = \mathfrak{Q}' : \mathfrak{P}'^\nu$ for $0 \leqq \nu \leqq \rho$; as usual, $\mathfrak{Q}' : \mathfrak{P}'^\nu$ means the ideal consisting of all the elements $R(Y)$ of $\mathfrak{O}'$ such that $R(Y) \cdot \mathfrak{P}'^\nu \subset \mathfrak{Q}'$, and $\mathfrak{P}'^0$ means the ring $\mathfrak{O}'$ itself. We have $\mathfrak{Q}'_0 = \mathfrak{Q}'$, $\mathfrak{Q}'_\rho = \mathfrak{O}'$, $\mathfrak{Q}'_0 \subset \mathfrak{Q}'_1 \subset \cdots \subset \mathfrak{Q}'_\rho$, and $\mathfrak{P}' \cdot \mathfrak{Q}'_{\nu+1} \subset \mathfrak{Q}'_\nu$ for every ν; and the $\mathfrak{Q}'_\nu$, as can be easily verified, are primary ideals belonging to the prime ideal $\mathfrak{P}'$. The rank of the k-module $\mathfrak{O}'/\mathfrak{Q}'$, i.e. of $\mathfrak{Q}'_\rho/\mathfrak{Q}'_0$, is the sum of the ranks of the modules $\mathfrak{Q}'_{\nu+1}/\mathfrak{Q}'_\nu$ for $0 \leqq \nu \leqq \rho - 1$; therefore we need only prove that each one of the latter ranks is a multiple of $[k(\alpha):k]$. In fact, for a given ν, let $R(Y)$ be any element of $\mathfrak{O}'$, and $S(Y)$ any element of $\mathfrak{Q}'_{\nu+1}$; then the product $R(Y) \cdot S(Y)$ is in $\mathfrak{Q}'_\nu$ if and only if either $R(Y)$ is in $\mathfrak{P}'$ or $S(Y)$ in $\mathfrak{Q}'_\nu$; from this it follows that the class of $R(Y) \cdot S(Y)$ modulo $\mathfrak{Q}'_\nu$ depends only upon the class of $R(Y)$ modulo $\mathfrak{P}'$ and the class of $S(Y)$ modulo $\mathfrak{Q}'_\nu$. This shows that the transformation $S(Y) \to R(Y) \cdot S(Y)$, for a given $R(Y)$ in $\mathfrak{O}'$, nduces a linear transformation of the module $\mathfrak{Q}'_{\nu+1}/\mathfrak{Q}'_\nu$ into itself, depending only upon the class of $R(Y)$ modulo $\mathfrak{P}'$; as the ring $\mathfrak{O}'/\mathfrak{P}'$ is isomorphic to $k(\alpha)$, this means that the k-module $\mathfrak{Q}'_{\nu+1}/\mathfrak{Q}'_\nu$ can also be considered as a module over the field $k(\alpha)$; its rank over k must then be the product of its rank over $k(\alpha)$ and of the degree of $k(\alpha)$ over k. This completes our proof.

3. Rings of power-series. In this §, we shall be mainly concerned with a ring of (formal) power-series, which we construct as follows. Let k be a field and

[2] See e.g. W. Krull, *Idealtheorie* (Berlin 1935), §13.

$(x) = (x_1, \cdots, x_r)$ a set of r independent variables over k (in the sense of Chap. I, §§1–2). Then the power-series in $x_1, \cdots, x_r$, with coefficients in k, constitute a ring, which we denote by $k\{x\} = k\{x_1, \cdots, x_r\}$; two power-series in that ring are considered equal if and only if every monomial in the x_i has the same coefficient in both, and the addition and multiplication of power-series are defined as usual. The ring $\mathfrak{o} = k\{x\}$ contains a subring, consisting of all the power-series with only a finite number of non-vanishing terms, which is isomorphic with the ring of polynomials in (x) with coefficients in k, and which we identify with that ring in the obvious manner. It is easily seen that the ring $\mathfrak{o} = k\{x\}$ contains no zero-divisors, so that we can construct its quotient-field Ω; the elements of Ω which can be written as quotients of two polynomials in (x) form a subfield of Ω, isomorphic to the field $k(x)$, which we identify with that field; Ω is thus defined as an "abstract field" containing the field $k(x)$. We shall also consider elements of algebraic extensions of Ω, which we may assume to be in an algebraic closure $\bar{\Omega}$ of Ω, abstractly constructed in the usual manner, and the same once for all.

As stated in §1, the ring $\mathfrak{o} = k\{x\}$ is Noetherian, and this implies that, if $(Y) = (Y_1, \cdots, Y_m)$ is any set of indeterminates, the ring $\mathfrak{o}[Y]$ of polynomials in (Y) with coefficients in $\mathfrak{o}$ is Noetherian. An element of the ring $\mathfrak{o}$ will be denoted by some such notation as $\varphi(x)$; by $\varphi(0)$ we understand, as natural, the constant term in $\varphi(x)$. Similarly, an element of the ring $\mathfrak{o}[Y]$ will be denoted by such a notation as $\varphi(x, Y)$; if in this polynomial in (Y), with coefficients in $\mathfrak{o}$, we replace each coefficient by its constant term, we get a polynomial in (Y) with coefficients in k, which we denote by $\varphi(0, Y)$; on the other hand, we may, in $\varphi(x, Y)$, substitute for (Y) any set (η) of m elements of any field containing $\mathfrak{o}$, e.g. of the field $\bar{\Omega}$, and we then get an element of the same field, which we write as $\varphi(x, \eta)$.

If the $\varphi_\nu(x)$ are elements of $\mathfrak{o}$, and if $P(U)$ is a polynomial in $k[U]$ such that $P[\varphi_1(x), \cdots, \varphi_h(x)] = 0$, then, writing that the constant term in the left-hand side is 0, we get $P[\varphi_1(0), \cdots, \varphi_h(0)] = 0$. This means that, by assigning to each element $\varphi(x)$ of $\mathfrak{o}$ the element $\varphi(0)$ of k, we have defined a specialization over k of the set of all elements in $\mathfrak{o}$. By th. 7 of Chap. II, §6, this specialization can be extended so as to include a specialization of any set of elements (η) in any field containing $\mathfrak{o}$; such a specialization of a set (η) will be called a *specialization of* (η) *at the center of* $\mathfrak{o}$. A specialization (y) of the set (η) at the center of $\mathfrak{o}$ will be called *isolated* if there does not exist a specialization (y') of (η) at the center of $\mathfrak{o}$, of higher dimension than (y) over k, and having (y) as a specialization over k; it will be called *proper* if it is finite, isolated, and algebraic over k. A set (η) will be called *finite at the center of* $\mathfrak{o}$ if every one of its specializations at the center of $\mathfrak{o}$ is finite.

PROPOSITION 1. *Let* (η) *be a set of elements of some field containing the ring* $\mathfrak{o} = k\{x\}$. *Let* $\mathfrak{A}$ *be the set of all the polynomials* $\theta(0, Y)$ *when one takes for* $\theta(x, Y)$ *all the polynomials in* $\mathfrak{o}[Y]$ *such that* $\theta(x, \eta) = 0$. *Then* $\mathfrak{A}$ *is an ideal in* $k[Y]$; *and the finite specializations of* (η) *at the center of* $\mathfrak{o}$ *are the zeros of that ideal.*

The first point is clear. Furthermore, a finite specialization of (η) at the center of $\mathfrak{o}$ is by definition a set of quantities (y) with the following property: whenever the elements $\varphi_\nu(x)$ of $\mathfrak{o}$, and the polynomial $P(U, Y)$ in $k[U, Y]$, are such that $P[\varphi_\nu(x), \eta] = 0$, then we have $P[\varphi_\nu(0), y] = 0$. Assume that (y) is such a specialization, and let $\theta(x, Y)$ be an element of $\mathfrak{o}[Y]$ such that $\theta(x, \eta) = 0$; then we can write $\theta(x, Y)$ in the form $\sum_\nu \varphi_\nu(x) \cdot M_\nu(Y)$, where the $M_\nu(Y)$ are monomials in (Y), and the assumption on (y) implies that we have

$$\sum_\nu \varphi_\nu(0) \cdot M_\nu(y) = 0,$$

i.e. $\theta(0, y) = 0$; this shows that (y) is then a zero of $\mathfrak{A}$. Conversely, let (y) be a zero of $\mathfrak{A}$, and let the $\varphi_\nu(x)$ and $P(U, Y)$ be such that $P[\varphi_\nu(x), \eta] = 0$; then, if we put $\theta(x, Y) = P[\varphi_\nu(x), Y]$, this is an element of $\mathfrak{o}[Y]$ such that $\theta(x, \eta) = 0$; therefore the polynomial $\theta(0, Y) = P[\varphi_\nu(0), Y]$ is in $\mathfrak{A}$, so that we have

$$\theta(0, y) = P[\varphi_\nu(0), y] = 0;$$

therefore (y) is a specialization of (η) at the center of $\mathfrak{o}$.

We remind the reader that an element η of a field containing a ring $\mathfrak{o}$ is called *integral over* $\mathfrak{o}$ if it satisfies a relation of the form $\eta^d + \omega_1 \cdot \eta^{d-1} + \cdots + \omega_d = 0$, where the ω_i are elements of $\mathfrak{o}$; it is then a fortiori algebraic over the quotient-field of $\mathfrak{o}$. A set of elements (η) will be called *integral over* $\mathfrak{o}$ if every one of the η_j is integral over $\mathfrak{o}$. It is well-known that, if $\mathfrak{o}$ is a Noetherian ring, and if a ring $\mathfrak{o}'$, containing $\mathfrak{o}$, is a finite $\mathfrak{o}$-module, i.e. has a finite basis over $\mathfrak{o}$, then every element of $\mathfrak{o}'$ is integral over $\mathfrak{o}$.

A set (η) of elements of a field containing the ring $\mathfrak{o} = k\{x\}$ is finite at the center of $\mathfrak{o}$ if and only if it is integral over $\mathfrak{o}$; the proof for this is exactly similar to that of prop. 21 and prop. 22 of Chap. II, §5 (where we avoided the phrase "integral over a ring"). For the sake of brevity, we shall prove only the direct proposition, together with the analogue of prop. 23 of Chap. II, §5:

PROPOSITION 2. *Let (η) be a set of integral elements over the ring $\mathfrak{o} = k\{x\}$ in some field containing $\mathfrak{o}$. Then every specialization of (η) at the center of $\mathfrak{o}$ is proper.*

It is enough to prove this for a single element η, i.e. to show that if η satisfies a relation $\eta^d + \varphi_1(x) \cdot \eta^{d-1} + \cdots + \varphi_d(x) = 0$, then every specialization α of η at the center of $\mathfrak{o}$ is finite and algebraic over k. In fact, if α is finite, it must satisfy the relation $\alpha^d + \varphi_1(0) \cdot \alpha^{d-1} + \cdots + \varphi_d(0) = 0$, and therefore is algebraic over k; moreover, we have $1 + \varphi_1(x) \cdot 1/\eta + \cdots + \varphi_d(x) \cdot (1/\eta)^d = 0$, which shows that 0 cannot be a specialization of $1/\eta$, i.e. that ∞ cannot be a specialization of η, at the center of $\mathfrak{o}$.

PROPOSITION 3. *Let Ω be the quotient-field of the ring $\mathfrak{o} = k\{x_1, \cdots, x_r\}$; let (η) be a set of elements in some field containing Ω, with a proper specialization (α) at the center of $\mathfrak{o}$. Let $\mathfrak{o}'$ be the subring of $\Omega(\eta)$ consisting of all the elements of the form $\varphi(x, \eta)/\psi(x, \eta)$ with $\varphi(x, Y)$ and $\psi(x, Y)$ in $\mathfrak{o}[Y]$, and $\psi(0, \alpha) \neq 0$. Let $\mathfrak{q}'$ be the ideal with the basis $x_1, \cdots, x_r$ in $\mathfrak{o}'$, i.e. the ideal $\mathfrak{q}' = \mathfrak{o}' \cdot x_1 + \cdots + \mathfrak{o}' \cdot x_r$.*

Then the residue-ring $\mathfrak{o}'/\mathfrak{q}'$ *is a* k*-module of finite rank, and its rank is a multiple of* $[k(\alpha):k]$. *Moreover, if* $(\omega_1, \cdots, \omega_n)$ *is a maximal set of linearly independent elements over* k *modulo* $\mathfrak{q}'$ *in* $\mathfrak{o}'$, *then every element* ω *of* $\mathfrak{o}'$ *can be written in the form* $\omega = \sum_i \omega_i \cdot \varphi_i(x)$, *with the* $\varphi_i(x)$ *in* $\mathfrak{o}$.

It should first be observed that implicit use is made of prop. 1 in the above definition of the ring $\mathfrak{o}'$; for this definition rests upon the fact that, when $\psi(x, Y)$ is in $\mathfrak{o}[Y]$ and $\psi(0, \alpha)$ is not 0, then $\psi(x, \eta)$ is not 0. Now call $\mathfrak{A}$, as in prop. 1, the ideal in $k[Y]$, consisting of all the polynomials $\theta(0, Y)$ when we take for $\theta(x, Y)$ all the elements of $\mathfrak{o}[Y]$ such that $\theta(x, \eta) = 0$. Then (α) is, by prop. 1, an isolated zero of $\mathfrak{A}$, so that we can apply lemma 6 of §2 to $\mathfrak{A}$ and (α); as in that lemma, we call $\mathfrak{O}'$ the subring of the quotient-field of $k[Y]$ which consists of the elements $R(Y) = P(Y)/Q(Y)$, with $P(Y)$ and $Q(Y)$ in $k[Y]$ and $Q(\alpha) \neq 0$; and we call $\mathfrak{Q}'$ the ideal in $\mathfrak{O}'$ which consists of the elements $P(Y)/Q(Y)$ with $P(Y) \in \mathfrak{A}$, $Q(Y) \in k[Y]$, and $Q(\alpha) \neq 0$; then the residue-ring $\mathfrak{O}'/\mathfrak{Q}'$ is a k-module of finite rank n, and this rank n is a multiple of $[k(\alpha):k]$. Therefore, in order to prove the first part of our proposition, we need only show that the ring $\mathfrak{o}'/\mathfrak{q}'$ which is defined there is isomorphic to the ring $\mathfrak{O}'/\mathfrak{Q}'$ which we have just defined. In fact, let $\varphi(x)$ be an element of $\mathfrak{o}$ such that $\varphi(0) = 0$; then we can write it in the form $\sum_i x_i \cdot \varphi_i(x)$, with the $\varphi_i(x)$ in $\mathfrak{o}$; applying this to the coefficients in a polynomial in $\mathfrak{o}[Y]$, we see that, if $\varphi(x, Y)$ is in $\mathfrak{o}[Y]$ and satisfies the condition $\varphi(0, Y) = 0$, then it can be written as $\sum_i x_i \cdot \varphi_i(x, Y)$, with the $\varphi_i(x, Y)$ in $\mathfrak{o}[Y]$. Therefore, if $\varphi(x, Y)$ and $\psi(x, Y)$ are in $\mathfrak{o}[Y]$ and such that $\varphi(0, Y) = 0$ and $\psi(0, \alpha) \neq 0$, then $\varphi(x, \eta)/\psi(x, \eta)$ is in the ideal $\mathfrak{q}'$. From this it follows that, if $\varphi(x, Y)$ and $\psi(x, Y)$ are in $\mathfrak{o}[Y]$, and if $\psi(0, \alpha) \neq 0$, then we have

$$(*) \qquad \varphi(x, \eta)/\psi(x, \eta) \equiv \varphi(0, \eta)/\psi(0, \eta) \mod. \mathfrak{q}';$$

in this congruence, both sides are in $\mathfrak{o}'$ because of the assumption $\psi(0, \alpha) \neq 0$. In particular, let $R(Y) = P(Y)/Q(Y)$ be any element of the ideal $\mathfrak{Q}'$ in $\mathfrak{O}'$; this means that we assume $P(Y)$ to be in $\mathfrak{A}$, i.e. of the form $P(Y) = \theta(0, Y)$ with $\theta(x, Y)$ in $\mathfrak{o}[Y]$ and such that $\theta(x, \eta) = 0$, and $Q(Y)$ to be in $k[Y]$ and such that $Q(\alpha) \neq 0$; then, applying the above congruence to $\theta(x, Y)$ and $Q(Y)$ instead of $\varphi(x, Y)$ and $\psi(x, Y)$, we get $0 \equiv R(\eta)$ mod. $\mathfrak{q}'$; in other words, if $R(Y)$ is in $\mathfrak{Q}'$, then $R(\eta)$ is in $\mathfrak{q}'$. Conversely, let $R(Y) = P(Y)/Q(Y)$ be an element of $\mathfrak{O}'$, $P(Y)$ and $Q(Y)$ being in $k[Y]$ and such that $Q(\alpha)$ is not 0, and assume that $R(\eta)$ is in $\mathfrak{q}'$, i.e. that there are elements $\varphi_i(x, Y)$ and $\psi(x, Y)$ of $\mathfrak{o}[Y]$ such that $\psi(0, \alpha)$ is not 0 and that we have $R(\eta) = \sum_i x_i \cdot \varphi_i(x, \eta)/\psi(x, \eta)$; then, if we put $\theta(x, Y) = P(Y) \cdot \psi(x, Y) - \sum_i x_i \cdot \varphi_i(x, Y) \cdot Q(Y)$, we have $\theta(x, \eta) = 0$, hence $\theta(0, Y) = P(Y) \cdot \psi(0, Y) \in \mathfrak{A}$, and $R(Y) = \theta(0, Y)/Q(Y)\psi(0, Y)$, which shows that $R(Y)$ is in $\mathfrak{Q}'$. We have thus shown that, if $R(Y)$ is in $\mathfrak{O}'$, then it is in $\mathfrak{Q}'$ if and only if $R(\eta)$ is in $\mathfrak{q}'$. Now we go back to the congruence (*); in the left-hand side we have an arbitrary element of $\mathfrak{o}'$; the right-hand side is of the form $R(\eta)$, with $R(Y) = \varphi(0, Y)/\psi(0, Y) \in \mathfrak{O}'$; this shows that, in every class in $\mathfrak{o}'$ modulo $\mathfrak{q}'$, there is an element of the form $R(\eta)$, with $R(Y) \in \mathfrak{O}'$;

moreover, by what we have just proved, two such elements $R(\eta)$ and $S(\eta)$, with $R(Y)$ and $S(Y)$ in $\mathfrak{O}'$, are in the same class in $\mathfrak{o}'$ modulo $\mathfrak{q}'$ if and only if $R(Y)$ and $S(Y)$ are in the same class in $\mathfrak{O}'$ modulo $\mathfrak{Q}'$. Therefore the correspondence between the class of $R(Y)$ modulo $\mathfrak{Q}'$ in $\mathfrak{O}'$, and the class of $R(\eta)$ modulo $\mathfrak{q}'$ in $\mathfrak{o}'$, is a one-to-one correspondence between $\mathfrak{O}'/\mathfrak{Q}'$ and $\mathfrak{o}'/\mathfrak{q}'$; it is then obviously an isomorphism, and this completes the proof of the first part of our proposition. Moreover, as the definition of $\mathfrak{Q}'$ implies that 1 is not in $\mathfrak{Q}'$, i.e. that $\mathfrak{Q}'$ is not $\mathfrak{O}'$, it also follows that we have $\mathfrak{q}' \neq \mathfrak{o}'$. Now we apply lemma 2 of §1 to the ring $\mathfrak{o}'$, to the ideal $\mathfrak{q}'$ with the basis $x_1, \cdots, x_r$ in $\mathfrak{o}'$, and to a maximal set $(\omega_1, \cdots, \omega_n)$ of linearly independent elements over k modulo $\mathfrak{q}'$ in $\mathfrak{o}'$; this shows that, if ω is any element of $\mathfrak{o}'$, there are n sequences of polynomials $P_{i\nu}(X)$ in $k[X]$, $P_{i\nu}(X)$ being homogeneous of degree ν in (X), such that we have, for every N, the congruence $\omega \equiv \sum_i \sum_{\nu=0}^{N-1} \omega_i P_{i\nu}(x) \bmod. \mathfrak{q}'^N$. For every i, we consider the expression $\sum_{\nu=0}^{\infty} P_{i\nu}(x)$, which is a power-series in (x) with coefficients in k, i.e. an element of $\mathfrak{o}$, which we denote by $\varphi_i(x)$. If, for any N, we call $M_\rho(X)$ all the monomials of degree N in $X_1, \cdots, X_r$, then

$$\varphi_i(x) - \sum_{\nu=0}^{N-1} P_{i\nu}(x)$$

can be written as a linear combination of the $M_\rho(x)$ with coefficients in $\mathfrak{o}$; from this it follows that the above congruence implies the congruence $\omega \equiv \sum_i \omega_i \varphi_i(x) \bmod. \mathfrak{q}'^N$ for every N; as $\mathfrak{q}'$ is not $\mathfrak{o}'$, lemma 4 of §1 shows that, in order to be able to conclude from this congruence to the equality $\omega = \sum_i \omega_i \varphi_i(x)$ which we set out to prove, it is enough to show that the ring $\mathfrak{o}'$ is Noetherian and without zero-divisors. The latter point is obvious, as $\mathfrak{o}'$ is contained in the field $\Omega(\eta)$. Moreover, the ring $\mathfrak{o}[\eta]$ is Noetherian, by the principles stated in §1; this ring consists of the elements $\varphi(x, \eta)$ with $\varphi(x, Y) \in \mathfrak{o}[Y]$. In this ring $\mathfrak{o}[\eta]$, the set of all elements $\varphi(x, \eta)$ with $\varphi(x, Y) \in \mathfrak{o}[Y]$ and $\varphi(0, \alpha) = 0$ is an ideal; it is a prime ideal, for a relation $\varphi(x, \eta)\varphi'(x, \eta) = \psi(x, \eta)$ implies $\varphi(0, \alpha)\varphi'(0, \alpha) = \psi(0, \alpha)$, by prop. 1, so that $\psi(0, \alpha) = 0$ then implies either $\varphi(0, \alpha) = 0$ or $\varphi'(0, \alpha) = 0$. As the ring $\mathfrak{o}'$ is the quotient-ring derived from the ring $\mathfrak{o}[\eta]$ and the prime ideal in $\mathfrak{o}[\eta]$ which we have just defined, it is therefore Noetherian by the principles noted in §1. This completes our proof.

THEOREM 1. *Let Ω be the quotient-field of the ring $\mathfrak{o} = k\{x\}$; and let (η) be a set of elements in some field containing Ω, with a proper specialization (α) at the center of $\mathfrak{o}$. Then (η) is integral over $\mathfrak{o}$, and every specialization of (η) at the center of $\mathfrak{o}$ is a conjugate of (α) over k.*

The ring $\mathfrak{o}'$ being defined as in prop. 3, prop. 3 shows that $\mathfrak{o}'$ is a finite $\mathfrak{o}$-module; as $\mathfrak{o}$ is Noetherian, it follows from this that every element of $\mathfrak{o}'$ is integral over $\mathfrak{o}$. This proves our first point. By prop. 2, this implies that all the specializations of (η) at the center of $\mathfrak{o}$ are proper; assume now that there is such a specialization (β), other than a conjugate of (α) over k. As (β) is algebraic over k, its specializations over k are its conjugates over k, by the coroll. of th. 3, Chap. II, §1; as (α) is not such, there is therefore a polynomial $Q(Y)$ in $k[Y]$, such that $Q(\beta) = 0$ and $Q(\alpha) \neq 0$. Then the element $1/Q(\eta)$ is in the ring $\mathfrak{o}'$, therefore integral over $\mathfrak{o}$, hence finite at the center of $\mathfrak{o}$ by prop. 2. This means that 0 is not a specialization of $Q(\eta)$ at the center of $\mathfrak{o}$. This is impossible; for, if it were so, the specialization $(\eta) \rightarrow (\beta)$ at the center of $\mathfrak{o}$ could not be extended to a specialization of $(\eta, Q(\eta))$ at the center of $\mathfrak{o}$, which is against th. 7 of Chap. II, §6.

An important addition to th. 1 concerns the relation between the degrees of $\Omega(\eta)$ over Ω and of $k(\alpha)$ over k when the assumptions are those of that theorem; this will be given in th. 2. As a first preliminary step to this, it is necessary to deal with the special case of a power-series ring in one variable; we write this ring as $K\{t\}$, K being a field and t a variable quantity over that field; this is defined just as the ring $k\{x\}$ has been defined at the beginning of this §, and we can apply to it the above results, and in particular prop. 3.

PROPOSITION 4. *Let Ω_1 be the quotient-field of the ring $\mathfrak{o}_1 = K\{t\}$, and let (η) be a set of elements in some field containing Ω_1, with a proper specialization (α) at the center of $\mathfrak{o}_1$. Then $[\Omega_1(\eta):\Omega_1]$ is a multiple of $[K(\alpha):K]$.*

We apply prop. 3 to $\mathfrak{o}_1$, Ω_1, (η), and (α); by that proposition, if we call $\mathfrak{o}_1'$ the ring consisting of the elements $\varphi(t, \eta)/\psi(t, \eta)$, with $\varphi(t, Y)$ and $\psi(t, Y)$ in $\mathfrak{o}_1[Y]$ and $\psi(0, \alpha) \neq 0$, and if we put $\mathfrak{q}_1' = \mathfrak{o}_1' \cdot t$, then $\mathfrak{o}_1'/\mathfrak{q}_1'$ is a K-module of finite rank n, n being a multiple of $[K(\alpha):K]$; and, if $(\omega_1, \cdots, \omega_n)$ is a maximal set of linearly independent elements over K modulo $\mathfrak{q}_1'$ in $\mathfrak{o}_1'$, then every element ω of $\mathfrak{o}_1'$ can be written in the form $\omega = \sum_i \omega_i \cdot \varphi_i(t)$, with $\varphi_i(t) \in \mathfrak{o}_1$. In particular, every monomial in (η) can be so written; on the other hand, by th. 1, $\Omega_1(\eta)$ is an algebraic extension of Ω_1, and therefore has a basis over Ω_1, consisting of such monomials; it follows from this that every element of $\Omega_1(\eta)$ can be expressed as a linear combination of the ω_i with coefficients in Ω_1, and therefore that the degree of $\Omega_1(\eta)$ over Ω_1 is at most equal to the number n of the ω_i. As n is a multiple of $[K(\alpha):K]$, it will now be enough to show that the degree of $\Omega_1(\eta)$ over Ω_1 is not less than n; we shall do this by showing that the ω_i are linearly independent over Ω_1. In fact, assume that there is a relation $\sum_i \omega_i \zeta_i = 0$, with the ζ_i in Ω_1 and not all 0; after multiplying this, if necessary, by a suitable element of $\mathfrak{o}_1$, we may assume that the ζ_i are in $\mathfrak{o}_1$, i.e. that our relation is of the form $\sum_i \omega_i \varphi_i(t) = 0$, where the $\varphi_i(t)$ are elements of $\mathfrak{o}_1$, not all 0. After dividing this, if necessary, by a suitable power of t, we may assume that the quantities $\varphi_i(0)$ are not all 0; as our relation implies the congruence $\sum_i \omega_i \varphi_i(0) \equiv 0$ mod. $\mathfrak{q}_1'$, this contradicts the definition of the ω_i.

We now extend to "abstract fields" the notion of a complete set of conjugates, as defined in Chap. I, §4. If Ω is any abstract field, and (η) a set of elements of an abstractly constructed algebraic closure $\bar{\Omega}$ of Ω, then we define, as in Chap. I, §4, a conjugate of (η) over Ω in $\bar{\Omega}$ as a transform of (η) by any automorphism of $\bar{\Omega}$ over Ω, and a complete set of conjugates of (η) over Ω in $\bar{\Omega}$ as a set consisting of all the conjugates of (η), each one being repeated p^n times if p^n is the inseparable factor of the degree of $\Omega(\eta)$ over Ω. If the field Ω is contained in a field Ω_1, and if $\bar{\Omega}_1$ is an algebraic closure of Ω_1, then we can take for $\bar{\Omega}$ the algebraic closure of Ω in $\bar{\Omega}_1$; that being so, if (η) is any set of elements of $\bar{\Omega}$, the proof of prop. 12 of Chap. I, §4, can be applied, without any other modification than obvious changes of notation, to a complete set of conjugates of (η) over Ω in $\bar{\Omega}$; it follows from this that such a complete set consists of complete sets of conjugates, over Ω_1, of conjugates of (η) over Ω, each such set being repeated a certain number of times.

Furthermore, in order to prove th. 2, or rather that part of it which is contained in prop. 6, we have to consider, beside the ring $\mathfrak{o} = k\{x\}$, the ring $\mathfrak{o}_0 = \bar{k}\{x\}$ of power-series in the same variables, with coefficients in the algebraic closure of k; $\mathfrak{o}$ will be considered, in an obvious manner, as being contained in $\mathfrak{o}_0$, and the quotient-field Ω of $\mathfrak{o}$ as being contained in the quotient-field Ω_0 of $\mathfrak{o}_0$; then, $\bar{\Omega}_0$ being an algebraic closure of Ω_0, we can take for $\bar{\Omega}$ the algebraic closure of Ω in $\bar{\Omega}_0$. That being so, if (η) is any set of elements of $\bar{\Omega}$, it is clear that a specialization of (η) at the center of $\mathfrak{o}_0$ is a fortiori a specialization of (η) at the center of $\mathfrak{o}$.

Proposition 5. *Let Ω_0 be the quotient-field of the ring $\mathfrak{o}_0 = \bar{k}\{x\}$, and Ω the quotient-field of the ring $\mathfrak{o} = k\{x\}$, the latter being considered as contained in the former. Let (η) be a set of algebraic elements over Ω in an algebraic closure $\bar{\Omega}_0$ of Ω_0. Then, if a finite specialization (α) of (η) at the center of $\mathfrak{o}_0$ is algebraic over k, every conjugate (α') of (α) over k is the specialization, at the center of $\mathfrak{o}_0$, of some conjugate (η') of (η) over Ω in $\bar{\Omega}_0$.*

Let σ be an automorphism of $\bar{k}$ over k, transforming (α) into (α'). If $\varphi(x)$ is any element of $\mathfrak{o}_0$, let $\varphi^\sigma(x)$ be the power-series obtained by applying σ to all the coefficients in the series $\varphi(x)$; by this definition, σ is thus extended to an automorphism of the ring $\mathfrak{o}_0$, in which every element of $\mathfrak{o}$ is invariant, and this determines, in an obvious manner, an automorphism of Ω_0 over Ω; we can then extend this to an automorphism of $\bar{\Omega}_0$, which we again denote by σ; as the latter automorphism leaves every element of Ω invariant, it transforms (η) into a conjugate (η') of (η) over Ω. Then, if $\theta(x, Y)$ is any element of $\mathfrak{o}_0[Y]$, i.e. any polynomial in (Y) with coefficients in $\mathfrak{o}_0$, and $\theta^\sigma(x, Y)$ is obtained by applying σ to the coefficients in $\theta(x, Y)$, the relations $\theta(x, \eta) = 0$ and $\theta^\sigma(x, \eta') = 0$ imply each other; therefore, if we call $\mathfrak{A}$ the set of all polynomials $\theta(0, Y)$ when we take for $\theta(x, Y)$ the elements of $\mathfrak{o}_0[Y]$ such that $\theta(x, \eta) = 0$, prop. 1 shows that the finite specializations of (η) and of (η') at the center of $\mathfrak{o}_0$ are the zeros of the ideals $\mathfrak{A}$ and $\mathfrak{A}^\sigma$, respectively. But it is clear that, if a zero (α) of $\mathfrak{A}$ is algebraic over k, its transform (α') by σ is a zero of $\mathfrak{A}^\sigma$. This completes our proof.

Proposition 6. *Let Ω be the quotient-field of the ring $\mathfrak{o} = k\{x\}$. Let (η) be a set of elements in an algebraic closure $\bar{\Omega}$ of Ω, with a proper specialization (α) at the center of $\mathfrak{o}$. Then every specialization, at the center of $\mathfrak{o}$, of a complete set of conjugates of (η) over Ω in $\bar{\Omega}$ consists of conjugates of (α) over k; all the conjugates of*

(α) over k occur in every such specialization, and they all occur therein the same number of times.

By th. 1, our assumptions imply that (η) is integral over $\mathfrak{o}$. If (η') is any conjugate of (η) over Ω, there is an isomorphism over Ω between $\Omega(\eta)$ and $\Omega(\eta')$, which maps (η) on (η'); this shows that (η') also is then integral over $\mathfrak{o}$, and furthermore (by the definition of a specialization) that (η') has the same specializations as (η) at the center of $\mathfrak{o}$, so that, by th. 1, every specialization of (η') at the center of $\mathfrak{o}$ is a conjugate of (α) over k. This proves our first assertion. As to our last two assertions, it is enough to show that they hold true for some specialization $(\alpha^{(1)}, \cdots, \alpha^{(n)})$, at the center of $\mathfrak{o}$, of a complete set $(\eta^{(1)}, \cdots, \eta^{(n)})$ of conjugates of (η) over Ω in $\bar{\Omega}$; for every other such specialization must then, by th. 1, be a conjugate of that one over k, i.e. must be the transform of that one by some automorphism of $\bar{k}$ over k, and we know that the effect of such an automorphism on the conjugates of (α) over k is merely to permute them among themselves. We now introduce, as in prop. 5, the ring $\mathfrak{o}_0 = \bar{k}\{x\}$, its quotient-field Ω_0, and an algebraic closure $\bar{\Omega}_0$ of Ω_0; then we may again consider $\mathfrak{o}$ as contained in $\mathfrak{o}_0$, Ω in Ω_0, and $\bar{\Omega}$ in $\bar{\Omega}_0$, so that (η) is now a set of elements of $\bar{\Omega}_0$. Let $(\eta^{(1)}, \cdots, \eta^{(n)})$ be, as before, a complete set of conjugates of (η) over Ω in $\bar{\Omega}$; and let $(\alpha^{(1)}, \cdots, \alpha^{(n)})$ be a specialization of this at the center of $\mathfrak{o}_0$, which must then a fortiori be a specialization of it at the center of $\mathfrak{o}$; we need only show that $(\alpha^{(1)}, \cdots, \alpha^{(n)})$ is as asserted. In fact, let $(\alpha'^{(1)}, \cdots, \alpha'^{(n)})$ be the transform of $(\alpha^{(1)}, \cdots, \alpha^{(n)})$ by any automorphism of $\bar{k}$ over k; by prop. 5, this is a specialization, at the center of $\mathfrak{o}_0$, of some conjugate of $(\eta^{(1)}, \cdots, \eta^{(n)})$ over Ω, i.e. of the transform of $(\eta^{(1)}, \cdots, \eta^{(n)})$ by some automorphism of $\bar{\Omega}$ over Ω; as every automorphism of $\bar{\Omega}$ over Ω merely permutes the $(\eta^{(\nu)})$ among themselves, this shows that $(\alpha'^{(1)}, \cdots, \alpha'^{(n)})$ is a permutation of some specialization of $(\eta^{(1)}, \cdots, \eta^{(n)})$ at the center of $\mathfrak{o}_0$. But every specialization of $(\eta^{(1)}, \cdots, \eta^{(n)})$ at the center of $\mathfrak{o}_0$ must, by th. 1, be a conjugate of $(\alpha^{(1)}, \cdots, \alpha^{(n)})$ over $\bar{k}$, i.e. it can be no other than $(\alpha^{(1)}, \cdots, \alpha^{(n)})$ itself. We have thus proved that the transform of $(\alpha^{(1)}, \cdots, \alpha^{(n)})$ by any automorphism of $\bar{k}$ over k is a permutation of $(\alpha^{(1)}, \cdots, \alpha^{(n)})$; this shows that every conjugate of any one of the $(\alpha^{(\nu)})$ must occur in the set $(\alpha^{(1)}, \cdots, \alpha^{(n)})$, and must occur the same number of times as $(\alpha^{(\nu)})$ itself; as every $(\alpha^{(\nu)})$ is a conjugate of (α) over k, this completes our proof.

We can now prove the result for the sake of which we needed prop. 4, 5 and 6, and in which prop. 4 and 6 are included:

THEOREM 2. *Let Ω be the quotient-field of the ring $\mathfrak{o} = k\{x\}$; and let (η) be a set of elements of an algebraic closure $\bar{\Omega}$ of Ω, with a proper specialization (α) at the center of $\mathfrak{o}$. Then $[\Omega(\eta):\Omega]$ is a multiple of $[k(\alpha):k]$; and every specialization, at the center of $\mathfrak{o}$, of a complete set of conjugates of (η) over Ω in $\bar{\Omega}$ consists of a complete set of conjugates of (α) over k, repeated a certain number of times.*

Using prop. 6, we first show that the two assertions in our theorem imply each other. In fact, put $n = [\Omega(\eta):\Omega]$, $n' = [k(\alpha):k]$, $p^m = [k(\alpha):k]_i$, $d = [k(\alpha):k]_s$. Then we have $n' = p^m \cdot d$; d is the number of distinct conjugates of (α) over k; and a complete set of conjugates of (η) over Ω consists of n conjugates $(\eta^{(1)}, \cdots, \eta^{(n)})$ of (η) over Ω. By prop. 6, every one of the d distinct conjugates of (α) over k is repeated the same number of times in a specialization of $(\eta^{(1)}, \cdots, \eta^{(n)})$ at the center of $\mathfrak{o}$; this number must then be equal to $n/d = p^m \cdot n/n'$; this is a multiple of p^m if and only if n is a multiple of n'. As every conjugate of (α) is repeated p^m times in a complete set of conjugates of (α) over k, the two assertions in our theorem have thus been shown to be equivalent. In particular, it now follows from prop. 4 that our theorem is true for any power-series ring in one variable. Now let t be any variable quantity over the field $k(x)$; put $u_i = x_i/t$ for $1 \leqq i \leqq r$; then we have $k(x, t) = k(u, t)$, which shows, since the field $k(x, t)$ has the dimension $r + 1$ over k, that (u, t) is a set of $r + 1$ independent variables over k, i.e. that (u) is a set of independent variables over k and that t is a variable quantity over the field $K = k(u)$. Consider the ring $\mathfrak{o}_1 = K\{t\}$ of power-series in t with coefficients in K; let Ω_1 be the quotient-field of $\mathfrak{o}_1$, and $\bar{\Omega}_1$ an algebraic closure of Ω_1. If $\varphi(x)$ is any element of the ring $\mathfrak{o}$, and if $P_\nu(x)$ is the homogeneous polynomial of degree ν, consisting of all the terms of degree ν in the power-series $\varphi(x)$, then we put $\bar{\varphi}(t) = \sum_{\nu=0}^{\infty} P_\nu(u) \cdot t^\nu$; this is an element of the ring $\mathfrak{o}_1$, and we have $\bar{\varphi}(0) = \varphi(0)$. The correspondence between $\varphi(x)$ and $\bar{\varphi}(t)$, which we have thus defined, is obviously an isomorphic mapping of $\mathfrak{o}$ into $\mathfrak{o}_1$; as we have $x_i = u_i \cdot t$ for $1 \leqq i \leqq r$, those elements of the ring $\mathfrak{o}$ which are polynomials in (x) with coefficients in k are transformed into themselves by that mapping of $\mathfrak{o}$ into $\mathfrak{o}_1$. Therefore we may identify every element of $\mathfrak{o}$ with its image in $\mathfrak{o}_1$ by that mapping; and we may consider Ω as contained in Ω_1, and $\bar{\Omega}$ in $\bar{\Omega}_1$. That being so, if (ζ) is any set of elements of $\bar{\Omega}$, it is at the same time a set of elements of $\bar{\Omega}_1$; and a specialization of (ζ) at the center of $\mathfrak{o}_1$ is a fortiori a specialization of (ζ) at the center of $\mathfrak{o}$, as follows from the relation $\bar{\varphi}(0) = \varphi(0)$ when $\varphi(x)$ and $\bar{\varphi}(t)$ are as above defined. We apply this to a complete set of conjugates of the set (η) over Ω in $\bar{\Omega}$; as this shows, all that we need now prove is that a specialization of such a complete set at the center of $\mathfrak{o}_1$ is as required by the last assertion in our theorem. But a complete set of conjugates of (η) over Ω consists of complete sets of conjugates, over Ω_1, of conjugates of (η) over Ω, each such set being repeated a certain number of times. As our theorem is true for power-series rings in one variable, and therefore for the ring $\mathfrak{o}_1$, it follows from this that any specialization $(\alpha^{(1)}, \cdots, \alpha^{(n)})$ of a complete set of conjugates of (η) over Ω at the center of $\mathfrak{o}_1$ consists of complete sets of conjugates of some of the $(\alpha^{(\nu)})$ over the field $K = k(u)$. But, by prop. 13 of Chap. I, §4, and coroll. 1 of th. 3, Chap. I, §6, a complete set of conjugates, over K, of any one of the $(\alpha^{(\nu)})$ is also a complete set of conjugates over k of that $(\alpha^{(\nu)})$, hence also of (α) since every $(\alpha^{(\nu)})$ is a conjugate of (α) over k. This completes our proof.

Theorems 1 and 2 sum up the results of our investigation so far as it concerns power-series rings and specializations at the center of such rings. In order to apply them to our algebraic problems, we need a result connecting such specializations with those of the purely algebraic type which was alone discussed in §§1–5 of Chap. II. This is contained in the following theorem:

THEOREM 3. *Let k be a field, (x) a set of independent variables over k, and (y) a set of algebraic quantities over the field $K = k(x)$. Let $(\bar{y})$ be a specialization of (y) over $(x) \rightarrow (0)$, with reference to k. Let Ω be the quotient-field of the power-series ring $\mathfrak{o} = k\{x\}$, and $\bar{\Omega}$ an algebraic closure of Ω. Then there exists an isomorphism of $k(x, y)$ over $k(x)$ into $\bar{\Omega}$, in which the set (y) is mapped on a set (η) such that $(\bar{y})$ is a specialization of (η) at the center of $\mathfrak{o}$.*

After applying a reciprocation to the set (y) if necessary, we may assume that the specialization $(\bar{y})$ is finite. Let $\mathfrak{P}$ be the ideal determined by (y) over the field $K = k(x)$, and let the $P_\mu(Y)$ be a basis of $\mathfrak{P}$. Let $\mathfrak{A}$ be the ideal with that basis in $\Omega[Y]$; we can write it as intersection of primary ideals $\mathfrak{Q}_\alpha$ in $\Omega[Y]$, belonging respectively to prime ideals $\mathfrak{P}_\alpha$. There is, for each α, an integer ρ such that we have $\mathfrak{Q}_\alpha \supset (\mathfrak{P}_\alpha)^\rho$; as the $\mathfrak{Q}_\alpha$ are in finite number, we may therefore choose ρ so that this relation is satisfied for every α. For any given α, we can construct the residue-ring of $\Omega[Y]$ modulo $\mathfrak{P}_\alpha$, and its quotient-field; if, in that residue-ring, we denote by η'_j the class of Y_j, we can write that ring as $\Omega[\eta']$, and its quotient-field as $\Omega(\eta')$; and, if $\Phi(Y)$ is any polynomial in $\Omega[Y]$, we have $\Phi(\eta') = 0$ if and only if we have $\Phi(Y) \equiv 0$ mod. $\mathfrak{P}_\alpha$, i.e. if and only if $\Phi(Y)$ is in $\mathfrak{P}_\alpha$; in particular, since we have $\mathfrak{P} \subset \mathfrak{A} \subset \mathfrak{Q}_\alpha \subset \mathfrak{P}_\alpha$, we have $P(\eta') = 0$ whenever $P(Y)$ is in $\mathfrak{P}$, i.e. whenever $P(Y)$ is a polynomial in $K[Y]$ such that $P(y) = 0$. As Ω contains K, the field $\Omega(\eta')$ contains $K(\eta')$; and, by prop. 25 of Chap. II, §6, there is a set of quantities (y') such that there is an isomorphism between $K(\eta')$ and $K(y')$ over K, in which (η') is mapped on (y'); then, if $P(Y)$ is in $K[Y]$, we have $P(y') = 0$ whenever $P(\eta')$ is 0, hence whenever $P(y)$ is 0; in other words, (y') is a specialization of (y) over K, hence, by the coroll. of th. 3, Chap. II, §1, a conjugate of (y) over K. Then there is an isomorphism between $K(y)$ and $K(y')$ over K, in which (y') corresponds to (y); combining this with the above-defined isomorphism between $K(\eta')$ and $K(y')$, we get an isomorphism between $K(\eta')$ and $K(y)$ over K, in which (y) corresponds to (η'). As (y) is algebraic over K, (η') is therefore algebraic over K, and a fortiori over Ω. Therefore $\Omega(\eta')$ is an algebraic extension of Ω, so that there is an isomorphic mapping of it over Ω into $\bar{\Omega}$; if that mapping transforms (η') into a set of elements $(\eta^{(\alpha)})$ of $\bar{\Omega}$, then it maps $\Omega(\eta')$ on $\Omega(\eta^{(\alpha)})$. We have thus defined, for the given value of α, a set $(\eta^{(\alpha)})$ of elements of $\bar{\Omega}$, such that a polynomial $\Phi(Y)$ in $\Omega[Y]$ is in $\mathfrak{P}_\alpha$ if and only if $\Phi(\eta^{(\alpha)})$ is 0, and that there is an isomorphism between $K(y)$ and $K(\eta^{(\alpha)})$ over K, in which (y) is transformed into $(\eta^{(\alpha)})$; and our theorem will be proved if we show that, for at least one value of α, $(\eta^{(\alpha)})$ has the specialization $(\bar{y})$ at the center of the ring $\mathfrak{o} = k\{x\}$. In fact, let us assume that this is not so. Then, by prop. 1, there is, for every α, an element $\varphi_\alpha(x, Y)$ of $\mathfrak{o}[Y]$, such that $\varphi_\alpha(x, \eta^{(\alpha)}) = 0$ and that $\varphi_\alpha(0, \bar{y}) \neq 0$. Put $\varphi(x, Y) = \prod_\alpha \varphi_\alpha(x, Y)^\rho$; as $\varphi_\alpha(x, Y)$ is in $\mathfrak{P}_\alpha$ for every α, it follows, by the definition of ρ, that $\varphi(x, Y)$ is in $\mathfrak{Q}_\alpha$ for every α, hence that it is in $\mathfrak{A}$; and we have $\varphi(0, \bar{y}) \neq 0$; we shall now show that this implies a contradiction. In fact, $\varphi(x, Y)$ is a polynomial in (Y), with coefficients in $\mathfrak{o}$; taking, among these coefficients, a maximal set $\psi_\lambda(x)$ of linearly independent elements over K, and expressing all the coefficients in $\varphi(x, Y)$ in terms of the

$\psi_\lambda(x)$, we get for $\varphi(x, Y)$ an expression of the form $\varphi(x, Y) = \sum_\lambda \psi_\lambda(x) \cdot Q_\lambda(Y)$, with $Q_\lambda(Y) \in K[Y]$ for every λ. We may apply lemma 1 of Chap. I, §6, to the ideal $\mathfrak{A}$ in $\Omega[Y]$ with the basis $P_\mu(Y)$ in $K[Y]$, and to the polynomial

$$\varphi(x, Y) = \sum_\lambda \psi_\lambda(x) \cdot Q_\lambda(Y)$$

in $\mathfrak{A}$, as can be seen by repeating the proof of that lemma; this shows that the $Q_\lambda(Y)$ are in $\mathfrak{P}$, i.e. that we have $Q_\lambda(y) = 0$ for every λ. But we can write the $Q_\lambda(Y)$ in the form $Q_\lambda(Y) = H_\lambda(x, Y)/G(x)$, with $H_\lambda(X, Y) \in k[X, Y]$, and $G(X) \in k[X]$; then we have $H_\lambda(x, y) = 0$ for every λ, and $G(x) \neq 0$. This gives the relation $G(x) \cdot \varphi(x, Y) = \sum_\lambda \psi_\lambda(x) \cdot H_\lambda(x, Y)$, with $G(x)$, $\varphi(x, Y)$, $\psi_\lambda(x)$, $H_\lambda(x, Y)$ as stated. Now, N being an arbitrary integer, call $\varphi_N(x, Y)$ the polynomial in $k[x, Y]$, of degree $N - 1$ in (x), derived from $\varphi(x, Y)$ by omitting, in every power-series in (x) which occurs in $\varphi(x, Y)$, all the terms of degree $\geqq N$; similarly, call $\psi_{\lambda N}(x)$ the polynomial derived from $\psi_\lambda(x)$ by omitting in it all the terms of degree $\geqq N$. Then the above relation implies that the polynomial $P_N(x, Y)$ defined by $P_N(x, Y) = G(x) \cdot \varphi_N(x, Y) - \sum_\lambda \psi_{\lambda N}(x) \cdot H_\lambda(x, Y)$ contains only terms of degree $\geqq N$ in (x), i.e. can be written in the form

$$P_N(x, Y) = \sum_\rho A_\rho(x, Y) \cdot M_\rho(x),$$

where the $M_\rho(X)$ are all the monomials of degree N in (X), and the $A_\rho(X, Y)$ are in $k[X, Y]$. Substituting (y) for (Y) in this, we get, since the $H_\lambda(x, y)$ are 0, $G(x) \cdot \varphi_N(x, y) = \sum_\rho A_\rho(x, y) \cdot M_\rho(x)$, or $G(x) = \sum_\rho M_\rho(x) \cdot A_\rho(x, y)/\varphi_N(x, y)$. As we have $\varphi_N(0, \bar{y}) = \varphi(0, \bar{y}) \neq 0$, this shows that, in the subring $\mathfrak{r}$ of the field $k(x, y)$ which consists of all elements $P(x, y)/Q(x, y)$ with $P(X, Y) \in k[X, Y]$, $Q(X, Y) \in k[X, Y]$, and $Q(0, \bar{y}) \neq 0$, $G(x)$ is in the ideal with the basis $M_\rho(x)$; in other words, putting $\mathfrak{c} = \mathfrak{r} \cdot x_1 + \cdots + \mathfrak{r} \cdot x_r$, we have $G(x) \in \mathfrak{c}^N$, and this holds true for every N. But $\mathfrak{r}$ is a Noetherian ring, for it is the quotient-ring derived from the Noetherian ring $k[x, y]$, and the prime ideal in that ring which consists of the elements $P(x, y)$ with $P(X, Y) \in k[X, Y]$ and $P(0, \bar{y}) = 0$. We can therefore apply lemma 4 of §1 to the ring $\mathfrak{r}$ and the ideal $\mathfrak{c}$; as $G(x)$, which is not 0, is in $\mathfrak{c}^N$ for every N, this shows that we must have $\mathfrak{c} = \mathfrak{r}$, i.e. $1 \in \mathfrak{c}$; therefore there are polynomials $L_i(X, Y)$, $M(X, Y)$ in $k[X, Y]$, such that $M(0, \bar{y}) \neq 0$ and that $1 = \sum_i x_i \cdot L_i(x, y)/M(x, y)$, hence $M(x, y) = \sum_i x_i \cdot L_i(x, y)$; as $(0, \bar{y})$ is a specialization of (x, y) over k, the latter relation implies $M(0, \bar{y}) = 0$; this is a contradiction.

With the same assumptions and notations as in th. 3, we shall now get the main result of this chapter, in preliminary form, by applying it to a complete set of conjugates of (y) over $k(x)$, and then making use of th. 1 and th. 2.

PROPOSITION 7. *Let k be a field, (x) a set of independent variables over k, (y) a set of algebraic quantities over the field $k(x)$, and $(y^{(1)}, \cdots, y^{(n)})$ a complete set of conjugates of (y) over $k(x)$. Let (a) be a set of elements of k, and (α) a set of algebraic quantities over k, such that (α) is an isolated specialization of (y) over $(x) \to (a)$,* *with reference to k. Then there is an integer* μ *such that, in every specialization* $(\bar{y}^{(1)}, \cdots, \bar{y}^{(n)})$ *of* $(y^{(1)}, \cdots, y^{(n)})$ *over* $(x) \to (a)$ *with reference to k, each conjugate of* (α) *over k appears exactly* μ *times among the* $(\bar{y}^{(\nu)})$*; and* μ *is a multiple of* $[k(\alpha):k]_i$.

Replacing the x_i by $x_i - a_i$, respectively, we may assume that we have $(a) = (0)$. As in th. 3, let Ω be the quotient-field of the ring $\mathfrak{o} = k\{x\}$, and $\bar{\Omega}$ an algebraic closure of Ω. Put $K = k(x)$; as K is contained in Ω, $\bar{\Omega}$ contains an algebraic closure Λ of K, which is isomorphic to the field $\bar{K}$, and which we may identify with that field. Let $(\bar{y}^{(1)}, \cdots, \bar{y}^{(n)})$ be a specialization of $(y^{(1)}, \cdots, y^{(n)})$ over $(x) \to (0)$, with reference to k; by th. 3, this is a specialization, at the center of $\mathfrak{o} = k\{x\}$, of the image of $(y^{(1)}, \cdots, y^{(n)})$ by some isomorphism σ of $K(y^{(1)}, \cdots, y^{(n)})$ into $\bar{\Omega}$ over K; since such an image is a conjugate over K of $(y^{(1)}, \cdots, y^{(n)})$, hence differs from that set merely by a permutation of the $(y^{(\nu)})$, we need therefore only show that our conclusion holds true for the specializations of $(y^{(1)}, \cdots, y^{(n)})$ at the center of $\mathfrak{o}$. But $(y^{(1)}, \cdots, y^{(n)})$ consists of complete sets of conjugates of some of the $(y^{(\nu)})$ over Ω, in $\bar{\Omega}$, each one repeated a certain number of times; hence we need only show that our conclusion holds true for the specializations, at the center of $\mathfrak{o}$, of a complete set of conjugates of any set $(y^{(\nu)})$ over Ω in $\bar{\Omega}$. In fact, for any given value of ν, a specialization of $(y^{(\nu)})$ at the center of $\mathfrak{o}$ is a fortiori a specialization of $(y^{(\nu)})$ over $(x) \to (0)$ with reference to k, as follows from the definition of such specializations, hence also one of (y) over $(x) \to (0)$ with reference to k. Therefore, if (α) is a specialization of $(y^{(\nu)})$ at the center of $\mathfrak{o}$, it must be a proper one; in that case, by th. 2, in every specialization at the center of $\mathfrak{o}$ of a complete set of conjugates of $(y^{(\nu)})$ over Ω, all the conjugates of (α) over k occur the same number of times, and this number is a multiple of $[k(\alpha):k]_i$. On the other hand, assume that (α) is not a specialization of $(y^{(\nu)})$ at the center of $\mathfrak{o}$; then prop. 1 shows that no conjugate of (α) over k can be a specialization, at the center of $\mathfrak{o}$, of any conjugate of $(y^{(\nu)})$ over Ω; in that case, therefore, (α) and its conjugates over k can never occur in any specialization, at the center of $\mathfrak{o}$, of a complete set of conjugates of $(y^{(\nu)})$ over Ω. This completes our proof.

4. The multiplicity of a specialization. The reader may now forget the whole of the contents of §§1–3 of this chapter, except prop. 7 of §3, which, in slightly more general terms, will presently appear as th. 4, and, in that form, will be the corner-stone for our theory of multiplicities in algebraic geometry. From now onwards, the conventions and restrictions of Chap. I, §1, are again in full force, and will remain so throughout this book.

Let (x) be a set of independent variables over a field k; let (y) be a set of algebraic quantities over $k(x)$, and let $(y^{(1)}, \cdots, y^{(n)})$ be a complete set of conjugates of (y) over $k(x)$. Then, if a set $(\bar{y})$ occurs exactly μ times among the $(\bar{y}^{(\nu)})$ in a specialization $(\bar{y}^{(1)}, \cdots, \bar{y}^{(n)})$ of $(y^{(1)}, \cdots, y^{(n)})$, we say that μ is the multiplicity of $(\bar{y})$ in that specialization. If a given set $(\bar{y})$ occurs with the same multiplicity μ in all the specializations of $(y^{(1)}, \cdots, y^{(n)})$ over a given specialization $(\bar{x})$ of (x), with reference to k, then we say that *the multiplicity of* $(\bar{y})$ *as a specialization of* (y) *over* $(x) \to (\bar{x})$, with reference to k, is defined and equal to μ.

PROPOSITION 8. *Let* (x) *be a set of independent variables over a field* k, *and* (y) *a set of algebraic quantities over* $k(x)$. *Let* $(\bar{x})$ *be a specialization of* (x) *over* k, *and* $(\bar{y})$ *an arbitrary set. Then the multiplicity of* $(\bar{y})$, *as a specialization of* (y) *over* $(x) \to (\bar{x})$ *with reference to* k, *is defined and equal to* 0 *if and only if* $(\bar{y})$ *is not a specialization of* (y) *over* $(x) \to (\bar{x})$ *with reference to* k.

Let $(y^{(1)}, \cdots, y^{(n)})$ be a complete set of conjugates of (y) over $k(x)$; by th. 1 of Chap. II, §1, $(x, y^{(\nu)})$ is, for every ν, a generic specialization of (x, y) over k, and therefore has the same specializations over k as (x, y). Hence, if $(\bar{y})$ is not a specialization of (y) over $(x) \to (\bar{x})$, with reference to k, it is not a specialization over $(x) \to (\bar{x})$ of any of the $(y^{(\nu)})$, and therefore its multiplicity in every specialization of $(y^{(1)}, \cdots, y^{(n)})$ over $(x) \to (\bar{x})$, with reference to k, is 0. On the other hand, if $(\bar{x}, \bar{y})$ is a specialization of (x, y) over k, then, by th. 6 of Chap. II, §2, it can be extended to a specialization of $(x, y^{(1)}, \cdots, y^{(n)})$, in which $(\bar{y})$ has then a multiplicity which is not 0.

Prop. 7 of §3 can now be interpreted as giving a sufficient condition for the multiplicity of a specialization to be defined; before we extend this to the more general criterion of th. 4, we introduce one more definition. Let (x) be a set of independent variables over a field k; let (y) be a set of algebraic elements over $k(x)$, and let $(\bar{x}, \bar{y})$ be a finite specialization of (x, y) over k; then we say that $(\bar{y})$ is a *proper specialization of* (y) *over* $(x) \to (\bar{x})$, with reference to k, if it is isolated over $(x) \to (\bar{x})$ with reference to k, and algebraic over $k(\bar{x})$.

THEOREM 4. *Let* (x) *be a set of independent variables over a field* k, *and* (y) *a set of algebraic quantities over* $k(x)$. *Let* $(\bar{y})$ *be a proper specialization of* (y) *over a given finite specialization* $(\bar{x})$ *of* (x), *with reference to* k. *Then the specialization* $(\bar{y})$ *of* (y) *over* $(x) \to (\bar{x})$, *with reference to* k, *has a well-defined multiplicity, which is a multiple of* $[k(\bar{x}, \bar{y}):k(\bar{x})]_i$.

This is contained in prop. 7 of §3, if the $\bar{x}_i$ are in k; the general case of our theorem will now be reduced to that special case. Let $(y^{(1)}, \cdots, y^{(n)})$ be a complete set of conjugates of (y) over $k(x)$; we have to show that $(\bar{y})$ occurs with the same multiplicity μ in all specializations of that complete set over $(x) \to (\bar{x})$, with reference to k, and that μ is a multiple of $[k(\bar{x}, \bar{y}):k(\bar{x})]_i$. In order to prove this, we may first replace $(x, y^{(1)}, \cdots, y^{(n)})$ by any generic specialization of it over k, this implying that we replace (x, y) by a generic specialization over k since (y) is one of the $(y^{(\nu)})$; for, when we do that, the specializations of $(x, y^{(1)}, \cdots, y^{(n)})$, and those of (x, y), over k remain the same. By doing so, we may, by th. 2 of Chap. II, §1, ensure that (x) be a set of independent variables over the field $K = k(\bar{x})$; it is therefore enough for us to prove our theorem under the additional assumption that this is so. Moreover, by prop. 21 of

Chap. I, §7, $k(x)$ is a regular extension of k; we can therefore apply prop. 8 of Chap. II, §3, to the specializations of $(x, y^{(1)}, \cdots, y^{(n)})$, and this shows that, in proving our theorem, it is enough to consider specializations of that set over the field $\bar{k}$. But every extension of $\bar{k}$ is regular; and, as (x) and $(\bar{x})$ are independent over k, the sets $(x, y^{(1)}, \cdots, y^{(n)})$ and $(\bar{x})$ are independent over $\bar{k}$; we can therefore make use of th. 4 of Chap. II, §1, which shows that every specialization of $(x, y^{(1)}, \cdots, y^{(n)})$ over $\bar{k}$ is also such over $\bar{k}(\bar{x})$, and a fortiori over K; in proving our theorem, it is therefore enough to consider specializations of that set over K. By prop. 12 of Chap. I, §4, $(y^{(1)}, \cdots, y^{(n)})$ consists of complete sets of conjugates of sets $(y^{(\nu)})$ over $K(x)$, each such complete set being taken a certain number of times. We need therefore only show that, for any given ν, the multiplicity of $(\bar{y})$, as a specialization of $(y^{(\nu)})$ over $(x) \rightarrow (\bar{x})$ with reference to the field K, is well-defined and is a multiple of $[k(\bar{x}, \bar{y}):k(\bar{x})]_i$, i.e. of $[K(\bar{y}):K]_i$. In fact, this is so for those values of ν for which $(\bar{y})$ is not a specialization of $(y^{(\nu)})$ over $(x) \rightarrow (\bar{x})$ with reference to K, for then, by prop. 8, that multiplicity is defined and equal to 0. Assume now that $(\bar{y})$ is a specialization of $(y^{(\nu)})$ over $(x) \rightarrow (\bar{x})$ with reference to K; then it is a proper one, as follows from its being a proper specialization of (y) over $(x) \rightarrow (\bar{x})$ with reference to k, and from the fact that every specialization of $(x, y^{(\nu)})$ over K is a fortiori a specialization of $(x, y^{(\nu)})$, hence also of (x, y), over k; then what we have to prove is contained in prop. 7 of §3 when we apply that proposition to the field K, to (x) and $(y^{(\nu)})$, to the specialization $(\bar{x})$ of (x) over K, and to the specialization $(\bar{y})$ of $(y^{(\nu)})$ over $(x) \rightarrow (\bar{x})$ with reference to K. This completes our proof.

PROPOSITION 9. *Let σ be an isomorphism of a field K on a field K'. Let (x) be a set of independent variables over K, (y) a set of algebraic quantities over $K(x)$, $(\bar{x})$ a finite specialization of (x) over K, and $(\bar{y})$ a proper specialization of (y), of multiplicity μ, over $(x) \rightarrow (\bar{x})$ with reference to K. Let (x', y') and $(\bar{x}', \bar{y}')$ be such that σ can be extended to an isomorphism of $K(x, y)$ on $K'(x', y')$, mapping (x, y) on (x', y'), and also to an isomorphism of $K(\bar{x}, \bar{y})$ on $K'(\bar{x}', \bar{y}')$, mapping $(\bar{x}, \bar{y})$ on $(\bar{x}', \bar{y}')$. Then $(\bar{x}', \bar{y}')$ is a specialization of (x', y') over K'; and $(\bar{y}')$ is a proper specialization, of multiplicity μ, of (y') over $(x') \rightarrow (\bar{x}')$ with reference to K'.*

Let the isomorphisms between $K(x, y)$ and $K'(x', y')$, and between $K(\bar{x}, \bar{y})$ and $K'(\bar{x}', \bar{y}')$, the existence of which is assumed in our proposition, be denoted, the former again by σ, and the latter by $\bar{\sigma}$. The first point in our proposition follows from prop. 16 of Chap. II, §4. In order to show that $(\bar{y}')$ is proper, we need only show that it is isolated, since the assumption on $(\bar{y})$ and the existence of the isomorphism $\bar{\sigma}$ make it obvious that $(\bar{y}')$ is finite and algebraic over $K'(\bar{x}')$. Let therefore $(\bar{x}', y'^*)$ be a specialization of (x', y') over K' which has the specialization $(\bar{x}', \bar{y}')$ over K'; by prop. 9 of Chap. I, §3, $\bar{\sigma}$ can be extended to an isomorphism between some extension $K(\bar{x}, \bar{y}, y^*)$ of $K(\bar{x}, \bar{y})$, and the field $K'(\bar{x}', \bar{y}', y'^*)$; then prop. 16 of Chap. II, §4, shows that $(\bar{x}, y^*)$ is a specialization of (x, y) over K and has the specialization $(\bar{x}, \bar{y})$ over K; as $(\bar{y})$ is proper, this implies that (y^*) is algebraic over $K(\bar{x})$, hence (y'^*) over $K'(\bar{x}')$, which is what we had to prove. As to the assertion on the multiplicities of $(\bar{y})$ and $(\bar{y}')$, these multiplicities are defined, by th. 4 and what we have just proved. Let $(y^{(1)}, \cdots, y^{(n)})$ be a complete set of conjugates of (y) over $K(x)$, and let

$$(\bar{y}^{(1)}, \cdots, \bar{y}^{(n)})$$

be a specialization of that set over $(x) \to (\bar{x})$ with reference to K. The isomorphism σ between $K(x, y)$ and $K'(x', y')$ can be extended to an isomorphism between the algebraic closures of these two fields, i.e. between the algebraic closures of $K(x)$ and of $K'(x')$; the image $(y'^{(1)}, \cdots, y'^{(n)})$ of $(y^{(1)}, \cdots, y^{(n)})$ by that isomorphism is then a complete set of conjugates of (y') over $K'(x')$. On the other hand, by prop. 9 of Chap. I, §3, $\bar{\sigma}$ can be extended to an isomorphism of $K(\bar{x}, \bar{y}^{(1)}, \cdots, \bar{y}^{(n)})$ on some extension $K'(\bar{x}', \bar{y}'^{(1)}, \cdots, \bar{y}'^{(n)})$ of $K'(\bar{x}', \bar{y}')$, in which $(\bar{x}, \bar{y})$ is mapped on $(\bar{x}', \bar{y}')$, and $(\bar{y}^{(1)}, \cdots, \bar{y}^{(n)})$ on $(\bar{y}'^{(1)}, \cdots, \bar{y}'^{(n)})$. Then, by prop. 16 of Chap. II, §4, $(\bar{x}', \bar{y}'^{(1)}, \cdots, \bar{y}'^{(n)})$ is a specialization of $(x', y'^{(1)}, \cdots, y'^{(n)})$ over K'. But, by the definition of these sets, $(\bar{y}')$ occurs among the $(\bar{y}'^{(\nu)})$ the same number of times as $(\bar{y})$ among the $(\bar{y}^{(\nu)})$. This proves our assertion on multiplicities.

Proposition 10. *Let (x) be a set of independent variables over a field k, (y) and (z) two sets of algebraic quantities over $k(x)$, and $(\bar{x}, \bar{y})$ a finite specialization of (x, y) over k. Assume that $(\bar{y})$ is a proper specialization, of multiplicity μ, of (y) over $(x) \to (\bar{x})$ with reference to k, and that (z) is finite over $(x, y) \to (\bar{x}, \bar{y})$ with reference to k. Then the specializations $(\bar{z}^{(\rho)})$ of (z) over $(x, y) \to (\bar{x}, \bar{y})$, with reference to k, are in finite number; for every ρ, $(\bar{y}, \bar{z}^{(\rho)})$ is a proper specialization of (y, z) over $(x) \to (\bar{x})$, with reference to k; and, if μ_ρ is the multiplicity of that specialization, we have the relation $\sum_\rho \mu_\rho = \mu \cdot [k(x, y, z):k(x, y)]$.*

Except for the latter relation, our assertions are immediate consequences of prop. 23 of Chap. II, §5, of prop. 5 of Chap. II, §2, and of prop. 6 of Chap. II, §3. Now let $(y^{(1)}, \cdots, y^{(n)})$ be a complete set of conjugates of (y) over $k(x)$, and, putting $\delta = [k(x, y, z):k(x, y)]$, call $(z^{(1)}, \cdots, z^{(\delta)})$ a complete set of conjugates of (z) over $k(x, y)$; furthermore, for every ν, consider some automorphism over $k(x)$ of the algebraic closure of $k(x)$, which transforms (y) into $(y^{(\nu)})$, and call $(z^{(\nu\lambda)})$ the image of $(z^{(\lambda)})$ by that automorphism. Then, by prop. 11 of Chap. I, §4, the $n\delta$ sets $(y^{(\nu)}, z^{(\nu\lambda)})$, for $1 \leqq \nu \leqq n$, $1 \leqq \lambda \leqq \delta$, constitute a complete set of conjugates of (y, z) over $k(x)$; let $(\bar{y}^{(\nu)}, \bar{z}^{(\nu\lambda)})$ be a specialization of that complete set over $(x) \to (\bar{x})$, with reference to k. Then there are μ values of ν for which we have $(\bar{y}^{(\nu)}) = (\bar{y})$; therefore there are $\mu\delta$ values of (ν, λ) for which $(\bar{y}^{(\nu)}, \bar{z}^{(\nu\lambda)})$ is of the form $(\bar{y}, \bar{z}^{(\rho)})$. This proves our assertion.

Proposition 11. *Let $k(x)$ and $k(y)$ be two linearly disjoint extensions of a field k; let (z) be a maximal set of independent variables over k in $k(x)$, and (t) a maximal set of independent variables over k in $k(y)$. Let $(\bar{z}, \bar{t})$ be a finite specialization of (z, t) over k; let $(\bar{x})$ be a proper specialization of (x), of multiplicity μ, over $(z) \to (\bar{z})$ with reference to k, and let $(\bar{y})$ be a proper specialization of (y), of multiplicity ν, over $(t) \to (\bar{t})$ with reference to k. Then $(\bar{x}, \bar{y})$ is a proper specialization of (x, y)*

over $(z, t) \to (\bar{z}, \bar{t})$, *with reference to* k; *and the multiplicity of this specialization is equal to* $\mu \cdot \nu$.

The statement of our proposition depends upon the fact that, under the above assumptions, (x) is algebraic over $k(z)$, (y) over $k(t)$, and (x, y) over $k(z, t)$, and furthermore that, by prop. 4 of Chap. I, §2, (z) and (t) are independent over k, so that (z, t) is a set of independent variables over k. That being so, our first assertion is an immediate consequence of the definitions. By th. 4, this implies that the multiplicity mentioned in the last assertion in our proposition is well-defined; it remains to be shown that it has the required value. In fact, let $(x^{(1)}, \cdots, x^{(d)})$ and $(y^{(1)}, \cdots, y^{(e)})$ be complete sets of conjugates of (x) over $k(z)$, and of (y) over $k(t)$, respectively. Then, by prop. 14 of Chap. I, §4, the $d \cdot e$ sets $(x^{(\alpha)}, y^{(\beta)})$, for $1 \leqq \alpha \leqq d$, $1 \leqq \beta \leqq e$, constitute a complete set of conjugates of (x, y) over $k(z, t)$; let $(\bar{x}^{(\alpha)}, \bar{y}^{(\beta)})$ be a specialization of that complete set over $(z, t) \to (\bar{z}, \bar{t})$, with reference to k. By the definition of μ and ν, there are exactly μ values of α and ν values of β such that $(\bar{x}^{(\alpha)}) = (\bar{x})$ and $(\bar{y}^{(\beta)}) = (\bar{y})$. Therefore there are exactly $\mu \cdot \nu$ values of (α, β) such that $(\bar{x}^{(\alpha)}, \bar{y}^{(\beta)}) = (\bar{x}, \bar{y})$. This completes our proof.

PROPOSITION 12. *Let* (x) *be a set of independent variables over a field* k, *and* (y) *a set of algebraic quantities over* $k(x)$. *Let* (x') *be a finite specialization of* (x) *over* k, $(\bar{x})$ *a finite specialization of* (x') *over* k, *and* $(\bar{y})$ *a proper specialization of* (y) *over* $(x) \to (\bar{x})$, *with respect to* k. *Then there exists a specialization* (x', y') *of* (x, y) *over* k, *which has the specialization* $(\bar{x}, \bar{y})$ *over* k.

Let $(y^{(1)}, \cdots, y^{(n)})$ be a complete set of conjugates of (y) over $k(x)$, and let $(y'^{(1)}, \cdots, y'^{(n)})$ be a specialization of that set over $(x) \to (x')$, with reference to k. The specialization $(\bar{x})$ of (x') over k can be extended to a specialization

$$(\bar{x}, \bar{y}^{(1)}, \cdots, \bar{y}^{(n)})$$

of $(x', y'^{(1)}, \cdots, y'^{(n)})$. By th. 4, since $(\bar{y})$ is a proper specialization of (y) over $(x) \to (\bar{x})$, it has a well-defined multiplicity, which cannot be 0 by prop. 8, and therefore it must occur at least once among the $(\bar{y}^{(\nu)})$. This shows that there is a value of ν such that $(\bar{x}, \bar{y})$ is a specialization of $(x', y'^{(\nu)})$, which itself is a specialization of $(x, y^{(\nu)})$, hence also of (x, y), over k. Our assertion is then satisfied by taking $(y') = (y'^{(\nu)})$.

PROPOSITION 13. *Let* (x) *and* (y) *be two sets of quantities, and* $(\bar{x}, \bar{y})$ *a finite specialization of* (x, y) *over a field* k. *Then, if* $(\bar{y})$ *is an isolated specialization of* (y) *over* $(x) \to (\bar{x})$ *with reference to* k, *the dimension of* $(\bar{y})$ *over* $k(\bar{x})$ *is at least equal to that of* (y) *over* $k(x)$.

We shall first prove that, if $(\bar{y})$ is algebraic over $k(\bar{x})$, (y) must be so over $k(x)$, and begin by proving this in the case in which (x) is a set of independent variables over k. Let s be the dimension of (y) over $k(x)$; if s is not 0, we may, after reordering the y_j if necessary, assume that $y_1, \cdots, y_s$ are independent variables over $k(x)$, and that (y) is algebraic over $k(x, y_1, \cdots, y_s)$. Then our assumptions imply that $(\bar{y}_{s+1}, \cdots, \bar{y}_m)$ is a proper specialization of $(y_{s+1}, \cdots, y_m)$ over $(x, y_1, \cdots, y_s) \rightarrow (\bar{x}, \bar{y}_1, \cdots, \bar{y}_s)$ with reference to k. Let $(y'_1, \cdots, y'_s)$ be a set of independent variables over $k(\bar{x})$; then $(\bar{x}, y'_1, \cdots, y'_s)$ is a specialization of $(x, y_1, \cdots, y_s)$ over k, and, by the coroll. of th. 5, Chap. II, §1, it has the specialization $(\bar{x}, \bar{y}_1, \cdots, \bar{y}_s)$ over k. By prop. 12, it follows from this that $(\bar{x}, y'_1, \cdots, y'_s)$ can be extended to a specialization $(\bar{x}, y')$ of (x, y) over k, such that $(\bar{x}, \bar{y})$ is a specialization of $(\bar{x}, y')$ over k; as $(\bar{x}, y')$ has at least the dimension s over $k(\bar{x})$, this contradicts the assumption about $(\bar{y})$ being isolated. Now, $(\bar{y})$ being still assumed to be algebraic over $k(\bar{x})$, assume that (x) is arbitrary, and let r be its dimension over k. Let $(u) = (u_{ji})$ be a set of $r \cdot n$ independent variables over $k(x, y, \bar{x}, \bar{y})$, n being the number of quantities x_i; put $K = k(u)$, and, for $1 \leqq j \leqq r$, $z_j = \sum_{i=1}^n u_{ji}x_i$ and $\bar{z}_j = \sum_{i=1}^n u_{ji}\bar{x}_i$. By prop. 24 of Chap. II, §5, (z) is then a set of independent variables over K, and (x) is algebraic over $K(z)$. By the coroll. of th. 5, Chap. II, §1, $(\bar{x}, \bar{y})$ is a specialization of (x, y) over K; moreover, as $(\bar{y})$ is an isolated specialization of (y) over $(x) \rightarrow (\bar{x})$ with reference to k, it is such a fortiori with reference to K. By prop. 13 of Chap. II, §4, (z) has the uniquely determined specialization $(\bar{z})$ over $(x) \rightarrow (\bar{x})$ with reference to K, and, by prop. 24 of Chap. II, §5, (x) is finite over $(z) \rightarrow (\bar{z})$ with reference to K; this, by prop. 23 of Chap. II, §5, implies that $(\bar{x})$ is algebraic over $K(\bar{z})$ and that it is an isolated specialization of (x) over $(z) \rightarrow (\bar{z})$ with reference to K. From what we have thus proved, it follows that $(\bar{x}, \bar{y})$ is algebraic over $K(\bar{z})$, and, by prop. 6 of Chap. II, §3, that it is an isolated specialization of (x, y) over $(z) \rightarrow (\bar{z})$ with reference to K; by the special case of our proposition which has been treated above, this implies that (x, y) must be algebraic over $K(z)$, hence also over $K(z, x) = k(u, x)$. Therefore the dimension of (x, y) over $k(u)$, which is equal to that of (x, y) over k since (x, y) and (u) are independent over k, is equal to that of (x) over $k(u)$, i.e., for the same reason, to that of (x) over k; this shows that, under the assumptions made above, (y) is algebraic over $k(x)$. We now consider the general case. If d is the dimension of $(\bar{y})$ over $k(\bar{x})$, we may assume, after reordering the y_j if necessary, that $(\bar{y}_1, \cdots, \bar{y}_d)$ is a set of independent variables over $k(\bar{x})$, and that $(\bar{y})$ is algebraic over $k(\bar{x}, \bar{y}_1, \cdots, \bar{y}_d)$. Then our assumptions imply that $(\bar{y})$ is an isolated specialization of (y) over $(x, y_1, \cdots, y_d) \rightarrow (\bar{x}, \bar{y}_1, \cdots, \bar{y}_d)$ with reference to k. By what we have proved, (y) must then be algebraic over $k(x, y_1, \cdots, y_d)$, and has therefore at most the dimension d over $k(x)$.

We conclude this chapter with the following important criterion for the multiplicity of a specialization to have the value 1.

THEOREM 5. *Let (x) be a set of independent variables over a field k, and (y) a set of m algebraic quantities over $k(x)$. Let $(\bar{x}, \bar{y})$ be a finite specialization of (x, y) over k, and assume that there are m polynomials $F_j(X, Y)$ in $k[X, Y]$, such that $F_j(x, y) = 0$ for $1 \leqq j \leqq m$ and that the determinant $|\partial F_j/\partial \bar{y}_h|$, for $1 \leqq j \leqq m$, $1 \leqq h \leqq m$, is not 0. Then $(\bar{y})$ is a proper specialization of (y) over $(x) \rightarrow (\bar{x})$ with reference to k; and its multiplicity is 1.*

Put $D(X, Y) = |\partial F_j/\partial Y_h|$. By the coroll. of th. 1, Chap. I, §5, the relation $D(\bar{x}, \bar{y}) \neq 0$ implies that $(\bar{y})$ is algebraic and separable over $k(\bar{x})$. Moreover, $D(\bar{x}, \bar{y}) \neq 0$ implies $D(x, y) \neq 0$, so that, by the same corollary, (y) is separable over $k(x)$; therefore, in a complete set of conjugates of (y) over $k(x)$, each conjugate of (y) over $k(x)$ occurs only once. If $(\bar{y})$ was not an isolated specialization of (y) over $(x) \rightarrow (\bar{x})$ with reference to k, there would be a specialization $(\bar{x}, y')$ of (x, y) over k, of dimension greater than that of $(\bar{x}, \bar{y})$, and having the specialization $(\bar{x}, \bar{y})$ over k. We should then have $F_j(\bar{x}, y') = 0$, for $1 \leqq j \leqq m$, and at the same time $D(\bar{x}, y') = 0$, for otherwise, again by the coroll. of th. 1, Chap. I, §5, (y') would be algebraic over $k(\bar{x})$, and $(\bar{x}, y')$ would not be of higher dimension over k than $(\bar{x}, \bar{y})$. But then $D(\bar{x}, y') = 0$ implies $D(\bar{x}, \bar{y}) = 0$, against our assumptions. It remains to be shown that no two distinct conjugates of (y) over $k(x)$, say $(y^{(1)})$ and $(y^{(2)})$, can be such that $(\bar{x}, \bar{y}, \bar{y})$ is a specialization of $(x, y^{(1)}, y^{(2)})$ over k. In fact, assume that $(y^{(1)})$ and $(y^{(2)})$ are such, and put $w_h = y_h^{(2)} - y_h^{(1)}$ for $1 \leqq h \leqq m$; then $(\bar{x}, \bar{y}, 0)$ is a specialization of $(x, y^{(1)}, w)$ over k. Putting $(Y + W) = (Y_h + W_h)$, and

$$H_j(X, Y, W) = F_j(X, Y + W) - F_j(X, Y),$$

we can apply prop. 11 of Chap. II, §3, to the sets of quantities $(x, y^{(1)})$ and (w), to the specialization $(\bar{x}, \bar{y}, 0)$ of $(x, y^{(1)}, w)$, and to the polynomials $H_j(X, Y, W)$; this shows that there exists a set of quantities z'_h, not all 0, such that we have $\sum_{h=1}^{m} \partial F_j/\partial \bar{y}_h \cdot z'_h = 0$. But this contradicts our assumption.

The converse of th. 5 is also true; the proof for this, however, can best be described in geometrical terms, and will therefore be postponed until Chap. V, §3.

CHAPTER IV
THE GEOMETRIC LANGUAGE

1. Points and varieties. By a *point in n-space*, we understand any set of n quantities $(x) = (x_1, \cdots, x_n)$; the x_i are called the *coordinates* of the point $P = (x)$. If $P = (x)$ is any point, and k a field, we write $k(P)$ for $k(x)$, $\dim_k(P)$ for $\dim_k(x)$, etc. Any finite specialization of a point in n-space is a point in n-space. A set (x) of n generalized quantities will be called a *pseudopoint* if it is not finite. Whenever we shall speak of a *set of points*, we shall understand by this, unless the contrary is specifically stated, an *indexed* set $(P_1, \cdots, P_h)$ consisting of points P_α, distinct or not, in finite number, which need not all be in the same space; two such sets $(P_1, \cdots, P_h)$ and $(Q_1, \cdots Q_h)$ are to be considered as equal if and only if we have $P_\alpha = Q_\alpha$ for every α; we shall occasionally write (P_α) for a set such as $(P_1, \cdots, P_h)$. If, for $1 \leqq \alpha \leqq h$, P_α is a point in n_α-space, then, according to the above definitions and to those in Chap. I, §1, the set $(P_1, \cdots, P_h)$ may be considered as a point in n-space, n being defined by $n = \sum_\alpha n_\alpha$. A set $(P_1, \cdots, P_h)$, where each P_α is either a point or a pseudopoint, is to be understood similarly, and may itself be considered as a point, if all the P_α are points, and as a pseudopoint otherwise; every specialization $(P'_1, \cdots, P'_h)$ of such a set over a field k is itself such a set. When we wish to speak of a "set of points" in the usual sense of point-set theory, i.e. of a subset of the set of all points in n-space, we shall use for this the word "*point-set*", two point-sets being considered as identical if every element of either one of them is also an element of the other. On the few occasions when we shall have to mention sets (in the sense of point-set theory) consisting both of points and of pseudopoints, we shall use the word "point-and-pseudopoint-set".

Among the couples (k, P), consisting of a field k and of a point P in n-space such that $k(P)$ is a regular extension of k, we introduce an equivalence relation as follows: two such couples (k, P) and (k', P') are to be put into the same class if and only if the finite specializations of P over k are the same as those of P' over k', i.e. if and only if every finite specialization of P over k is also one of P' over k' and conversely; this is an equivalence relation, as it is obviously symmetric, reflexive and transitive, and therefore determines, among the couples (k, P) satisfying the above conditions, classes of equivalence, each of which is said to define a *variety in n-space*; if V is such a variety, and if (k, P) is a couple in the class which defines it, then we say that k is a *field of definition for* V, that V is *defined over* k, that V is *the locus of* P *over* k, and that P is a *generic point of* V *over* k. From these definitions it follows that, if P is a point in n-space, and k a field, then P has a locus over k if and only if $k(P)$ is a regular extension of k, i.e., by th. 5 of Chap. I, §7, if and only if k is algebraically closed in $k(P)$ and $k(P)$ separably generated over k. In particular, if P is any point and k any field, P always has a locus over the algebraic closure $\bar{k}$ of k.

Let V be a variety in n-space, k a field of definition for V, and P a generic point of V over k; a point P' in n-space is then said to be *a point of* V, or to be *in* or *on* V, if it is a specialization of P over k; it follows from the definition of a variety that this does not depend upon the choice of k and P when V is given; from this, and from the fact that P itself is a specialization of P over k, it follows that every generic point of V, over every field of definition for V, is a point of V. The point-set, consisting of all the points in a variety V, will be called the point-set *attached to* V, and will be denoted by $\{V\}$; conversely, the variety V, which by our definitions is uniquely determined by the point-set $\{V\}$, will be said to be attached to that point-set. If two varieties V and W are such that $\{W\}$ is contained in $\{V\}$, i.e. if every point of W is a point of V, then we write $W \subset V$ and $V \supset W$, and we say that W is a *subvariety of* V, that it is *contained in* V, that it is (or lies) *in* or *on* V, and that V *contains* W. These definitions show that, if we have $V \supset W$ and $W \supset V$, then we have $V = W$, and also that, if V contains W, V contains every subvariety of W.

If k is any field, and (x) a set of n independent variables over k, then, by prop. 21 of Chap. I, §7, the point (x) has a locus over k, which is a variety such that the point-set attached to it consists of all the points in n-space; this variety, which is therefore uniquely determined and independent of the choice of k and (x), and which is defined over every field, will be denoted by S^n. As every point and every variety in n-space is in S^n, and conversely, we may, without contradicting our previous definitions, call S^n *the n-space*. If P is any point, or V any variety, in S^n, then we say that S^n is *the ambient space* for P or for V.

Let $P = (x)$ be a point in S^n, and k a field containing all the coordinates of P; then we have $k(P) = k$; as this is a regular extension of k, P has then a locus over k; as P has then no other specialization over k than P itself, this locus depends only upon P, and not upon the choice of k when P is given, and will be said to be the variety *reduced to* P. The variety reduced to a point P will henceforward be *identified* with that point; the point-set $\{P\}$ attached to it has P as its only element. In view of this identification, care should be taken, whenever one defines for varieties a notion which is also defined for points (or vice versa), to verify that the two definitions agree together in the case of a variety reduced to a point.

PROPOSITION 1. *Let V be the locus of a point P over a field k. Then a point P' is a generic point of V over k if and only if it is a generic specialization of P over k.*

In fact, if it is such a specialization, then the specializations of P and those of P' over k are the same; moreover, by th. 1 of Chap. II, §1, there is an isomorphism of $k(P)$ on $k(P')$ over k; therefore, as k is algebraically closed in $k(P)$, and $k(P)$ separably generated over k, $k(P')$ has the same properties and is thus a regular extension of k. This shows that P' has then a locus over k, which is the same as that of P over k. Conversely, if both P and P' have the locus V over k, then P', being a point of V, must be a specialization of P over k, and similarly P must be a specialization of P' over k.

It follows from prop. 1, and from th. 1 of Chap. II, §1, that, if a variety V is given, and is defined over a field k, then the field generated over k by a generic point of V over k is uniquely determined except for an isomorphism over k.

Let V be a variety, and k a field of definition for V; let $P = (x)$ be a generic point of V over k, and let $\mathfrak{P}$ be the ideal in $k[X]$ determined by (x) over k; prop. 1 means that a point $P' = (x')$ is a generic point of V over k if and only if the ideal determined by (x') over k is $\mathfrak{P}$; V is therefore uniquely determined by k and by the ideal $\mathfrak{P}$, and conversely $\mathfrak{P}$ is uniquely determined when V and k are given. When a point $P = (x)$ has a locus V over a field k, we shall therefore say that the ideal $\mathfrak{P}$ determined by (x) over k is *the ideal defining V over k*, and that V is *defined over k by the ideal* $\mathfrak{P}$; if then the polynomials $F_\mu(X)$ are a basis for $\mathfrak{P}$, we say that the equations $F_\mu(X) = 0$ are *a set of equations for V over k*, and that V is *defined over k by the set of equations* $F_\mu(X) = 0$, or more briefly *by the equations* $F_\mu(X) = 0$. It follows immediately from our definitions that, if a variety V is defined over a field k by a set of equations $F_\mu(X) = 0$, then a point $P = (x)$ is in V if and only if it satisfies all these equations, i.e. if and only if we have $F_\mu(x) = 0$ for every μ. This property, however, is not characteristic of a set of equations for V; for instance, it also belongs to the set of equations $F_\mu(X)^m = 0$ if m is any integer, although this is not a set of equations for V unless m is 1.

THEOREM 1. *If a point P has a locus V over a field k, and if K is a field containing k, then P has the locus V over K if and only if K is free over k with respect to P; and then K and $k(P)$ are linearly disjoint over k. On the other hand, if a point P has a locus V over a field K, and if k is a field contained in K, then P has the locus V over k if and only if K and $k(P)$ are linearly disjoint over k; and then K is free over k with respect to P.*

If P has the locus V over k, then $k(P)$ is regular over k; therefore, by th. 4 of Chap. II, §1, if K is free over k with respect to P, the specializations of P over K are the same as those over k; moreover, by th. 5 of Chap. I, §7, $K(P)$ is then regular over K; this proves that the condition in the first part of our theorem is sufficient. Similarly, if P has the locus V over K, and if K and $k(P)$ are linearly disjoint over k, then, by prop. 4 of Chap. I, §2, K is free over k with respect to P, and, by prop. 22 of Chap. I, §7, $k(P)$ is regular over k, so that P has a locus over k, which is V by what we have already proved. Assume now that P has the locus V over k, and let r be the dimension of P over k; then, by th. 2 of Chap. II, §1, there is a generic specialization P' of P over k, i.e., by prop. 1, a generic point P' of V over k, which has the dimension r over K; if now we assume that P has the locus V also over K, P' must be a specialization of P over K, which, by th. 3 of Chap. II, §1, implies here that the dimension of P over K cannot be less than r, i.e. that K is free over k with respect to P, and therefore, by th. 5 of Chap. I, §7, that K and $k(P)$ are linearly disjoint over k. This completes our proof.

COROLLARY 1. *If a point P has a locus V over a field k, then it has the same locus V over the algebraic closure $\bar{k}$ of k.*

COROLLARY 2. *Let k be a field of definition for a variety V. Then every field K containing k is a field of definition for V; and every generic point of V over a field K containing k is a generic point of V over k.*

Let P be a generic point of V over k, and r its dimension over k; by th. 2 of Chap. II, §1, if K contains k, there is a generic specialization P' of P over k, i.e., by prop. 1, a generic point P' of V over k, which has the dimension r over K; as K is then free over k with respect to P', P', by th. 1, has the locus V over K. Let now $\bar{P}$ be any generic point of V over K; by prop. 1, $\bar{P}$ is a generic specialization of P' over K, hence a fortiori over k, and is therefore, by prop. 1, a generic point of V over k.

COROLLARY 3. *Let V be a variety, defined over a field k; let $\mathfrak{P}$ be the ideal defining V over k, and let k_0 be the smallest field such that $\mathfrak{P}$ has a basis with coefficients in k_0. Then a field K is a field of definition for V if and only if it contains the field k_0.*

In fact, by th. 1, and by th. 7 of Chap. I, §7, k_0 is a field of definition for V, and the smallest such field contained in k. This shows already that, of all the fields of definition for V which are contained in a given one, there is a smallest one. Furthermore, by coroll. 2, every field containing k_0 is a field of definition for V. Let now K be a field of definition for V, and let K_0 be its compositum with k_0; by what we have proved, K_0 is a field of definition for V, and, of all the fields of definition for V contained in K_0, there is a smallest one k_0', which is therefore contained in K and in k_0; by what we have proved above, k_0' cannot then be other than k_0, so that we have $k_0' = k_0$, hence $k_0 \subset K$.

COROLLARY 4. *If a variety V is the locus of a point P over a field k, and also of a point P' over a field k', then the specializations of P over k are the same as those of P' over k'.*

For finite specializations, this is contained in the definition of a variety. In general, let k_0, according to coroll. 3, be the smallest field of definition for V; then, by coroll. 2, P and P' are generic points of V over k_0, hence, by prop. 1, generic specializations of each other over k_0; they have therefore the same specializations over k_0. On the other hand, by th. 1, and by th. 4 of Chap. II, §1, the specializations of P over k are the same as those of P over k_0, and those of P' over k' the same as those of P' over k_0.

COROLLARY 5. *Let $F_\mu(X) = 0$ be a set of equations for a variety V over a field k. Then every field k' containing the coefficients in the polynomials $F_\mu(X)$ is a field of definition for V, and the $F_\mu(X) = 0$ are a set of equations for V over every such field.*

The first assertion follows from coroll. 3 and from the definitions. Now, k and k' being as stated, put $k_1 = k \cap k'$; the $F_\mu(X)$ are then in $k_1[X]$, so that k_1

is a field of definition for V. Let (x) be a generic point of V over some field containing k and k', hence also, by coroll. 2, over k, over k' and over k_1; let $\mathfrak{P}$, $\mathfrak{P}'$ and $\mathfrak{P}_1$ be the ideals determined by (x) over k, over k' and over k_1, respectively. By th. 3 of Chap. I, §6, the $F_\mu(X)$ are a basis for $\mathfrak{P}_1$; moreover, by coroll. 3, $\mathfrak{P}'$ must have a basis in $k_1[X]$, consisting therefore of polynomials in $\mathfrak{P}_1$; as such polynomials can be expressed in terms of the basis $F_\mu(X)$ for $\mathfrak{P}_1$, and as the $F_\mu(X)$ themselves are in $\mathfrak{P}'$, this implies that the $F_\mu(X)$ are a basis for $\mathfrak{P}'$.

COROLLARY 6. *Let $P = (x)$ be a point with a locus V over a field k, and let $P' = (x')$ be a point with a locus V' over a field k'. Then we have $V = V'$ if and only if the ideals respectively determined by (x) over k, and by (x') over k', have a basis in common.*

Put $k_1 = k \cap k'$; if $V = V'$, then, by coroll. 3, k_1 is a field of definition for V, and, by coroll. 5, any basis for the ideal defining V over k_1 will be a common basis for the two ideals in our corollary. The converse follows immediately from coroll. 5.

It follows from coroll. 4 of th. 1 that, if a variety V is the locus of a point P over a field k, the point-and-pseudopoint-set consisting of all the specializations of P over k depends only upon V; this set will be said to be *attached to* V.

Furthermore, as a consequence of coroll. 5 of th. 1, it is permissible to speak of *a set of equations for a variety* without any mention of a field of reference; the field of reference is then understood to be any field containing all the coefficients in the given equations.

If V is any variety, then its smallest field of definition, the existence of which has been proved in coroll. 3 of th. 1, will be denoted by $\text{def}(V)$. Let now V be a variety; put $k_0 = \text{def}(V)$; let P_0 be a generic point of V over k_0, and r its dimension over k_0; by prop. 1, and by th. 3 of Chap. II, §1, all generic points of V over k_0 have then the dimension r over k_0; moreover, if k is any field of definition for V, and P any generic point of V over k, then, by coroll. 2 of th. 1, P is also a generic point of V over k_0 and has therefore the dimension r over k_0; and, by th. 1, k is free over k_0 with respect to P, so that P has the same dimension r over k as over k_0. We have thus proved that, if V is a variety, there is an integer r such that, k being any field of definition for V, every generic point of V over k has the dimension r over k; this integer r will be called *the dimension of* V, and denoted by $\dim(V)$. A superscript, attached to the symbol for a variety, will always denote the dimension of that variety; and, except in the case of the symbol S^n for the n-space (where the superscript n belongs to the symbol and may never be omitted), we shall use interchangeably the symbols with and without superscript, e.g. V and V^r for a variety V of dimension r, even within one and the same theorem, according as it may seem desirable or not to draw attention upon the dimension. When we say "Let V^r be a variety . . .", this should be understood as being equivalent to "Let V be a variety of dimension r . . .". The n-space S^n, as follows immediately from the definitions, has the dimension n. It also follows from the definitions that a variety reduced to a point P has the dimension 0; in view of our identification of such varieties with the points to which they are reduced, it should be observed here that we continue, nevertheless, to speak of the dimension of a point over a field, which need of course not be 0; it will be found that no ambiguity arises from this in practice.

THEOREM 2. *Let V^r be a variety, k a field of definition for V, and P a point of V. Then the dimension of P over k is at most equal to r, and it is equal to r if and only if P is a generic point of V over k. Moreover, every finite specialization of P is a point of V.*

Let $\bar{P}$ be a generic point of V over k; then $\bar{P}$ has the dimension r over k, and P is a specialization of $\bar{P}$ over k. Our assertions now follow immediately from the definitions, from th. 3 of Chap. II, §1, and from prop. 1.

COROLLARY 1. *Let V be a variety, defined over a field k; let W be the locus of a point P over a field K containing k. Then W is contained in V if and only if P is a point of V.*

The condition is necessary, by our definitions. Assume now that P is on V; every point of W is a specialization of P over K, hence a fortiori over k, and is therefore, by th. 2, a point of V.

COROLLARY 2. *Let W be a subvariety of a variety V. Then* $\dim(W) \leqq \dim(V)$; *and, if W has the same dimension as V, it is V.*

Let k be a common field of definition for V and for W (e.g. the compositum of any field of definition for V and of any field of definition for W); and let P be a generic point of W over k. Then, by th. 2, the dimension of P over k is not greater than $\dim(V)$, and cannot be equal to $\dim(V)$ unless the locus of P over k is V.

COROLLARY 3. *Let V and V' be two varieties in n-space, both defined over a field k; let $\mathfrak{P}$ and $\mathfrak{P}'$ be the ideals defining V and V', respectively, over k. Then we have $V \supset V'$ if and only if $\mathfrak{P} \subset \mathfrak{P}'$.*

In fact, let (x) and (x') be generic points of V and of V', respectively, over k; by coroll. 1, we have $V \supset V'$ if and only if (x') is a specialization of (x) over k; our assertion follows immediately from this and from the definitions.

Coroll. 2 of th. 2 shows that there is only one variety of dimension n in n-space, viz. the n-space S^n itself; as we have already seen, this is a variety which is defined over every field k; and, by th. 2, a point $P = (x)$ is a generic point of S^n over k if and only if (x) has the dimension n over k, i.e. if and only if (x) is a set of n independent variables over k. The n-space S^n is defined over a field k by the ideal (0) in $k[X]$, and can therefore be defined over any field by an empty set of equations (or, what amounts to the same, by the equation $0 = 0$). On the other hand, a variety is of dimension 0 if and only if it is reduced to a point;

in fact, we have already observed that this condition is sufficient; conversely, if k is a field of definition for a variety V of dimension 0, and if P is a generic point of V over k, then $k(P)$ must be algebraic over k, which, since k must at the same time be algebraically closed in $k(P)$ by the definition of a variety, implies that we have $k = k(P)$. This shows at the same time that a field k is a field of definition for the variety reduced to the point P if and only if it contains all the coordinates of P.

Less trivial examples of varieties than those which are mentioned above are supplied by the following result:

PROPOSITION 2. *Let k be a field, and $F(X)$ a polynomial in*

$$k[X] = k[X_1, \cdots, X_n].$$

Then the equation $F(X) = 0$ defines a variety in S^n if and only if $F(X)$ is irreducible in $\bar{k}[X]$; and, when that is so, that variety is of dimension $n - 1$. Conversely, every variety of dimension $n - 1$ in S^n, defined over k, can be defined by such an equation.

Assume that $F(X) = 0$ defines a variety V in S^n; by coroll. 5 of th. 1, $\bar{k}$ is a field of definition for V, and $F(X)$ is a basis for the ideal defining V over $\bar{k}$, i.e. for the ideal determined over $\bar{k}$ by a generic point (x) of V over $\bar{k}$; if (x) is such a point, we have then $F(x) = 0$. If we have $F(X) = G(X) \cdot H(X)$, with $G(X)$ and $H(X)$ in $\bar{k}[X]$, the relation $F(x) = 0$ implies either $G(x) = 0$ or $H(x) = 0$, so that one of the two polynomials $G(X)$ and $H(X)$ must be a multiple of $F(X)$; the other must then be of degree 0. This shows that $F(X)$ is then irreducible in $\bar{k}[X]$. Conversely, if $F(X)$ is irreducible in $\bar{k}[X]$, then, by prop. 10 of Chap. I, §3, there is a point (x) in S^n, of dimension $n - 1$ over $\bar{k}$, such that $F(X) = 0$ is the irreducible equation for (x) over $\bar{k}$, i.e., by the definitions, is an equation for the locus of (x) over $\bar{k}$. Finally, if V^{n-1} is in S^n and defined over k, and if (x) is a generic point of V over k, then the irreducible equation for (x) over k is an equation for V.

The following result, which will not be used in this book, is given here in order to show that a variety V is uniquely determined, not only by the point-set attached to it, but even by the subset of that point-set, consisting of all the points in V which are algebraic over some field of definition for V.

PROPOSITION 3. *Let V be a variety, not reduced to a point; let the V_i, for $1 \leqq i \leqq m$, be m varieties in the same space as V, none of which contains V; let k be a common field of definition for V and all the V_i. Then there are infinitely many points on V which are algebraic over k and do not lie on any of the V_i.*

Let (x) be a generic point of V over k, and $\mathfrak{P}$ the ideal determined by (x) over k; and let $\mathfrak{P}_i$, for $1 \leqq i \leqq m$, be the ideal defining V_i over k. By coroll. 3 of th. 2, there is, for every i, a polynomial $F_i(X)$ which is in $\mathfrak{P}_i$ and not in $\mathfrak{P}$; then we have $F_i(x) \neq 0$ for $1 \leqq i \leqq m$; and the polynomial $F(X) = \prod_i F_i(X)$ is in $\mathfrak{P}_i$ for every i, and it is such that $F(x) \neq 0$. By prop. 12 of Chap. II, §3, there exists a finite specialization (x') of (x) over k, which is algebraic over k and such that $F(x') \neq 0$. Then (x') is on V; and, as we have $F(x') \neq 0$ while $F(X)$ is in $\mathfrak{P}_i$, (x') is not in V_i for any i. This proves the existence of one point (x') with the required properties. Assume now that N such points have been found, and let $W_1, \cdots, W_N$ be the varieties respectively reduced to these N points; none of them contains V since V is not reduced to a point; and $\bar{k}$ is a common field of definition for V, for the V_i, and for the W_ν; applying therefore, to these varieties and to the field $\bar{k}$, what we have already proved, we get one more point, distinct from those already found, which has the required properties.

2. Isomorphisms, conjugate varieties, specialization-rings. Let V be a variety, defined by an ideal $\mathfrak{P}$ over a field K; let σ be an isomorphism of K on a field K'; then, if the transform $\mathfrak{P}^\sigma$ of $\mathfrak{P}$ by σ (as defined in Chap. I, §3) defines a variety over K', this variety will be called *the transform of V by σ*, and will be denoted by V^σ. The existence of this variety under those conditions is proved in the following theorem:

THEOREM 3. *Let V be a variety, defined by an ideal $\mathfrak{P}$ over a field K. Let σ be an isomorphic mapping of K on a field K'. Then there is a variety V^σ defined over K' by the ideal $\mathfrak{P}^\sigma$; V^σ has the same dimension as V; and, if P is a generic point of V over K, a point P' is a generic point of V^σ over K' if and only if σ can be extended to an isomorphism of $K(P)$ on $K'(P')$ in which P is mapped on P'; moreover, when P' is such, this isomorphism of $K(P)$ on $K'(P')$ is uniquely determined.*

By prop. 9 of Chap. I, §3, σ can be extended to an isomorphism of $K(P)$ on some extension of K'; if this isomorphism maps P on $\bar{P}'$, it maps $K(P)$ on $K'(\bar{P}')$. From the existence of such an isomorphism between $K(P)$ and $K'(\bar{P}')$, it follows that $\bar{P}'$ has the same dimension over K' as P over K, and, since $K(P)$ is regular over K, that $K'(\bar{P}')$ is regular over K'; therefore $\bar{P}'$ has a locus over K', which, by prop. 8 of Chap. I, §3, is defined over K' by the ideal $\mathfrak{P}^\sigma$; our other assertions then follow from that same proposition and from prop. 1 of §1.

COROLLARY 1. *If a variety V is defined over a field K by a set of equations $F_\mu(X) = 0$, and if σ is an isomorphism of K on a field K', then a set of equations for the transform V^σ of V by σ is $F_\mu^\sigma(X) = 0$.*

COROLLARY 2. *If V and V' are two varieties, both defined over a field K, and if σ is an isomorphism of K on a field K', then the relation $V \supset V'$ implies $V^\sigma \supset V'^\sigma$, and conversely.*

This follows from th. 3, and from coroll. 3 of th. 2, §1.

By th. 3, if a variety V is reduced to a point P, and if K is a field of definition for V, i.e., as we have shown in §1, a field containing the coordinates of P, then an isomorphism σ of K on a field K' transforms V into the variety V^σ reduced to the point $P' = P^\sigma$. This shows that, for zero-dimensional varieties, our definition of the transform of a variety by an isomorphism coincides, as it should in view of the identifications of §1, with the corresponding definition for a point.

PROPOSITION 4. *Let K and K_1 be two fields of definition for a variety V. Let σ be an isomorphism of K on a field K', and σ_1 an isomorphism of K_1 on a field K_1'. Then we have $V^\sigma = V^{\sigma_1}$ if and only if every element of the field $k_0 = \text{def}(V)$ is transformed into the same quantity by σ and by σ_1.*

From coroll. 1 of th. 3, and from the fact that V can be defined by a set of equations with coefficients in k_0, it follows that our condition is sufficient. Assume now that we have $V^\sigma = V^{\sigma_1}$; put $k_0' = \text{def}(V^\sigma)$, and let $F_\mu(X) = 0$ be a set of equations for V over k_0; as V^σ can then, by coroll. 1 of th. 3, be defined by the equations $F_\mu^\sigma(X) = 0$, and as these equations have their coefficients in the transform k_0^σ of the field k_0 by σ, we have $k_0^\sigma \supset k_0'$; similarly, as we have $V = (V^\sigma)^{\sigma^{-1}}$, we have $(k_0')^{\sigma^{-1}} \supset k_0$, hence $k_0' \supset k_0^\sigma$; this gives $k_0' = k_0^\sigma$. The same reasoning, applied to σ_1, shows that σ_1 also maps k_0 on k_0'; therefore the product $\sigma^{-1}\sigma_1$ is defined on k_0 and is an automorphism of k_0, transforming a set of equations for V over k_0 into a set of equations for V over k_0, and transforming therefore into itself the ideal which defines V over k_0; by lemma 2 of Chap. I, §7, that automorphism must therefore leave invariant every element of k_0.

The most important application of the above results is to the following case. A variety V is said to be *algebraic over a field k* if the algebraic closure $\bar{k}$ of k is a field of definition for V; when that is so, every transform V^σ of V by an automorphism σ of $\bar{k}$ over k is called a *conjugate of V over k*. Here again one has to verify that, in the case of zero-dimensional varieties, these definitions coincide with the corresponding definitions for points; this follows immediately from the fact that $\bar{k}$ is a field of definition for the variety reduced to a point P if and only if the coordinates of P are in $\bar{k}$, i.e. algebraic over k.

PROPOSITION 5. *Let V be a variety, algebraic over a field k. Then, of all the fields of definition for V which contain k, there is a smallest one k_1; this field k_1 is an algebraic extension of k, and is the smallest field generated over k by the coefficients in a basis of the ideal defining V over $\bar{k}$. Moreover, the number of distinct conjugates of V over k is then equal to $[k_1 : k]_s$.*

Coroll. 3 of th. 1, §1, applied to V, to $\bar{k}$, and to the ideal defining V over $\bar{k}$, shows that there is a field k_1 with the properties asserted in the first part of our proposition, viz. the compositum of k and of the field $k_0 = \text{def}(V)$. Furthermore, by prop. 4, two automorphisms σ and σ_1 of $\bar{k}$ over k transform V into the same variety if and only if they coincide on k_0, hence if and only if they coincide on the compositum k_1 of k and k_0. As the number of distinct isomorphic mappings of k_1 onto the conjugate fields of k_1 over k is equal to $[k_1 : k]_s$, this proves our last assertion.

THEOREM 4. *Let P be a point, k a field, and let V be the locus of P over the algebraic closure $\bar{k}$ of k. Then every generic specialization of P over k is a generic point over $\bar{k}$ of a conjugate of V over k, and is a point of only one such conjugate;*

conversely, every generic point over $\bar{k}$ *of a conjugate of* V *over* k *is a generic specialization of* P *over* k. *Moreover, every finite specialization of* P *over* k *is a point of a conjugate of* V *over* k, *and every such point is a specialization of* P *over* k.

Let σ be an automorphism of $\bar{k}$ over k, and let P' be a generic point of V^σ over $\bar{k}$. Then, by th. 3, σ can be extended to an isomorphism of $\bar{k}(P)$ on $\bar{k}(P')$, mapping P on P'; therefore, by th. 1 of Chap. II, §1, P' is a generic specialization of P over k; every point of V^σ is a specialization of P' over $\bar{k}$ and a fortiori over k, hence also one of P over k; moreover, if r is the dimension of V, hence also of the conjugates of V by th. 3, P' has the dimension r over $\bar{k}$, so that, by th. 2 of §1, a conjugate of V which contains P' must be the locus V^σ of P' over $\bar{k}$. Let now, conversely, P' be any generic specialization of P over k; by th. 1 of Chap. II, §1, there is an isomorphism of $k(P)$ on $k(P')$ over k, mapping P on P'; this can be extended to an isomorphism between the algebraic closures of these fields, which must leave $\bar{k}$ invariant, inducing on it an automorphism σ over k, and which must therefore map $\bar{k}(P)$ on $\bar{k}(P')$; by th. 3, this implies that P' is a generic point of V^σ over $\bar{k}$. By prop. 7 of Chap. II, §3, it follows from this that every finite specialization of P over k is a point of some V^σ. This completes our proof.

We now reconsider, from our present point of view, the results of Chap. II, §4. If k is a field, P a point, and P' a finite specialization of P over k, we have defined there the specialization-ring of P' in $k(P)$; and this ring, by prop. 15 of Chap. II, §4, remains the same if P' is replaced by any generic specialization of P' over k. The most important case for us is that in which P has a locus V over k, P' being then a point of V. In particular, V being the locus of P over k, let W be a subvariety of V; let K and K' be two fields of definition for W, both containing k; then, if P' is a generic point of W over K, and P'' a generic point of W over K', both P' and P'' are, by coroll. 2 and 3 of th. 1, §1, generic points of W over the field $K \cap K'$, hence, by prop. 1 of §1, generic specializations of each other over $K \cap K'$ and a fortiori over k, and therefore they have the same specialization-ring in $k(P)$; this specialization-ring, therefore, depends only upon V, P, k and W, and will be called *the specialization-ring of* W *in* $k(P)$; if W is reduced to a point P', this definition coincides, as it should, with our earlier definitions. We shall now re-state, in more convenient terms, some of the results of Chap. II, §4.

PROPOSITION 6. *Let* V *be a variety, defined over a field* k; *let* K *be a field containing* k, *and* P *a generic point of* V *over* K. *Then, if an element* z *of* $k(P)$ *is in the specialization-ring, in* $K(P)$, *of a subvariety* W *of* V, *it is in the specialization-ring of* W *in* $k(P)$.

In fact, under those assumptions, th. 1 of §1 shows that K is free over k with respect to P; our assertion now follows immediately from prop. 17 of Chap. II, §4, and from the definitions.

PROPOSITION 7. *Let* V *be a variety,* W *a subvariety of* V, *and* K *a common field of definition for* V *and for* W. *Let* σ *be an isomorphism of* K *on a field* K'; *let*

P and P' be generic points of V over K, and of V^σ over K', respectively. Then σ can be extended to an isomorphism of $K(P)$ on $K'(P')$, mapping P on P'; this isomorphism is uniquely determined, and it maps the specialization-ring of W in $K(P)$ on that of W^σ in $K'(P')$.

This follows immediately from prop. 16 of Chap. II, §4, combined with th. 3.

PROPOSITION 8. *Let V be the locus of a point P over a field k; let W be a subvariety of V, algebraic over k. Let K be a free field over k with respect to P; let z be an element of $K(P)$ of the form $z = \sum_\lambda \omega_\lambda w_\lambda$, where the w_λ are elements of $k(P)$ and the ω_λ are linearly independent elements of K over k. Then the w_λ are all in the specialization-ring of W in $k(P)$ if and only if z is in the specialization-ring, in $K(P)$, of every one of the conjugates of W over k.*

In fact, let P' be a generic point of W over $\bar{k}$; then, by th. 4, the locus over $\bar{k}$ of any generic specialization P'' of P' over k is a conjugate of W over k; if such a point P'' has the same dimension over K as over k, so that the compositum K_1 of K and $\bar{k}$ is free over $\bar{k}$ with respect to P'', then, by th. 1 of §1, the locus of P'' over K_1 is the same as its locus over $\bar{k}$, i.e. a conjugate of W over k. Our proposition follows immediately from this and from prop. 20 of Chap. II, §4.

3. Product-varieties and projections. Let V and W be two varieties, in the same or in different spaces; let k be a common field of definition for V and for W; then we say that P and Q are independent generic points of V and of W, respectively, over k, if P is a generic point of V over k, Q a generic point of W over k, and if P and Q are independent over k. When that is so, then, by th. 1 of §1, Q is a generic point of W over $k(P)$, and P a generic point of V over $k(Q)$. Conversely, if P is any generic point of V over k, and Q any generic point of W over $k(P)$, then, by coroll. 2 of th. 1, §1, and by the definitions of Chap. I, §2, P and Q are independent generic points of V and of W, respectively, over k. Similar remarks apply to varieties $V_1, \cdots, V_h$, in any number, all defined over a field k; one can always obtain a set of independent generic points P_α of the V_α over k, by induction, by taking for P_1 a generic point of V_1 over k, and for P_α, after $P_1, \cdots, P_{\alpha-1}$ have been chosen, a generic point of V_α over $k(P_1, \cdots, P_{\alpha-1})$; and every such set can be so obtained.

Let V be a variety in S^n, and W a variety in S^m; let k be a common field of definition for V and for W; let P and Q be independent generic points of V and of W, respectively, over k; then, by th. 6 of Chap. I, §7, the point (P, Q) in the space S^{n+m} has a locus Z over k; every point of Z, i.e. every finite specialization of (P, Q) over k, is then of the form (P', Q'), where P' is a finite specialization of P over k, i.e. a point of V, and where similarly Q' is a point of W; conversely, th. 5 of Chap. II, §1, shows that, if P' is any point of V and Q' any point of W, then (P', Q') is a point of Z. This shows that the point-set $\{Z\}$ attached to the variety Z is, in the sense of abstract set-theory, the "direct product" (or "Cartesian product") $\{V\} \times \{W\}$ of the point-sets $\{V\}$ and $\{W\}$ respectively attached to V and to W; in particular, this shows that Z depends only upon

V and W, and not upon the choice of k, P and Q when V and W are given. The variety Z, defined as we have said, will be called *the product-variety* or *the product of V and of W*, and will be denoted by $V \times W$; V and W will be called *the factors* of that product; we have, with that notation, $\{V \times W\} = \{V\} \times \{W\}$. More generally, if V_α, for $1 \leqq \alpha \leqq h$, is a variety in a space S^{n_α}, then we define the *product-variety*, or the *product*, $\prod_{\alpha=1}^{h} V_\alpha$, of these varieties, as being equal to V_1 for $h = 1$, and by induction, for $h \geqq 2$, as being equal to $(\prod_{\alpha=1}^{h-1} V_\alpha) \times V_h$; the V_α are called the *factors* of that product, which, for $h \geqq 2$, we also write as $V_1 \times V_2 \times \cdots \times V_h$. By induction on h, it follows from this definition that the point-set attached to the product $\prod_\alpha V_\alpha$ is the direct product of the point-sets $\{V_\alpha\}$; this implies that the product of varieties is associative. It should be observed that it is meaningless to speak of the factors of a variety except with reference to a definite representation of that variety as a product; for instance, the product $U \times V \times W$ of three factors U, V, W can also be written as a product of two factors, e.g. as $(U \times V) \times W$.

Let the V_α, for $1 \leqq \alpha \leqq h$, be h varieties; let $\alpha_1, \cdots, \alpha_r$ be any non-empty set of distinct indices from among the set of indices $(1, 2, \cdots, h)$; then, by the *partial product* of the product $\prod_\alpha V_\alpha$, corresponding to the set of indices (α_i), we understand the product $\prod_i V_{\alpha_i}$; this includes the factors of the product $\prod_\alpha V_\alpha$ as a special case, viz. the case $r = 1$.

In the next theorem, where we have to write equations for varieties in a space S^n and also for varieties in a space S^m (where m and n are any two integers, which need not be distinct), we shall use indeterminates $X_1, \cdots, X_n$ for the former, indeterminates $Y_1, \cdots, Y_m$ for the latter, and then use the $n + m$ indeterminates $X_1, \cdots, X_n, Y_1, \cdots, Y_m$ for writing equations of varieties in S^{n+m}; such notational devices will be used very frequently throughout this book (cf. also the remarks at the beginning of Chap. VI, §1).

THEOREM 5. *Let V^r be a variety in S^n, and W^s a variety in S^m; let k be a common field of definition for V and W. Then the product $V \times W$ is a variety of dimension $r + s$ in S^{n+m}, defined over k; if P is any point of V, and Q any point of W, (P, Q) is a point of $V \times W$, and conversely every point of $V \times W$ can be written as (P, Q), where P is a point of V and Q a point of W; moreover, such a point is a generic point of $V \times W$ over k if and only if P and Q are independent generic points of V and of W, respectively, over k. Finally, if V is defined by a set of equations $F_\mu(X) = 0$, and W by a set of equations $G_\nu(Y) = 0$, then the equations $F_\mu(X) = 0$, $G_\nu(Y) = 0$, taken jointly, are a set of equations for $V \times W$.*

Part of this has been proved above; in particular, we have shown that, if P and Q are independent generic points of V and of W over k, then (P, Q) is a generic point of $V \times W$ over k; this implies that $V \times W$ has the dimension $r + s$. Conversely, assume now that P is a point of V, and Q a point of W, such that (P, Q) is a generic point of $V \times W$ over k; then (P, Q) must have the dimension $r + s$ over k; as this dimension is the sum of the dimension of P over k, which is not greater than r by th. 2 of §1, and of the dimension of Q over $k(P)$, which is not greater than s by the same theorem, this implies that P has the dimension r over k, and Q the dimension s over $k(P)$, hence, by th. 2 of §1, that they are independent generic points of V and of W over k. The last assertion in our theorem follows immediately from the definitions, from th. 4 of Chap. I, §6, and from th. 6 of Chap I, §7.

COROLLARY 1. *Let V and W be two varieties, both defined over a field K; let σ be an isomorphism of K on a field K'. Then we have* $(V \times W)^\sigma = V^\sigma \times W^\sigma$.

This follows from the last assertion in th. 5, and from coroll. 1 of th. 3, §2 (or also from th. 5 and from th. 3, §2).

COROLLARY 2. *Let V_α, for $1 \leqq \alpha \leqq h$, be a variety of dimension r_α in S^{n_α}; let k be a common field of definition for the V_α; put $n = \sum_\alpha n_\alpha$, and $r = \sum_\alpha r_\alpha$. Then the product $V = \prod_\alpha V_\alpha$ is a variety of dimension r in S^n; if, for $1 \leqq \alpha \leqq h$, P_α is a point in V_α, then $(P_1, \cdots, P_h)$ is a point of V, and conversely every point of V is of that form; moreover, such a point is a generic point of V over k if and only if the P_α are independent generic points of the V_α over k.*

This follows from th. 5 by induction on h.

Our definition of the product applies in particular to the case in which the factors are spaces; by coroll. 2 of th. 5, if the n_α are integers, and if we put $n = \sum_\alpha n_\alpha$, then we have $S^n = \prod_\alpha S^{n_\alpha}$. On the other hand, we can also apply our definition to the case in which some of the factors, or all the factors, are of dimension 0; in view of our identification of zero-dimensional varieties with the points to which they are reduced, this shows that, if P_α is a point in S^{n_α} for $1 \leqq \alpha \leqq h$, then the product $\prod_\alpha P_\alpha = P_1 \times P_2 \times \cdots \times P_h$ is the point $(P_1, \cdots, P_h)$ in the space $S^n = \prod_\alpha S^{n_\alpha}$; this provides us with an alternative notation, to be used for such a point whenever convenient; in particular, a point (P, Q) may always be written as $P \times Q$.

Let now U be a subvariety of a product-variety $V \times W$; let k be a common field of definition for U, V and W; and let M be a generic point of U over k, which, by th. 5, can be written as $M = (P, Q)$, where P is a point of V and Q a point of W. By prop. 20 of Chap. I, §7, P has then a locus U' over k; moreover, by th. 2, §1, and by th. 6 of Chap. II, §2, the points of U' are all those points $\bar{P}$ of V which are such that there exists a specialization of M over k of the form $\bar{M} = (\bar{P}, \bar{Q})$, where $\bar{Q}$ is a point or a pseudopoint; therefore, by coroll. 4 of th. 1, §1, the point-set $\{U'\}$, hence also the variety U', depends only upon U, V and W, and not upon the choice of k and of M; the variety U', defined as we have said, will then be called *the projection of U on* the first factor V of the product $V \times W$, or more briefly (when no misunderstanding can arise) *on V*. It should be observed that the point-set $\{U'\}$ is not necessarily the projection on $\{V\}$, in the sense of abstract set-theory, of the subset $\{U\}$ of the direct product $\{V\} \times \{W\}$; it can be shown that the latter projection is always the complement in $\{U'\}$ of the union of point-sets attached to some subvarieties of U'. The parallelism of our definitions with those of abstract set-theory could be fully restored by considering the point-and-pseudopoint-sets attached to V, W, U and U', as follows easily from th. 6 of Chap. II, §2.

It follows from the above definitions that, if V is a variety in S^n, W a variety in S^m, and U a subvariety of $V \times W$, hence also of the product-space

$$S^{n+m} = S^n \times S^m,$$

the projection U' of U on V, when U is considered as contained in $V \times W$, is the same as the projection of U on S^n when U is considered as contained in $S^n \times S^m$. Furthermore, our definition, applied to a zero-dimensional subvariety of a product $V \times W$, shows that, if a point of $V \times W$ is written as (P, Q), with P in V and Q in W, then its projections on V and on W are respectively P and Q.

We now extend, in the usual manner, the above definitions to the case of an arbitrary product $\prod_\alpha V_\alpha$ and to projections on any partial product; this more general case could also be reduced to the case treated above, by a suitable reordering and grouping of the factors. Let $V = \prod_\alpha V_\alpha$ be a product of h varieties V_α; let U be a subvariety of V, and k a common field of definition for U and for the V_α; and let P be a generic point of U over k, which, according to coroll. 2 of th. 5, can be written as $P = \prod_\alpha P_\alpha$, where P_α is, for every α, a point of V_α. Let now $(\alpha_1, \cdots, \alpha_r)$ be a set of distinct indices from among $(1, 2, \cdots, h)$, and let $V' = \prod_i V_{\alpha_i}$ be the partial product of the product V defined by that set; then, by prop. 20 of Chap. I, §1, the point $P' = \prod_i P_{\alpha_i}$, which is in V' by coroll. 2 of th. 5, has a locus U' over k; moreover, by th. 2 of §1, and by th. 6 of Chap. II, §2, the points of U' are those points $\bar{P}' = \prod_i \bar{P}_{\alpha_i}$ of V' which are such that there is a specialization of P over k, of the form $(\bar{P}_1, \cdots, \bar{P}_h)$, where the $\bar{P}_\alpha$ are points or pseudopoints; the variety U', which therefore, in view of coroll. 4 of th. 1, depends only upon U and the V_α, will be called *the projection of U, considered* as a subvariety of the product $V = \prod_\alpha V_\alpha$, *on the partial product $V' = \prod_i V_{\alpha_i}$* of that product. In particular, if U is zero-dimensional, hence reduced to the point $P = \prod_\alpha P_\alpha$, its projection on the partial product V' is $P' = \prod_i P_{\alpha_i}$; more particularly, the projections of the point $P = \prod_\alpha P_\alpha$ of V on the factors V_α are the points P_α.

THEOREM 6. *Let U^r be a subvariety of a product $V \times W$; and let k be a field of definition for U. Then the projection U' of U on V is a variety of dimension not greater than r, defined over k; the projection on V of every point of U is a point of U'; the projection on V of every generic point of U over k is a generic point of U' over k, and conversely every generic point of U' over k is the projection on V of a generic point of U over k. Moreover, if S^n and S^m are the ambient spaces for V and for W, respectively, and if U is defined over k by an ideal $\mathfrak{P}$ in*

$$k[X, Y] = k[X_1, \cdots, X_n, Y_1, \cdots, Y_m],$$

then U' is defined over k by the ideal $\mathfrak{P} \cap k[X]$.

The variety U has the same projection U' on V as on the first factor S^n of $S^{n+m} = S^n \times S^m$ if it is considered as contained in this product-space. Let

$(P, Q) = P \times Q$ be a generic point of U over k, with the projections P on V and Q on W; P and Q are then also the projections of (P, Q), considered as a point in $S^n \times S^m$, on S^n and on S^m; therefore, by what we have proved above, U' is the locus of P over k; as (P, Q) has the dimension r over k, P has at most that dimension over k. If $(\bar{P}, \bar{Q})$ is any point of U, i.e. any finite specialization of (P, Q) over k, then $\bar{P}$ is the projection of that point on V and is a finite specialization of P over k, i.e. a point of U'. Let now P' be any generic point of U' over k, i.e., by prop. 1 of §1, a generic specialization of P over k; by prop. 4 of Chap. II, §2, this can be extended to a generic specialization (P', Q') of (P, Q) over k, which is then, by prop. 1 of §1 and by our definitions, a generic point of U over k with the projection P' on V. Finally, if we put $P = (x)$, and $Q = (y)$, the ideal $\mathfrak{P}$, defining U over k, is the ideal determined by (x, y) over k; therefore the ideal defining U' over k, which is the ideal determined by (x) over k, is $\mathfrak{P} \cap k[X]$.

Corollary 1. *Let U be a subvariety of a product $V \times W$, and let U' be its projection on V; let K be a common field of definition for U, V and W, and σ an isomorphism of K on a field K'. Then U^σ is a subvariety of $V^\sigma \times W^\sigma$, and its projection on V^σ is U'^σ.*

The first assertion follows from coroll. 2 of th. 3, §2, and coroll. 1 of th. 5; the second one, from the last assertion in th. 6, and from coroll. 1 of th. 3, §2 (or also from th. 3 of §2, applied to generic points of U over K and of U^σ over K').

Corollary 2. *Let U be a subvariety of a product $V = \prod_{\alpha=1}^{h} V_\alpha$, and let, for $1 \leqq \alpha \leqq h$, U'_α be its projection on the α-th factor V_α of that product. Then, if P is any point of U, and P_α its projection on V_α, P_α is a point of U'_α; if, moreover, k is a field of definition for U, and if P is a generic point of U over k, then, for every α, k is a field of definition for U'_α, and P_α a generic point of U'_α over k.*

This follows from the definitions and from what was proved above.

Corollary 3. *Let U and Z be two subvarieties of a product $V = \prod_{\alpha=1}^{h} V_\alpha$; let, for $1 \leqq \alpha \leqq h$, U'_α and Z'_α be the projections of U and of Z, respectively, on the α-th factor V_α of that product. Then, if Z is contained in U, Z'_α is contained in U'_α for every α.*

This follows from coroll. 2, applied to a generic point of Z over some common field of definition for U and for Z, and from coroll. 1 of th. 2, §1.

Corollary 4. *Let the V_α be h varieties, and let W_α, for $1 \leqq \alpha \leqq h$, be a variety in the same space as V_α. Then the product $W = \prod_\alpha W_\alpha$ is contained in the product $V = \prod_\alpha V_\alpha$ if and only if W_α is contained in V_α for every α; and, when that is so, the projections of W on the factors V_α of V are respectively the factors W_α of W.*

As the point-sets $\{V\}$ and $\{W\}$ are the direct products of the point-sets $\{V_\alpha\}$, and of the point-sets $\{W_\alpha\}$, respectively, the first assertion follows from the corresponding result in abstract set-theory. The second one follows from coroll. 2 of th. 5, and from the above coroll. 2, applied to a generic point of W over some common field of definition for all the V_α and for all the W_α.

COROLLARY 5. *Let the V_α be h varieties; let W_α, for $1 \leqq \alpha \leqq h$, be a subvariety of V_α; let U be a subvariety of the product $V = \prod_\alpha V_\alpha$, and let the U'_α, for $1 \leqq \alpha \leqq h$, be its projections on the factors V_α of V. Then the relation $U \subset \prod_\alpha W_\alpha$ holds if and only if we have $U'_\alpha \subset W_\alpha$ for every α; and, when that is so, U'_α is the projection of U, considered as a subvariety of the product $\prod_\alpha W_\alpha$, on the factor W_α of that product.*

In the first assertion, the condition is necessary, by coroll. 3 and 4; it is sufficient because, by coroll. 2, the point-set $\{U\}$ is contained in the direct product of the point-sets $\{U'_\alpha\}$, hence also in that of the $\{W_\alpha\}$ if we have $U'_\alpha \subset W_\alpha$ for every α. The second assertion follows from coroll. 2.

COROLLARY 6. *Let U be a subvariety of a product $V \times W$, having on V a projection reduced to a point P; then, if Z is the projection of U on W, we have $U = P \times Z$.*

Let r be the dimension of U. By coroll. 5, U is contained in $P \times Z$, which, by th. 6 and th. 5, has at most the dimension r; by coroll. 2 of th. 2, §1, this implies $U = P \times Z$.

COROLLARY 7. *Let U be a subvariety of a product $V_1 \times V_2 \times V_3$; let U'_{12} and U'_1 be its projections on the partial product $V_1 \times V_2$, and on V_1, respectively. Then U'_1 is the projection on V_1 of U'_{12}, considered as a subvariety of the product $V_1 \times V_2$.*

In fact, let k be a field of definition for U, and P a generic point of U over k; if P_α is, for $\alpha = 1, 2, 3$, the projection of P on V_α, we have $P = P_1 \times P_2 \times P_3$, and U'_{12} and U'_1 are respectively the loci of $P_1 \times P_2$ and of P_1 over k. Our assertion follows from this and from the definitions.

Similar results to coroll. 2, 3, 4 and 7 hold for projections on partial products but have been omitted for brevity. Concerning the language to be used in speaking of projections, a word of caution may be necessary. If U is a subvariety of a product $V \times W$, one usually speaks of "the projection of U on V" instead of "the projection of U on the first factor of the product $V \times W$", etc.; as long as V and W are different, or at any rate as long as one is using different symbols for them, no ambiguity can arise from such manners of speaking. However, products frequently have to be considered where some or all factors are identical; when for instance, as in Chap. VI, we have to consider subvarieties of a product-space $S^N \times S^M \times S^N \times S^M$, where N and M are two integers (which need not be different), it is obviously meaningless to speak of the projection of such a variety on S^N, or on the partial product $S^N \times S^M$; in such cases, care should be taken to use such language as will make unmistakably clear the projection that one has in mind.

4. Unions and intersections of varieties. From the point-sets in n-space which are attached to the varieties in S^n, one can derive further point-sets by the operations of intersection and union. The structure of such point-sets will now be examined from the point of view of algebraic geometry.

By a *maximal variety* belonging to a point-set $\mathfrak{M}$ consisting of points in n-space, we understand a variety V, every point of which is an element of $\mathfrak{M}$, and which is not contained in any other variety having that property. If a variety W is such that $\{W\} \subset \mathfrak{M}$, and if V is a variety of highest dimension in S^n, such that $V \supset W$ and $\{V\} \subset \mathfrak{M}$, then, by coroll. 2 of th. 2, §1, V is a maximal variety belonging to $\mathfrak{M}$. Therefore, if the point-set $\mathfrak{M}$ is given, and if W is any variety such that every point of W is an element of $\mathfrak{M}$, W is contained in at least one maximal variety belonging to $\mathfrak{M}$; this applies in particular to a variety W reduced to a point of $\mathfrak{M}$, and shows that $\mathfrak{M}$ is the union of the point-sets attached to the maximal varieties belonging to $\mathfrak{M}$.

We now introduce a new sort of geometric object. Every finite set of varieties in S^n is said to define a *bunch of varieties*, or more briefly a *bunch*, in S^n; two such sets $V_1, \cdots, V_q$ and $W_1, \cdots, W_r$ are said to define the same bunch of varieties if and only if the unions $\{V_1\} \cup \cdots \cup \{V_q\}$ and $\{W_1\} \cup \cdots \cup \{W_r\}$ of the point-sets respectively attached to the V_i and to the W_j are the same. As this is an equivalence relation between sets of varieties, our definition of bunches of varieties, as being in one-to-one correspondence with the classes determined among such sets by that relation, is legitimate. The bunch of varieties defined by an empty set of varieties will be called *empty*. If a bunch of varieties can be defined by a set consisting of one variety only, it can be so defined only in one way, and will then be identified with that variety; in view of this, care should be taken that definitions for bunches be in agreement with definitions for varieties. If a bunch $\mathfrak{B}$ is defined by a set of varieties $V_1, \cdots, V_q$, then we say that $\mathfrak{B}$ is *the union* of the varieties V_i, and we write

$$\mathfrak{B} = V_1 \cup \cdots \cup V_q ;$$

when that is so, we also say that the point-set $\{V_1\} \cup \cdots \cup \{V_q\}$, which, by our definition, is uniquely determined by $\mathfrak{B}$ and determines $\mathfrak{B}$ uniquely, is the point-set *attached to* $\mathfrak{B}$, and that $\mathfrak{B}$ is the bunch *attached to* that point-set, and we denote that point-set by $\{\mathfrak{B}\}$. If we have two bunches $\mathfrak{B} = V_1 \cup \cdots \cup V_q$ and $\mathfrak{B}' = V'_1 \cup \cdots \cup V'_r$, then we write $\mathfrak{B} \cup \mathfrak{B}'$ for the union of the $q + r$ varieties V_i, V'_j, which is uniquely determined by $\mathfrak{B}$ and $\mathfrak{B}'$ since the point-set attached to it is $\{\mathfrak{B}\} \cup \{\mathfrak{B}'\}$, and we call this *the union* of $\mathfrak{B}$ and $\mathfrak{B}'$; this operation is associative and commutative, as follows from the corresponding properties of the union for the attached point-sets, and the union of bunches in any number is then to be defined as usual in such cases.

Let $\mathfrak{B}$ and $\mathfrak{B}'$ be two bunches of varieties; we say that $\mathfrak{B}'$ is *contained in* $\mathfrak{B}$, and we write $\mathfrak{B}' \subset \mathfrak{B}$ and $\mathfrak{B} \supset \mathfrak{B}'$, if we have $\{\mathfrak{B}'\} \subset \{\mathfrak{B}\}$; this applies in particular to the case in which $\mathfrak{B}'$ is a variety W, and more particularly when it is a variety reduced to a point P; in the latter case, we say that P is *in* $\mathfrak{B}$ and that it is *a point of* $\mathfrak{B}$. A maximal variety belonging to the point-set $\{\mathfrak{B}\}$ attached to a bunch $\mathfrak{B}$ is therefore a variety contained in $\mathfrak{B}$, and not contained in any other variety contained in $\mathfrak{B}$; such a variety will be called a *component of* $\mathfrak{B}$, and we also say that such a variety is *maximal in* $\mathfrak{B}$.

PROPOSITION 9. *Let $\mathfrak{B}$ be a bunch of varieties in S^n, defined by*

$$\mathfrak{B} = V_1 \cup \cdots \cup V_q .$$

Then the components of $\mathfrak{B}$ are those varieties among the V_i which are not contained in any V_j of higher dimension than themselves; a variety, or a point, is contained in $\mathfrak{B}$ if and only if it is contained in some component of $\mathfrak{B}$; and $\mathfrak{B}$ is the union of its components. Moreover, if $\mathfrak{B}'$ is a bunch of varieties in S^n, defined by

$$\mathfrak{B}' = W_1 \cup \cdots \cup W_r ,$$

$\mathfrak{B}'$ is contained in $\mathfrak{B}$ if and only if every W_j is contained in some V_i; and it is the same as $\mathfrak{B}$ if and only if every W_j is contained in some V_i, and every V_i in some W_j.

Let W be any variety in S^n, k a common field of definition for W and for all the V_i, and P a generic point of W over k; then, if W is contained in $\mathfrak{B}$, P is in $\mathfrak{B}$, hence in one of the V_i, so that, by coroll. 1 of th. 2, §1, W is contained in one of the V_i; as every V_i is contained in $\mathfrak{B}$, it follows from this that every component of $\mathfrak{B}$ must be one of the V_i. All our assertions are now immediate consequences of this and of the definitions.

It follows from prop. 9 that, of all the expressions of a given bunch $\mathfrak{B}$ as a union of varieties, there is a shortest one, viz. the one where $\mathfrak{B}$ is written as the union of its components, each component being written only once; this will be called the *reduced expression* for $\mathfrak{B}$. In particular, if V is a variety, then the reduced expression for the bunch V is V itself. If all the components of a bunch of varieties are defined over a field k, we say that $\mathfrak{B}$ is *defined over* k; if all the components of $\mathfrak{B}$ are algebraic over k, we say that $\mathfrak{B}$ is *algebraic over* k.

PROPOSITION 10. *Let the V_i, for $1 \leqq i \leqq q$, be varieties in S^n, all defined over a field K; let $\mathfrak{B} = V_1 \cup \cdots \cup V_q$ be their union; and let σ be an isomorphism of K on a field K'. Then a variety W is a component of $\mathfrak{B}$ if and only if W^σ is a component of the bunch $\mathfrak{B}' = V_1^\sigma \cup \cdots \cup V_q^\sigma$.*

This follows from prop. 9 and from the fact that, by th. 3 of §2 and coroll. 2 of that theorem, V_j^σ contains V_i^σ and is of higher dimension than V_i^σ if and only if V_j contains V_i and is of higher dimension than V_i.

It follows from prop. 10 that, under the assumptions and with the notations of that proposition, the bunch $\mathfrak{B}'$ depends only upon $\mathfrak{B}$ and σ, and not upon the expression of $\mathfrak{B}$ as a union of varieties V_i; we shall call that bunch $\mathfrak{B}'$ *the transform of* $\mathfrak{B}$ *by* σ, and denote it by $\mathfrak{B}^\sigma$; this is defined whenever, with those same notations, $\mathfrak{B}$ is defined over K. In particular, if a bunch of varieties is algebraic over a field k, its transforms by the automorphisms of $\bar{k}$ over k will be called its *conjugates over* k. When $\mathfrak{B}$ is a variety, these definitions coincide, as they should, with the corresponding ones for varieties. If a bunch of varieties is algebraic over a field k and coincides with all its conjugates over k, then we say that it is *normally algebraic over* k; for instance, by prop. 5 of §2, a variety V is normally algebraic over k if and only if it has a field of definition which is purely inseparable over k.

PROPOSITION 11. *Let* $V_1, \cdots, V_q$ *be* q *varieties in* S^n, *all algebraic over* k, *such that every conjugate of every* V_i *over* k *is contained in some* V_j. *Then the bunch* $\mathfrak{B} = V_1 \cup \cdots \cup V_q$ *is normally algebraic over* k.

In fact, let σ be an automorphism of $\bar{k}$ over k; then $\mathfrak{B}^\sigma$ is the union of the V_i^σ. Every V_i^σ is contained in some V_j; on the other hand, every $V_j^{\sigma^{-1}}$ is contained in some V_i, hence, by coroll. 2 of th. 3, §2, every V_j in some V_i^σ. By prop. 9, this proves our assertion.

PROPOSITION 12. *Let* $\mathfrak{B}$ *be a bunch of varieties, and* k *a field. Then* $\mathfrak{B}$ *is normally algebraic over* k *if and only if every finite specialization over* k *of every point of* $\mathfrak{B}$ *is a point of* $\mathfrak{B}$; *and when that is so, every conjugate over* k *of a component of* $\mathfrak{B}$ *is a component of* $\mathfrak{B}$, *and* $\mathfrak{B}$ *is normally algebraic over every field* K *containing* k.

Assume that the above condition is satisfied, and let V be a component of $\mathfrak{B}$; let K be a field of definition for V, containing $\bar{k}$, and let P be a generic point of V over K; from our assumption, and from th. 4 of §2, it follows that the locus $\bar{V}$ of P over $\bar{k}$, and every conjugate of that locus over k, are contained in $\mathfrak{B}$; as $\bar{V}$ contains V by coroll. 1 of th. 2, §1, this implies that we have $V = \bar{V}$, i.e. that V is algebraic over k, and also that every conjugate of V over k is contained in $\mathfrak{B}$, hence, by prop. 9, in some component of $\mathfrak{B}$; therefore the reduced expression for $\mathfrak{B}$ satisfies the condition in prop. 11, and $\mathfrak{B}$ is normally algebraic over k. Assume now, conversely, that a bunch $\mathfrak{B}$ is normally algebraic over k; let P be a point of $\mathfrak{B}$; by prop. 9, P is in some component V of $\mathfrak{B}$, and is therefore a specialization over $\bar{k}$, and a fortiori over k, of a generic point $\overline{P}$ of V over $\bar{k}$; a finite specialization of P over k is then also one of $\overline{P}$ over k, hence, by th. 4 of §2, a point in a conjugate of V over k and therefore a point of $\mathfrak{B}$. If now K is any field containing k, every finite specialization of a point of $\mathfrak{B}$ over K is a fortiori one over k, hence a point of $\mathfrak{B}$. This completes our proof.

We shall now prove that, if the V_i are varieties in S^n, the intersection of the point-sets $\{V_i\}$ attached to the V_i is a point-set attached to a certain bunch of varieties in S^n. This will be a consequence of the following stronger result:

THEOREM 7. *Let* V^r *be a variety in* S^n, *defined over a field* k; *and let the* $F_j(X)$, *for* $1 \leqq j \leqq s$, *be* s *polynomials in* $k[X]$. *Then there is a uniquely determined bunch of varieties* $\mathfrak{B}$ *in* S^n, *such that a point of* S^n *is in* $\mathfrak{B}$ *if and only if it is in* V *and satisfies all the equations* $F_j(X) = 0$ $(1 \leqq j \leqq s)$; *this bunch is normally algebraic over* k, *and all its components have a dimension at least equal to* $r - s$.

Let (x) be a generic point of V over k; put $y_j = F_j(x)$ for $1 \leqq j \leqq s$, and let $\mathfrak{M}$ be the point-set consisting of all the points of V which satisfy the equations $F_j(X) = 0$. As a point $(\bar{x})$ in S^n is in V if and only if it is a specialization of (x) over k, and as the y_j, by prop. 13 of Chap. II, §4, have then the uniquely determined specializations $\bar{y}_j = F_j(\bar{x})$ over $(x) \to (\bar{x})$ with reference to k, a point $(\bar{x})$ of S^n is in $\mathfrak{M}$ if and only if it is a specialization of (x) over $(y) \to (0)$ with reference to k; this implies that, if $\mathfrak{M}$ is not empty, (0) must be a specialization of (y) over k; we shall assume that this is the case. If $(\bar{x}')$ is a finite specialization over k of a point $(\bar{x})$ of $\mathfrak{M}$, $(0, \bar{x}')$ is a specialization over k of $(0, \bar{x})$, hence of (y, x), so that $(\bar{x}')$ is a point of $\mathfrak{M}$. Let now Z be a maximal variety belonging to $\mathfrak{M}$; let K be a field of definition for Z, containing $\bar{k}$, and let (x') be a generic point of Z over K; by what we have just proved, every finite specialization of (x') over $\bar{k}$, i.e. every point of the locus of (x') over $\bar{k}$, is in $\mathfrak{M}$; as this locus contains Z by coroll. 1 of th. 2, §1, it must be Z itself by the definition of Z; this shows that Z is algebraic over k. We now show that (x') must be an isolated specialization of (x) over $(y) \to (0)$ with reference to k; in fact, if $(0, x')$ is a specialization of $(0, \bar{x})$, and $(0, \bar{x})$ a specialization of (y, x), over k, then $(\bar{x})$ is finite, as it has the finite specialization (x') over k, and, by what we have proved above, is a point of $\mathfrak{M}$; if then $\bar{Z}$ is the locus of $(\bar{x})$ over $\bar{k}$, th. 4 of §2, together with what we have proved above, shows that every point of $\bar{Z}$ and of its conjugates over k is contained in $\mathfrak{M}$, and also that (x'), hence, by coroll. 1 of th. 2, §1, the variety Z, are contained in one of these conjugates; therefore, by the definition of Z, Z must be a conjugate of $\bar{Z}$ over k, so that (x') and $(\bar{x})$ have the same dimension over k; this proves our assertion about (x') being isolated. This, by prop. 13 of Chap. III, §4, implies that the dimension of (x) over $k(y)$, which is equal to $r - \dim_k(y)$, hence at least equal to $r - s$, is not greater than that of (x') over k, i.e. than the dimension of Z. Our proof will now be complete if we show that the maximal varieties belonging to $\mathfrak{M}$ are in finite number; for then, by what we have proved and by prop. 12, the union of these varieties will be a bunch with the required properties. This will be proved by induction on s; we first consider the case $s = 1$. In this case, if we have $y_1 = F_1(x) = 0$, then V is a maximal variety belonging to $\mathfrak{M}$, and the only one; we may therefore assume $y_1 \neq 0$; then a maximal variety Z, belonging to $\mathfrak{M}$, is a subvariety of V, other than V, of dimension at least $r - 1$, and has therefore, by coroll. 2 of th. 2, §1, exactly the dimension $r - 1$, so that, if (x') is a generic point of Z over $\bar{k}$, there is at least one choice of the indices $i_1, \cdots, i_{r-1}$ such that $(x'_{i_1}, \cdots, x'_{i_{r-1}})$ is a set of independent variables over $\bar{k}$; it will therefore be enough to show that there can be only a finite number of maximal varieties Z which have this property for a given choice of the indices $i_1, \cdots, i_{r-1}$. After reordering the coordinates in our space, what we have to show is that there are only a finite number of maximal varieties Z belonging to $\mathfrak{M}$, with the property that, if (x') is a generic point of Z over $\bar{k}$, $(x'_1, \cdots, x'_{r-1})$ are independent variables over k. In fact, let $(t_1, \cdots, t_{r-1})$ be a set of independent variables over k; if Z and (x') are as we have just said, then $(t_1, \cdots, t_{r-1})$ is a generic specialization of $(x_1', \cdots, x_{r-1}')$ over $\bar{k}$, which, by prop. 4 of Chap. II, §2, can be extended to a generic specialization (t) of (x') over $\bar{k}$; (t) is then a generic point of Z over $\bar{k}$, and, being a point of $\mathfrak{M}$, it is a specialization of (x), with reference to k, over $y_1 \to 0$, hence also over $(y_1, x_1, \cdots, x_{r-1}) \to (0, t_1, \cdots, t_{r-1})$. Now, as y_1 is not 0, a specialization of (x) over $(y_1, x_1, \cdots, x_{r-1}) \to (0, t_1, \cdots, t_{r-1})$, with reference to k, cannot be generic, and must therefore, by th. 3 of Chap. II, §1, be at most of dimension $r - 1$ over k, which implies that it must be algebraic over $k(t_1, \cdots, t_{r-1})$; prop. 5 of Chap. II, §2, then shows that such specializations, hence also their loci over $\bar{k}$, are in finite number; as every variety Z, with the properties stated above, is such a locus, this completes the proof of our theorem in the case $s = 1$. Now, taking again s to be arbitrary, we may, by the induction assumption, assume that there is a bunch $\mathfrak{B}'$ such that a point is in $\mathfrak{B}'$ if and only if it is in V and satisfies the equations $F_1(X) = \cdots = F_{s-1}(X) = 0$. If then the Z_ρ' are the components of $\mathfrak{B}'$, there is for every ρ, by the case $s = 1$ of our theorem, a bunch $\mathfrak{B}_\rho$ such that a point is in $\mathfrak{B}_\rho$ if and only if it is in Z_ρ' and satisfies the equation $F_s(X) = 0$. Then the point-set $\mathfrak{M}$ is the union of the point-sets $\{\mathfrak{B}_\rho\}$, so that the maximal varieties belonging to $\mathfrak{M}$ are the components of the union $\mathfrak{B}$ of the bunches $\mathfrak{B}_\rho$.

Corollary 1. *Let V be a variety in S^n, defined over a field K; let the $F_j(X)$ be polynomials in $K[X]$; and let σ be an isomorphism of K on a field K'. Let $\mathfrak{B}$ be the bunch of varieties, such that a point is in $\mathfrak{B}$ if and only if it is in V and satisfies the equations $F_j(X) = 0$; and let $\mathfrak{B}'$ be the bunch similarly defined by means of V^σ and of the equations $F_j^\sigma(X) = 0$. Then $\mathfrak{B}$ is defined over $\bar{K}$; and, if $\bar{\sigma}$ is any isomorphism of $\bar{K}$ on $\bar{K}'$ coinciding with σ on K, we have $\mathfrak{B}' = \mathfrak{B}^{\bar{\sigma}}$.*

By th. 7, $\mathfrak{B}$ is defined over $\bar{K}$; let Z be a component of $\mathfrak{B}$, P a generic point of Z over $\bar{K}$, and P' a generic point of $Z^{\bar{\sigma}}$ over $\bar{K}'$; th. 3 of §2, and its coroll. 2, show that P' is in $\mathfrak{B}'$, hence in a component Z' of $\mathfrak{B}'$; as Z', by th. 7, is defined over $\bar{K}'$, this implies $Z^{\bar{\sigma}} \subset Z'$; one shows in the same way, by using the isomorphism $\bar{\sigma}^{-1}$ of $\bar{K}'$ on $\bar{K}$, that, if Z' is any component of $\mathfrak{B}'$, there is a component Z of $\mathfrak{B}$ such that $Z' \subset Z^{\bar{\sigma}}$. Our assertion now follows from prop. 9, applied to the reduced expressions for $\mathfrak{B}^{\bar{\sigma}}$ and for $\mathfrak{B}'$.

Corollary 2. *Let V and W be two varieties in S^n, defined over a field k. Then there is a bunch of varieties $\mathfrak{B}$ in S^n, normally algebraic over k, such that a point is in $\mathfrak{B}$ if and only if it is both in V and in W.*

This follows from th. 7, applied e.g. to V and to a set of equations for W over k.

By coroll. 2 of th. 7, if two varieties V and W are given in S^n, there is a bunch of varieties $\mathfrak{B}$ such that the point-set $\{\mathfrak{B}\}$ attached to it is the intersection of the point-sets $\{V\}$ and $\{W\}$ respectively attached to V and to W; the bunch $\mathfrak{B}$, which is uniquely determined by this condition, and which may be empty, will be called *the intersection of V and of W*, and will be denoted by $V \cap W$. If now two bunches of varieties, $\mathfrak{B} = V_1 \cup \cdots \cup V_q$ and $\mathfrak{B}' = W_1 \cup \cdots \cup W_r$, are given in S^n, the point-set $\{\mathfrak{B}\} \cap \{\mathfrak{B}'\}$ is the union of the point-sets $\{V_i\} \cap \{W_j\}$, i.e. the union of the point-sets respectively attached to the bunches $V_i \cap W_j$; the union of the bunches $V_i \cap W_j$ for $1 \leqq i \leqq q$, $1 \leqq j \leqq r$, which therefore depends only upon the bunches $\mathfrak{B}$ and $\mathfrak{B}'$, will be called *the intersection of $\mathfrak{B}$ and of $\mathfrak{B}'$*, and will be denoted by $\mathfrak{B} \cap \mathfrak{B}'$; we have then $\{\mathfrak{B} \cap \mathfrak{B}'\} = \{\mathfrak{B}\} \cap \{\mathfrak{B}'\}$; in particular, if $\mathfrak{B}$ and $\mathfrak{B}'$ are varieties, this definition coincides with the one given above for that case. From the corresponding properties of the union and intersection in abstract set-theory, it follows immediately that the union and intersection of bunches of varieties have all the usual properties of a so-called "Boolean algebra", associativity, commutativity, distributivity; in particular, one can define, in the usual manner, the intersection of bunches in any number.

THEOREM 8. *Let $V_1, \cdots, V_q$ be q varieties in S^n, all defined over a field k. Then their intersection $\mathfrak{B} = V_1 \cap \cdots \cap V_q$ is a bunch of varieties, normally algebraic over k; every point, and every variety, contained in all the V_i is contained in at least one component of $\mathfrak{B}$; every component of $\mathfrak{B}$ is algebraic over k, and every conjugate of a component of $\mathfrak{B}$ over k is also a component of $\mathfrak{B}$.*

Let $F_\mu^{(i)}(X) = 0$ $(1 \leqq \mu \leqq m_i)$ be, for every i, a set of equations for V_i over k; a point of S^n is in all the V_i if and only if it satisfies all the equations

$$F_\mu^{(i)}(X) = 0 \qquad (1 \leqq i \leqq q, 1 \leqq \mu \leqq m_i);$$

our first assertion follows then from th. 7, applied to S^n and to this set of equations. The rest follows from prop. 9 and from the definitions.

COROLLARY 1. *Let the $\mathfrak{B}_i$ be q bunches of varieties in S^n, all defined over a field K; and let σ be an isomorphism of K on a field K'. Then the union of the $\mathfrak{B}_i$ is defined over K, and its transform by σ is the union of the $\mathfrak{B}_i^\sigma$; the intersection of the $\mathfrak{B}_i$ is defined over $\bar{K}$, and its transform by any isomorphism $\bar{\sigma}$ of $\bar{K}$ on $\bar{K}'$ coinciding with σ on K is the intersection of the $\mathfrak{B}_i^\sigma$.*

The first assertion follows, by induction on q, from the definitions and from prop. 10. As to the latter, if one replaces the $\mathfrak{B}_i$ by their reduced expressions, and uses the distributivity of the intersection with respect to the union, one sees that it is enough to prove it for an intersection of varieties V_i, defined over K. Let then $F_\mu^{(i)}(X) = 0$ $(1 \leqq \mu \leqq m_i)$ be, for $1 \leqq i \leqq q$, a set of equations for V_i over K; then our result follows from coroll. 1 of th. 7, applied to S^n and to the set of equations $F_\mu^{(i)}(X) = 0$ $(1 \leqq i \leqq q, 1 \leqq \mu \leqq m_i)$, and from coroll. 1 of th. 3, §2.

COROLLARY 2. *If some bunches of varieties in S^n are normally algebraic over a field k, so is every bunch derived from them by the operations of union and intersection.*

This follows immediately from coroll. 1.

COROLLARY 3. *Let $V_1, \cdots, V_q$ and W be $q + 1$ varieties in S^n, defined over a field K; and let σ be an isomorphism of K on a field K'. Then W is a component of $V_1 \cap \cdots \cap V_q$ if and only if W^σ is a component of $V_1^\sigma \cap \cdots \cap V_q^\sigma$.*

This follows from coroll. 1, from prop. 10, and from prop. 4 of §2.

COROLLARY 4. *Let, for $1 \leqq i \leqq q$, V_i be a variety in S^n, and W_i a variety in S^m. Then the components of the intersection of the q products $V_i \times W_i$ are the varieties of the form $X \times Y$, where X is any one of the components of $V_1 \cap \cdots \cap V_q$, and Y any one of the components of $W_1 \cap \cdots \cap W_q$.*

By coroll. 4 of th. 6, §3, every one of the varieties $X \times Y$ is contained in all the $V_i \times W_i$, and none of them is contained in any other variety $X \times Y$. By th. 5 of §3, every point in the intersection of the $V_i \times W_i$ can be written as $P \times Q$, where P is in all the V_i, hence in some X by th. 8, and where Q is in all the W_i, hence in some Y. Therefore the union of the $X \times Y$ is contained in the intersection of the $V_i \times W_i$ and contains it, and, by prop. 9, the $X \times Y$ are its components.

5. Linear varieties. By a *linear variety in* S^n, we understand a variety which can be defined by a set of linear equations

$$\sum_{j=1}^{n} c_{\mu j} X_j - a_\mu = 0 \qquad (1 \leqq \mu \leqq m).$$

As S^n can be defined by an empty set of equations, and as a variety, reduced to a point (a) in S^n, can be defined by the equations $X_i - a_i = 0$ $(1 \leqq i \leqq n)$, S^n and all varieties of dimension 0 are linear varieties. More generally, if $(a_1, \cdots, a_r)$ is a set of r elements of a field k, and if $(u_1, \cdots, u_{n-r})$ is a set of $n - r$ independent variables over k, then, by prop. 21 of Chap. I, §7, the point $(a_1, \cdots, a_r, u_1, \cdots, u_{n-r})$ in S^n has a locus L over k, and it is easily seen that L, which is of dimension $n - r$, can be defined over k by the set of equations $X_i - a_i = 0$ $(1 \leqq i \leqq r)$.

PROPOSITION 13. *Let $\|c_{ij}\|$, for $1 \leqq i \leqq n$, $1 \leqq j \leqq n$, be a matrix with coefficients in a field k, and with a non-vanishing determinant; let (a) be a set of n elements of k; and let the $\bar{X}_i$ be the n linear polynomials in k[X] defined by*

$$\bar{X}_i = \textstyle\sum_{j=1}^{n} c_{ij} X_j - a_i \qquad (1 \leqq i \leqq n).$$

Then, if for every polynomial F(X) in k[X] we put $\bar{F}(X) = F(\bar{X})$, the correspondence between F(X) and $\bar{F}(X)$ is an automorphism of k[X]. Moreover, if (x) is a point in S^n, there is a point $(\bar{x})$ in S^n such that $x_i = \sum_{j=1}^{n} c_{ij}\bar{x}_j - a_i$, for $1 \leqq i \leqq n$; if (x) has a locus V over k, then $(\bar{x})$ has a locus $\bar{V}$ over k; and, if the $F_\mu(X) = 0$ are a set of equations for V cver k, the transforms $\bar{F}_\mu(X) = 0$ of these by the above-defined automorphism of k[X] are a set of equations for $\bar{V}$ over k.

As the determinant $|c_{ij}|$ is not 0, the matrix $\|c_{ij}\|$ has an inverse $\|d_{ij}\|$ with coefficients in k. Then, if $F(X)$ is in $k[X]$, and if $\bar{F}(X)$ is defined as above, i.e. by $\bar{F}(X) = F[\sum_j c_{ij}X_j - a_i]$, we have $F(X) = \bar{F}[\sum_j d_{ij}(X_j + a_j)]$, and conversely; this makes our first assertion obvious. If (x) is in S^n, and if we have $x_i = \sum_j c_{ij}\bar{x}_j - a_i$, for $1 \leqq i \leqq n$, we have $\bar{x}_i = \sum_j d_{ij}(x_j + a_j)$ for $1 \leqq i \leqq n$, and conversely; and then we have $k(\bar{x}) = k(x)$, which implies that, if (x) has a locus V over k, $(\bar{x})$ has a locus $\bar{V}$ over k. That being so, let $\mathfrak{P}$ and $\bar{\mathfrak{P}}$ be the ideals defining V and $\bar{V}$, respectively, over k; a polynomial $F(X)$ in $k[X]$ is then in $\mathfrak{P}$ if and only if we have $F(x) = 0$, i.e. $F[\sum_j c_{ij}\bar{x}_j - a_i] = 0$, i.e. if and only if the corresponding polynomial $\bar{F}(X)$ in the above-defined automorphism of $k[X]$ is in the ideal $\bar{\mathfrak{P}}$; this shows that $\bar{\mathfrak{P}}$ is the transform of $\mathfrak{P}$ by that automorphism, so that, if the $F_\mu(X)$ are a basis of $\mathfrak{P}$, the corresponding polynomials $\bar{F}_\mu(X)$ in that automorphism are a basis of $\bar{\mathfrak{P}}$.

Theorem 9. *Let $||c_{ij}||$, for $1 \leqq i \leqq r$, $1 \leqq j \leqq n$, be a matrix of rank r, with coefficients in a field k; and let (a) be a set of r elements of k. Then there is a linear variety L^{n-r} in S^n, defined over k by the set of equations $\sum_{j=1}^n c_{ij}X_j - a_i = 0$ $(1 \leqq i \leqq r)$. Moreover, there is a generic point (z) of that variety L over k, with coordinates of the form $z_i = \sum_{h=1}^{n-r} e_{ih}u_h + f_i$ $(1 \leqq i \leqq n)$, where the e_{ih} and f_i are elements of k, and $(u) = (u_h)$ is a set of $n - r$ independent variables over k.*

As the matrix $||c_{ij}||$ is of rank r, the r linear forms $\sum_j c_{ij}X_j$ are linearly independent over k, and it is therefore possible to find $n - r$ linear forms $\sum_j c_{r+h,j}X_j$ $(1 \leqq h \leqq n - r)$, such that the n forms $\sum_j c_{ij}X_j$, for $1 \leqq i \leqq n$, are linearly independent over k, i.e. that their determinant is not 0; then the matrix $||c_{ij}||$ of these n forms has an inverse $||d_{ij}||$. Now, put $a_{r+h} = 0$ for $1 \leqq h \leqq n - r$; let $(u) = (u_h)$ be a set of $n - r$ independent variables over k, and put $x_i = 0$ for $1 \leqq i \leqq r$, $x_{r+h} = u_h$ for $1 \leqq h \leqq n - r$; as we have seen, the point

$$(x) = (0, \cdots, 0, u_1, \cdots, u_{n-r})$$

has a locus over k, which is defined over k by the set of equations

$$X_i = 0 \qquad (1 \leqq i \leqq r).$$

Therefore, by prop. 13, there is a point $(\bar{x})$ such that $x_i = \sum_j c_{ij}\bar{x}_j - a_i$ for $1 \leqq i \leqq n$, and this point has a locus L over k, which is defined over k by the set of equations $\sum_j c_{ij}X_j - a_i = 0$ $(1 \leqq i \leqq r)$. Moreover, the relations by which $(\bar{x})$ is defined imply that we have $\bar{x}_i = \sum_j d_{ij}(x_j + a_j)$ for $1 \leqq i \leqq n$; this shows that we have $k(\bar{x}) = k(x) = k(u)$, hence that L has the dimension $n - r$. The last assertion in our theorem follows by writing (z) instead of $(\bar{x})$, e_{ih} insead of $d_{i,r+h}$, and f_i instead of $\sum_j d_{ij}a_j$.

Corollary. *Let the $F_\mu(X) = \sum_{j=1}^n c_{\mu j}X_j - a_\mu$, for $1 \leqq \mu \leqq m$, be any set of linear polynomials in (X) with coefficients in a field k. Then there is a variety L, defined in S^n by the set of equations $F_\mu(X) = 0$ $(1 \leqq \mu \leqq m)$, if and only if there is at least one point in S^n which satisfies all these equations; this is the case if and only if the matrices $||c_{\mu j}\ a_\mu||$ and $||c_{\mu j}||$ have the same rank r; when that is so, L has the dimension $n - r$, and can also be defined by the set of equations*

$$F_{\mu_i}(X) = 0 \qquad (1 \leqq i \leqq r)$$

if the $F_{\mu_i}(X)$ are any maximal set of linearly independent polynomials over k among the $F_\mu(X)$.

Put $F'_\mu(X) = \sum_{j=1}^n c_{\mu j} X_j$ $(1 \leqq \mu \leqq m)$, and call r and r' the ranks of the matrices $\|c_{\mu j}\ a_\mu\|$ and $\|c_{\mu j}\|$, respectively; then r and r' are the maximal numbers of linearly independent polynomials over k among the $F_\mu(X)$, and among the $F'_\mu(X)$, respectively; and we have $r \geqq r'$. If r' is less than r, then, if we consider r linearly independent polynomials $F_{\mu_i}(X)$, the corresponding $F'_{\mu_i}(X)$ cannot be linearly independent, so that we have a non-trivial relation $\sum_{i=1}^r b_i F'_{\mu_i}(X) = 0$, with coefficients b_i in k; this gives $\sum_i b_i F_{\mu_i}(X) = -\sum_i b_i a_{\mu_i}$, where the right-hand side cannot be 0 since the $F_{\mu_i}(X)$ are linearly independent; this shows that in this case no point can satisfy all the equations $F_\mu(X) = 0$. On the other hand, assume that we have $r = r'$, and let the $F_{\mu_i}(X)$, for $1 \leqq i \leqq r$, be any maximal set of linearly independent polynomials among the $F_\mu(X)$; then all the $F_\mu(X)$ are linear combinations of the $F_{\mu_i}(X)$, hence all the $F'_\mu(X)$ are linear combinations of the $F'_{\mu_i}(X)$, which therefore must be linearly independent, since otherwise there would not be r linearly independent forms among the $F'_\mu(X)$; this shows that the matrix $\|c_{\mu_i j}\|$ is then of rank r. By th. 9, therefore, there is a linear variety L of dimension $n - r$, defined by the equations $F_{\mu_i}(X) = 0$; the $F_{\mu_i}(X)$ are then a basis of the ideal defining L over k; the $F_\mu(X)$ are a fortiori also such a basis, since they include the $F_{\mu_i}(X)$ among themselves and are linear combinations of the $F_{\mu_i}(X)$ with coefficients in k; hence L is also defined by the set of equations $F_\mu(X) = 0$.

If k is a field, and $\mathfrak{A}$ any ideal in the ring $k[X]$, then the set of all linear polynomials in $\mathfrak{A}$ is obviously a finite k-module; th. 9 and its corollary give important information about this module in the case when $\mathfrak{A}$ is the ideal defining a linear variety over k; this is contained in the following theorem:

THEOREM 10. *Let L^{n-r} be a linear variety in S^n; let k be a field of definition for L, and let $\mathfrak{P}$ be the ideal defining L over k. Then the set of all linear polynomials in $\mathfrak{P}$ is a k-module of rank r; and a set of linear polynomials is a basis for that module if and only if it is a basis for $\mathfrak{P}$.*

We first show that $\mathfrak{P}$ has a basis consisting of linear polynomials. Let the $\Phi_\mu(X) = 0$ be a set of linear equations for L; let k' be a field containing k and the coefficients in the $\Phi_\mu(X)$, and let the ω_λ be a maximal set of linearly independent elements over k among the coefficients in the $\Phi_\mu(X)$. By coroll. 5 of th. 1, §1, the $\Phi_\mu(X)$ are a basis for the ideal $\mathfrak{P}'$ which defines L over k'. Expressing the coefficients in the $\Phi_\mu(X)$ as linear combinations of the ω_λ, we get

$$\Phi_\mu(X) = \sum_\lambda \omega_\lambda F_{\mu\lambda}(X),$$

where the $F_{\mu\lambda}(X)$ are linear polynomials with coefficients in k, which, by lemma 1 of Chap. I, §6, must all be in $\mathfrak{P}$; as the $\Phi_\mu(X)$ are a basis for $\mathfrak{P}'$, this implies that the $F_{\mu\lambda}(X)$ are also such a basis, hence also a basis for the ideal $\mathfrak{P} = \mathfrak{P}' \cap k[X]$. Now let the $G_\rho(X)$ be any basis for the k-module of the linear polynomials in $\mathfrak{P}$; then the $F_{\mu\lambda}(X)$ are linear combinations of the $G_\rho(X)$, with coefficients in k, and this implies that the $G_\rho(X)$ also are a basis for $\mathfrak{P}$. Conversely, if a set of linear polynomials $G_\rho(X)$ is a basis for the ideal $\mathfrak{P}$, so that the set of equations $G_\rho(X) = 0$ defines L over k, then, by the coroll. of th. 9, there are r and no more than r linearly independent polynomials among the $G_\rho(X)$; moreover, if $H(X)$ is any linear polynomial in $\mathfrak{P}$, then the $G_\rho(X)$ and $H(X)$, taken together, are still a basis for $\mathfrak{P}$, so that, by the same corollary, there are no more than r linearly independent polynomials over k among them; $H(X)$ must then be a linear combination, with coefficients in k, of any r linearly independent polynomials among the $G_\rho(X)$. This shows that, in that case, the $G_\rho(X)$ are a basis for the k-module of the linear polynomials in $\mathfrak{P}$, and also that this module is of rank r.

COROLLARY. *If L^{n-r} is a linear variety, defined over a field k in S^n, it can be defined by a set of r linear equations, with coefficients in k, and not by any lesser number of linear equations. Moreover, if $F_i(X) = 0$ $(1 \leqq i \leqq r)$ is a set of r linear equations for L over k, then the $F_i(X)$ are linearly independent over k; and, if we have $F_i(X) = \sum_{j=1}^{n} c_{ij}X_j - a_i$, the matrix $\|c_{ij}\|$ is of rank r.*

This follows at once from th. 10, and from the coroll. of th. 9.

A set of r linear equations, defining a linear variety L of dimension $n - r$ in the n-space S^n, will be called a *minimal set of linear equations* for L, and will be denoted, whenever convenient, by a German capital with a superscript denoting the number of equations in the set, e.g. $\mathfrak{S}^r$ for a minimal set of r linear equations. By the coroll. of th. 10, every linear variety can be defined by a minimal set of linear equations; by th. 9 and its corollary, a set of linear equations

$$\sum_{j=1}^{n} c_{ij}X_j - a_i = 0 \qquad (1 \leqq i \leqq r)$$

is a minimal set for some linear variety if and only if the matrix $\|c_{ij}\|$ is of rank r.

It is an immediate consequence of our definitions, and of th. 5 of §3, that, if L and M are two linear varieties, the product $L \times M$ also is a linear variety; the same then follows, by induction on the number of factors, for the product $\prod_\alpha L_\alpha$ of linear varieties L_α in any number. The corresponding result for projections is a consequence of the following theorem:

THEOREM 11. *Let k be a field, (u) a set of m independent variables over k, and (x) a point in S^n, with coordinates of the form $x_i = \sum_\mu e_{i\mu}u_\mu + f_i$ $(1 \leqq i \leqq n)$, where the $e_{i\mu}$ and f_i are elements of k. Then the point (x) has a locus over k, which is a linear variety of dimension equal to the rank of the matrix $\|e_{i\mu}\|$.*

Let r be the rank of the matrix $\|e_{i\mu}\|$; after reordering the x_i and the u_μ if necessary, we may assume that the determinant $|e_{i\mu}|$, for $1 \leqq i \leqq r$, $1 \leqq \mu \leqq r$, is not 0. Then, if we denote by (U) a set of m indeterminates, and if we put $F_i(U) = \sum_\mu e_{i\mu}U_\mu$ for $1 \leqq i \leqq n$, the forms $F_1(U), \cdots, F_r(U)$ are linearly independent, and there are no more than r linearly independent forms over k among the n forms $F_i(U)$; we can therefore write $F_{r+h}(U) = \sum_{i=1}^{r} d_{hi}F_i(U)$, for $1 \leqq h \leqq n - r$, the d_{hi} being elements of k. Now put $z_i = x_i$ for $1 \leqq i \leqq r$, and $z_{r+h} = x_{r+h} - \sum_{i=1}^{r} d_{hi}x_i$ for $1 \leqq h \leqq n - r$; as we have $x_i = F_i(u) + f_i$ for

$1 \leqq i \leqq n$, these relations, together with the above relations between the $F_i(U)$, imply that we have $z_{r+h} = f_{r+h} - \sum_{i=1}^{r} d_{hi}f_i$ for $1 \leqq h \leqq n - r$, hence that $z_{r+1}, \cdots, z_n$ are in k. On the other hand, we have $z_i = F_i(u) + f_i$ for $1 \leqq i \leqq r$; as the determinant $|e_{i\mu}|$ for $1 \leqq i \leqq r$, $1 \leqq \mu \leqq r$, is not 0, we can solve these r relations for $u_1, \cdots, u_r$, which shows that $u_1, \cdots, u_r$ can be expressed as linear polynomials in $z_1, \cdots, z_r, u_{r+1}, \cdots, u_m$, with coefficients in k; therefore the dimension of $(u_1, \cdots, u_r)$ over the field $K = k(u_{r+1}, \cdots, u_m)$, which is r since the u_μ are independent variables over k, is not greater than the dimension of $(z_1, \cdots, z_r)$ over K. This shows that $z_1, \cdots, z_r$ are independent variables over K, and a fortiori over k. That being so, the point (z) has a locus over k, which is the linear variety of dimension r defined over k by the set of equations $X_{r+h} - z_{r+h} = 0$ $(1 \leqq h \leqq n - r)$. The relations

$$z_i = x_i \qquad (1 \leqq i \leqq r), \qquad z_{r+h} = x_{r+h} - \textstyle\sum_{i=1}^{r} d_{hi}x_i \qquad (1 \leqq h \leqq n - r),$$

which imply that we have $x_{r+h} = z_{r+h} + \sum_{i=1}^{r} d_{hi}z_i$ $(1 \leqq h \leqq n - r)$, show that we have $k(x) = k(z)$, hence that (x) also has a locus of dimension r over k; and prop. 13, applied to the loci of (z) and of (x) over k, shows that the latter is the linear variety defined by the set of equations

$$X_{r+h} - \textstyle\sum_{i=1}^{r} d_{hi}X_i - z_{r+h} = 0 \qquad (1 \leqq h \leqq n - r).$$

COROLLARY. *Let L be a linear variety in a product-space $S^n \times S^m$; then the projection L' of L on S^n is a linear variety. Moreover, if L is defined over a field k by a set of linear equations $F_\mu(X, Y) = 0$, where the $F_\mu(X, Y)$ are in*

$$k[X, Y] = k[X_1, \cdots, X_n, Y_1, \cdots, Y_m],$$

then L' can be defined by any maximal set of linearly independent equations from among those linear combinations of the $F_\mu(X, Y) = 0$, with coefficients in k, which do not contain any of the Y_j.

The first assertion is an immediate consequence of the last assertion in th. 9, of the definition of a projection, and of th. 11. The rest then follows from th. 6 of §3, and from th. 10.

We now consider the application to linear varieties of the definitions and results of §4 concerning intersections.

PROPOSITION 14. *Let the L_i, for $1 \leqq i \leqq m$, be m linear varieties in S^n, respectively of dimension $n - r_i$. Then, either the intersection of the L_i is empty, or it is a linear variety L' of dimension at least equal to $n - \sum_i r_i$. Moreover, if, for every i, the $F_\mu^{(i)}(X) = 0$ $(1 \leqq \mu \leqq m_i)$ are a set of linear equations for L_i, then the intersection of the L_i is the linear variety defined by the set of all equations*

$$F_\mu^{(i)}(X) = 0 \qquad (1 \leqq i \leqq m, 1 \leqq \mu \leqq m_i),$$

if there is such a variety, and is empty otherwise.

We prove the last assertion first. Let k be a field containing the coefficients in all the $F_\mu^{(i)}(X)$. A point (x) is in the intersection of the L_i if and only if it satisfies all the equations $F_\mu^{(i)}(X) = 0$; by the coroll. of th. 9, either there is no such point, or else these equations define a variety L'. In the latter case, a point (x) is thus in the intersection of the L_i if and only if it is in L'; hence L' is that intersection. This proves our proposition except for the assertion on the dimension of L'. As to that, we may take for the $F_\mu^{(i)}(X) = 0$, for every i, a minimal set of linear equations for L_i, consisting of r_i equations; L', if it exists, is then defined by a set of $\sum_i r_i$ equations, and therefore, by the coroll. of th. 9, has at least the dimension $n - \sum_i r_i$.

If L^{n-r} and M^{n-s} are two linear varieties in S^n, and if $L \cap M$ is not empty and has the dimension $n - r - s$, then we say that L and M are *transversal* to each other; this cannot be the case unless we have $r + s \leqq n$. If $\mathfrak{S}^r$ and $\mathfrak{T}^s$ are minimal sets of linear equations for L^{n-r} and for M^{n-s}, respectively, then, by prop. 14 and the coroll. of th. 9, L and M are transversal to each other if and only if the set of equations $(\mathfrak{S}^r, \mathfrak{T}^s)$, consisting of all the $r + s$ equations in $\mathfrak{S}^r$ and in $\mathfrak{T}^s$, is a minimal set of equations for a linear variety, and then that set defines the intersection $L \cap M$; if $\mathfrak{S}^r$ consists of the equations

$$\textstyle\sum_j c_{ij}X_j - a_i = 0 \qquad (1 \leqq i \leqq r),$$

and $\mathfrak{T}^s$ of the equations

$$\textstyle\sum_j d_{hj}X_j - b_h = 0 \qquad (1 \leqq h \leqq s),$$

then, by th. 9 and its corollary, L and M are transversal to each other if and only if the matrix

$$\begin{Vmatrix} c_{ij} \\ d_{hj} \end{Vmatrix}$$

is of rank $r + s$; in particular, if we have $r + s = n$, this will be the case if and only if the determinant of that matrix is not 0.

Two linear varieties will be called *parallel* when they have the same dimension and can be defined by two minimal sets of linear equations which differ only in their constant terms; it is easily seen that there always exists one and only one linear variety, through a given point, parallel to a given variety. That being so, it is clear, from what has been said above, that, if two linear varieties L and M are transversal to each other, any linear varieties, respectively parallel to L and to M, are also transversal to each other.

We now apply the idea of specialization to sets of linear equations, confining ourselves to what will be needed in the following chapters. Let

$$\textstyle\sum_{j=1}^n u_{\mu j}X_j - v_\mu = 0 \qquad (1 \leqq \mu \leqq m)$$

be a set of m linear equations, where the coefficients are any set $(u_{\mu j}, v_\mu)$ of $(n + 1)m$ quantities; by a *specialization* of that set of equations over a field k, we shall understand (according to the context) *either* any finite specialization $(u_{\mu j}, v_\mu) \to (u'_{\mu j}, v'_\mu)$ of the set of coefficients $(u_{\mu j}, v_\mu)$ over k, *or* a set of m linear equations $\sum_{j=1}^n u'_{\mu j}X_j - v'_\mu = 0$ $(1 \leqq \mu \leqq m)$ having such a specialization as set of coefficients. By a *generic set of m linear equations* over a field k, we understand any set of m linear equations $\sum_{j=1}^{n} u_{\mu j}X_j - v_\mu = 0$ $(1 \leqq \mu \leqq m)$ in which the set of coefficients $(u_{\mu j}, v_\mu)$ is a set of $(n+1)m$ independent variables over k; every set of m linear equations is a specialization of such a generic set over k. If the coefficients in a matrix are independent variables over a field k, then no determinant belonging to that matrix can vanish, so that the rank of that matrix is equal to the number of rows or to the number of columns in it, whichever is smaller; from this, and from th. 9 and its corollary, it follows that a generic set of m linear equations in n indeterminates defines a linear variety L^{n-m} in S^n, and is a minimal set of linear equations for that variety, whenever m is not greater than n; for $m > n$, such a set defines no variety. Furthermore, it is obvious that the rank of a matrix (defined as the maximal order of non-vanishing determinants belonging to that matrix) cannot increase if the set of coefficients in the matrix is replaced by any finite specialization of that set over some field; the next two propositions are immediate consequences of this fact and of th. 9 and its corollary:

PROPOSITION 15. *Let L be a linear variety, defined by a set of linear equations $F_\mu(X) = 0$; and let L' be a linear variety, defined by a specialization of that set of equations over some field. Then the dimension of L' is not less than that of L.*

PROPOSITION 16. *Let the $F_i(X) = 0$ $(1 \leqq i \leqq r)$ be a set of linear equations, and let the $F'_i(X) = 0$ $(1 \leqq i \leqq r)$ be a specialization of that set over some field. Then, if the latter set is a minimal set of equations for some linear variety L', the former also is a minimal set of equations for some linear variety L, and L has the same dimension as L'.*

PROPOSITION 17. *Let L^{n-r} be a linear variety, defined over a field k in S^n. Let M^{n-s} and M'^{n-s} be two linear varieties, respectively defined in S^n by minimal sets of linear equations $\mathfrak{S}^s$ and $\mathfrak{S}'^s$ such that $\mathfrak{S}'^s$ is a specialization of $\mathfrak{S}^s$ over k. Then, if M' is transversal to L, so is M.*

Let $\mathfrak{T}^r$ be a minimal set of linear equations defining L over k. Our assumptions imply that $(\mathfrak{T}^r, \mathfrak{S}'^s)$ is a minimal set of $r + s$ linear equations for $L \cap M'$, and that it is a specialization of $(\mathfrak{T}^r, \mathfrak{S}^s)$ over k; by prop. 16, therefore, the latter set is a minimal set of linear equations for some variety, hence for $L \cap M$. This proves our assertion.

PROPOSITION 18. *Let L^{n-r} be a linear variety, defined over a field k in S^n; and, s being such that $r + s \leqq n$, let $\mathfrak{S}^s$ be a generic set of s linear equations over k, defining a variety M^{n-s} in S^n. Then M is transversal to L.*

In fact, consider a minimal set of linear equations

$$\sum_{j=1}^{n} c_{ij}X_j - a_i = 0 \qquad (1 \leqq i \leqq r)$$

for L over k; then the r linear forms $F_i(X) = \sum_j c_{ij}X_j$ are linearly independent; as we have $s \leqq n - r$, we can find s linear forms $G_h(X)$ in $k[X]$, for instance among the X_j, such that the $r + s$ forms $F_i(X)$, $G_h(X)$ are linearly independent. That being so, the s equations $G_h(X) = 0$ are a minimal set $\mathfrak{S}'^s$, defining a linear variety which is transversal to L. Our assertion now follows by applying prop. 17 to L, to $\mathfrak{S}^s$, and to $\mathfrak{S}'^s$.

6. Simple points. Let (x) be a point in S^n, k a field, and $P(X)$ a polynomial in $k[X]$, such that $P(x) = 0$. Then we associate with $P(X)$ the linear form with coefficients in $k(x)$ which is defined by

$$\Delta_x P(X) = \sum_{i=1}^n \partial P/\partial x_i \cdot X_i .$$

This process (which, for obvious reasons, might be called linearization at the given point) will now be applied to the definition of simple points and tangent linear varieties. We write $(X - x)$ for $(X_1 - x_1, \cdots, X_n - x_n)$, so that, whenever (x) and $P(X)$ are as above, the equation $\Delta_x P(X - x) = 0$ is a linear equation with coefficients in $k(x)$, which is satisfied by the point (x); therefore, by the coroll. of th. 9, §5, any set of equations of that form defines a linear variety which goes through the point (x).

Proposition 19. *Let V be a variety in S^n, and (x) a point on V. Then, if k is any field of definition for V, and $\mathfrak{P}$ the ideal defining V over k, there is a linear variety L through (x), defined by any maximal set of linearly independent equations from among the equations $\Delta_x P(X - x) = 0$, where one takes for $P(X)$ all the polynomials in $\mathfrak{P}$; and, V and (x) being given, this variety L does not depend upon the choice of k. The variety L is also defined by the set of linear equations*

$$\Delta_x F_\mu(X - x) = 0$$

if the $F_\mu(X) = 0$ are any set of equations for V; and its dimension is ρ if $n - \rho$ is the rank of the matrix $\|\partial F_\mu/\partial x_i\|$.

Let k and $\mathfrak{P}$ be as stated, and take first for the $F_\mu(X)$ a basis of $\mathfrak{P}$. Then any polynomial $P(X)$ in $\mathfrak{P}$ can be written in the form

$$P(X) = \sum_\mu A_\mu(X) \cdot F_\mu(X),$$

with the $A_\mu(X)$ in $k[X]$, and this implies the relation $\Delta_x P(X) = \sum_\mu A_\mu(x) \cdot \Delta_x F_\mu(X)$. This shows that the linear polynomials of the form $w \cdot \Delta_x P(X - x)$, with $w \in k(x)$ and $P(X) \in \mathfrak{P}$, constitute a module over the field $k(x)$, and that the $\Delta_x F_\mu(X - x)$ are a basis for that module. By th. 10 of §5, any maximal set of linearly independent equations of the form $\Delta_x P(X - x) = 0$ therefore defines the same linear variety L as the set of equations $\Delta_x F_\mu(X - x) = 0$. Now let the $H_\nu(X) = 0$ be a set of equations for V with coefficients in the smallest field of definition for V; by coroll. 5 of th. 1, §1, the $H_\nu(X)$ are a basis for $\mathfrak{P}$, so that the above-defined variety L, by what we have proved, can also be defined by the set of equations $\Delta_x H_\nu(X - x) = 0$, hence is independent of the choice of k. Now, if the $F_\mu(X) = 0$ are an arbitrary set of equations for V, we can take for k a field containing all the coefficients in the $F_\mu(X)$, and apply what has been proved above. This completes our proof, except for the last assertion, which follows from the coroll. of th. 9, §5.

If V is a variety in S^n, (x) a point on V, and k a field of definition for V, then the variety defined by a maximal set of linearly independent equations of the form $\Delta_x P(X - x) = 0$, when one takes for $P(X)$ all the polynomials in the ideal defining V over k, will be called *the linear variety attached to V at (x)*; by prop. 19, it does not depend upon k, and can also be defined by the equations

$$\Delta_x F_\mu(X - x) = 0$$

if the $F_\mu(X) = 0$ are any set of equations for V. If V' is a subvariety of V, (x) a point of V', and if L and L' are the linear varieties respectively attached to V and to V' at (x), then L' is contained in L, as follows from coroll. 3 of th. 2, §1.

PROPOSITION 20. *Let V be a variety, defined over a field k in S^n. Let (x) be a point of V, and (x') a finite specialization of (x) over k, with coordinates x'_i in k. Let t be any quantity, and let (y) be the point defined by*

$$y_i = x'_i + t(x_i - x'_i) \qquad (1 \leqq i \leqq n).$$

Then every finite specialization (y') of (y) over $(x) \rightarrow (x')$, with reference to k, is a point of the linear variety attached to V at (x').

Our statement implies that (x') is a point of V; this follows from th. 2 of §1. Now, (y') being as stated, (x', y') is a specialization of (x, y) over k, which can be extended to a specialization (x', y', t') of (x, y, t) over k. If t' is finite, then, by prop. 13 of Chap. II, §4, the y'_i are the quantities obtained by substituting (x', t') for (x, t) in the expressions $x'_i + t(x_i - x'_i)$; this gives $(y') = (x')$, so that our assertion is true in that case. Assuming now that we have $t' = \infty$, put $u = 1/t$, so that $(x', y', 0)$ is a specialization of (x, y, u) over k. Let $P(X)$ be any polynomial in the ideal $\mathfrak{P}$ defining V over k. We have

$$x_i = x'_i + u(y_i - x'_i) \qquad (1 \leqq i \leqq n);$$

substituting the right-hand sides of these relations for the x_i in the relation $P(x) = 0$, we get a relation of the form

$$u \cdot \Delta_{x'} P(y - x') + u^2 \cdot Q(x', y, u) = 0,$$

where $Q(X, Y, U)$ is a polynomial in $k[X, Y, U]$; dividing by u and substituting $(y', 0)$ for (y, u), we get $\Delta_{x'} P(y' - x') = 0$. This shows that (y') satisfies the equation $\Delta_{x'} P(X - x') = 0$ whenever $P(X)$ is in $\mathfrak{P}$, which was to be proved.

PROPOSITION 21. *Let V^r be a variety, defined over a field k in S^n. Then the dimension of the linear variety attached to V at a point (x) of V is at least equal to r; it is equal to r whenever (x) is a generic point of V over k. Moreover, if (x) is any point of V, (x') a finite specialization of (x) over k, and if ρ and ρ' are the dimensions of the linear varieties attached to V at (x) and at (x') respectively, then we have $\rho \leqq \rho'$.*

As to the last assertion, (x') is a point of V by th. 2 of §1; if the $F_\mu(X) = 0$ are a set of equations for V over k, then ρ and ρ' are the dimensions of the linear varieties respectively defined by the sets of equations $\Delta_x F_\mu(X - x) = 0$ and $\Delta_{x'} F_\mu(X - x') = 0$; as the latter set of equations is a specialization of the former over k, the inequality $\rho \leqq \rho'$ follows by prop. 15 of §5. Now, if (x) is a generic point of V over k, the matrix $\|\partial F_\mu/\partial x_i\|$ has the rank $n - r$ by th. 2 of Chap. I, §5, and th. 5 of Chap. I, §7; therefore, by prop. 19, we have in that case $\rho = r$; as every point of V is then a specialization of (x) over k, our first assertion follows from this by what we have already proved.

If V^r is a variety, and P a point of V, we shall say that P is *simple on* V, and that it is a *simple point of* V, if the linear variety attached to V at P has the dimension r, and in this case this linear variety will be called *the tangent linear variety to* V *at* P; otherwise, i.e., by prop. 21, if the linear variety attached to V at P has a dimension greater than r, we say that P is *multiple on* V, and that it is a *multiple point of* V. A subvariety W of V, every point of which is multiple on V, is said to be *multiple on* V, and is called a *multiple subvariety of* V; any other subvariety of V is said to be *simple on* V and is called a *simple subvariety of* V. A maximal variety belonging to the point-set which consists of the multiple points of a variety V is, according to these definitions, multiple on V, and will be called a *maximal multiple subvariety of* V. A point $P = (x)$, on a variety V^r defined in S^n by a set of equations $F_\mu(X) = 0$, is simple or multiple on V according as the rank of the matrix $\|\partial F_\mu/\partial x_i\|$ is $n - r$ or less than $n - r$.

Proposition 22. *If W is a simple subvariety of a variety V, every generic point of W over a common field of definition for V and for W is simple on V.*

In fact, if k is such a field, and P a generic point of W over k, every point of W is a specialization of P over k, and therefore, by prop. 21, would be multiple on V if P were so.

Theorem 12. *Let V^r be a variety in S^n, defined over a field k. Then there is a bunch of varieties $\mathfrak{B}$, contained in V and normally algebraic over k, such that the points of $\mathfrak{B}$ are the multiple points of V; the components of $\mathfrak{B}$ are the maximal multiple subvarieties of V, and are at most of dimension $r - 1$; and a point of V, or a subvariety of V, is simple on V if and only if it is not contained in $\mathfrak{B}$.*

Let the $F_\mu(X) = 0$ be a set of equations for V over k; let the $D_\nu(X)$ be all the determinants of order $n - r$ belonging to the matrix $\|\partial F_\mu/\partial X_i\|$. By th. 7 of §4, there is a bunch of varieties $\mathfrak{B}$, normally algebraic over k, the points of which are the points of V which satisfy all the equations $D_\nu(X) = 0$; as these points are the multiple points of V, this, together with the definitions, proves all our assertions, provided one remarks that the components of $\mathfrak{B}$ are subvarieties of V and are not V by prop. 21, and have therefore, by coroll. 2 of th. 2, §1, a dimension at most equal to $r - 1$.

Corollary 1. *Let V^r be a variety in S^n, defined over a field K; let σ be an isomorphism of K on a field K'. Let $\mathfrak{B}$ and $\mathfrak{B}'$ be the bunches of varieties, such that* *the points of* $\mathfrak{B}$ *are the multiple points of* V, *and the points of* $\mathfrak{B}'$ *are those of* V^σ. *If then* $\bar{\sigma}$ *is an isomorphism of* $\bar{K}$ *on* $\bar{K}'$, *coinciding with* σ *on* K, *we have* $\mathfrak{B}' = \mathfrak{B}^{\bar{\sigma}}$.

In fact, if the $F_\mu(X) = 0$ are a set of equations for V over K, and the $D_\nu(X)$ the determinants of order $n - r$, belonging to the matrix $||\partial F_\mu/\partial X_i||$, then the polynomials $D_\nu^\sigma(X)$ are respectively equal to the determinants similarly derived from the matrix $||\partial F_\mu^\sigma/\partial X_i||$; our result now follows from coroll. 1 of th. 7, §4, applied to V, to the equations $D_\nu(X) = 0$, to σ and to $\bar{\sigma}$.

Corollary 2. *Let* W *be a subvariety of a variety* V; *let* K *be a common field of definition for* V *and for* W, *and let* σ *be an isomorphism of* K *on a field* K'. *Then* W^σ *is simple or multiple on* V^σ *according as* W *is simple or multiple on* V; *and it is a maximal multiple subvariety of* V^σ *if and only if* W *is such a subvariety of* V.

This follows from coroll. 1, from prop. 10 of §4, from th. 12, and from coroll. 2 of th. 3, §2.

The tangent linear variety to a variety V at a point P is defined whenever P is a simple point of V, and is then a linear variety containing P, of the same dimension as V. If V^r is a variety in S^n, defined over a field k by an ideal $\mathfrak{P}$, and if $P = (x)$ is a point of V, then P is simple on V if and only if there are $n - r$ polynomials $P_\rho(X)$ in $\mathfrak{P}$, such that the $n - r$ linear equations $\Delta_x P_\rho(X - x) = 0$, i.e. the equations $\sum_{i=1}^n \partial P_\rho/\partial x_i \cdot (X_i - x_i) = 0$ $(1 \leqq \rho \leqq n - r)$, are linearly independent, and then these equations are a minimal set of linear equations for the tangent linear variety to V at P. If V^r is defined in S^n by a set of equations $F_\mu(X) = 0$, then a point $P = (x)$ of V is simple on V if and only if the matrix $||\partial F_\mu/\partial x_i||$ is of rank $n - r$, and then the tangent linear variety to V at P is defined by the set of equations $\sum_{i=1}^n \partial F_\mu/\partial x_i \cdot (X_i - x_i) = 0$. This, applied to a linear variety L^r in S^n, and to a set of linear equations for L^r, shows that every point of such a variety L is simple on L, the tangent linear variety to L at every point being L itself. Furthermore, all that we have proved above for the linear variety attached to a variety can be applied to tangent linear varieties; in particular, we have the following result:

Proposition 23. *Let* W *be a subvariety of a variety* V, *and let* P *be a point of* W, *simple both on* W *and on* V; *then the tangent linear variety to* W *at* P *is contained in the tangent linear variety to* V *at* P. *In particular, if* W *is a subvariety of a linear variety* L, *then the tangent linear variety to* W *at any simple point of* W *is contained in* L.

Let now again V^r be a variety in S^n, defined by a set of equations $F_\mu(X) = 0$, and let (x) be a point of V; then, by a *uniformizing set of linear forms for* V *at* (x), we understand a set of r linear forms $H_i(X) = \sum_{j=1}^n c_{ij}X_j$ $(1 \leqq i \leqq r)$ such that there are n linearly independent forms among the forms

$$\Delta_x F_\mu(X) = \sum_{j=1}^n \partial F_\mu/\partial x_j \cdot X_j, \qquad H_i(X).$$

The existence of such a set implies that there are $n - r$ linearly independent forms among the $\Delta_x F_\mu(X)$, i.e. that (x) is simple on V; and, when that is so, the $H_i(X)$ are a uniformizing set for V at (x) if and only if they are linearly independent and the equations $H_i(X) = 0$ define a linear variety transversal to the tangent linear variety to V at (x); this shows that, V and (x) being given, the definition of a uniformizing set of linear forms for V at (x) is independent of the choice of the set of equations $F_\mu(X) = 0$ for V. A simple point (x) being given on a variety V^r, there always exists a uniformizing set of linear forms for V at (x), which for instance may be chosen from among the X_j; moreover, if k is a field of definition for V, hence $k(x)$ for the tangent linear variety to V at (x), prop. 18 of §5 shows that the forms $H_i(X) = \sum_{j=1}^n u_{ij}X_j$, for $1 \leqq i \leqq r$, are a uniformizing set of linear forms for V at (x) whenever (u_{ij}) is a set of $r \cdot n$ independent variables over $k(x)$.

Proposition 24. *Let V^r be a variety, defined over a field k in S^n; and let the $H_i(X) = \sum_{j=1}^n c_{ij} X_j$ $(1 \leqq i \leqq r)$ be r linear forms with coefficients in k. Let (x) be a generic point of V over k, and put $y_i = H_i(x)$ for $1 \leqq i \leqq r$. Then the $H_i(X)$ are a uniformizing set of linear forms for V at (x) if and only if the field $k(x)$ is separably algebraic over $k(y)$.*

Let the $H_i(X)$ be a uniformizing set for V at (x). Then there are $n - r$ polynomials $P_\rho(X)$, in the ideal determined by (x) over k, such that the n linear forms $\Delta_x P_\rho(X)$ and $H_i(X)$ are linearly independent. The point (x) satisfies the n equations $P_\rho(X) = 0$ $(1 \leqq \rho \leqq n - r)$, $H_i(X) - y_i = 0$ $(1 \leqq i \leqq r)$, the left-hand sides of which are polynomials in (X) with coefficients in $k(y)$; applying to these equations the coroll. of th. 1, Chap. I, §5, we see that $k(x)$ must therefore be separable over $k(y)$, since the determinant in that corollary is in the present case the determinant of the coefficients of the n forms $\Delta_x P_\rho(X)$, $H_i(X)$. As to the converse, assume first that (x) is algebraic over $k(y)$; then (y) must have the dimension r over k, hence is a set of r independent variables over k. Let, for every j, $Q_j(Y, X_j) = 0$ be the irreducible equation for (y, x_j) over k; by prop. 10 of Chap. I, §3, $Q_j(y, X_j) = 0$ is then the irreducible equation for x_j over $k(y)$. Therefore, if we now assume that (x) is separable over $k(y)$, we have $\partial Q_j/\partial x_j \neq 0$, for $1 \leqq j \leqq n$. Put $F_j(X) = Q_j[H_1(X), \cdots, H_r(X), X_j]$, for $1 \leqq j \leqq n$; the $F_j(X)$ are in $k[X]$, and, as we have $Q_j(y, x_j) = 0$, we have $F_j(x) = 0$ for $1 \leqq j \leqq n$, so that the $F_j(X)$ are in the ideal determined by (x) over k. An easy calculation gives $\Delta_x F_j(X) = \partial Q_j/\partial x_j \cdot X_j + \sum_{i=1}^r \partial Q_j/\partial y_i \cdot H_i(X)$; as we have $\partial Q_j/\partial x_j \neq 0$ for every j, this shows that the X_j can all be expressed as linear combinations of the $n + r$ linear forms $\Delta_x F_j(X)$, $H_i(X)$. The forms $H_i(X)$ are linearly independent, for otherwise there would be a linear relation between them, with coefficients in k, and then the quantities $y_i = H_i(x)$ would satisfy the same relation and would not be independent variables over k. Therefore there are, among the n forms $\Delta_x F_j(X)$, $n - r$ forms which, together with the $H_i(X)$, make up a set of n linearly independent forms. This completes our proof.

Proposition 25. *Let V^r be a variety in S^n, k a field of definition for V, (x) a point of V, and (x') a finite specialization of (x) over k. Then, if r forms*

$$H_i(X) = \sum_{j=1}^{n} c_{ij}X_j \qquad (1 \leqq i \leqq r),$$

with coefficients in k, are a uniformizing set of linear forms for V at (x'), they are also such for V at (x), and both (x) and (x') are simple on V.

As we have seen, the existence of a uniformizing set of linear forms for V at (x') implies that (x') is simple on V. Therefore there are $n - r$ polynomials $P_\rho(X)$ in the ideal defining V over k, such that the equations

$$\sum_{j=1}^{n} \partial P_\rho/\partial x'_j \cdot (X_j - x'_j) = 0 \qquad (1 \leqq \rho \leqq n - r)$$

are a minimal set of linear equations for the tangent linear variety L' to V at (x'). This set is a specialization over k of the set of linear equations

$$\sum_{j=1}^{n} \partial P_\rho/\partial x_j \cdot (X_j - x_j) = 0 \qquad (1 \leqq \rho \leqq n - r),$$

and L' is transversal to the linear variety defined by the minimal set of equations $H_i(X) = 0$ $(1 \leqq i \leqq r)$. Our assertion now follows from this by prop. 16 and 17 of §5.

Let W be a subvariety of a variety V^r in S^n; let K be a common field of definition for V and W, and let the $H_i(X)$ be r linear forms with coefficients in K; then prop. 25 shows that, if the $H_i(X)$ are a uniformizing set of linear forms for V at some point of W, they are also such at every generic point of W over K, and that W must be simple on V; when that is so, we say that the $H_i(X)$ are a *uniformizing set of linear forms for V along W*; it should be observed that this does *not* imply that they are such at every point of W (since such a point need not even be simple on V). From what has been said above, it follows that, if W is a simple subvariety of a variety V^r in S^n, then a uniformizing set of linear forms $H_i(X)$ for V along W can always be chosen from among the X_j, and also that such a set can be defined by $H_i(X) = \sum_{j=1}^{n} u_{ij}X_j$ $(1 \leqq i \leqq r)$, where $(u) = (u_{ij})$ is any set of $r \cdot n$ independent variables over any common field of definition K for V and W; for, in the latter case, if (x) is a generic point of W over $K(u)$, then (u) is a set of independent variables over $K(x)$.

Theorem 13. *Let P be a point on a variety V^r in S^n, and Q a point on a variety W^s in S^m. Then the point $P \times Q$ is simple on $V \times W$ if and only if P is simple on V and Q on W. Moreover, if that is so, and if L^r and M^s are the tangent linear varieties to V at P, and to W at Q, respectively, then $L \times M$ is the tangent linear variety to $V \times W$ at $P \times Q$; and, if the r forms $H_i(X)$, for $1 \leqq i \leqq r$, and the s forms $E_j(Y)$, for $1 \leqq j \leqq s$, are uniformizing sets of linear forms for V at P, and for W at Q, respectively, then these $r + s$ forms, taken together, are a uniformizing set of linear forms for $V \times W$ at $P \times Q$.*

Put $P = (x)$ and $Q = (y)$; let the $F_\mu(X) = 0$ be a set of equations for V, and the $G_\nu(Y) = 0$ a set of equations for W. Then the number of linearly independent forms, among the linear forms

$$\Delta_x F_\mu(X) = \sum_{i=1}^{n} \partial F_\mu/\partial x_i \cdot X_i,$$

is at most equal to $n - r$, and it is equal to $n - r$ if and only if P is simple on V; similarly, the number of linearly independent forms, among the forms

$$\Delta_y G_\nu(Y) = \sum_{j=1}^{m} \partial G_\nu/\partial y_j \cdot Y_j,$$

is at most $m - s$, and it is $m - s$ if and only if Q is simple on W. Now, by th. 5 of §3, the equations $F_\mu(X) = 0$, $G_\nu(Y) = 0$ are a set of equations for $V \times W$; therefore the point $P \times Q = (x, y)$ is simple on $V \times W$ if and only if there are $n + m - r - s$ linearly independent forms among the forms $\Delta_x F_\mu(X)$, $\Delta_y G_\nu(Y)$; therefore, when that is so, P must be simple on V, and Q on W. Moreover, the tangent linear variety to $V \times W$ at $P \times Q$ is then the variety defined by the set of equations $\Delta_x F_\mu(X - x) = 0$, $\Delta_y G_\nu(Y - y) = 0$, i.e., by th. 5 of §3, the product of the varieties respectively defined in S^n by the equations $\Delta_x F_\mu(X - x) = 0$, and in S^m by the equations $\Delta_y G_\nu(Y - y) = 0$; these are the tangent linear varieties to V at P, and to W at Q, respectively. The last assertion is then an immediate consequence of the definition of a uniformizing set of linear forms.

Corollary 1. *Let U be a subvariety of the product $V \times W$ of two varieties V^r and W^s. Then U is simple on $V \times W$ if and only if its projections on V and on W are respectively simple on V and simple on W; and, when that is so, any uniformizing set of r linear forms $H_i(X)$ for V along the projection of U on V, together with any uniformizing set of s linear forms $E_j(Y)$ for W along the projection of U on W, constitutes a uniformizing set of $r + s$ linear forms for $V \times W$ along U.*

This is an immediate consequence of th. 13 and the definitions.

Corollary 2. *Let U be a subvariety of the product $V = \prod_\alpha V_\alpha$ of h varieties V_α. Then U is simple on V if and only if its projection on every one of the factors V_α of V is simple on that factor.*

This follows at once from coroll. 1 by induction on h.

Theorem 14. *Let V^r be a variety, defined over a field k in a product-space $S^n \times S^m$; let $(\bar{x}, \bar{y}) = (\bar{x}_1, \cdots, \bar{x}_n, \bar{y}_1, \cdots, \bar{y}_m)$ be a generic point of V over k, and (x, y) any point of V; and assume that the $\bar{y}_j$, for $1 \leqq j \leqq m$, are in the specialization-ring of (x) in $k(\bar{x})$. Then the point (x, y) is simple on V if and only if (x) is simple on the projection V' of V on S^n. Moreover, if that is so, and if L is the tangent linear variety to V at (x, y), then the tangent linear variety to V' at (x) is the projection L' of L on S^n; and any uniformizing set of linear forms for V' at (x) is also such for V at (x, y).*

Our assumptions imply that we have $k(\bar{x}, \bar{y}) = k(\bar{x})$, so that V', which is the locus of $(\bar{x})$ over k, has the same dimension r as V; they also imply that the $\bar{y}_j$

can be written in the form $\bar{y}_j = F_j(\bar{x})/G(\bar{x})$, with the $F_j(X)$ and $G(X)$ in $k[X]$, and $G(x) \neq 0$. That being so, the m polynomials $Q_j(X, Y) = G(X) \cdot Y_j - F_j(X)$ are in the ideal determined by $(\bar{x}, \bar{y})$ over k, i.e. in the ideal defining V over k. Now assume that (x) is simple on V'; this means that there are $n - r$ polynomials $P_\rho(X)$, in the ideal determined by $(\bar{x})$ over k, such that the $n - r$ linear forms $\Delta_x P_\rho(X) = \sum_{i=1}^n \partial P_\rho/\partial x_i \cdot X_i$ $(1 \leqq \rho \leqq n - r)$ are linearly independent. Then the $n + m - r$ forms $\Delta_x P_\rho(X)$ and

$$\Delta_{x,y} Q_j(X, Y) = G(x) \cdot Y_j + y_j \cdot \Delta_x G(X) - \Delta_x F_j(X) \qquad (1 \leqq j \leqq m)$$

are linearly independent, since we have $G(x) \neq 0$; this shows that (x, y) is a simple point on V. Moreover, the tangent linear variety L to V at (x, y) is then defined by the minimal set of equations

$$\Delta_x P_\rho(X - x) = 0 \qquad (1 \leqq \rho \leqq n - r),$$

$$\Delta_{x,y} Q_j(X - x, Y - y) = 0 \qquad (1 \leqq j \leqq m);$$

a linear combination of these $n + m - r$ equations will be a linear polynomial in the X_i if and only if it is a linear combination of the equations $\Delta_x P_\rho(X - x) = 0$ only. Therefore, by the coroll. of th. 11, §5, the projection of L on S^n is the linear variety defined in S^n by the equations $\Delta_x P_\rho(X - x) = 0$; this is the tangent linear variety to V' at (x). Under the same assumptions, if r forms $E_i(X)$ are a uniformizing set of linear forms for V' at (x), the n forms $E_i(X)$ and $\Delta_x P_\rho(X)$ are linearly independent; these, and the m forms $\Delta_{x,y} Q_j(X, Y)$, are then a set of $n + m$ linearly independent forms in (X, Y), which shows that the $E_i(X)$ are a uniformizing set of linear forms for V at (x, y). It remains to be shown that, conversely, if (x, y) is simple on V, then (x) is simple on V'. Assume therefore that (x, y) is simple on V; this means that there are $n + m - r$ forms in any maximal set of linearly independent forms among the linear forms $\Delta_{x,y} Q(X, Y)$, when we take for $Q(X, Y)$ all the polynomials in the ideal $\mathfrak{Q}$ defining V over k. As the $Q_j(X, Y)$, for $1 \leqq j \leqq m$, are in $\mathfrak{Q}$, and as the m forms $\Delta_{x,y} Q_j(X, Y)$ are linearly independent, we can then find, in $\mathfrak{Q}$, $n - r$ polynomials $Q_{m+1}(X, Y), \cdots, Q_{n+m-r}(X, Y)$ such that, if we put

$$L_h(X, Y) = \Delta_{x,y} Q_h(X, Y) \qquad (1 \leqq h \leqq n + m - r),$$

the $n + m - r$ forms $L_h(X, Y)$ are linearly independent. That being so, if we take for d a sufficiently large integer, and if we put

$$H_\rho(X) = G(X)^d \cdot Q_{m+\rho}[X, F_j(X)/G(X)] \qquad (1 \leqq \rho \leqq n - r),$$

the $H_\rho(X)$ will be polynomials in $k[X]$; and, as we have $Q_{m+\rho}(\bar{x}, \bar{y}) = 0$ for every ρ, $G(\bar{x}) \neq 0$, and $F_j(\bar{x})/G(\bar{x}) = \bar{y}_j$ for $1 \leqq j \leqq m$, we have $H_\rho(\bar{x}) = 0$ for every ρ, so that the $n - r$ polynomials $H_\rho(X)$ are in the ideal defining V' over k. An easy calculation now gives

$$\Delta_x H_\rho(X) = G(x)^d \cdot L_{m+\rho}(X, Y) - G(x)^{d-1} \cdot \sum_{j=1}^m \partial Q_{m+\rho}/\partial y_j \cdot L_j(X, Y);$$

from this, and the linear independence of the $n + m - r$ forms $L_h(X, Y)$, it follows, since we have $G(x) \neq 0$, that the $n - r$ forms $\Delta_x H_\rho(X)$ are linearly independent. This completes our proof.

COROLLARY. *Let V^r be a variety, defined over a field k in a product-space $S^n \times S^m$; let W be a subvariety of V; let V' and W' be the projections of V and of W on S^n; and, (x, y) being a generic point of V over k, assume that the y_j are all in the specialization-ring of W' in $k(x)$. Then W is simple on V if and only if W' is so on V'; and, when that is so, every uniformizing set of linear forms for V' along W' is also such for V along W.*

This follows immediately from th. 14 and the definitions.

7. Projection from a variety and birational correspondences. Let U be a subvariety of a product $V \times W$, and U' its projection on the first factor V of that product; then, by coroll. 5 of th. 6, §3, U is contained in $U' \times W$, and the projection on V of every point or subvariety of U, considered as contained in $V \times W$, is the same as its projection on U' when it is considered as contained in $U' \times W$, and is also the same as its projection on the ambient space S^n for V when it is considered as contained in the product $S^n \times S^m$ of S^n and of the ambient space S^m for W. This correspondence between the points and subvarieties of U and their projections on U' will be called *the projection from U to U'*. The following results give as much information as will be needed in this book on points and subvarieties of U with given projections on U'.

PROPOSITION 26. *Let U be a subvariety of a product $V \times W$, and U' its projection on V. Let Z be a subvariety of U, with the projection Z' on V. Then Z is contained in $U \cap (Z' \times W)$; every component $\bar{Z}$ of $U \cap (Z' \times W)$ containing Z has the projection Z' on V; and, if r, r' and s' are the dimensions of U, of U' and of Z', respectively, then every such component $\bar{Z}$ has at least the dimension $s' + r - r'$.*

The first assertion follows from coroll. 5 of th. 6, §3. If a subvariety $\bar{Z}$ of U contains Z, then, by coroll. 3 of th. 6, §3, its projection $\bar{Z}'$ on V contains Z', and it must be contained in Z' if $\bar{Z}$ is contained in $Z' \times W$; this proves the second assertion. Let now k be a common field of definition for U, Z' and $\bar{Z}$; let (x, y) and $(\bar{x}, \bar{y})$ be generic points of U and of $\bar{Z}$, respectively, over k, with respectively the projections (x) and $(\bar{x})$ on V, and (y) and $(\bar{y})$ on W. Then (x, y) is also a generic point of U over $\bar{k}$, so that $(\bar{x}, \bar{y})$ is a specialization of (x, y) over $\bar{k}$. Moreover, $(\bar{y})$ is an isolated specialization of (y) over $(x) \rightarrow (\bar{x})$ with reference to $\bar{k}$; for, if this were not so, there would be a specialization $(\bar{x}, y')$ of (x, y) over $\bar{k}$, of higher dimension than $(\bar{x}, \bar{y})$ over $\bar{k}$, and having $(\bar{x}, \bar{y})$ as a specialization over $\bar{k}$; and then the locus of $(\bar{x}, y')$ over $\bar{k}$ would be a subvariety of U, containing $\bar{Z}$ and with the projection Z' on V, and of greater dimension than $\bar{Z}$, so that $\bar{Z}$ would not be maximal in $U \cap (Z' \times W)$. Our last assertion now follows from prop. 13 of Chap. III, §4.

It follows from prop. 26 that if, with the notations of that proposition, some component of $U \cap (Z' \times W)$, having the projection Z' on V, has the same dimension as Z', U must have the same dimension as U'. In particular, if U is a subvariety of a product $V \times W$, and P' a point of its projection U' on V, and if some component of $U \cap (P' \times W)$ is reduced to a point, then U and U' have the same dimension. This case will now be considered more in detail. We first introduce some definitions.

Let U be a subvariety of a product $V \times W$; let $P' = (\bar{x})$ be a point in the projection U' of U on V; let k be a field of definition for U, and let (x, y) be a generic point of U over k, with the projections (x) on V and (y) on W; we shall say that U is *finite over* P' if (y) is finite over $(x) \rightarrow (\bar{x})$ with reference to k; it follows from coroll. 4 of th. 1, §1, that this definition depends only upon U and P', and not upon the choice of k and of (x, y). With these same notations, if U is finite over P', then, by th. 6 of Chap. II, §2, there exists at least one point of U with the projection P' on V, and, by prop. 23 of Chap. II, §5, and prop. 5 of Chap. II, §2, such points are in finite number and algebraic over $k(P')$; as stated above, this implies that U and U' have the same dimension.

Let now U be a subvariety of a product $V \times W$, having the same dimension as its projection U' on V; put $k_0 = \text{def}(U)$, and let (x, y) be a generic point of U over k_0, with the projections (x) on V and (y) on W; then the dimensions of (x, y) and of (x) over k_0, being respectively equal to the dimensions of U and of U', are the same, so that $k_0(x, y)$ is an algebraic extension of $k_0(x)$; that being so, we define the symbol $[U:U']$ as having the value $[k_0(x, y):k_0(x)]$, this being a positive integer which, by prop. 1 of §1 and by th. 1 of Chap. II, §1, is independent of the choice of the generic point (x, y) of U over k_0. On the other hand, if a subvariety U of a product $V \times W$ is of higher dimension than its projection U' on V, then we define the symbol $[U:U']$ as having the value 0.

PROPOSITION 27. *Let U be a subvariety of a product $V \times W$, having the same dimension as its projection U' on V. Let k be a field of definition for U, and let P' be a generic point of U' over k. Then U is finite over P'; the points of U with the projection P' on V are all conjugates of each other over $k(P')$; and, if P is any one of these points, we have $[k(P):k(P')] = [U:U']$.*

Let r be the dimension of U, hence also of U'; and put $P' = (x)$; then (x) has the dimension r over k. By th. 6 of §3, there is a generic point of U with the projection P' on V; conversely, if $P = (x, y)$ is any point of U with the projection P' on V, it has at least the dimension r over k and is therefore, by th. 2 of §1, a generic point of U over k; it must then have exactly the dimension r over k, so that (y) must be algebraic over $k(x)$. If $(\bar{y})$ is any specialization of (y) over $(x) \rightarrow (x)$ with reference to k, then, by prop. 2 of Chap. II, §1, and the coroll. of th. 3, Chap. II, §1, $(\bar{y})$ must be a conjugate of (y) over $k(x)$, and therefore is finite; $(x, \bar{y})$ is then a conjugate of (x, y) over $k(x)$. As to our last assertion, (x, y) and (x) have, by th. 1 of §1 and its coroll. 2, the dimension r over the field $k_0 = \text{def}(U)$, so that (y) is algebraic over $k_0(x)$; and, by the same results and by prop. 13 of Chap. I, §4, $[k(x, y):k(x)]$ must be equal to $[k_0(x, y):k_0(x)]$, i.e., by definition, to $[U:U']$. This completes our proof.

An important special case, with which we shall be mainly concerned in the rest of this chapter, is that in which a subvariety U of a product $V \times W$, and its projection U' on V, are such that $[U:U'] = 1$; when that is so, we say that *the projection from U to U' is regular.* If k is any field of definition for U, and P any generic point of U over k, with the projection P' on V, prop. 27 shows that the projection from U to U' is regular if and only if we have $k(P) = k(P')$, and that, when that is so, P is the only point of U with the projection P' on V.

PROPOSITION 28. *Let U be a subvariety of a product $V \times W$, and U' its projection on V. Let k be a field of definition for U, and (x, y) a generic point of U over k, with the projections (x) on V and (y) on W. Let $(\bar{x})$ be a point of U' such that all the y_j are in the specialization-ring of $(\bar{x})$ in $k(x)$. Then we have $[U:U'] = 1$; U is finite over $(\bar{x})$; there is one and only one point $(\bar{x}, \bar{y})$ of U with the projection $(\bar{x})$ on V; we have $k(\bar{x}, \bar{y}) = k(\bar{x})$; and $(\bar{x}, \bar{y})$ is simple on U if and only if $(\bar{x})$ is so on U'. Moreover, if k' is a field of definition for U, and (x', y') a point of U, such that $(\bar{x}, \bar{y})$ is a specialization of (x', y') over k', then every y'_j is in the specialization-ring of $(\bar{x})$ in $k'(x')$, and the specialization-ring of $(\bar{x}, \bar{y})$ in $k'(x', y')$ is the same as that of $(\bar{x})$ in $k'(x')$.*

As we have $k(x, y) = k(x)$, prop. 27 shows that we have $[U:U'] = 1$. Prop. 13 of Chap. II, §4, shows that (y) has a uniquely determined and finite specialization $(\bar{y})$ over $(x) \rightarrow (\bar{x})$ with reference to k, and that every $\bar{y}_j$ is in $k(\bar{x})$; this, together with th. 14 of §6, proves the first part of our proposition. By the definition of the symbol $[U:U']$, if we put $k_0 = \text{def}(U)$, we have $k_0(x, y) = k_0(x)$; every y_j is therefore in $k_0(x)$, hence, by our assumptions and by prop. 6 of §2, in the specialization-ring of $(\bar{x})$ in $k_0(x)$. As k and k' contain k_0, (x', y') is a specialization of (x, y), and $(\bar{x}, \bar{y})$ is one of (x', y'), over k_0; then prop. 15 of Chap. II, §4, shows that all the y'_j are in the specialization-ring of $(\bar{x})$ in $k_0(x')$ and a fortiori in that of $(\bar{x})$ in $k'(x')$. Let now w' be any element of the specialization-ring of $(\bar{x}, \bar{y})$ in $k'(x', y')$; it can be written as $w' = F(x', y')/G(x', y')$, with $F(X, Y)$ and $G(X, Y)$ in $k'[X, Y]$, and $G(\bar{x}, \bar{y}) \neq 0$. Put $u' = F(x', y')$, $v' = G(x', y')$, and $z' = 1/v'$; as the y'_j are in the specialization-ring of $(\bar{x})$ in $k'(x')$, the same is true of u' and of v'; therefore, by prop. 13 of Chap. II, §4, v' has the uniquely determined specialization $\bar{v} = G(\bar{x}, \bar{y})$ over $(x') \rightarrow (\bar{x})$ with reference to k', so that z' has the specialization $\bar{z} = 1/\bar{v}$ over $(x') \rightarrow (\bar{x})$ with reference to k'. As $\bar{v}$ is not 0, $\bar{z}$ is not ∞; prop. 13 of Chap. II, §4, applied to z', shows then that z' is in the specialization-ring of $(\bar{x})$ in $k'(x')$; the same is therefore true of $w' = u' \cdot z'$. As it follows immediately from the definitions that the specialization-ring of $(\bar{x})$ in $k'(x')$ is contained in that of $(\bar{x}, \bar{y})$ in $k'(x', y')$, this completes our proof.

Let U be a subvariety of a product $V \times W$; let $P' = (\bar{x})$ be a point in the projection U' of U on V; let k be a field of definition for U, and (x, y) a generic point of U over k, with the projection (x) on V; we shall say that *the projection from U to U' is regular at P'* if all the y_j are in the specialization-ring of $(\bar{x})$ in $k(x)$; prop. 28 shows that this definition is independent of the choice of k and of (x, y), when U and P' are given, for, if k' is any field of definition for U, and (x', y') any generic point of U over k', then the point $(\bar{x}, \bar{y})$ of U with the projection $(\bar{x})$ on V is a specialization of (x', y') over k', so that, by prop. 28, if the y_j are in the specialization-ring of $(\bar{x})$ in $k(x)$, the y'_j are in that of $(\bar{x})$ in $k'(x')$. If the projection from U to U' is regular at some point of U', then, by prop. 28, it is regular; on the other hand, prop. 14 of Chap. II, §4, shows that, if the projection from U to U' is regular, then it is regular at every generic point of U' over any field of definition for U.

PROPOSITION 29. *Let U be a subvariety of a product $V \times W$, with the projection U' on V. Let k be a field of definition for U, and let P' and $\bar{P}'$ be two points of U', such that $\bar{P}'$ is a specialization of P' over k. If then the projection from U to U' is regular at $\bar{P}'$, it is also regular at P'.*

Let (x, y) be a generic point of U over k, with the projection (x) on V; put $P' = (x')$, and $\bar{P}' = (\bar{x}')$; our assertion is an immediate consequence of the definitions and of prop. 15 of Chap. II, §4, applied to k, (x), (x'), $(\bar{x}')$ and to the y_j.

Let again U be a subvariety of a product $V \times W$; let U' be the projection of U on V, and Z' a subvariety of U'; we shall say that *the projection from U to U' is regular along Z'* if it is regular at some point of Z'; prop. 29 shows that, if k is any common field of definition for U and Z', then the projection from U to U' is regular along Z' if and only if it is regular at every generic point of Z' over k. If Z' is reduced to a point P', then it is the same thing to say that the projection from U to U' is regular at P' or along P'.

THEOREM 15. *Let U be a subvariety of a product $V \times W$, with the projection U' on V; let k be a field of definition for U, and let (P, Q) be a generic point of U over k, with the projections P on V, and $Q = (y)$ on W. Let Z' be a subvariety of U'; then the projection from U to U' is regular along Z' if and only if all the y_j are in the specialization-ring of Z' in $k(P)$; when that is so, there is one and only one subvariety Z of U with the projection Z' on V; Z is a component of $U \cap (Z' \times W)$, and is simple on U if and only if Z' is so on U'; we have $[Z:Z'] = 1$, and the specialization-ring of Z in $k(P, Q)$ is the same as that of Z' in $k(P)$. Conversely, if Z is any subvariety of U, with the projection Z' on V, such that the specialization-ring of Z in $k(P, Q)$ is the same as that of Z' in $k(P)$, then the projection from U to U' is regular along Z'.*

Let K be a common field of definition for Z' and for W, containing k; let P' be a generic point of Z' over K; as we have seen, the projection from U to U' is regular along Z' if and only if it is so at P'; in view of our definitions, this proves the first assertion. When that is so, there is, by prop. 28, a uniquely determined and finite specialization Q' of Q over $P \to P'$ with reference to k, and we have $k(P', Q') = k(P')$, hence a fortiori $K(P', Q') = K(P')$; therefore (P', Q') has a locus Z over K, which, by coroll. 1 of th. 2, §1, is contained in U, and which has the projection Z' on V; it follows then from prop. 27 and 28, and from the definitions, that we have $[Z:Z'] = 1$, and that the specialization-ring of Z in $k(P, Q)$ is the same as that of Z' in $k(P)$; and the coroll. of th. 14, §6, shows that Z is simple on U if and only if Z' is so on U'. Let now r be the dimension over K of the field $K(P', Q') = K(P')$; then Z and Z' have the dimension r. Assume that Z_1 is a subvariety of U with the projection Z' on V; then Z_1 has at least the dimension r, and, by prop. 26, it is contained in a component $\bar{Z}_1$ of $U \cap (Z' \times W)$, having also the projection Z' on V; by th. 8 of §4, $\bar{Z}_1$ must then be algebraic over K. As P' is a generic point of Z' over $\bar{K}$, there is therefore, by th. 6 of §3, a generic point of $\bar{Z}_1$ over $\bar{K}$ of the form (P', Q''); as this point is in U, it is a specialization of (P, Q) over k, so that, by prop. 28, we have $Q'' = Q'$, hence $\bar{Z}_1 = Z$. This shows that Z_1 is contained in Z; as Z has the dimension r, and as Z_1 has at least that dimension, they are therefore the same; and this shows also that Z is a component of $U \cap (Z' \times W)$. If now Z and Z' are as in the last part of our theorem, then every y_j, being in the specialization-ring of Z in $k(P, Q)$ by the definitions, must be in that of Z' in $k(P)$, and our assertion follows by what we have proved above.

Corollary. *Let U be a subvariety of a product $V \times W$, with the projection U' on V. Let Z' be a subvariety of U'; let K be a common field of definition for U and Z', and P' a generic point of Z' over K. Then, if the projection from U to U' is regular at some point $\bar{P}'$ of Z', it is regular at P', and along Z'; if (P', Q') is the point of U with the projection P' on V, (P', Q') has a locus over K, which is the subvariety Z of U with the projection Z' on V; and the projection from Z to Z' is regular at $\bar{P}'$.*

The first assertion follows from the definitions and from prop. 29; the second one follows, as above, from the relation $K(P', Q') = K(P')$, which is contained in prop. 28. Let now (P, Q) be a generic point of U over K; let $\bar{Q}'$ be a specialization of Q' over $P' \rightarrow \bar{P}'$ with reference to K; then $(\bar{P}', \bar{Q}')$ is also a specialization of (P, Q) over K, and is therefore, by prop. 28, the point of U with the projection $\bar{P}'$ on V; that being so, the last assertion in our corollary follows from the last part of prop. 28, applied to K, (P, Q), (P', Q') and $(\bar{P}', \bar{Q}')$.

Let now V be a variety in some space, and W a variety in the same or in another space; by a *birational correspondence between V and W*, we understand a subvariety T of the product $V \times W$, having the projections V and W, respectively, on the first factor V and on the second factor W of that product, and such that the projections from T to V and from T to W are both regular. We say that two varieties are *birationally equivalent* if there exists a birational correspondence between them, and that they are so over a field k if there exists such a birational correspondence, defined over that field; when that is so, k must be a common field of definition for these varieties, and they must have the same dimension.

Let T be a birational correspondence between two varieties V and W; and let V' be a subvariety of V, such that the projection from T to V is regular along V', so that, by th. 15, there is one and only one subvariety T' of T with the projection V' on V; when that is so, and when, moreover, the projection from T to W is regular along the projection W' of T' on W, then we say that the birational correspondence T is *biregular along* V' and *along* W', and that V' and W' are *regularly corresponding subvarieties of* V *and of* W *by* T, and we write $W' = T(V')$, and $V' = T^{-1}(W')$, this notation being justified by the fact that, by what we have said and by th. 15, all three varieties V', W' and T' are uniquely determined when any one of them is given; there is therefore a one-to-one correspondence between the regularly corresponding subvarieties of V and of W by T; moreover, by th. 15, regularly corresponding subvarieties of V and of W by T have the same dimension.

In particular, T being again a birational correspondence between V and W, if two regularly corresponding subvarieties of V and of W are of dimension 0, and therefore respectively reduced to a point P of V and to a point Q of W, we say that P and Q are *regularly corresponding points of* V *and of* W *by* T, and we also say that T is *biregular at* P and *at* Q; this is so if and only if (P, Q) is a point of T such that the projection from T to V is regular at P, and that from T to W regular at Q.

Let again T be a birational correspondence between two varieties V and W; by th. 6 of §3, if k is a field of definition for T, and (P, Q) a generic point of T over k, then P and Q are generic points of V and of W, respectively, over k; when that is so, we shall say that P and Q are *corresponding generic points of* V *and of* W *over* k *by* T.

THEOREM 16. *Let* T *be a birational correspondence between two varieties* V *and* W; *and let* k *be a field of definition for* T. *Then any corresponding generic points of* V *and of* W *over* k *by* T *are regularly corresponding points of* V *and of* W *by* T. *Moreover, if* P *is any generic point of* V *over* k, T *is biregular at* P; P *and the point* $Q = T(P)$ *are then corresponding generic points of* V *and of* W *over* k *by* T, *and we have* $k(P) = k(Q)$.

As to the first assertion, let (P, Q) be a generic point of T over k, so that, by th. 6 of §3, P and Q are generic points of V and of W, respectively, over k; then, as we have already seen above, it follows from prop. 14 of Chap. II, §4, that the projection from T to V is regular at P, and similarly that the projection from T to W is so at Q. If now P is any generic point of V over k, then, by th. 6 of §3, there is a generic point of T over k, of the form (P, Q). From what we have proved, and from prop. 27, it follows that $k(P, Q) = k(P) = k(Q)$. This completes the proof.

COROLLARY 1. *Let* V *and* W *be two varieties, defined over a field* k; *let* P *and* Q *be generic points of* V *and of* W *over* k. *Then there exists a birational correspondence* T, *defined over* k, *between* V *and* W, *such that* P *and* Q *are corresponding generic points of* V *and of* W *over* k *by* T, *if and only if* P *and* Q *satisfy the condition* $k(P) = k(Q)$; *and, when that is so,* T *is the locus of* (P, Q) *over* k.

The condition is necessary by th. 16, and then, by definition, T is the locus of (P, Q) over k. Conversely, if $k(P) = k(Q)$, then we have $k(P, Q) = k(P)$, which shows that (P, Q) has a locus T over k; T is then, by prop. 27, a birational correspondence between V and W.

COROLLARY 2. *Let V and W be two varieties, defined over a field k; let P and Q be generic points of V and of W over k. Then V and W are birationally equivalent over k if and only if there is an isomorphism over k between the fields $k(P)$ and $k(Q)$.*

If there is such an isomorphism, then it must transform P into a point P' such that $k(P') = k(Q)$; P' is then, by th. 1 of Chap. II, §1, and by prop. 1 of §1, a generic point of V over k, and, by coroll. 1, (P', Q) has a locus over k which is a birational correspondence between V and W. Conversely, if there exists such a birational correspondence T, defined over k, then, by th. 16, if we put $Q' = T(P)$, we have $k(P) = k(Q')$, and Q' is a generic point of W over k, so that, by prop. 1 of §1 and th. 1 of Chap. II, §1, there is an isomorphism of $k(Q')$ on $k(Q)$ over k.

COROLLARY 3. *Let V and W be two varieties, both algebraic over a field k; let P and Q be generic points of V and of W over $\bar{k}$. Then, if there exists an isomorphism between $k(P)$ and $k(Q)$ over k, W is birationally equivalent over $\bar{k}$ to one of the conjugates of V over k.*

The given isomorphism transforms P into a point P' such that $k(P') = k(Q)$, hence a fortiori $\bar{k}(P') = \bar{k}(Q)$; therefore the loci of P' and of Q over $\bar{k}$ are birationally equivalent over $\bar{k}$, by coroll. 1. This proves our assertion, by th. 4 of §2 and by th. 1 of Chap. II, §1. It should be observed that the converse of this corollary is not true.

THEOREM 17. *Let T be a birational correspondence, defined over a field k, between two varieties V and W; let P and Q be corresponding generic points of V and of W over k by T. Let T' be a subvariety of T, with the projections V' on V, and W' on W. Then V' and W' are regularly corresponding subvarieties of V and of W by T if and only if the specialization-ring of V' in $k(P)$ is the same as that of W' in $k(Q)$; when that is so, T' is a birational correspondence between V' and W'; and W' is simple or not on W according as V' is simple or not on V, or also according as T' is simple or not on T.*

By th. 15 and the definitions, if V' and W' are regularly corresponding subvarieties of V and of W by T, then the specialization-rings of V' in $k(P)$, and of W' in $k(Q)$, are both the same as that of T' in $k(P, Q)$. Conversely, if the specialization-rings of V' in $k(P)$, and of W' in $k(Q)$, are the same, then every coordinate of Q, being in the latter, is in the former, so that, by th. 15, the projection from T to V is regular along V', and similarly the projection from T to W is regular along W'. Our other assertions are immediate consequences of th. 15.

COROLLARY 1. *Let T be a birational correspondence, defined over a field k, between two varieties V and W; let P and Q be corresponding generic points of V*

and of W over k by T; let (P', Q') be a point of T, with the projections P' on V and Q' on W. Then P' and Q' are regularly corresponding points of V and of W by T if and only if the specialization-rings of P' in $k(P)$, and of Q' in $k(Q)$, are the same; when that is so, we have $k(P') = k(Q')$; and Q' is then simple on W' if and only if P' is so on V'.

In fact, this is a special case of th. 17, except for the relation $k(P') = k(Q')$ which follows from our definitions and from prop. 28.

COROLLARY 2. *Let T be a birational correspondence, defined over a field k, between two varieties V and W. Let V' be a subvariety of V; let K be a field of definition for V', containing k; and let P' be a generic point of V' over K. Then T is biregular along V' if and only if it is biregular at P'; and, when that is so, then, if we put $W' = T(V')$ and $Q' = T(P')$, W' is the locus of Q' over K, and the point (P', Q') has over K a locus T' which is the subvariety of T with the projections V' on V and W' on W.*

If T is biregular along V', then there exist subvarieties T' of T, and $W' = T(V')$ of W, with the properties stated in th. 17; by the coroll. of th. 15, T' is then the locus over K of a point (P', Q') with the projection P' on V, so that W' is the locus of Q' over K; the projection from T to V is regular along V', hence at P', and the projection from T to W is regular along W', hence at Q'; therefore P' and Q' are then regularly corresponding points of V and of W by T. Assume now, conversely, that T is biregular at P'; then, if we put $Q' = T(P')$, we have, by coroll. 1, $k(P') = k(Q')$, hence a fortiori $K(P') = K(Q') = K(P', Q')$, so that Q' and (P', Q') have loci W' and T' over K; it follows now from the coroll. of th. 15 that V' and W' are regularly corresponding subvarieties of V and of W by T.

COROLLARY 3. *Let T be a birational correspondence, defined over a field k between two varieties V and W. Let P and P' be two points of V, such that T is biregular at P' and that P' is a specialization of P over k. Then T is biregular at P; if we put $Q = T(P)$ and $Q' = T(P')$, then Q' is the uniquely determined specialization of Q over $P \rightarrow P'$ with reference to k, and the specialization-ring of Q' in $k(Q)$ is the same as that of P' in $k(P)$.*

It follows from prop. 29 that the projection from T to V is regular at P; let (P, Q) be the point of T with the projection P on V; if then $(\bar{P}, \bar{Q})$ is a generic point of T over k, (P, Q) is a specialization of $(\bar{P}, \bar{Q})$ over k; therefore, if (P', Q'') is any specialization of (P, Q) over $P \rightarrow P'$ with reference to k, this is also one of $(\bar{P}, \bar{Q})$ over k, so that, by the definitions, we must then have $Q'' = Q'$; it then follows from prop. 29 that the projection from T to W is regular at Q. Now, by the last assertion in prop. 28, the specialization-rings of P' in $k(P)$, and of Q' in $k(Q)$, are both the same as that of (P', Q') in $k(P, Q)$.

COROLLARY 4. *Let T be a birational correspondence between two varieties V and W; let V' be a subvariety of V, and V'' a subvariety of V', such that T is biregular* *along V''. Then T is biregular along V', and the variety $W'' = T(V'')$ is contained in $W' = T(V')$; moreover, if T' and T'' are the subvarieties of T with the projections V' and V'' on V, respectively, then T' contains T'' and is a birational correspondence between V' and W'; and V'' and W'' are regularly corresponding subvarieties of V' and of W' by T'.*

Let k be a common field of definition for T, V' and V''; let P' and P'' be generic points of V' and of V'' over k; by coroll. 2, T is biregular at P'', hence at P' by coroll. 3, hence along V' by coroll. 2. Put $Q' = T(P')$, and $Q'' = T(P'')$; by coroll. 2, T', W', T'' and W'' are respectively the loci of (P', Q'), of Q', of (P'', Q'') and of Q'' over k; by coroll. 3, (P'', Q'') is a specialization of (P', Q') over k, and the specialization-rings of P'' in $k(P')$, and of Q'' in $k(Q')$, are the same; all our assertions follow from that by th. 17 and coroll. 1.

COROLLARY 5. *Let T be a birational correspondence, defined over a field k, between two varieties V and W. Let V' be a subvariety of V, such that T is biregular along V'. Let K be a field of definition for V', containing k; and let σ be an isomorphism of K over k on a field K'. Then V'^{σ} is a subvariety of V, along which T is biregular; moreover, if we put $W' = T(V')$, then W' is defined over K, and we have $T(V'^{\sigma}) = W'^{\sigma}$.*

Let T' be the subvariety of T with the projections V' on V and W' on W; by coroll. 2, T' and W' are defined over K; by coroll. 2 of th. 3, §2, by prop. 4 of §2, and by coroll. 1 of th. 6, §3, T'^{σ} is a subvariety of T with the projections V'^{σ} on V and W'^{σ} on W. Let (P, Q) and (P', Q') be generic points of T' over K, and of T'^{σ} over K', respectively; by th. 3 of §2, σ can be extended to an isomorphism between $K(P, Q)$ and $K'(P', Q')$ in which (P, Q) is mapped on (P', Q'); by th. 1 of Chap. II, §1, this implies that (P', Q') is a generic specialization of (P, Q) over k. By coroll. 2, T is biregular at P, so that we can write $Q = T(P)$; then coroll. 3 shows that T is biregular at P' and that we have $Q' = T(P')$; by coroll. 2, this proves our assertions.

THEOREM 18. *Let, for $1 \leqq \alpha \leqq h$, T_α be a birational correspondence, defined over a field k, between two varieties V_α and W_α; let the P_α be independent generic points of the V_α over k, and put, for $1 \leqq \alpha \leqq h$, $Q_\alpha = T_\alpha(P_\alpha)$. Then there is one and only one birational correspondence T between the product-varieties $V = \prod_\alpha V_\alpha$ and $W = \prod_\alpha W_\alpha$, such that the points $P = \prod_\alpha P_\alpha$ and $Q = \prod_\alpha Q_\alpha$ are corresponding generic points of V and of W over k by T; and T depends only upon the T_α, V_α and W_α, and not upon the choice of k and of the P_α. Moreover, if $P' = \prod_\alpha P'_\alpha$ is any point of V, with the projection P'_α on V_α for $1 \leqq \alpha \leqq h$, then T is biregular at P' if and only if, for $1 \leqq \alpha \leqq h$, T_α is biregular at P'_α; and, when that is so, we have $T(P') = \prod_\alpha T_\alpha(P'_\alpha)$.*

For every α, by th. 16, Q_α is a generic point of W_α over k, and $k(P_\alpha) = k(Q_\alpha)$; this, together with our assumptions, implies that the h points Q_α are independent over k. Therefore, by coroll. 2 of th. 5, §3, P and Q are generic points of V and of W, respectively, over k. As $k(P)$ is the compositum of the h fields $k(P_\alpha)$, and $k(Q)$ the compositum of the h fields $k(Q_\alpha)$, this also shows that we have $k(P) = k(Q)$; our first assertion follows from this by coroll. 1 of th. 16, which also shows that the birational correspondence T of our theorem is the locus of (P, Q) over k. By the definition of the projection on a partial product in §3, T is then the projection of the variety $\prod_\alpha T_\alpha$, in the product of $2h$ factors

$$V_1 \times W_1 \times \cdots \times V_h \times W_h,$$

on the partial product $V_1 \times \cdots \times V_h \times W_1 \times \cdots \times W_h$ of that product (or, as one could also say, it is obtained from that variety by reordering the factors in that product as we have indicated); therefore it depends only upon the T_α, the V_α and the W_α. Let now $P' = \prod_\alpha P'_\alpha$ be a point of V, such that, for every α, T_α is biregular at P'_α; put $Q'_\alpha = T_\alpha(P'_\alpha)$, and $Q' = \prod_\alpha Q'_\alpha$. For every α, every coordinate of Q_α is in the specialization-ring of P'_α in $k(P_\alpha)$, and Q'_α is the uniquely determined specialization of Q_α over $P_\alpha \rightarrow P'_\alpha$ with reference to k; by the definition of specialization-rings, this implies that every coordinate of every Q_α, i.e. every coordinate of Q, is in the specialization-ring of P' in $k(P)$, and that Q' is the uniquely determined specialization of Q over $P \rightarrow P'$ with reference to k; therefore the projection from T to V is regular at P', and (P', Q') is the point of T with the projection P' on V. Moreover, for every α, every coordinate of P_α is in the specialization-ring of Q'_α in $k(Q_\alpha)$; as before, this implies that the projection from T to W is regular at Q'. Therefore T is biregular at P', and we have $Q' = T(P')$. Now, conversely, assume that $P' = \prod_\alpha P'_\alpha$ and $Q' = \prod_\alpha Q'_\alpha$ are regularly corresponding points of V and of W by T; we shall prove that then, for every α, P'_α and Q'_α are regularly corresponding points of V_α and of W_α by T_α. As our assumptions and conclusion depend only upon T, and not upon the choice of (P, Q), we may assume that (P, Q) is not only, as above, a generic point of T over k, but also over the field $k(P', Q')$, so that (P, Q) and (P', Q') are independent over k. Let now z be any element of the specialization-ring of Q'_1 in $k(Q_1)$; this is then a fortiori, by the definition of specialization-rings, an element of the specialization-ring of Q' in $k(Q)$, hence also, by coroll. 1 of th. 17, of the specialization-ring of P' in $k(P)$. Put

$$K = k(P_2, \cdots, P_h);$$

as the P_α are independent over k, this is a free field over k with respect to P_1, and we have $k(P) = K(P_1)$. Put $\bar{P}_1 = P'_1$, $\bar{P}_\beta = P_\beta$ for $2 \leqq \beta \leqq h$, and $\bar{P} = \prod_{\alpha=1}^h \bar{P}_\alpha$. As $\bar{P}$ is a point of V, it is a specialization of P over k; as P and P' are independent over k, the locus of $\bar{P}$ over $k(P')$ is $P'_1 \times V_2 \times \cdots \times V_h$, which contains P', so that P' is a specialization of $\bar{P}$ over $k(P')$ and a fortiori over k. That being so, prop. 15 of Chap. II, §4, shows that z, which is in the specialization-ring of P' in $k(P)$, must a fortiori be in that of $\bar{P}$ in $k(P)$, hence also, by the definition of specialization-rings, in that of P'_1 in $K(P_1)$. As z is in the field $k(Q_1) = k(P_1)$, prop. 6 of §2 shows that z is in the specialization-ring of P'_1 in $k(P_1)$. The same proof can be applied to show that, for every α, the specialization-ring of Q'_α in $k(Q_\alpha)$ is contained in that of P'_α in $k(P_\alpha)$, and similarly that the latter is contained in the former, so that they are the same. As (P'_α, Q'_α) is, for every α, a specialization of (P_α, Q_α) over k and therefore a point of T_α, our conclusion follows now from coroll. 1 of th. 17.

COROLLARY. *Assumptions and notations being as in th.* 18, *let* U *be a subvariety of* V, *with the projection* U'_α *on* V_α *for* $1 \leqq \alpha \leqq h$. *Then* T *is biregular along* U *if and only if, for every* α, T_α *is biregular along* U'_α; *and, when that is so,* $T(U)$ *is a subvariety of* W *with the projection* $T_\alpha(U'_\alpha)$ *for* $1 \leqq \alpha \leqq h$.

This is an immediate consequence of the definitions, of th. 18, of coroll. 2 of th. 17, and of coroll. 2 of th. 6, §3, when one applies those results to a generic point of U over some common field of definition for T and U.

CHAPTER V

INTERSECTION-MULTIPLICITIES (SPECIAL CASE)

1. Intersections of dimension 0. In this chapter, we shall define and study intersection-multiplicities for the components of the intersection of an arbitrary variety and of a linear variety in n-space; this is the "special case" referred to in the title of the chapter. We begin by two results concerning the dimension of such components, in general and in an important particular case.

PROPOSITION 1. *Let V^r be a variety, and L^{n-s} a linear variety, in S^n. Then every component of $V \cap L$ has at least the dimension $r - s$. Moreover, if k is a common field of definition for V and L, every component of $V \cap L$ is algebraic over k; and every conjugate of such a component over k is also a component of $V \cap L$.*

Let the $F_i(X) = 0$ $(1 \leqq i \leqq s)$ be a minimal set of linear equations for L over k. A point (x) is in $V \cap L$ if and only if it is in V and satisfies the s equations $F_i(X) = 0$; all our assertions then follow from th. 7 of Chap. IV, §4.

PROPOSITION 2. *Let V^r be a variety, defined over a field k in S^n; and let (x) be a generic point of V over k. Let L^{n-s} be the linear variety in S^n defined by the set of equations $F_i(X) - v_i = 0$ $(1 \leqq i \leqq s)$, where the $F_i(X) = \sum_{j=1}^{n} c_{ij}X_j$ are s linearly independent linear forms in $k[X]$, and (v) is a set of s independent variables over k. Then $V \cap L$ is not empty if and only if the s quantities $y_i = F_i(x)$ are independent variables over k; when that is so, the components of $V \cap L$ are all of dimension $r - s$, and are the conjugates of each other over the field $K = k(v)$; and every generic point of any one of them over $\bar{K}$ is a generic point of V over k.*

Assume that (y) is a set of independent variables over k; then (v) is a generic specialization of (y) over k, which, by prop. 4 of Chap. II, §2, can be extended to a generic specialization (v, z) of (y, x) over k. Then the relations $y_i = F_i(x)$ imply $v_i = F_i(z)$, so that (z) satisfies the equations for L and is therefore in L; as (z) is a specialization of (x) over k it is in V, hence in $V \cap L$. Now, conversely, assume that $V \cap L$ is not empty, and let W be any component of $V \cap L$, which, by prop. 1, must be algebraic over the field $K = k(v)$, and of a dimension $d \geqq r - s$; and let (z) be a generic point of W over $\bar{K}$. Then the dimension of (z) over K is d; and (z) satisfies the equations for L, so that we have $v_i = F_i(z)$ for $1 \leqq i \leqq s$, hence $k(v) \subset k(z)$. As $k(v)$ has the dimension s over k, and (z) the dimension d over $k(v)$, (z) must therefore have the dimension $d + s$ over k; as (z) is on V, th. 2 of Chap. IV, §1, shows that we must then have $d + s \leqq r$. This gives $d = r - s$, and it also shows that, W and (z) being as stated, (z) has the dimension r over k, hence, by th. 2 of Chap. IV, §1, is a generic point of V over k. Now let W' be any other component of $V \cap L$, and (z') a generic point of W' over $\bar{K}$; as above, we find that (z') must be a generic point of V over k, hence a generic specialization of (z) over k, which can be extended, by prop. 4 of Chap. II, §2, to a generic specialization (z', v') of (z, v) over k. The relations $v_i = F_i(z)$ then imply $v'_i = F_i(z')$; but, as (z') is on L, we have $v_i = F_i(z')$, hence $v_i = v'_i$ for $1 \leqq i \leqq s$. Prop. 2 of Chap. II, §1, now shows that (z) and (z') are generic specializations of each other over the field $K = k(v)$; therefore, by th. 4 of Chap. IV, §2, their loci over $\bar{K}$ are conjugate to each other over K. Finally, by prop. 1, every conjugate of W over K is a component of $V \cap L$. This completes our proof.

If V^r is a variety, and L^{n-s} a linear variety, in S^n, a component of $V \cap L$ will be called *proper* if it has the dimension $r - s$; such a component can exist only if we have $r \geqq s$. In the case $r = s$, every proper component is of dimension 0, i.e. reduced to a point; such a point will then be called a *proper point of intersection* of V^r and L^{n-r}. In the rest of this §, we shall deal exclusively with proper components of dimension 0, i.e. with proper points of intersection.

PROPOSITION 3. *Let V^r be a variety, and L^{n-r} a linear variety, both defined over a field k in S^n; and let P be a proper point of intersection of V and L. Then P is algebraic over k; and, if a point P' in $V \cap L$ has P as a specialization over k, it is a conjugate of P over k.*

The first assertion is a special case of prop. 1. Now, P and P' being as stated, prop. 7 of Chap. II, §3, shows that there is a generic specialization P'' of P' over k, which has P as a specialization over $\bar{k}$. Then P is on the locus W of P'' over $\bar{k}$; moreover, P'', hence also W, is in V and in L, so that, by our assumption on P, W must be reduced to P, hence P'' is the same as P. Our conclusion follows from this by the coroll. of th. 3, Chap. II, §1.

PROPOSITION 4. *Let V^r be a variety, defined over a field k in S^n. Let L^{n-r} and L'^{n-r} be two linear varieties in S^n, respectively defined by the minimal sets of linear equations $\sum_{j=1}^n u_{ij}X_j - v_i = 0$ $(1 \leqq i \leqq r)$ and $\sum_{j=1}^n u'_{ij}X_j - v'_i = 0$ $(1 \leqq i \leqq r)$, the latter being a specialization of the former over k, and (v) being a set of independent variables over the field $k(u)$. Then, if (x) is a point in $V \cap L$, a point (x') is in $V \cap L'$ if and only if it is a specialization of (x) over $(u, v) \rightarrow (u', v')$ with reference to k; and it is a proper point of intersection of V and L' if and only if it is an isolated specialization of (x) over $(u, v) \rightarrow (u', v')$ with reference to k, and is algebraic over $k(u', v')$.*

By prop. 2, applied to V, L, and to the field $k(u)$, (x) is a generic point of V over $k(u)$, and is algebraic over $k(u, v)$. Let (x') be a finite specialization of (x) over $(u, v) \rightarrow (u', v')$ with reference to k; then (x') is on V; and the relations $\sum_j u_{ij}x_j - v_i = 0$ imply $\sum_j u'_{ij}x'_j - v'_i = 0$, which shows that (x') is in L', hence in $V \cap L'$. Conversely, assume that (x') is a point in $V \cap L'$; as it is on V, it is a specialization of (x) over $k(u)$, hence also over k. As (x) is a generic point of V over $k(u)$, th. 1 of Chap. IV, §1, shows that (x) and (u) are independent over k, and that (x) is a generic point of V over k, so that $k(x)$ is a regular extension of k; that being so, th. 5 of Chap. II, §1, shows that (x', u') is a specialization of (x, u) over k. Then the relations $v_i = \sum_j u_{ij}x_j$ show, by prop. 13 of Chap. II, §4, that (v) has a uniquely determined specialization over $(x, u) \rightarrow (x', u')$, which is no other than (v') since we have $v'_i = \sum_j u'_{ij}x'_j$ for $1 \leqq i \leqq r$; therefore (x', u', v') is a specialization of (x, u, v) over k, which completes the proof of the first part of our proposition. Now assume that the point (x') is algebraic over the field $K = k(u', v')$, and that it is an isolated specialization of (x) over $(u, v) \rightarrow (u', v')$ with reference to k. By what we have already proved, (x') is then in $V \cap L'$, hence in some component Z of $V \cap L'$, which is algebraic over K. Then, (x'') being a generic point of Z over $\bar{K}$, (x') is a specialization of (x'') over $\bar{K}$, hence also over K; as (x'') is in $V \cap L'$, it is, by what we have proved above, a specialization of (x) over $(u, v) \rightarrow (u', v')$ with reference to k; as (x') has been assumed to be isolated, this implies that (x'') has the same dimension as (x') over K, i.e. that it is algebraic over K; therefore Z is of dimension 0, and, as it contains the point (x'), it is reduced to (x'), which is thus shown to be a proper point of intersection of V and L'. Conversely, assume that (x') is a proper point of intersection of V and L', hence, by prop. 3, algebraic over $K = k(u', v')$; let (x'') be a specialization of (x) over $(u, v) \rightarrow (u', v')$ with reference to k, having (x') as a specialization over K; then, by what we have proved above, (x'') is in $V \cap L'$, and therefore, by prop. 3, it must be a conjugate of (x') over K; this shows that (x') is an isolated specialization of (x) over $(u, v) \rightarrow (u', v')$.

We shall now apply prop. 2 and 4 to the case where the linear variety L in those propositions is defined by a generic set of linear equations over the field of reference. This gives in the first place the following result:

THEOREM 1. *Let V^r be a variety, defined over a field k in S^n. Let*

$$\sum_{j=1}^{n} u_{ij}X_j - v_i = 0 \qquad (1 \leqq i \leqq r)$$

be a generic set of r linear equations over k, and L^{n-r} the linear variety defined by that set in S^n. Then $V \cap L$ is not empty; all the points in $V \cap L$ are separably algebraic over $k(u, v)$, and are the conjugates of each other over $k(u, v)$; moreover, each one of these points is a proper point of intersection of V and L, and is a generic point of V over $k(u)$.

Let (x) be a generic point of V over $k(u)$; then, by th. 1 of Chap. IV, §1, (x) and (u) are independent over k. As (u) is a set of independent variables over k, it is therefore also such over $k(x)$; hence, by prop. 24 of Chap. II, §5, the quantities $y_i = \sum_j u_{ij}x_j$ are independent variables over $k(u)$. We can now apply prop. 2 to V, L and the field $k(u)$; this proves all our assertions, except for the separability of the points in $V \cap L$ over $k(u, v)$. As to that, let $(\bar{x})$ be a point in $V \cap L$; it is a generic point of V over $k(u)$, hence simple on V. As above in the case of (x), the fact that $(\bar{x})$ is a generic point of V over $k(u)$ implies that (u) is a set of independent variables over $k(\bar{x})$. From this it follows that the forms $H_i(X) = \sum_j u_{ij}X_j$, for $1 \leqq i \leqq r$, are a uniformizing set of linear forms for V at $(\bar{x})$. That being so, our assertion on separability follows from prop. 24 of Chap. IV, §6, applied to V, to the forms $H_i(X)$, to the field $k(u)$, and to the point $(\bar{x})$, if we observe that $(\bar{x})$ is on L, so that we have $v_i = H_i(\bar{x})$ for $1 \leqq i \leqq r$.

Now let V^r be a variety, and L^{n-r} a linear variety, in S^n. Let k be a field of definition for V; let $\mathfrak{S}^r$ be a minimal set of linear equations for L; let $\bar{\mathfrak{S}}^r$ be a generic set of r linear equations over k, and $\bar{L}^{n-r}$ the variety defined by that set in S^n. Let the $\bar{P}^{(\nu)}$, for $1 \leqq \nu \leqq d$, be all the distinct points of intersection of V and $\bar{L}$, which are in finite number by th. 1, each of them being taken once; and let $(P^{(1)}, \cdots, P^{(d)})$ be a specialization of $(\bar{P}^{(1)}, \cdots, \bar{P}^{(d)})$ over $\bar{\mathfrak{S}}^r \rightarrow \mathfrak{S}^r$ with reference to k; as this specialization need not be finite, each one of the $P^{(\nu)}$ is either a point or a pseudopoint (according to the definition at the beginning of Chap. IV, §1); but, by prop. 4, if any one of the $P^{(\nu)}$ is a point, then it is a point in $V \cap L$. That being so, the set of points derived from $(P^{(1)}, \cdots, P^{(d)})$ by removing every pseudopoint $P^{(\nu)}$ which may occur there will be called a *complete set of intersections of V and L*; each point in such a set is therefore a point in $V \cap L$, but need not be proper; such a complete set (and even the number of points in it) may depend, not only upon V and L, but also upon the choice of k, of the sets of equations $\mathfrak{S}^r$ and $\bar{\mathfrak{S}}^r$, and of the specialization $(P^{(1)}, \cdots, P^{(d)})$ of $(\bar{P}^{(1)}, \cdots, \bar{P}^{(d)})$. The notations being the same as above, it follows from our definition that, if a minimal set of equations $\mathfrak{S}'^r$, for a linear variety L'^{n-r} in S^n, is a specialization of $\mathfrak{S}^r$ over k, then every specialization over $\mathfrak{S}^r \rightarrow \mathfrak{S}'^r$, with reference to k, of a complete set of intersections of V and L will give, after again removing any pseudopoints which may occur in it, a complete set of intersections of V and L'. Still with the same notations, if $\mathfrak{S}^r$ is itself a generic set of linear equations over k, then we may take it as $\bar{\mathfrak{S}}^r$, so that we get $\bar{L} = L$; in that case, therefore, we get a complete set of intersections of V and L by taking all the points in $V \cap L$, each of them being taken only once.

THEOREM 2. *Let P be a proper point of intersection of a variety V^r and of a linear variety L^{n-r} in S^n. Then there is a positive integer μ such that P occurs exactly μ times in every complete set of intersections of V and L.*

Let $\sum_{j=1}^n u_{ij}X_j - v_i = 0$ $(1 \leqq i \leqq r)$ be a minimal set of equations for L; let k_0 be the smallest field of definition for V; let $\sum_{j=1}^n \bar{u}_{ij}X_j - \bar{v}_i = 0$ $(1 \leqq i \leqq r)$ be a generic set of r linear equations over k_0, and $\bar{L}$ the variety defined by that set in S^n. By th. 1, there exists a point $\bar{P} = (\bar{x})$ in $V \cap \bar{L}$, and the set of all points of intersection of V and $\bar{L}$ is a complete set of conjugates of $\bar{P}$ over $k_0(\bar{u}, \bar{v})$. By prop. 4, if the point $P = (x)$ is a proper point of intersection of V and L, it is a proper specialization of $(\bar{x})$ over $(\bar{u}, \bar{v}) \rightarrow (u, v)$, with reference to k_0, and, as such, by th. 4 of Chap. III, §4, it has a well-defined multiplicity μ; μ is then the number of times that P will occur in every specialization, over $(\bar{u}, \bar{v}) \rightarrow (u, v)$, with reference to k_0, of the set of all points of intersections of V and $\bar{L}$. Now let k be an arbitrary field of definition for V; let $\sum_j \bar{u}'_{ij}X_j - \bar{v}'_i = 0$ $(1 \leqq i \leqq r)$

be any generic set of r linear equations over k, hence a fortiori over k_0 since k_0 is contained in k, and let $\bar{L}'$ be the variety defined by that set. As $(\bar{u}', \bar{v}')$ is a generic specialization of $(\bar{u}, \bar{v})$ over k_0, it can be extended, by prop. 4 of Chap. II, §2, to a generic specialization $(\bar{u}', \bar{v}', \bar{x}')$ of $(\bar{u}, \bar{v}, \bar{x})$ over k_0; then, by th. 1 of Chap. II, §1, there is an isomorphism of $k_0(\bar{u}, \bar{v}, \bar{x})$ on $k_0(\bar{u}', \bar{v}', \bar{x}')$ over k_0, which maps $(\bar{u}, \bar{v}, \bar{x})$ on $(\bar{u}', \bar{v}', \bar{x}')$; moreover, by prop. 4, $(\bar{x}')$ is then a point in $V \cap \bar{L}'$, so that, by th. 1, the set of all points of intersections of V and $\bar{L}'$ is a complete set of conjugates of $(\bar{x}')$ over $k(\bar{u}', \bar{v}')$ and also over $k_0(\bar{u}', \bar{v}')$. That being so, prop. 9 of Chap. III, §4, shows that the point $P = (x)$ has a multiplicity equal to μ as a specialization of $(\bar{x}')$ over $(\bar{u}', \bar{v}') \rightarrow (u, v)$ with reference to k_0, hence also with reference to k since every specialization over k is a fortiori a specialization over k_0. In order to complete the proof of our theorem, it only remains to show that, V, L and P being given as above, the multiplicity μ, as above defined, is independent of the choice of a minimal set of equations for L. In fact, let $\sum_{j=1}^{n} u_{ij}X_j - v_i = 0$ $(1 \leqq i \leqq r)$ and $\sum_{j=1}^{n} u'_{ij}X_j - v'_i = 0$ $(1 \leqq i \leqq r)$ be two such sets, and put $K = k_0(u, v, u', v')$. By th. 10 of Chap. IV, §5, the equations in either one of the above sets for L are linear combinations, with coefficients in K, of the equations in the other, i.e. there are two matrices $\|c_{ih}\|$ and $\|d_{ih}\|$, with $1 \leqq i \leqq r$, $1 \leqq h \leqq r$, which are of rank r and inverse to each other and consist of elements of K, such that we have

$$u'_{ij} = \sum_{h=1}^{r} c_{ih}u_{hj}, \qquad v'_i = \sum_{h=1}^{r} c_{ih}v_h$$
$$u_{ij} = \sum_{h=1}^{r} d_{ih}u'_{hj}, \qquad v_i = \sum_{h=1}^{r} d_{ih}v'_h \qquad (1 \leqq i \leqq r,\ 1 \leqq j \leqq n).$$

Let now

$$\sum_{j=1}^{n} \bar{u}_{ij}X_j - \bar{v}_i = 0 \qquad (1 \leqq i \leqq r)$$

be a generic set of r linear equations over K; let $\bar{L}$ be the variety defined by that set, and put

$$\bar{u}'_{ij} = \sum_h c_{ih}\bar{u}_{hj}, \qquad \bar{v}'_i = \sum_h c_{ih}\bar{v}_h \qquad (1 \leqq i \leqq r,\ 1 \leqq j \leqq n);$$

then we have

$$\bar{u}_{ij} = \sum_h d_{ih}\bar{u}'_{hj}, \qquad \bar{v}_i = \sum_h d_{ih}\bar{v}'_h \qquad (1 \leqq i \leqq r,\ 1 \leqq j \leqq n),$$

which, by th. 10 of Chap. IV, §5, shows that $\bar{L}$ can also be defined by the set of equations

$$\sum_{j=1}^{n} \bar{u}'_{ij}X_j - \bar{v}'_i = 0 \qquad (1 \leqq i \leqq r);$$

moreover, we have $K(\bar{u}', \bar{v}') = K(\bar{u}, \bar{v})$, which shows that the dimension of $(\bar{u}', \bar{v}')$ over K is the same as that of $(\bar{u}, \bar{v})$, i.e. $r(n + 1)$, hence that $(\bar{u}', \bar{v}')$ is a set of independent variables over K. Furthermore, the above relations show, by prop. 13 of Chap. II, §4, that $(\bar{u}', \bar{v}')$ has the uniquely determined specialization (u', v') over $(\bar{u}, \bar{v}) \rightarrow (u, v)$ with reference to K. That being so, a specialization of the set of all intersections of V and $\bar{L}$ over $(\bar{u}, \bar{v}) \rightarrow (u, v)$, with reference to K, is also such over $(\bar{u}', \bar{v}') \to (u', v')$, with reference to K; hence the multiplicity of a proper point of intersection P of V and L in such a specialization is the same in either case. This completes our proof.

Corollary. *Let V^r be a variety, and L^{n-r} a linear variety, in S^n, such that all the points in $V \cap L$ are proper points of intersections of V and L. Then any two complete sets of intersections of V and L are the same, except for a permutation of the points in those sets.*

This is an obvious consequence of th. 2.

If a point P is a proper point of intersection of a variety V^r and of a linear variety L^{n-r} in S^n, then the number of times, always the same by th. 2, that P occurs in every complete set of intersections of V and L will be called *the multiplicity of P* as point of intersection of V and L, or *the intersection-multiplicity of V and L at P*, and will be denoted by the symbol $j(V \cdot L, P)$.

Proposition 5. *Let P be a proper point of intersection of a variety V^r and of a linear variety L^{n-r} in S^n; let K be a common field of definition for V and L, containing the coordinates of P; and let σ be an isomorphism of K on a field K'. Then the transform P^σ of P by σ is a proper point of intersection of V^σ and L^σ, and we have $j(V^\sigma \cdot L^\sigma, P^\sigma) = j(V \cdot L, P)$.*

Put $P = (x)$, $P^\sigma = (x')$; let $\sum_{j=1}^{n} u_{ij}X_j - v_i = 0$ $(1 \leqq i \leqq r)$ be a minimal set of linear equations for L over K, and let (u', v') be the image of (u, v) by σ, so that, by coroll. 1 of th. 3, Chap. IV, §2, L^σ is defined by the minimal set of linear equations $\sum_j u'_{ij}X_j - v'_i = 0$ $(1 \leqq i \leqq r)$. Let $\sum_j \bar{u}_{ij}X_j - \bar{v}_i = 0$ $(1 \leqq i \leqq r)$ be a generic set of r linear equations over K, defining a variety $\bar{L}$, and let $(\bar{x})$ be a point in $V \cap \bar{L}$. By prop. 9 of Chap. I, §3, σ can be extended to an isomorphism of $K(\bar{u}, \bar{v}, \bar{x})$ on an extension $K'(\bar{u}', \bar{v}', \bar{x}')$ of K', mapping $(\bar{u}, \bar{v}, \bar{x})$ on $(\bar{u}', \bar{v}', \bar{x}')$. Then $(\bar{u}', \bar{v}')$ is a set of independent variables over K', so that the equations $\sum_j \bar{u}'_{ij}X_j - \bar{v}'_i = 0$ $(1 \leqq i \leqq r)$ are a generic set of linear equations over K', defining a variety $\bar{L}'$. As $(\bar{x})$ satisfies the equations for $\bar{L}$, $(\bar{x}')$ satisfies the equations for $\bar{L}'$; similarly, writing a set of equations for V over K, and using coroll. 1 of th. 3, Chap. IV, §2, we see that, since $(\bar{x})$ is on V, $(\bar{x}')$ is on V^σ, hence in the intersection of V^σ and $\bar{L}'$. Now, if we write $\mu = j(V \cdot L, P)$, (x) is, by prop. 4 and the definition of intersection-multiplicities, a proper specialization, of multiplicity μ, of $(\bar{x})$ over $(\bar{u}, \bar{v}) \to (u, v)$, with reference to K; hence, by prop. 9 of Chap. IV, §4, (x') is a proper specialization, of multiplicity μ, of $(\bar{x}')$ over $(\bar{u}', \bar{v}') \to (u', v')$, with reference to K'. By prop. 4 and the definition of intersection-multiplicities, this proves our proposition.

Proposition 6. *Let V^r be a variety, defined over a field k in S^n; let L^{n-r} and L'^{n-r} be two linear varieties in S^n, defined respectively by two minimal sets of linear equations $\mathfrak{S}^r$ and $\mathfrak{S}'^r$ such that $\mathfrak{S}'^r$ is a specialization of $\mathfrak{S}^r$ over k. Let P' be a proper point of intersection of V and L', and let P be a point in $V \cap L$, such that P'*

is a specialization of P over $\mathfrak{S}^r \to \mathfrak{S}'^r$ with reference to k. Then P is a proper point of intersection of V and L, and we have $j(V \cdot L, P) \leqq j(V \cdot L', P')$.

Put $P = (x)$, $P' = (x')$; let the sets $\mathfrak{S}^r$ and $\mathfrak{S}'^r$ consist respectively of the equations $\sum_{j=1}^{n} u_{ij}X_j - v_i = 0$ $(1 \leqq i \leqq r)$ and $\sum_{j=1}^{n} u'_{ij}X_j - v'_i = 0$ $(1 \leqq i \leqq r)$. The point P is in some component W of $V \cap L$, which is algebraic over $k(u, v)$; let $(\bar{x})$ be a generic point of W over the algebraic closure of $k(u, v)$; then $P = (x)$ is a specialization of $(\bar{x})$ over that algebraic closure, and a fortiori over $k(u, v)$, so that, by prop. 2 of Chap. II, §1, (u, v, x) is a specialization of $(u, v, \bar{x})$ over k. By our assumptions, (u', v', x') is a specialization of (u, v, x) over k, hence also of $(u, v, \bar{x})$ by what we have just proved; we shall now show that (x') is an isolated specialization of $(\bar{x})$ over $(u, v) \to (u', v')$ with reference to k. In fact, let (u', v', x'') be a specialization of $(u, v, \bar{x})$, having the specialization (u', v', x') over k; as (x') is finite, (x'') must also be finite, so that the relations

$$\textstyle\sum_j u_{ij}\bar{x}_j - v_i = 0 \qquad (1 \leqq i \leqq r),$$

which express that $(\bar{x})$ is in L, imply $\sum_j u'_{ij}x''_j - v'_i = 0$ $(1 \leqq i \leqq r)$, showing that (x'') is in L'; moreover, as $(\bar{x})$ is in V, (x'') is in V by th. 2 of Chap. IV, §1, hence in $V \cap L'$. By prop. 3, applied to V, L', (x'), (x'') and to the field $k(u', v')$, (x'') must then be a conjugate of (x') over $k(u', v')$, which proves our assertion about (x') being isolated. Prop. 13 of Chap. III, §4, now shows that $(\bar{x})$ must be algebraic over $k(u, v)$, so that W is of dimension 0 and therefore reduced to P, which is thus shown to be a proper point of intersection of V and L. Now put $\mu = j(V \cdot L, P)$, and consider a complete set of intersections of V and L, in which P will appear μ times; then P' will appear at least μ times in a specialization of that complete set over $(u, v, x) \to (u', v', x')$ with reference to k. This completes our proof.

PROPOSITION 7. *Let P be a simple point on a variety V^r in S^n, and let L^{n-r} be a linear variety through P, transversal to the tangent linear variety to V at P. Then P is a proper point of intersection of multiplicity 1 of V and L.*

Put $P = (x)$, and let k be a field of definition for V. As (x) is simple on V, there are $n - r$ polynomials $P_\rho(X)$, in the ideal defining V over k, such that the matrix $\|\partial P_\rho/\partial x_j\|$ is of rank $n - r$; then the tangent linear variety to V at (x) is defined by the set of linear equations $\sum_{j=1}^{n} \partial P_\rho/\partial x_j \cdot (X_j - x_j) = 0$ $(1 \leqq \rho \leqq n - r)$. Let the equations $\sum_j u_{ij}X_j - v_i = 0$ $(1 \leqq i \leqq r)$ be a minimal set of linear equations for L; let $\sum_j \bar{u}_{ij}X_j - \bar{v}_i = 0$ $(1 \leqq i \leqq r)$ be a generic set of linear equations over k, defining a variety $\bar{L}$, and let $(\bar{x})$ be a point in $V \cap \bar{L}$, which therefore satisfies the equations for $\bar{L}$ and also the equations $P_\rho(X) = 0$. Then $(\bar{u}, \bar{v})$ is a set of independent variables over k; by th. 1, $(\bar{x})$ is algebraic over $k(\bar{u}, \bar{v})$, and, by prop. 4, (x) is a specialization of $(\bar{x})$ over $(\bar{u}, \bar{v}) \to (u, v)$, with reference to k. Apply th. 5 of Chap. III, §4, to the specialization (x) of $(\bar{x})$ over $(\bar{u}, \bar{v}) \to (u, v)$, with reference to k, and to the n polynomials $P_\rho(X)$, for $1 \leqq \rho \leqq n - r$, and $F_i(U, V, X) = \sum_j U_{ij}X_j - V_i$, for $1 \leqq i \leqq r$, which are all in $k[U, V, X]$ and vanish if we substitute $(\bar{u}, \bar{v}, \bar{x})$ for (U, V, X). The determinant in that theorem becomes here the determinant of the coefficients in the n linear forms

$$\textstyle\sum_j \partial P_\rho/\partial x_j \cdot X_j, \qquad \sum_j u_{ij} X_j,$$

which does not vanish since L is transversal to the tangent linear variety to V at (x); therefore th. 5 of Chap. III, §4, shows that (x) is a proper specialization, of multiplicity 1, of $(\bar{x})$ over $(\bar{u}, \bar{v}) \rightarrow (u, v)$, with reference to k. By prop. 4 and the definition of intersection-multiplicities, this proves our result.

Let V be a variety, algebraic over a field k; and let P be a generic point of V over $\bar{k}$; then the order of inseparability $[k(P):k]_\iota$ of $k(P)$ over k, as defined in Chap. I, §8, will be called *the order of inseparability of V over k*; by th. 1 of Chap. II, §1, prop. 1 of Chap. IV, §1, and th. 4 of Chap. IV, §2, the order of inseparability, when V and k are given as above, does not depend upon the choice of P, and is the same for V and all the conjugates of V over k.

PROPOSITICN 8. *Let V^r be a variety, algebraic over a field k in S^n, and let p^f be its order of inseparability over k. Let $\sum_{j=1}^n u_{ij} X_j - v_i = 0$ $(1 \leqq i \leqq r)$ be a generic set of r linear equations over k, and L^{n-r} the linear variety defined by that set in S^n. Then $V \cap L$ is not empty; if (x) is any point in $V \cap L$, it is algebraic over $k(u, v)$, and we have $[k(u, v, x):k(u, v)]_i = p^f$; and the conjugates of (x) over $k(u, v)$ are the points in the intersections $V^\sigma \cap L$ of L and of all the conjugate varieties V^σ to V over k.*

As (u, v) is a set of independent variables over k, it is also such over $\bar{k}$; therefore th. 1 shows that $V \cap L$ is not empty, and that, if (x) is any point in $V \cap L$, (x) is separably algebraic over $\bar{k}(u, v)$, hence algebraic over $k(u, v)$; it also shows that (x) is a generic point of V over $\bar{k}(u)$, hence that it has the dimension r over $\bar{k}(u)$ and therefore also over the field $K = k(u)$. The relations $v_i = \sum_j u_{ij} x_j$, which express that (x) is in L, show that the v_i are in $K(x)$; as (v) is a set of r independent variables over K, and as r is the dimension of (x) over K, this shows that (v) is a maximal set of independent variables over K in $K(x)$; since (x) is separably algebraic over $\bar{k}(u, v)$ and a fortiori over $\bar{K}(v)$, it follows from this that the order of inseparability $[K(x):K]_\iota$ of $K(x)$ over K is equal to $[K(x):K(v)]_i$, i.e. to $[k(u, v, x):k(u, v)]_i$. On the other hand, as (x) is a generic point of V over $\bar{k}(u)$, it is such a fortiori over $\bar{k}$, and therefore has the same dimension r over $k(u)$ and over k; hence (x) and (u) are independent over k. By coroll. 1 of th. 3, Chap. I, §6, and prop. 26 of Chap. I, §8, it follows from this that $[K(x):K]_\iota$ is equal to $[k(x):k]_\iota$, which is no other than the order of inseparability p^f of V over k since (x) is a generic point of V over $\bar{k}$. Now, as to the last assertion, let (x') be a conjugate of (x) over $k(u, v)$; then (x') satisfies the equations for L; moreover, being a generic specialization of (x) over $k(u, v)$ by the coroll. of th. 3, Chap. II, §1, it is a fortiori a generic specialization of (x) over k, and therefore, by th. 4 of Chap. IV, §2, it is in a conjugate V^σ of V over k, hence in $V^\sigma \cap L$. Conversely, let V^σ be the transform of V by any automorphism σ of $\bar{k}$ over k, and let (x') be any point in $V^\sigma \cap L$. By prop. 8 of Chap. I, §3, σ can be extended to an automorphism of $\bar{k}(u)$, transforming (u) into itself, which we again denote by σ, and which, by prop. 4 of Chap. IV, §2, still transforms V into V^σ. By th. 1, applied to V^σ, L, (x') and to the field $\bar{k}$, (x') is a generic point of V^σ over $\bar{k}(u)$; by th. 3 of Chap. IV, §2, the automorphism σ of $\bar{k}(u)$ can therefore be extended to an isomorphism of $\bar{k}(u, x)$ on $\bar{k}(u, x')$, mapping (x) on (x'). The relations $v_i = \sum_j u_{ij}x_j$, $v_i = \sum_j u_{ij}x'_j$ $(1 \leqq i \leqq r)$, which express that (x) and (x') are on L, then show that this isomorphism transforms (v) into itself, and therefore that it is an isomorphism of $\bar{k}(u, x)$ on $\bar{k}(u, x')$ over $k(u, v)$. As (x) is algebraic over $k(u, v)$, this implies that (x') is a conjugate of (x) over $k(u, v)$, which completes our proof.

Proposition 9. *Let V^r be a variety, algebraic over a field k in S^n, and let p^f be its order of inseparability over k. Let L^{n-r} be a linear variety, defined over k in S^n, and let P be a proper point of intersection of V and L. Then P is algebraic over k, and its multiplicity $j(V \cdot L, P)$ is a multiple of $p^{-f} \cdot [k(P):k]_i$.*

Put $P = (x)$, and let $\sum_{j=1}^n u_{ij}X_j - v_i = 0$ $(1 \leqq i \leqq r)$ be a minimal set of linear equations for L over k. Let $\sum_{j=1}^n \bar{u}_{ij}X_j - \bar{v}_i = 0$ $(1 \leqq i \leqq r)$ be a generic set of r linear equations over k, and $\bar{L}$ the variety defined by that set. Let k' be the extension of k generated over k by the coefficients in some set of equations for V over $\bar{k}$, this being an algebraic extension of k and a field of definition for V; and let k'' be the field consisting of all separable elements of k' over k, so that k' is a purely inseparable extension of k'', and k'' a separable extension of k. By th. 1 and prop. 4, there is a point $(\bar{x})$ in $V \cap \bar{L}$, and (x) is then a proper specialization of $(\bar{x})$ over $(\bar{u}, \bar{v}) \rightarrow (u, v)$ with reference to k'; since, by prop. 3 of Chap. II, §1, a specialization of any set of quantities over k'' is still such over k', it follows from this, and from the definition of a proper specialization, that (x) is also a proper specialization of $(\bar{x})$ over $(\bar{u}, \bar{v}) \rightarrow (u, v)$ with reference to k''; by th. 4 of Chap. III, §4, therefore, it has as such a multiplicity μ' which is a multiple of $[k''(u, v, x):k''(u, v)]_i$. But since the u_{ij} and v_i are in k, we have $k''(u, v) = k''$, and $k''(u, v, x) = k''(x)$; at the same time we have, e.g. by prop. 25 of Chap. I, §8, $[k''(x):k'']_i = [k(x):k]_i$. Therefore μ' is a multiple of $[k(x):k]_i$. On the other hand, by prop. 25 of Chap. I, §8, V has the same order of inseparability over k'' as over k, viz. p^f. Moreover, the smallest field of definition for V containing k'' is contained in k', hence purely inseparable over k'', which implies, by prop. 5 of Chap. IV, §2, that V has no conjugate over k'', other than V itself. That being so, prop. 8 shows that a complete set of conjugates of $(\bar{x})$ over $k''(\bar{u}, \bar{v})$ consists of all the intersections of V and $\bar{L}$, each of them being repeated p^f times; therefore, in a specialization of such a complete set over $(\bar{u}, \bar{v}) \rightarrow (u, v)$ with reference to k', (x) will occur $p^f \cdot j(V \cdot L, P)$ times. As observed above, a specialization over k' is the same thing as a specialization over k'', so that, comparing this with the definition of μ', we see that $p^f \cdot j(V \cdot L, P)$ must be equal to μ', hence to a multiple of $[k(x):k]_i$.

THEOREM 3. *Let V^r be a variety, defined over a field k in S^n Let the*

$$F_i(X) = \sum_{j=1}^{n} c_{ij} X_j \qquad (1 \leqq i \leqq r)$$

be r linearly independent linear forms in $k[X]$, and (v) a set of r independent variables over k; and let L^{n-r} be the variety defined by the set of equations

$$F_i(X) - v_i = 0 \qquad (1 \leqq i \leqq r).$$

Then, if there is a point $P = (x)$ in $V \cap L$, this point is algebraic over $k(v)$; the points of intersection of V and L are the conjugates of (x) over $k(v)$, and are all proper; moreover, we have $j(V \cdot L, P) = [k(x):k(v)]_i$, and every complete set of intersections of V and L is a complete set of conjugates of (x) over $k(v)$.

Prop. 2. shows that, if $P = (x)$ is in $V \cap L$, (x) is algebraic over $k(v)$, and that the points of intersection of V and L are the conjugates of (x) over $k(v)$ and are proper. Then prop. 5, applied to V, L, P, and to the automorphisms over $k(v)$ of the algebraic closure of $k(v)$, shows that the conjugates of P over $k(v)$ all have the same multiplicity, equal to $j(V \cdot L, P)$, as points of intersection of V and L. As P is in L, we have $v_i = F_i(x)$ for $1 \leqq i \leqq r$, hence $k(v) \subset k(x)$; then, putting $\mu = j(V \cdot L, P)$ and $p^m = [k(x):k(v)]_i$, and applying prop. 9 to V, L, P and to the field $k(v)$, we see that μ is a multiple of p^m, so that we can write $\mu = p^m \cdot \mu_0$. That being so, by th. 2, every complete set of intersections of V and L consists of the conjugates of (x) over $k(v)$, each of them being repeated μ times; this is the same as a complete set of conjugates of (x) over $k(v)$, repeated μ_0 times; hence the last two assertions in our theorem are equivalent, and amount to $\mu_0 = 1$; this will be proved by induction on p^m. Assume first that we have $p^m = 1$; as (x) is a generic point of V over k by prop. 2, we can apply prop. 24 of Chap. IV, §6, which shows that the $F_i(X)$ are then a uniformizing set of linear forms for V at (x), i.e., by the definition of such a set, that L is transversal to the tangent linear variety to V at (x); by prop. 7, this implies $\mu = 1$. Now assume that we have $p^m > 1$; then one at least of the x_i, say x_1, is inseparable over $k(v)$, so that, if we put $p^e = [k(v, x_1):k(v)]_i$, we have $p^e > 1$. Then we have, by prop. 11 of Chap. I, §4,

$$[k(x):k(v, x_1)]_i = p^{m-e} < p^m.$$

Let $P(V, X_1) = 0$ be the irreducible equation for (v, x_1) over k; then, by prop. 10 of Chap. I, §3, x_1 is a root of multiplicity p^e of the equation $P(v, X_1) = 0$; as we have $p^e > 1$, this implies $\partial P/\partial x_1 = 0$. On the other hand, since $k(x)$ is a regular extension of k, the same is true, by prop. 20 of Chap. I, §7, of $k(v, x_1)$, which therefore, by th. 5 of Chap. I, §7, is separably generated over k; by th. 2 of Chap. I, §5, this, together with the relation $\partial P/\partial x_1 = 0$, implies that the r quantities $\partial P/\partial v_i$ cannot all be 0. Now let (t) be a set of r independent variables over $k(x)$, and put $K = k(t)$. Then the locus of (v, x_1) over k, which is a variety defined in S^{r+1} by the equation $P(V, X_1) = 0$, is also the locus of (v, x_1) over K, by th. 1 of Chap. IV, §1. Put $w_i = v_i + t_i x_1$, for $1 \leqq i \leqq r$, so that we have

$v_i = w_i - t_i x_1$; we can then apply prop. 13 of Chap. IV, §5, to the loci of the points (v, x_1) and (w, x_1) over K; this shows that, if we put

$$Q(T, W, X_1) = P(W_i - T_i X_1, X_1),$$

the point (w, x_1) has a locus over K, defined by the equation $Q(t, W, X_1) = 0$, which therefore is the irreducible equation for (w, x_1) over K; by prop. 10 of Chap. I, §3, this implies that $Q(t, w, X_1) = 0$ is the irreducible equation for x_1 over $K(w) = k(t, w)$. We have $\partial Q/\partial x_1 = -\sum_{i=1}^{r} t_i \cdot \partial P/\partial v_i$, and this is not 0 since the $\partial P/\partial v_i$ are not all 0 and the t_i are independent variables over $k(x)$; therefore x_1 is a simple root of $Q(t, w, X_1) = 0$, hence is separably algebraic over $K(w)$; in other words, the field $K(w, x_1) = K(v, x_1)$ is separably algebraic over $K(w)$. As (x) is algebraic over $k(v)$, hence a fortiori over $K(v, x_1)$, it follows from this that (x) is algebraic over $K(w)$; as (x) has the same dimension r over K as over k, (w) must therefore be a set of r independent variables over K. By prop. 13 of Chap. I, §4, and th. 5 of Chap. I, §7, we have

$$[K(x):K(v, x_1)]_i = [k(x):k(v, x_1)]_i = p^{m-e};$$

as we have found that $K(v, x_1)$ is separable over $K(w)$, this gives

$$[K(x):K(w)]_i = p^{m-e}.$$

By the same results, if we put $d_0 = [k(x):k(v, x_1)]_s$, we have

$$[K(x):K(v, x_1)] = [k(x):k(v, x_1)] = p^{m-e} d_0 .$$

Now put $G_i(X) = F_i(X) + t_i \cdot X_1$, for $1 \leqq i \leqq r$; these are linearly independent forms with coefficients in K, so that the equations $G_i(X) - w_i = 0$ $(1 \leqq i \leqq r)$ define a linear variety M^{n-r}. Moreover, from the relations $v_i = F_i(x)$ and $w_i = v_i + t_i x_1$, we get $w_i = G_i(x)$ for $1 \leqq i \leqq r$, which shows that (x) is in M, hence in $V \cap M$. As (w) is a set of independent variables over $K = k(t)$, (t, w) is a set of independent variables over k; and the set of equations

$$G_i(X) - w_i = 0 \qquad (1 \leqq i \leqq r),$$

which defines M, has, over $(t, w) \to (0, v)$, the specialization

$$F_i(X) - v_i = 0 \qquad (1 \leqq i \leqq r)$$

with reference to k; therefore, by prop. 4, applied to these two sets of equations and to the point (x) in $V \cap M$, the finite specializations of (x) over $(t, w) \to (0, v)$, with reference to k, are the points in $V \cap L$, i.e. (x) and its conjugates over $k(v)$, and they are all proper, and, as such, by th. 4 of Chap. III, §4, they have a multiplicity μ', the same for all of them. Furthermore, all the assumptions in our theorem hold for V, the field K, the forms $G_i(X)$, the set (w) of independent variables over K, and the point (x), and, as we have $[K(x):K(w)]_i = p^{m-e} < p^m$, the induction assumption shows that a complete set of intersections of V and M is a complete set of conjugates of (x) over $K(w)$; but any specialization of such a set over $(t, w) \to (0, v)$, with reference to k, gives, after removing any pseudo-points which may occur in it, a complete set of intersections of V and L; as (x)

and its conjugates over $k(v)$ will occur μ' times in such a specialization, what we have to prove is that we have $\mu' = p^m$. In fact, let the $(x^{(\rho)})$ be all those among the distinct conjugates of (x) over $k(v)$ which are such that $x_1^{(\rho)} = x_1$; these are the conjugates of (x) over $k(v, x_1)$, so that their number is equal to $d_0 = [k(x):k(v, x_1)]_s$; each one of them is then a specialization of (x) over

$$(t, w, x_1) \rightarrow (0, v, x_1),$$

with reference to k. Conversely, let (x') be any specialization of (x) over $(t, w, x_1) \rightarrow (0, v, x_1)$ with reference to k; the relations $v_i = w_i - t_i x_1$, and prop. 13 of Chap. II, §4, show that (v) has, over that specialization, the uniquely determined specialization (v), so that (x') is then, by prop. 2 of Chap. II, §1, a specialization of (x) over $k(v)$, hence, by the coroll. of th. 3, Chap. II, §1, a conjugate of (x) over $k(v)$, and therefore one of the $(x^{(\rho)})$. This implies that (x) is finite over $(t, w, x_1) \rightarrow (0, v, x_1)$ with reference to k. Now x_1 itself is a proper specialization of x_1 over $(t, w) \rightarrow (0, v)$, with reference to k, and as such has the multiplicity p^e, as follows from prop. 9 of Chap. II, §3, applied to the irreducible equation $Q(t, w, X_1) = 0$ for x_1 over $k(t, w)$, and from the fact that x_1 is a root of multiplicity p^e of the polynomial $Q(0, v, X_1) = P(v, X_1)$. We can now apply prop. 10 of Chap. III, §4, to the proper specialization x_1 of x_1 over $(t, w) \rightarrow (0, v)$, and to the specializations $(x^{(\rho)})$ of (x) over $(t, w, x_1) \rightarrow (0, v, x_1)$; and the formula in that proposition becomes in the present case

$$d_0 \cdot \mu' = p^e \cdot [k(t, w, x):k(t, w, x_1)].$$

As we have $k(t, w, x) = K(x)$, and $k(t, w, x_1) = K(v, x_1)$, the second factor in the right-hand side of this formula is $[K(x):K(v, x_1)]$, which, as we have seen, is equal to $p^{m-e} \cdot d_0$. Our formula now gives $\mu' = p^m$, which was to be proved.

COROLLARY. *Let V^r be a variety, defined over a field k in S^n; let $(\bar{x})$ be a generic point of V over k, and (x) any point on V. Let the $F_i(X)$, for $1 \leqq i \leqq r$, be r linearly independent linear forms in $k[X]$; put $\bar{v}_i = F_i(\bar{x})$ and $v_i = F_i(x)$, for $1 \leqq i \leqq r$, and let L^{n-r} be the linear variety defined by the set of equations*

$$F_i(X) - v_i = 0 \qquad (1 \leqq i \leqq r).$$

Then (x) is a proper point of intersection of V and L if and only if $(\bar{v})$ is a set of independent variables over k, and (x) a proper specialization of $(\bar{x})$ over $(\bar{v}) \rightarrow (v)$ with reference to k; and, when that is so, the intersection-multiplicity of V and L at (x) is equal to the multiplicity of the specialization (x) of $(\bar{x})$ over $(\bar{v}) \rightarrow (v)$ with reference to k.

As (x) is on V, it is a specialization of $(\bar{x})$ over k; and (v) is, by prop. 13 of Chap. II, §4, the uniquely determined specialization of $(\bar{v})$ over $(\bar{x}) \rightarrow (x)$ with reference to k. Let $\bar{L}$ be the variety defined by the set of equations

$$F_i(X) - \bar{v}_i = 0 \qquad (1 \leqq i \leqq r);$$

this set has, over $(\bar{x}) \rightarrow (x)$, with reference to k, the specialization

$$F_i(X) - v_i = 0 \qquad (1 \leqq i \leqq r).$$

Therefore, if (x) is proper in $V \cap L$, prop. 6 shows that $(\bar{x})$ is proper in $V \cap \bar{L}$, hence algebraic over $k(\bar{v})$; as $(\bar{x})$ has the dimension r over k, this implies that $(\bar{v})$ is a set of independent variables over k. All our assertions now follow from prop. 4, except for the assertion on multiplicities. As to that, $(\bar{v})$ being assumed to be a set of independent variables over k, th. 3 shows that a complete set of intersections of V and $\bar{L}$ is the same thing as a complete set of conjugates of $(\bar{x})$ over $k(\bar{v})$; as every specialization of such a set over $(\bar{v}) \rightarrow (v)$, with reference to k, gives, after the removal of pseudopoints if any should occur, a complete set of intersections of V and L, our last assertion now follows from this and from the definitions.

PROPOSITION 10. *Let V^r be a variety, and L^{n-r} a linear variety, in S^n; let W^s be a variety, and M^{m-s} a linear variety, in S^m. Then, if P is a point in S^n and Q a point in S^m, the point $P \times Q$ in S^{n+m} is a proper point of intersection of $V \times W$ and of $L \times M$ if and only if P and Q are proper points of intersection of V and L, and of W and M, respectively; and, when that is so, we have*

$$j[(V \times W)\cdot(L \times M), P \times Q] = j(V \cdot L, P)\cdot j(W \cdot M, Q).$$

Except for the last formula, this follows from coroll. 4 of th. 8, Chap. IV, §4. Now put $\mu = j(V \cdot L, P)$, $\nu = j(W \cdot M, Q)$, $P = (x)$, and $Q = (y)$. Let k be a common field of definition for V, W, L and M; let L and M be defined over k by minimal sets of equations $F_i(X) - a_i = 0$ $(1 \leqq i \leqq r)$, $G_j(Y) - b_j = 0$ $(1 \leqq j \leqq s)$, respectively, where the $F_i(X)$ are linear forms in $k[X]$, and the $G_j(Y)$ linear forms in $k[Y]$; then, by th. 5 of Chap. IV, §3, these two sets, taken together, define the variety $L \times M$ in S^{n+m}; this is then a minimal set of linear equations for $L \times M$. Now call $(\bar{x})$ and $(\bar{y})$ two independent generic points of V and of W, respectively, over k, so that $(\bar{x}, \bar{y})$ is a generic point of $V \times W$ over k; and put $\bar{v}_i = F_i(\bar{x})$ $(1 \leqq i \leqq r)$, $\bar{w}_j = G_j(\bar{y})$ $(1 \leqq j \leqq s)$. As (x) and (y) are proper in $V \cap L$ and in $W \cap M$, respectively, the coroll. of th. 3 shows that $(\bar{v})$ and $(\bar{w})$ are two sets of independent variables over k. As the $\bar{v}_i$ are in $k(\bar{x})$, and the $\bar{w}_j$ in $k(\bar{y})$, and as $k(\bar{x})$ and $k(\bar{y})$ are independent extensions of k, it follows from this that $(\bar{v}, \bar{w})$ is a set of $r + s$ independent variables over k. As (x) is in L, we have $F_i(x) = a_i$ $(1 \leqq i \leqq r)$; the coroll. of th. 3 now shows that (x) is a proper specialization of $(\bar{x})$, of multiplicity μ, over $(\bar{v}) \rightarrow (a)$, with reference to k; similarly (y) is a proper specialization of $(\bar{y})$, of multiplicity ν, over $(\bar{w}) \rightarrow (b)$ with reference to k. As $k(\bar{x})$ and $k(\bar{y})$ are linearly disjoint over k by th. 6 of Chap. I, §7, we can now apply prop. 11 of Chap. III, §4; this, combined with the coroll. of th. 3, proves our result.

PROPOSITION 11. *Let V^r be a variety in a product-space $S^n \times S^m$, such that its projection V' on the first factor S^n of that product has the same dimension as V. Let L^{n-r} be a linear variety in S^n, and let P' be a proper point of intersection of V' and L, such that V is finite over P'. Then the points $P^{(\rho)}$ of V which have the projection P' on S^n are proper points of intersection of V and of $L \times S^m$, and we have $[V:V']\cdot j(V' \cdot L, P') = \sum_\rho j[V\cdot(L \times S^m), P^{(\rho)}]$.*

Let k be a common field of definition for V and for L; let $(\bar{x}, \bar{y})$ be a generic point of V over k, with the projection $(\bar{x})$ on S^n, so that V' is the locus of $(\bar{x})$ over k, and that we have, by prop. 27 of Chap. IV, §8, $[V:V'] = [k(\bar{x}, \bar{y}):k(\bar{x})]$. Put $P' = (x)$; then $(\bar{y})$, by our assumptions, is finite over $(\bar{x}) \to (x)$, with reference to k; and, if we call $(y^{(\rho)})$ all the specializations of $(\bar{y})$ over $(\bar{x}) \to (x)$ with reference to k, the points $P^{(\rho)}$ are given by $P^{(\rho)} = (x, y^{(\rho)})$. Now let L be defined over k by a minimal set of equations $F_i(X) - a_i = 0$ $(1 \leqq i \leqq r)$, where the $F_i(X)$ are r linearly independent linear forms in $k[X]$, and (a) a set of elements of k. Then, by th. 5 of Chap. IV, §3, this same set of equations defines in $S^n \times S^m$ the linear variety $L \times S^m$. As P' is in L, we have $F_i(x) = a_i$ for $1 \leqq i \leqq r$. Put $\bar{v}_i = F_i(\bar{x})$ for $1 \leqq i \leqq r$; by the coroll. of th. 3, $(\bar{v})$ is a set of independent variables over k, and $P' = (x)$ is a proper specialization of $(\bar{x})$, of multiplicity equal to $j(V' \cdot L, P')$, over $(\bar{v}) \to (a)$, with reference to k. Our result is now an immediate consequence of prop. 10 of Chap. III, §4, combined again with the coroll. of th. 3.

2. Intersections of arbitrary dimension. We shall now define and study intersection-multiplicities for the proper components of the intersection of a variety V^r and of a linear variety L^{n-s} in S^n, when s is any integer not greater than r.

THEOREM 4. *Let V^r be a variety and L^{n-s} a linear variety in S^n, and let W^{r-s} be a proper component of $V \cap L$. Let k be a common field of definition for V and L, and let $\mathfrak{S}^{r-s}$ be a generic set of $r - s$ linear equations over k, defining a variety M^{n-r+s} in S^n. Then $W \cap M$ is not empty; every point P in $W \cap M$ is a generic point of W over $\bar{k}$ and a proper point of intersection of V and of the linear variety $L \cap M$; and the intersection-multiplicity of V and of $L \cap M$ at P depends only upon V, L and W, and not upon the choice of k, of $\mathfrak{S}^{r-s}$, and of P, subject to the above conditions.*

The statement of our theorem depends upon the fact that, L and M being as above, M is transversal to L by prop. 18 of Chap. IV, §5, so that the intersection $L \cap M$ is a linear variety of dimension $n - r$. By prop. 1 of §1, W is defined over $\bar{k}$; as the set of linear equations $\mathfrak{S}^{r-s}$ is generic over k, it is also such over $\bar{k}$; therefore, by th. 1 of §1, $W \cap M$ is not empty; and, if P is a point in $W \cap M$, it is a generic point of W over $\bar{k}$, and a proper point of intersection of W and M. As W is in $V \cap L$, P is in $V \cap (L \cap M)$, hence in some component Z of $V \cap (L \cap M)$; then Z is in $V \cap L$, hence in some component X of $V \cap L$, which must be algebraic over k. As P is in X, the locus W of P over $\bar{k}$ must therefore be contained in X; as W is maximal in $V \cap L$, this implies $W = X$, so that Z is contained in W, hence in $W \cap M$; as P is in Z and is maximal in $W \cap M$, this implies that Z is reduced to P, which shows that P is a proper point of intersection of V and of $L \cap M$. Now let k' be any common field of definition for V and L, $\mathfrak{S}'^{r-s}$ a generic set of $r - s$ linear equations over k', and P' an intersection of W and of the linear variety M' defined by that set; put

$P = (x)$, $P' = (x')$, and let (u, v) and (u', v') be the sets of coefficients in $\mathfrak{S}^{r-s}$ and in $\mathfrak{S}'^{r-s}$ respectively. Put $k_0 = k \cap k'$; this is also a common field of definition for V and L; and (u, v) and (u', v'), being sets of independent variables over k and over k' respectively, are both such over k_0, and therefore are generic specializations of each other over k_0. Then, by prop. 4 of §1, applied to W and to $\mathfrak{S}^{r-s}$ and $\mathfrak{S}'^{r-s}$, (x') is a specialization of (x) over $(u, v) \to (u', v')$, and (x) a specialization of (x') over $(u', v') \to (u, v)$, with reference to k_0. Therefore (u, v, x) and (u', v', x') are generic specializations of each other over k_0, hence, by th. 1 of Chap. II, §1, they are the transforms of each other in a certain isomorphism between $k_0(u, v, x)$ and $k_0(u', v', x')$ over k_0. Now, applying prop. 5 of §1 to that isomorphism, we get $j[V\cdot(L \cap M'), P'] = j[V\cdot(L \cap M), P]$. This completes our proof.

As in th. 4, let W^{r-s} be a proper component of the intersection of a variety V^r and of a linear variety L^{n-s} in S^n; let M be the linear variety defined by a generic set of $r - s$ linear equations over some common field of definition for V and L; then the intersection-multiplicity of V and of $L \cap M$ at any point of $W \cap M$ will be called *the multiplicity of W* as component of the intersection of V and L, or *the intersection-multiplicity of V and L along W*, and will be denoted by $j(V\cdot L, W)$. By th. 4, this depends only upon V, L and W. Moreover, when we have $s = r$, so that W must be reduced to a point P, then the variety we have denoted by M is the space S^n, and $j(V\cdot L, W)$ is the same as $j(V\cdot L, P)$.

Proposition 12. *Let W^{r-s} be a proper component of the intersection of a variety V^r and of a linear variety L^{n-s} in S^n; let K be a common field of definition for V, L and W; and let σ be an isomorphism of K on a field K'. Then W^σ is a proper component of $V^\sigma \cap L^\sigma$, and we have $j(V^\sigma\cdot L^\sigma, W^\sigma) = j(V\cdot L, W)$.*

The first assertion follows at once from coroll. 3 of th. 8, Chap. IV, §4. Now let $\mathfrak{S}^{r-s}$ be a generic set of $r - s$ linear equations over K, defining a variety M; let (u, v) be the set of the coefficients in those equations; and let $P = (x)$ be a point in $W \cap M$. By prop. 9 of Chap. I, §3, σ can be extended to an isomorphism of $K(u, v, x)$ on an extension $K'(u', v', x')$ of K', mapping (u, v, x) on (u', v', x'); this, by prop. 4 of Chap. IV, §2, transforms V, L and W into V^σ, L^σ and W^σ; it transforms $\mathfrak{S}^{r-s}$ into a generic set of linear equations over K', M into the variety M' defined by that set, and P into the point $P' = (x')$. By coroll. 2 of th. 3, Chap. IV, §2, P' is in $W^\sigma \cap M'$; our assertion on multiplicities now follows from the definitions and from prop. 5 of §1.

Proposition 13. *Let V^r be a variety, algebraic over a field k in S^n; let L^{n-s} be a linear variety defined over k in S^n; and let W^{r-s} be a proper component of $V \cap L$. Then, if p^f and p^g are the orders of inseparability of V and of W, respectively, over k, the intersection-multiplicity $j(V\cdot L, W)$ is a multiple of p^{g-f}.*

Let $\mathfrak{S}^{r-s}$ be a generic set of linear equations over $\bar{k}$, defining a linear variety M; let (u, v) be the set of the coefficients in those equations, and let $P = (x)$ be a point in $W \cap M$. As (u, v) is a set of independent variables over k, the order of inseparability of V over $k(u, v)$ is equal to p^f, by the definitions, by prop. 26 of Chap. I, §8, and by coroll. 1 of th. 3, Chap. I, §6. On the other hand, by prop. 8 of §1, applied to W, M and P, we have $[k(u, v, x):k(u, v)]_i = p^g$. Our assertion now follows from the definitions and from prop. 9 of §1, applied to V, to $L \cap M$, to P, and to the field $k(u, v)$.

PROPOSITION 14. *Let V^r be a variety in S^n, algebraic over a field k; and let L^{n-s} be the linear variety defined in S^n by the set of equations*

$$F_i(X) - v_i = 0 \qquad (1 \leqq i \leqq s),$$

where the $F_i(X)$ are s linearly independent linear forms in $k[X]$, and (v) is a set of s independent variables over k. Then, if $V \cap L$ is not empty, every component of $V \cap L$ is proper and algebraic over the field $K = k(v)$; and, if W is any such component, if p^g is its order of inseparability over K, and p^f the order of inseparability of V over k, we have $j(V \cdot L, W) = p^{g-f}$.

Except for the last assertion, this is contained in prop. 2 of §1. Now let W be a component of $V \cap L$, and $P = (x)$ a generic point of W over $\bar{K}$; by prop. 2 of §1, P must then be a generic point of V over $\bar{k}$. Put

$$G_h(X) = \textstyle\sum_{j=1}^{n} u_{hj}X_j \qquad (1 \leqq h \leqq r - s),$$

where (u) is a set of $n(r - s)$ independent variables over $K(x)$; and put $G_h(x) \doteq w_h$ for $1 \leqq h \leqq r - s$. As (x) has the dimension $r - s$ over K, prop. 24 of Chap. II, §5, shows that (w) is a set of independent variables over $K(u) = k(u, v)$. Therefore the set of linear equations $G_h(X) - w_h = 0$ $(1 \leqq h \leqq r - s)$ is generic over K; let M^{n-r+s} be the variety defined by that set in S^n. Then P is in $W \cap M$, so that the multiplicity $j(V \cdot L, W)$ is, by definition, equal to $j[V \cdot (L \cap M), P]$; as (v, w) is a set of independent variables over $k(u)$, we can apply th. 3 of §1 to V, to the field $\bar{k}(u)$, and to the variety $L \cap M$ defined by the set of equations $F_i(X) - v_i = 0$ $(1 \leqq i \leqq s)$, $G_h(X) - w_h = 0$ $(1 \leqq h \leqq r - s)$; this shows that $j[V \cdot (L \cap M), P]$ is equal to $[\bar{k}(u, x):\bar{k}(u, v, w)]_i$. On the other hand, prop. 8 of §1, applied to W, M, P and K, gives $p^g = [K(u, w, x):K(u, w)]_i$; as we have $K(u, w) = k(u, v, w)$, and $K(u, w, x) = k(u, v, w, x) = k(u, x)$ since the v_i and w_h are in $k(u, x)$, this can be written as $p^g = [k(u, x):k(u, v, w)]_i$, and the right-hand side of this relation, by th. 8 of Chap. I, §8, is the product of

$$[\bar{k}(u, x):\bar{k}(u, v, w)]_i$$

and of the order of inseparability of $k(u, x)$ over $k(u)$; of these two factors, the first one has been shown to be equal to $j(V \cdot L, W)$, and the other, by prop. 26 of Chap. I, §8, and by coroll. 1 of th. 3, Chap. I, §6, is equal to $[k(x):k]_i$, i.e. to p^f. This completes our proof.

The next result embodies, for the case with which we are dealing in the present chapter, the principle of associativity for intersection-multiplicities.

PROPOSITION 15. *Let V be a variety in S^n; let L and M be two linear varieties, transversal to each other in S^n; and let W be a proper component of the intersection of V and of $L \cap M$. Then, if the Z_α are all those components of $V \cap L$ which contain W, Z_α is a proper component of $V \cap L$, and W a proper component of $Z_\alpha \cap M$, for every α; and we have $j[V\cdot(L \cap M), W] = \sum_\alpha j(V\cdot L, Z_\alpha)\cdot j(Z_\alpha\cdot M, W)$.*

Let r, u, $n - s$ and $n - t$ be the dimensions of V, of W, of L and of M, respectively; then our assumptions imply that the dimension of $L \cap M$ is $n - s - t$, and that we have $u = r - s - t$. Every variety W' contained in $Z_\alpha \cap M$ is contained in $V \cap (L \cap M)$; if such a variety W' contains W, it must be the same as W since W is maximal in $V \cap (L \cap M)$. This shows that, for every α, W is maximal in $Z_\alpha \cap M$; by prop. 1 of §1, this implies that we have

$$\dim(Z_\alpha) \leqq r - s;$$

as we have $\dim(Z_\alpha) \geqq r - s$ by that same proposition, this shows that, for every α, Z_α has the dimension $r - s$, hence is proper in $V \cap L$; and it follows from this that W, being maximal in $Z_\alpha \cap M$ and having the required dimension, is proper in $Z_\alpha \cap M$. Now put

$$\mu = j[V\cdot(L \cap M), W], \quad \mu_\alpha = j(V\cdot L, Z_\alpha), \quad \nu_\alpha = j(Z_\alpha\cdot M, W).$$

Let k be a common field of definition for V, L and M; it then follows from prop. 1 of §1 that $\bar{k}$ is a common field of definition for all the varieties in our proposition. Let now $\mathfrak{S}^s$ and $\mathfrak{T}^t$ be minimal sets of linear equations for L and for M, respectively, over k, so that $(\mathfrak{S}^s, \mathfrak{T}^t)$ is a minimal set of linear equations for $L \cap M$. Furthermore, consider a generic set of $r - s$ linear equations over k, and denote by $\bar{\mathfrak{T}}^t$ the set consisting of the first t among these $r - s$ equations, and by $\mathfrak{U}^u$ the set consisting of all the others, so that our set of $r - s$ equations can be written as $(\bar{\mathfrak{T}}^t, \mathfrak{U}^u)$; and let $\bar{M}^{n-t}$ and N^{n-u} be the varieties defined by $\bar{\mathfrak{T}}^t$ and by $\mathfrak{U}^u$, respectively, so that $\bar{M} \cap N$ is the linear variety, of dimension $n - r + s$, defined by $(\bar{\mathfrak{T}}^t, \mathfrak{U}^u)$. By prop. 18 of Chap. IV, §5, $\bar{M} \cap N$ is transversal to L, so that $(\mathfrak{S}^s, \bar{\mathfrak{T}}^t, \mathfrak{U}^u)$ is a minimal set of equations for $L \cap \bar{M} \cap N$; similarly, N is transversal to $L \cap M$, so that $(\mathfrak{S}^s, \mathfrak{T}^t, \mathfrak{U}^u)$ is a minimal set of equations for $L \cap M \cap N$. Now let $(\bar{P}^{(1)}, \cdots, \bar{P}^{(d)})$ be a complete set of intersections of V and of $L \cap \bar{M} \cap N$; and let $(P^{(1)}, \cdots, P^{(d)})$ be a specialization of this over $(\mathfrak{S}^s, \bar{\mathfrak{T}}^t, \mathfrak{U}^u) \rightarrow (\mathfrak{S}^s, \mathfrak{T}^t, \mathfrak{U}^u)$ with reference to $\bar{k}$; if we remove from this specialization any pseudopoints which may occur among the $P^{(\lambda)}$, we get a complete set of intersections of V and of $L \cap M \cap N$. By the definition of the multiplicity μ, if P is any point in $W \cap N$, then μ is the number of times that P occurs among the $P^{(\lambda)}$. Now, if, for some λ, we have $P^{(\lambda)} = P$, then P is a specialization of $\bar{P}^{(\lambda)}$ over $\bar{k}$; that point $\bar{P}^{(\lambda)}$, being in $V \cap L$, is in some component X of $V \cap L$, which is algebraic over k; then, by th. 2 of Chap. IV, §1, X must contain P, hence also the locus of P over $\bar{k}$, which is W by th. 4; this shows that X must be one of the varieties Z_α, so that $\bar{P}^{(\lambda)}$, being in that variety and in $\bar{M} \cap N$, is in $Z_\alpha \cap (\bar{M} \cap N)$ for some α. Therefore, in counting how many of the $\bar{P}^{(\lambda)}$ have the specialization P in the above specialization of $(\bar{P}^{(1)}, \cdots, \bar{P}^{(d)})$, we need only consider those $\bar{P}^{(\lambda)}$ which are in $Z_\alpha \cap (\bar{M} \cap N)$ for some α. But, by the definition of μ_α, each point in $Z_\alpha \cap (\bar{M} \cap N)$ occurs exactly μ_α times among the $\bar{P}^{(\lambda)}$; moreover, by the definition of ν_α, there are, among the distinct points in $Z_\alpha \cap (\bar{M} \cap N)$ for a given α, exactly ν_α points which have the specialization P in any specialization of the set of all those points over

$$(\mathfrak{T}^t, \mathfrak{U}^u) \rightarrow (\mathfrak{T}^t, \mathfrak{U}^u)$$

with reference to $\bar{k}$. Putting all this together, we get $\mu = \sum_\alpha \mu_\alpha \nu_\alpha$, which was to be proved.

Proposition 16. *Let V^r be a variety in S^n, and P a simple point of V. Let L^{n-s} be a linear variety in S^n, containing P, and transversal to the tangent linear variety N^r to V at P. Then P lies on one and only one component of $V \cap L$; and, if W is that component, it is proper, and we have $j(V \cdot L, W) = 1$. Moreover, if M^{n-r+s} is any linear variety containing P and transversal to $N \cap L$, then P is a proper point of intersection of W and M, and we have $j(W \cdot M, P) = 1$.*

By our assumptions, $N \cap L$ is a linear variety of dimension $r - s$, and, if M is as stated, $N \cap L \cap M$ is reduced to P, so that, if we call d the dimension of $L \cap M$, we have, by prop. 1 of §1 (or by prop. 14 of Chap. IV, §5), $d \leqq n - r$; as we have, by the same proposition, $d \geqq n - r$, this shows that $L \cap M$ is a linear variety of dimension $n - r$, and therefore, since its intersection with N is reduced to P, that it is transversal to N. By prop. 7 of §1, it follows from this that P is a proper intersection of V and of $L \cap M$, and that we have $j[V \cdot (L \cap M), P] = 1$; hence, by prop. 15, if the Z_α are those components of $V \cap L$ which contain P, they are all proper, and we have

$$1 = \textstyle\sum_\alpha j(V \cdot L, Z_\alpha) \cdot j(Z_\alpha \cdot M, P);$$

this implies that there is only one term in the right-hand side of this formula, i.e. that there is only one Z_α, and that this has the properties asserted of W in our proposition.

As a special case of prop. 16, we note the formula $j(V \cdot S^n, V) = 1$, which holds for every variety V in S^n; we get this by putting $s = 0$ in prop. 16, and taking for P any simple point of V; it could also easily be deduced from the definitions.

Proposition 17. *Let V be a variety, and L a linear variety, in S^n; let W be a variety, and M a linear variety, in S^m. Then the proper components of the intersection of $V \times W$ and of $L \times M$ in S^{n+m} are the varieties $X \times Y$, where X and Y are any proper components of $V \cap L$ and of $W \cap M$, respectively; and, if X and Y are such components, we have*

$$j[(V \times W) \cdot (L \times M), X \times Y] = j(V \cdot L, X) \cdot j(W \cdot M, Y).$$

Let r, $n - r'$, s, $m - s'$ be the dimensions of V, of L, of W, and of M, respectively; by prop. 1 of §1, every component of $V \cap L$ has at least the dimension $r - r'$, and every component of $W \cap M$ has at least the dimension $s - s'$.

Our first assertion now follows from coroll. 4 of th. 8, Chap. IV, §4, if dimensions are taken into account. As to the last formula, let X and Y be as stated; put $\mu = j(V\cdot L, X)$, and $\nu = j(W\cdot M, Y)$; let k be a common field of definition for V, L, W and M. Furthermore, let $R^{n-r+r'}$ be a variety defined in S^n by a generic set of $r - r'$ linear equations over k; then, by th. 4, there is a point P in $X \cap R$, which is a generic point of X over $\bar{k}$, and we have $\mu = j[V\cdot(L \cap R), P]$; moreover, a complete set of intersections of X and R consists of all the points in $X \cap R$, taken only once, so that we have $j(X\cdot R, P) = 1$. Similarly, let $T^{m-s+s'}$ be a variety defined in S^m by a generic set of $s - s'$ linear equations over k; then there is a point Q in $Y \cap T$, which is a generic point of Y over $\bar{k}$, and we have $\nu = j[W\cdot(M \cap T), Q]$ and $j(Y\cdot T, Q) = 1$. By prop. 10 of §1, the point $P \times Q$ is a proper intersection, of multiplicity equal to $\mu\nu$, of $V \times W$ and of the linear variety $(L \cap R) \times (M \cap T)$, which, by coroll. 4 of th. 8, Chap. IV, §4, is the same as $(L \times M) \cap (R \times T)$. By prop. 18 of Chap. IV, §5, $L \cap R$ and $M \cap T$ have the dimensions $n - r$ and $m - s$, respectively; this shows that the variety $(L \times M) \cap (R \times T)$ has the dimension $n + m - r - s$, hence that $R \times T$ is transversal to $L \times M$ in S^{n+m}. We can now apply prop. 15 to $V \times W$, to $L \times M$ and $R \times T$, and to the proper intersection $P \times Q$ of $V \times W$ and of $(L \times M) \cap (R \times T)$. This shows in the first place that, if Z is any component, containing $P \times Q$, of $(V \times W) \cap (L \times M)$, it must be proper, hence, by what we have proved above, of the form $X' \times Y'$, where X' and Y' are proper components of $V \cap L$ and of $W \cap M$, respectively; moreover, by th. 5 of Chap. IV, §3, if $P \times Q$ is in the variety $Z = X' \times Y'$, P must be in X', and Q in Y'; then X', being algebraic over k, must contain the locus X of P over $\bar{k}$, which, since X is maximal in $V \cap L$, implies that $X' = X$; similarly $Y' = Y$, hence $Z = X \times Y$. This shows that $X \times Y$ is the only component of $(V \times W) \cap (L \times M)$ which contains $P \times Q$. That being so, prop. 15, applied as we have said, together with what has been proved above, shows that $\mu\nu$ is equal to the product of $j[(V \times W)\cdot(L \times M), X \times Y]$ and of $j[(X \times Y)\cdot(R \times T), P \times Q]$. The latter factor, by prop. 10 of §1, is itself the product of $j(X\cdot R, P)$ and of $j(Y, T, Q)$, and therefore, by what has been proved above, equal to 1. This completes our proof.

PROPOSITION 18. *Let V be a variety in a product-space $S^n \times S^m$, with the projection V' on the first factor S^n of that product. Let L^{n-s} be a linear variety in S^n; and let W' be a proper component of $V' \cap L$, such that the projection from V to V' is regular along W'. Then, if W is the subvariety of V with the projection W' on V', W is a proper component of $V \cap (L \times S^m)$, and we have*

$$j(V'\cdot L, W') = j[V\cdot(L \times S^m), W].$$

As W is contained in $V \cap (L \times S^m)$, it is contained in a component $\overline{W}$ of that intersection; then the projection of $\overline{W}$ on S^n is contained in V' and in L, and contains W', so that it must be W' since W' is maximal in $V' \cap L$. As W is the only subvariety of V with the projection W' on S^n, this shows that we have $W = \bar{W}$. As the projection from V to V' is regular, V' has the same dimension r as V, so that W' must have the dimension $r - s$; by th. 15 of Chap. IV, §7, the projection from W to W' is regular, and therefore W has the same dimension $r - s$ as W'. This proves our first assertion. Now let k be a common field of definition for V and L; and let M^{n-r+s} be a linear variety defined in S^n by a generic set of $r - s$ linear equations over k. Then, by th. 4 of §2, there is a point P' in $W' \cap M$, which is a generic point of W' over $\bar{k}$ and a proper point of intersection of V' and of $L \cap M$; and, by definition, the multiplicity $j(V' \cdot L, W')$ is equal to $j[V' \cdot (L \cap M), P']$. By th. 6 of Chap. IV, §3, there is a generic point P of W over $\bar{k}$, with the projection P' on W'. The projection from V to V' is regular at P'; therefore, by prop. 28 of Chap. IV, §7, P is the only point of V with the projection P' on V', and V is finite over P'. By prop. 11 of §1, P is then a proper point of intersection of V and of $(L \cap M) \times S^m$; and, if we call μ its multiplicity, the formula in that proposition shows that μ is the product of $[V:V']$, which is equal to 1, and of $j[V' \cdot (L \cap M), P']$, which we have shown to be equal to $j(V' \cdot L, W')$. Now, by coroll. 4 of th. 8, Chap. IV, §4, we have

$$(L \cap M) \times S^m = (L \times S^m) \cap (M \times S^m);$$

if dimensions are taken into account, this implies that $M \times S^m$ is transversal to $L \times S^m$ in $S^n \times S^m$. Moreover, as every component of $V \cap (L \times S^m)$ is algebraic over k, such a component cannot contain P without containing its locus W over $\bar{k}$; as W is maximal in $V \cap (L \times S^m)$, this shows that it is the only component of $V \cap (L \times S^m)$ which contains P. We can now calculate the intersection-multiplicity μ of V and of $(L \cap M) \times S^m$ at P by applying prop. 15 to V, to $L \times S^m$ and $M \times S^m$, and to P; this shows that μ is the product of $j[V \cdot (L \times S^m), W]$ and of $j[W \cdot (M \times S^m), P]$; and our proof will be complete if we show that the latter factor is equal to 1. In fact, as we have $[W:W'] = 1$, prop. 27 of Chap. IV, §7, shows that W is finite over P' and that P is the only point of W with the projection P' on W'; by prop. 11 of §1, $j[W \cdot (M \times S^m), P]$ is therefore equal to $j(W' \cdot M, P')$, which is itself equal to 1 since W' is defined over $\bar{k}$ and M is defined by a generic set of linear equations over k, so that every point in $W' \cap M$ occurs just once in a complete set of intersections of W' and M.

3. The theory of simple points. In this §, we shall prove the converse of prop. 16 of §2, i.e. the fact that the "criterion of multiplicity 1" contained in that proposition is necessary as well as sufficient, and Zariski's theorem which states that the specialization-ring of a simple point is "integrally closed".[1]

PROPOSITION 19. *Let K be a field, $(\bar{v})$ a set of independent variables over K, $\bar{y}$ an algebraic quantity over $K(\bar{v})$, and $F(V, Y) = 0$ the irreducible equation for $(\bar{v}, \bar{y})$ over K. Let y be a proper specialization of $\bar{y}$, of multiplicity* 1, *over a finite*

[1] Owing to some difference in the definitions, the theorem, as given here, is not quite equivalent to Zariski's, and is somewhat less comprehensive (cf. O. Zariski, Am. J. of Math. 62 (1940), p. 187).

specialization (v) of $(\bar{v})$ with reference to K. Then we have $\partial F/\partial y \neq 0$; and, if an element $\bar{z}$ of $K(\bar{v}, \bar{y})$ is finite over $(\bar{v}) \to (v)$ with reference to K, it is in the specialization-ring of (v, y) in $K(\bar{v}, \bar{y})$.

As y is proper, we have $F(v, Y) \neq 0$; for otherwise, u being a variable quantity over $K(v)$, (v, u) would be a specialization of $(\bar{v}, \bar{y})$ over K, and, by prop. 2 of Chap. II, §1, it would have the specialization (v, y) over K, so that y would not be an isolated specialization of $\bar{y}$ over $(\bar{v}) \to (v)$ with reference to K. From this, and from our assumption about the multiplicity of y, it follows, by prop. 9 of Chap. II, §3, that y is a simple root of $F(v, Y) = 0$, i.e. that we have $\partial F/\partial y \neq 0$. Now let $\bar{z}$ be as stated in our proposition; let t be a variable quantity over $K(\bar{v})$; and put $w = \bar{y} + t \cdot \bar{z}$; w is in $K(t, \bar{v}, \bar{y})$, hence algebraic over $K(t, \bar{v})$ since $\bar{y}$ is algebraic over $K(\bar{v})$. As we have $\bar{y} - w = -t \cdot \bar{z}$, and as $\bar{z}$ is finite over $(\bar{v}) \to (v)$ with reference to K, the quantity $\bar{y} - w$ has no other specialization than 0 over $(t, \bar{v}) \to (0, v)$ with reference to K, so that $\bar{y}$ and w have the same specializations over $(t, \bar{v}) \to (0, v)$ with reference to K; from this, and from what we have proved above, it follows that, if u is a variable quantity over $K(v)$, $(0, v, u)$ cannot be a specialization of $(t, \bar{v}, w)$ over K. Therefore, if $P(T, V, W) = 0$ is the irreducible equation for $(t, \bar{v}, w)$ over K, we have $P(0, v, W) \neq 0$. On the other hand, the relation $P(t, \bar{v}, w) = 0$ can be written as $P(t, \bar{v}, \bar{y} + t \cdot \bar{z}) = 0$; as $\bar{y}$ and $\bar{z}$ are algebraic over $K(\bar{v})$, and as t is not so, this implies that we have

$$P(T, \bar{v}, \bar{y} + T \cdot \bar{z}) = 0,$$

where the left-hand side is a polynomial in T with coefficients in $K(\bar{v}, \bar{y})$. Substituting 0 for T in that relation, we get $P(0, \bar{v}, \bar{y}) = 0$, which, by the definition of $F(V, Y)$, implies that $P(0, V, Y)$ is a multiple of $F(V, Y)$. But, by prop. 10 of Chap. I, §3, the degree of $F(V, Y)$ in Y is equal to $d = [K(\bar{v}, \bar{y}):K(\bar{v})]$; and the degree of $P(0, V, Y)$ in Y is at most equal to the degree of $P(T, V, W)$ in W, which, by prop. 10 of Chap. I, §3, is equal to the degree d' of w over $K(t, \bar{v})$; as w is in $K(t, \bar{v}, \bar{y})$, d' is at most equal to the degree of $\bar{y}$ over $K(t, \bar{v})$, which, by prop. 6 of Chap. I, §2, is not greater than d. This shows that the degree in Y of $P(0, V, Y)$ is not greater than that of $F(V, Y)$; as the former polynomial is a multiple of the latter, we can therefore write $P(0, V, Y) = G(V) \cdot F(V, Y)$, with $G(V)$ in $K[V]$; moreover, as we have seen that $P(0, v, Y)$ cannot be 0, we have $G(v) \neq 0$. Now put $P'(T, V, W) = \partial P/\partial T$; if then we differentiate the relation $P(T, \bar{v}, \bar{y} + T \cdot \bar{z}) = 0$ with respect to T, and substitute 0 for T, we get

$$P'(0, \bar{v}, \bar{y}) + \bar{z} \cdot G(\bar{v}) \cdot \partial F/\partial \bar{y} = 0.$$

Since we have $G(v) \neq 0$ and $\partial F/\partial y \neq 0$, this shows that $\bar{z}$ is in the specialization-ring of (v, y) in $K(\bar{v}, \bar{y})$.

THEOREM 5. *Let V^r be a variety in S^n, and $P = (x)$ a point on V. Then P is simple on V if and only if there exists a linear variety L^{n-r} through P, such that P is a proper point of intersection of V and L of multiplicity 1. Moreover, if that is so, and if k is a field of definition for V and $(\bar{x})$ a generic point of V over k, then* *an element of $k(\bar{x})$ is in the specialization-ring of (x) in $k(\bar{x})$ if and only if it is finite over $(\bar{x}) \rightarrow (x)$ with reference to k.*

The above conditions, for a point P of V to be simple, and for an element of $k(\bar{x})$ to be in the specialization-ring of (x), are necessary, the former as a consequence of prop. 7 of §1, and the latter as a consequence of prop. 13 of Chap. II, §4; we have now to show that they are sufficient. Assume that P is a proper point of intersection, of multiplicity 1, of V and of some linear variety L'^{n-r}; as P is in L', a minimal set of linear equations for L' can be written in the form $\sum_{j=1}^{n} u'_{ij}(X_j - x_j) = 0$ $(1 \leqq i \leqq r)$. Consider now $r + 1$ linear forms

$$F_i(X) = \sum_{j=1}^{n} u_{ij}X_j \quad (1 \leqq i \leqq r), \qquad F_{r+1}(X) = \sum_{j=1}^{n} t_jX_j,$$

(u, t) being a set of $n(r + 1)$ independent variables over $k(x, \bar{x})$; put $K = k(u, t)$, $\bar{v}_i = F_i(\bar{x})$ and $v_i = F_i(x)$ for $1 \leqq i \leqq r$, $\bar{y} = F_{r+1}(\bar{x})$, and $y = F_{r+1}(x)$. Let L^{n-r} be the linear variety defined by the set of equations

$$F_i(X) - v_i = 0 \qquad (1 \leqq i \leqq r);$$

this can also be written as $\sum_{j=1}^{n} u_{ij}(X_j - x_j) = 0$ $(1 \leqq i \leqq r)$; as (u', x) is a specialization of (u, x) over k by prop. 2 of Chap. II, §1, we can apply prop. 6 of §1 to the sets of equations which we have written for L and L', to the variety V, and to the point P; this shows that P is a proper intersection of V and L, of multiplicity 1. On the other hand, by th. 1 of Chap. IV, §1, $(\bar{x})$ is a generic point of V over the field K; as we have $K(\bar{x}, \bar{v}, \bar{y}) = K(\bar{x})$, the point $(\bar{x}, \bar{v}, \bar{y})$, in the space $S^n \times S^{r+1}$, has a locus Z over K, which has the projection V on the first factor S^n of that product-space, and has on the other factor S^{r+1} a projection W which is the locus of $(\bar{v}, \bar{y})$ over K; moreover, the formulae by which we have defined the $\bar{v}_i$ and $\bar{y}$ show that the projection from Z to V is regular at every point of V. It will now be shown that Z is a birational correspondence between V and W, and that (x) and (v, y) are regularly corresponding points of V and of W by Z. In fact, we can apply prop. 11 of §1 to Z, to its projection V on S^n, to L, and to the point $P = (x)$; as we have $j(V \cdot L, P) = 1$, and as the projection from Z to V is regular at P, so that (x, v, y) is the only point of Z with the projection $P = (x)$ on V, this shows that the point (x, v, y) is a proper intersection, of multiplicity 1, of Z and of the linear variety $L \times S^{r+1}$. As the latter variety is defined in $S^n \times S^{r+1}$ by the set of equations $F_i(X) - v_i = 0$ $(1 \leqq i \leqq r)$, it follows from this, by the coroll. of th. 3, §1, that (x, v, y) is a proper specialization of $(\bar{x}, \bar{v}, \bar{y})$, of multiplicity 1, over $(\bar{v}) \rightarrow (v)$, with reference to K. On the other hand, by prop. 24 of Chap. II, §5, $(\bar{x})$ is finite over $(\bar{v}) \rightarrow (v)$ with reference to $k(u)$, and therefore, by prop. 23 of Chap. II, §5, every specialization of $(\bar{x})$ over $(\bar{v}) \rightarrow (v)$ with reference to $k(u)$ is algebraic over $k(u, v)$; this implies a fortiori that every specialization of $(\bar{x})$ over $(\bar{v}) \rightarrow (v)$ with reference to K is finite and algebraic over $k(u, v)$, hence also over $k(u, x)$. Let now y' be a specialization of $\bar{y}$ over $(\bar{v}) \rightarrow (v)$ with reference to K; this can be extended to a specialization (v, y', x') of $(\bar{v}, \bar{y}, \bar{x})$ over K, where (x'), as we have just seen, must be finite, so that, by prop. 13 of Chap. II, §4, we must have $y' = F_{r+1}(x')$, since we have $\bar{y} = F_{r+1}(\bar{x})$; moreover, there can then be no more than one specialization (x') of $(\bar{x})$ over $(\bar{v}, \bar{y}) \to (v, y')$ with reference to K, for, if (x'') was another one, we should also have $y' = F_{r+1}(x'')$, hence $0 = F_{r+1}(x'' - x') = \sum_j t_j(x''_j - x'_j)$, where (x') and (x''), as we have seen, must be algebraic over $k(u, x)$, and this is impossible since (t) is a set of independent variables over $k(u, x)$. This proves that $\bar{y}$ is finite over $(\bar{v}) \to (v)$ with reference to K, so that, by prop. 23 of Chap. II, §5, every specialization of $\bar{y}$ over $(\bar{v}) \to (v)$ with reference to K must be proper; and it also shows that (x) is the only specialization of $(\bar{x})$ over $(\bar{v}, \bar{y}) \to (v, y)$ with reference to K. We can now apply prop. 10 of Chap. III, §4, to the proper specialization y of $\bar{y}$ over $(\bar{v}) \to (v)$ with reference to K, and to the set $(\bar{x}, \bar{v})$, the only specialization of which over $(\bar{v}, \bar{y}) \to (v, y)$ with reference to K is (x, v); this shows that the multiplicity of (x, v, y) as a proper specialization of $(\bar{x}, \bar{v}, \bar{y})$ over $(\bar{v}) \to (v)$, with reference to K, is the product of $[K(\bar{x}, \bar{v}, \bar{y}):K(\bar{v}, \bar{y})]$ and of the multiplicity of y as a proper specialization of $\bar{y}$ over $(\bar{v}) \to (v)$ with reference to K. As the former multiplicity has been shown to be equal to 1, it follows from this that the latter is also equal to 1, and furthermore that we have

$$[K(\bar{x}, \bar{v}, \bar{y}):K(\bar{v}, \bar{y})] = 1,$$

i.e. that the $\bar{x}_j$ are in $K(\bar{v}, \bar{y})$; as $(\bar{x})$ is finite over $(\bar{v}) \to (v)$ with reference to K, it follows from this, by prop. 19, that the $\bar{x}_j$ are in the specialization-ring of (v, y) in $K(\bar{v}, \bar{y})$, i.e. that the projection from Z to W is regular at (v, y). As we have seen that the projection from Z to V is regular at (x), this shows, as we had asserted, that Z is a birational correspondence between V and W, and that (x) and (v, y) are regularly corresponding points of V and of W by Z. Moreover, prop. 19 also shows that, if $F(V, Y) = 0$ is the irreducible equation for $(\bar{v}, \bar{y})$ over K, we have $\partial F/\partial y \neq 0$, and therefore that the point (v, y) is simple on W; by coroll. 1 of th. 17, Chap. IV, §7, this implies that (x) is simple on V. Let now $\bar{z}$ be an element of $k(\bar{x})$, finite over $(\bar{x}) \to (x)$ with reference to k; then $\bar{z}$ is in $K(\bar{x}) = K(\bar{v}, \bar{y})$; we shall prove that $\bar{z}$ is finite over $(\bar{v}) \to (v)$ with reference to K. In fact, assume that (v, ∞) is a specialization of $(\bar{v}, \bar{z})$ over K; this can be extended to a specialization (v, ∞, x') of $(\bar{v}, \bar{z}, \bar{x})$ over K, where we must have $(x') \neq (x)$ by our assumption on $\bar{z}$. As the dimension of $(\bar{z}, \bar{x})$ over k is equal to the dimension r of V, and as (∞, x') is a specialization of $(\bar{z}, \bar{x})$ over K, hence also over k, which is not generic, th. 3 of Chap. II, §1, shows that the dimension of this specialization over k, i.e. the dimension of (x') over k, is less than r. As $(\bar{x})$ is finite over $(\bar{v}) \to (v)$ with reference to K, (x') is finite; as we have $\bar{v}_i = F_i(\bar{x})$, we must therefore have $v_i = F_i(x')$, hence

$$0 = F_i(x' - x) = \sum_{j=1}^{n} u_{ij}(x'_j - x_j),$$

for $1 \leqq i \leqq r$. As we have $(x') \neq (x)$, we may assume that we have, for instance, $x'_n \neq x_n$; then we have $u_{in} = -\sum_{h=1}^{n-1} u_{ih}(x'_h - x_h)/(x'_n - x_n)$. If we call K_1 the field generated over k by the $r(n-1)$ quantities u_{ih} for $1 \leqq i \leqq r$, $1 \leqq h \leqq n - 1$, this shows that the u_{in} are in $K_1(x, x')$, and therefore that the dimension of $(u_{1n}, \cdots, u_{rn})$ over $K_1(x)$ is not greater than the dimension of (x') over $K_1(x)$ and a fortiori not greater than the dimension of (x') over k, which we have shown to be less than r. As this contradicts the assumption that (u) is a set of rn independent variables over $k(x)$, we have thus proved our assertion that $\bar{z}$ is finite over $(\bar{v}) \rightarrow (v)$ with reference to K. By prop. 19, it follows from this that $\bar{z}$ is in the specialization-ring of (v, y) in $K(\bar{v}, \bar{y})$, which, by what we have proved above and by coroll. 1 of th. 17, Chap. IV, §7, is the same as the specialization-ring of (x) in $K(\bar{x})$; as $\bar{z}$ is in $k(\bar{x})$, it is therefore also, by prop. 6 of Chap. IV, §2, in the specialization-ring of (x) in $k(\bar{x})$. This completes our proof.

PROPOSITION 20. *Let P be a proper point of intersection of a variety V^r and of a linear variety L^{n-r} in S^n. Then we have $j(V \cdot L, P) = 1$ if and only if P is simple on V, and L transversal to the tangent linear variety to V at P.*

The direct assertion is contained in prop. 7 of §1. Conversely, th. 5 shows that, if P is proper in $V \cap L$, and if we have $j(V \cdot L, P) = 1$, then P is simple on V. Assume now that, this being so, L is not transversal to the tangent linear variety M^r to V at P, i.e. that the intersection $M \cap L$ has a dimension $s > 0$. Put $P = (x)$, and let k be a common field of definition for V and L, containing the coordinates x_i of P. Let L be defined over k by a minimal set of linear equations $F_i(X) = 0$ $(1 \leqq i \leqq r)$, with $F_i(X) = \sum_{j=1}^{n} c_{ij}X_j - a_i$ for $1 \leqq i \leqq r$; as (x) is in L, these equations can also be written as

$$\textstyle\sum_j c_{ij}(X_j - x_j) = 0 \quad (1 \leqq i \leqq r).$$

If $G_\rho(X) = 0$ $(1 \leqq \rho \leqq n - r)$ is a minimal set of linear equations for M, prop. 14 of Chap. IV, §5, shows that $M \cap L$ is defined by the set of equations $G_\rho(X) = 0$, $F_i(X) = 0$, hence, by the coroll. of th. 9, Chap. IV, §5, that a minimal set of equations for $M \cap L$ consists of a maximal set of linearly independent equations among these; in such a maximal set, we can include the $n - r$ equations $G_\rho(X) = 0$, and, as it must consist of $n - s$ equations, we may then assume, after reordering the $F_i(X)$ if necessary, that it consists of the equations

$$G_\rho(X) = 0 \quad (1 \leqq \rho \leqq n - r), \qquad F_i(X) = 0 \quad (1 \leqq i \leqq r - s).$$

That being so, let N^{n-r+s} be the linear variety defined by the $r - s$ equations $F_i(X) = 0$ $(1 \leqq i \leqq r - s)$; this variety contains L, and we have

$$M \cap L = M \cap N.$$

As P is in $V \cap N$, it is in a component W of $V \cap N$, which is algebraic over k, and which, by prop. 1 of §1, has at least the dimension s. Let $(\bar{x})$ be a generic point of W over $\bar{k}$; then $(\bar{x})$ has the specialization (x) over $\bar{k}$, and has at least the dimension s over k, so that we have $(\bar{x}) \neq (x)$ since the x_i are in k. We can now apply prop. 10 of Chap. II, §3, to the specialization (x) of $(\bar{x})$ over $\bar{k}$, and to the n quantities $\bar{x}_j - x_j$ which are not all 0. This shows that there is a value j_0 of j, which we may assume to be $j_0 = n$, such that, if we put

$$\bar{z}_j = (\bar{x}_j - x_j)/(\bar{x}_n - x_n) \qquad (1 \leqq j \leqq n),$$

$(\bar{z})$ has a finite specialization (z) over $(\bar{x}) \to (x)$ with reference to $\bar{k}$; this implies that we have $\bar{x}_n \neq x_n$, and $\bar{z}_n = z_n = 1$. Then, if we put $t = 1/(\bar{x}_n - x_n)$, and $\bar{y}_j = x_j + t(\bar{x}_j - x_j) = x_j + \bar{z}_j$ for $1 \leqq j \leqq n$, the set $(\bar{y})$ has, over $(\bar{z}) \to (z)$, with reference to $\bar{k}$, the uniquely determined specialization (y) defined by $y_j = x_j + z_j$ $(1 \leqq j \leqq n)$. We can then apply prop. 20 of Chap. IV, §6, to V, to the points (x), $(\bar{x})$ and $(\bar{y})$, and to the field $\bar{k}$; this shows that (y) is in M. Also, as $(\bar{x})$ is in N, we have, for $1 \leqq i \leqq r - s$, $\sum_j c_{ij}(\bar{x}_j - x_j) = 0$, hence

$$\textstyle\sum_j c_{ij}(\bar{y}_j - x_j) = 0 \qquad (1 \leqq i \leqq r - s),$$

so that $(\bar{y})$ is in N; as N is defined over k, this implies, by th. 2 of Chap. IV, §1, that (y) is in N. As (y) is in M and in N, it is therefore in $M \cap N = M \cap L$, hence in L, so that we have $\sum_{j=1}^{n} c_{ij}(y_j - x_j) = 0$, i.e. $\sum_{j=1}^{n} c_{ij}z_j = 0$, hence $c_{in} = -\sum_{h=1}^{n-1} c_{ih}z_h$, for $1 \leqq i \leqq r$. Now let (u_{ih}), for $1 \leqq i \leqq r$, $1 \leqq h \leqq n-1$, be a set of $r(n-1)$ independent variables over $k(\bar{x})$; and define the r quantities u_{in}, for $1 \leqq i \leqq r$, by the relations $\sum_{j=1}^{n} u_{ij}(\bar{x}_j - x_j) = 0$, i.e. by

$$u_{in} = -\sum_{h=1}^{n-1} u_{ih}\bar{z}_h \qquad (1 \leqq i \leqq r).$$

As the u_{ih}, for $1 \leqq i \leqq r$, $1 \leqq h \leqq n-1$, are independent variables over the field $k(\bar{x}) = k(\bar{x}, \bar{z})$, the coroll. of th. 5, Chap. II, §1, shows that (x, z, c_{ih}) is a specialization of $(\bar{x}, \bar{z}, u_{ih})$ over k; then, by prop. 13 of Chap. II, §4, the r quantities $u_{in} = -\sum_{h=1}^{n-1} u_{ih}\bar{z}_h$ have over that specialization, with reference to $\bar{k}$, the uniquely determined specializations $c_{in} = -\sum_{h=1}^{n-1} c_{ih}z_h$; therefore (x, z, c_{ij}), with $1 \leqq i \leqq r$, $1 \leqq j \leqq n$, is a specialization of $(\bar{x}, \bar{z}, u_{ij})$ over $\bar{k}$. This shows in the first place that the set of equations $\sum_j c_{ij}(X_j - x_j) = 0$ $(1 \leqq i \leqq r)$, which defines L, is a specialization over $\bar{k}$ of the set of equations

$$\textstyle\sum_j u_{ij}(X_j - x_j) = 0 \qquad (1 \leqq i \leqq r),$$

and therefore, by prop. 16 of Chap. IV, §5, that the latter set defines a linear variety $\bar{L}^{n-r}$. Moreover, (x) and $(\bar{x})$ satisfy the equations for $\bar{L}$; applying prop. 6 of §1 to the sets of equations for L and for $\bar{L}$, to either one of the points (x) and $(\bar{x})$ in $V \cap \bar{L}$, and to the proper point of intersection (x) of V and L, we see that (x) and $(\bar{x})$ are both proper in $V \cap \bar{L}$. Let now $(\bar{P}^{(1)}, \cdots, \bar{P}^{(d)})$ be a complete set of intersections of V and $\bar{L}$; by th. 2 of §1, both (x) and $(\bar{x})$ must occur among the $\bar{P}^{(\nu)}$, and, as we have $(\bar{x}) \neq (x)$, we may assume that we have $\bar{P}^{(1)} = (x)$, $\bar{P}^{(2)} = (\bar{x})$. Let $(P^{(1)}, \cdots, P^{(d)})$ be a specialization of $(\bar{P}^{(1)}, \cdots, \bar{P}^{(d)})$ over $(\bar{x}, u_{ij}) \to (x, c_{ij})$ with reference to $\bar{k}$; this, after the removal of any pseudopoints which may occur among the $P^{(\nu)}$, gives a complete set of intersections of V and L. But we have $P^{(1)} = P^{(2)} = (x)$; this contradicts the assumption $j(V \cdot L, P) = 1$.

PROPOSITION 21. *Let V^r be a variety, and L^{n-s} a linear variety, in S^n; let W be a component of $V \cap L$, and P a point on W. Then P is simple on V, and L transversal to the tangent linear variety to V at P, if and only if the component W of $V \cap L$ is proper and of multiplicity* 1, *has P as a simple point, and is the only component of $V \cap L$ which contains P.*

The fact that our condition is necessary is contained in prop. 16 of §2, combined with th. 5. As to the converse, assume that W is proper, $j(V \cdot L, W)$ equal to 1, P simple on W, and that P is on no other component of $V \cap L$ than W; and let M^{n-r+s} be a linear variety through P, transversal to the tangent linear variety to W at P. Let $n - d$ be the dimension of $L \cap M$, so that, by prop. 1 of §1 (or by prop. 14 of Chap. IV, §5), we have $d \leqq r$. As P is in the intersection of V and of $L \cap M$, it is in a component X of that intersection, which, by prop. 1 of §1, has at least the dimension $r - d$. Then X is contained in V and in L, hence in some component Z of $V \cap L$; as P is in X, it is also in Z, so that Z must be the same as W. Therefore X is in $W \cap M$; as it contains P, and as P, by prop. 7 of §1, is proper in $W \cap M$, this implies that X is reduced to P, hence that P is proper in the intersection of V and of $L \cap M$, and also that we have $r - d = 0$, so that M is transversal to L. We can now apply prop. 15 of §2 to V, to $L \cap M$, and to P; this shows that $j[V \cdot (L \cap M), P]$ is equal to the product of $j(V \cdot L, W)$, which we have assumed to be 1, and of $j(W \cdot M, P)$, which is 1 by prop. 7 of §1. Therefore, by prop. 20, P is simple on V, and $L \cap M$ is transversal to the tangent linear variety N to V at P; hence $N \cap L \cap M$ is reduced to P; this, by prop. 1 of §1 (or by prop. 14 of Chap. IV, §5), implies that $N \cap L$ has at most the dimension $r - s$, i.e. that L is transversal to N.

CHAPTER VI

GENERAL INTERSECTION-THEORY

1. Definition of the symbol $i(A \cdot B, C; U)$. In this chapter, we shall constantly have to consider the product $S^N \times S^N$ of a space S^N by itself, and frequently products of more such factors. If the symbols $X_1, \cdots, X_N$ are used to denote the indeterminates in the equations for varieties in S^N, then we use the symbols $X_1, \cdots, X_N, X'_1, \cdots, X'_N$ for the indeterminates in the equations of varieties in $S^N \times S^N$. For instance, if two varieties U and V in S^N are respectively defined by the sets of equations $F_\mu(X) = 0$ $(1 \leqq \mu \leqq m)$ and $G_\nu(X) = 0$ $(1 \leqq \nu \leqq n)$, then, according to th. 5 of Chap. IV, §3, a set of equations for the product $U \times V$ in $S^N \times S^N$ will be $F_\mu(X) = 0$ $(1 \leqq \mu \leqq m)$, $G_\nu(X') = 0$ $(1 \leqq \nu \leqq n)$. As usual, we write (X) for $(X_1, \cdots, X_N)$, (X') for $(X'_1, \cdots, X'_N)$, and also $(X - X')$ for $(X_1 - X'_1, \cdots, X_N - X'_N)$, $(X - x)$ for $(X_1 - x_1, \cdots, X_N - x_N)$ if (x) is a set of N quantities, etc. For a product $S^N \times S^N \times S^N$ of three factors identical to the space S^N, we use in a similar manner the symbols

$$(X, X', X'') = (X_1, \cdots, X_N, X'_1, \cdots, X'_N, X''_1, \cdots, X''_N)$$

for writing equations of varieties in that product.

We shall also have to consider such products as $(S^N \times S^M) \times (S^N \times S^M)$; this is a product of two identical factors, each of which is the product of a space S^N and of a space S^M (where N and M may differ or be equal). If we use, in the manner illustrated in Chap. IV, §3, the indeterminates

$$(X, Y) = (X_1, \cdots, X_N, Y_1, \cdots, Y_M)$$

for the equations of varieties in $S^N \times S^M$, then we shall use (X, Y, X', Y') for the space $(S^N \times S^M) \times (S^N \times S^M)$. It should be observed once more (as we have done in Chap. IV, §3) that products such as $(S^N \times S^M) \times (S^N \times S^M)$, $S^N \times S^M \times S^N \times S^M$, $(S^N \times S^M \times S^N) \times S^M$, etc., are one and the same space, but that they differ as products; it is when we speak of the projections of a variety in that space that it has to be made clear how that space is to be considered as a product, and on which factor or partial product the projection is being taken, since otherwise the notion of projection would be meaningless.

In a product-space, a permutation of the factors can be effected by a suitable permutation of the coordinates of the points in that space, and by a corresponding permutation of the indeterminates used in writing the equations of the varieties in that space; such a permutation should always be understood to be applied simultaneously to all the points and all the varieties in the space under consideration. For instance, if the second and third factor of the product

$$S^N \times S^M \times S^N \times S^M$$

are interchanged (as will be done in the proof of th. 7, §2), this product is transformed into $S^N \times S^N \times S^M \times S^M$; if a variety in the former product is the locus of a point (x, y, x', y') over a field k, where (x), (y), (x') and (y') are the projections of that point on the four factors of that product, respectively, then the transform of this variety by the given permutation is the locus of (x, x', y, y') over k. If, at the same time, we denote by (X, Y, X', Y') the indeterminates for the former product-space, and by (X, X', Y, Y') the indeterminates for the latter, then a set of equations for a variety in the former space remains a set of equations for the transform of that variety, in the latter space, by the given permutation. The definition of the symbol $j(V \cdot L, W)$ in Chap. V, §§1–2, shows that it is invariant under any permutation of coordinates, simultaneously effected on V, L and W; in particular, if the ambient space is given as a product-space, it is invariant under any permutation of the factors in that product.

The indeterminates in the product-space $S^N \times S^N$ being denoted by (X, X'), th. 9 of Chap. IV, §5, shows that the set of equations $X_i - X'_i = 0$ $(1 \leqq i \leqq N)$ defines in that space a linear variety of dimension N, which will be called the *diagonal* of $S^N \times S^N$ and will be denoted by Δ_0. If (t) is a generic point of S^N over a field k, i.e. a set of N independent variables over k, then the point (t, t) is in Δ_0, and therefore, by th. 2 of Chap. IV, §1, is a generic point of Δ_0 over k; it follows from this that the projections of Δ_0 on the two factors of the product $S^N \times S^N$ are those factors themselves, and that the projection from Δ_0 to either one of them is regular at every point. Therefore, according to the definitions of Chap. IV, §7, Δ_0 is a birational correspondence between S^N and itself, which is everywhere biregular, i.e. biregular at every point and along every variety in S^N. Every point of Δ_0 must be of the form (x, x), so that every such point, hence also every subvariety of Δ_0, has the same projection on both factors of $S^N \times S^N$; in other words, every point, and every subvariety, of S^N corresponds regularly to itself by the birational correspondence Δ_0. If U is any variety in S^N, then the subvariety of Δ_0 which has the projection U on either one of the factors of $S^N \times S^N$ will be denoted by Δ_U and will be called *the diagonal of the product* $U \times U$, in which it is contained by coroll. 5 of th. 6, Chap. IV, §3.

PROPOSITION 1. *If U is any variety in a space S^N, the diagonal Δ_U is a birational correspondence between U and itself, which is everywhere biregular, and by which every point and every subvariety of U corresponds regularly to itself. If U is the locus of a point P over a field k, then Δ_U is the locus of (P, P) over k. Moreover, every subvariety of Δ_U is of the form Δ_V, where V is a subvariety of U; conversely, if V is any subvariety of U, then Δ_V is contained in Δ_U, and we have*

$$\Delta_V = \Delta_U \cap (V \times U) = \Delta_U \cap (U \times V) = \Delta_U \cap (V \times V).$$

The first assertion follows from coroll. 4 of th. 17, Chap. IV, §7, applied to the diagonal Δ_0 of $S^N \times S^N$, to the subvariety U of S^N, and to an arbitrary subvariety or point of U; the second assertion follows from coroll. 2 of the same theorem. It also follows from the same results that, if a subvariety of Δ_U has the projection V on either one of the two factors of the product $U \times U$, then that subvariety is Δ_V, and that conversely, if V is a given subvariety of U, Δ_V is the subvariety of Δ_U with the projection V on U. It now follows from coroll. 5 of th. 6, Chap. IV, §3, that Δ_V is contained in every one of the three intersections which occur in the final formula of our proposition; on the other hand, every component of any one of these intersections, being contained in Δ_U, must be of the form Δ_Z, where in every case Z must be contained in V by the same corollary; those three intersections are therefore all contained in Δ_V. This completes our proof.

PROPOSITION 2. *Let U, A and B be three varieties in S^N. Then we have $\Delta_U \cap (A \times B) = \Delta_U \cap \Delta_A \cap \Delta_B$; and the components of $\Delta_U \cap (A \times B)$ are the varieties Δ_C, where C is any one of the components of $U \cap A \cap B$.*

If a point of $S^N \times S^N$ is in $\Delta_U \cap (A \times B)$, then it is in Δ_0, and its projection on either factor of the product S^N is in U, in A and in B, so that such a point is in $\Delta_U \cap \Delta_A \cap \Delta_B$; the converse follows from the fact that the projections, on the two factors of $S^N \times S^N$, of any point of $\Delta_A \cap \Delta_B$ are in $A \cap B$, so that such a point must be in $A \times B$. A component of $\Delta_U \cap \Delta_A \cap \Delta_B$ must then be of the form Δ_Z, where Z must be contained in $U \cap A \cap B$ and must be maximal in that intersection; the converse also follows from prop. 1.

Now, k being a field, let the $F_i(X) = \sum_{j=1}^N c_{ij}X_j$, for $1 \leqq i \leqq n$, be n linearly independent linear forms in $k[X]$; then the forms

$$F_i(X - X') = \sum_{j=1}^N c_{ij}(X_j - X'_j),$$

for $1 \leqq i \leqq n$, are n linearly independent linear forms in $k[X, X']$; therefore, by th. 9 of Chap. IV, §5, the set of equations $F_i(X - X') = 0$ $(1 \leqq i \leqq n)$ defines in $S^N \times S^N$ a linear variety Λ^{2N-n}; and this variety contains the diagonal Δ_0 of $S^N \times S^N$, for, if (t) is a generic point of S^N over k, the point (t, t) is a generic point of Δ_0 over k, and is in Λ since it satisfies the equations for Λ. Varieties such as Λ will play an essential part in this chapter.

PROPOSITION 3. *Let U^n be a variety, defined over a field k in S^N; let P be a simple point on U, and let the forms $F_i(X) = \sum_{j=1}^N c_{ij}X_j$, for $1 \leqq i \leqq n$, be a uniformizing set of linear forms for U at P, with coefficients in k. Let the forms*

$$\bar{F}_i(X) = \sum_{j=1}^N u_{ij}X_j \qquad (1 \leqq i \leqq n)$$

be such that $(c) = (c_{ij})$ is a specialization of the set $(u) = (u_{ij})$ over k; and let $\bar{\Lambda}$ be the linear variety defined in $S^N \times S^N$ by the set of equations

$$\bar{F}_i(X - X') = 0 \qquad (1 \leqq i \leqq n).$$

Then, if a point in $(U \times U) \cap \bar{\Lambda}$ is such that it has the specialization (P, P) over $(u) \to (c)$ with reference to k, that point must be in Δ_0.

Put $P = (x)$; and consider a point in $(U \times U) \cap \bar{\Lambda}$, with the specialization (x, x) over $(u) \to (c)$ with reference to k; by th. 5 of Chap. IV, §3, this point can be written as (x', x''), with (x') and (x'') in U. By the definition of a uniformizing set, the n forms $F_i(X)$ are linearly independent; and, if we denote by $\mathfrak{S}^n$ the set of linear equations consisting of the n equations $F_i(X - x) = 0$ $(1 \leqq i \leqq n)$, this is a minimal set for a linear variety L^{N-n} which is transversal to the tangent linear variety to U at P; therefore, by prop. 7 of Chap. V, §1, P is a proper intersection of V and of L, with the multiplicity 1. Let $\bar{\mathfrak{S}}^n$ be the set of equations $\bar{F}_i(X - x') = 0$ $(1 \leqq i \leqq n)$; as (c, x, x) is a specialization of (u, x', x'') over k, $\mathfrak{S}^n$ is a specialization of $\bar{\mathfrak{S}}^n$ over k, so that, by prop. 16 of Chap. IV, §5, $\bar{\mathfrak{S}}^n$ defines a linear variety $\bar{L}^{N-n}$; as the point (x', x'') is in $\bar{\Lambda}$ and therefore satisfies the equations $\bar{F}_i(X - X') = 0$, we have $\bar{F}_i(x') = \bar{F}_i(x'')$ for $1 \leqq i \leqq n$, so that both (x') and (x'') are in $\bar{L}$. Then prop. 6 of Chap. V, §1, shows that both (x') and (x'') are proper intersections of U and $\bar{L}$. That being so, let $(\bar{P}^{(1)}, \cdots, \bar{P}^{(d)})$ be a complete set of intersections of U and $\bar{L}$, and let $(P^{(1)}, \cdots, P^{(d)})$ be a specialization of that set over $(u, x', x'') \rightarrow (c, x, x)$ with reference to k; the latter set, after the removal of any pseudopoints which may occur among the $P^{(\nu)}$, gives a complete set of intersections of U and L, so that P must occur in it once and no more than once. On the other hand, both (x') and (x'') must occur among the $\bar{P}^{(\nu)}$; if they were distinct, we could assume $\bar{P}^{(1)} = (x')$, $\bar{P}^{(2)} = (x'')$, and this would imply $P^{(1)} = P^{(2)} = (x)$. As this would be a contradiction, we must therefore have $(x') = (x'')$, so that (x', x'') is in Δ_0.

THEOREM 1. *Let A and B be two subvarieties of a variety U^n in S^N. Let Z be a variety contained in $A \cap B$, and simple on U. Let the $F_i(X)$, for $1 \leqq i \leqq n$, be a uniformizing set of linear forms for U along Z; and let Λ be the linear variety defined in $S^N \times S^N$ by the set of equations $F_i(X - X') = 0$ $(1 \leqq i \leqq n)$. Then the variety Δ_Z is contained in $(A \times B) \cap \Lambda$; and the components of $(A \times B) \cap \Lambda$ which contain Δ_Z are the varieties Δ_C, where C is any one of the components of $A \cap B$ which contain Z.*

If Z is contained in $A \cap B$, then Δ_Z is contained in $(A \times B) \cap \Delta_0$ by prop. 2, hence a fortiori in $(A \times B) \cap \Lambda$. Now let k be a common field of definition for U, A, B and Z, containing the coefficients in the $F_i(X)$; let P be a generic point of Z over k; then P is simple on U, and the $F_i(X)$ are a uniformizing set of linear forms for U at P. Let W be a component of $(A \times B) \cap \Lambda$, containing Δ_Z; this must be algebraic over k, by th. 8 of Chap. IV, §4; and, by th. 5 of Chap. IV, §3, a generic point of W over $\bar{k}$ can be written as (P', P''), with P' in A and P'' in B, and therefore is in $U \times U$. As Δ_Z is in W, (P, P) is a specialization of (P', P'') over $\bar{k}$. We can now apply prop. 3 to (P', P''), to (P, P), to the forms $F_i(X)$, and to the field $\bar{k}$, taking for the forms $\bar{F}_i(X)$ of that proposition the forms $F_i(X)$ themselves, so that the variety $\bar{\Lambda}$ of that proposition is in the present case the same as Λ. This shows that the point (P', P''), hence also its locus W over $\bar{k}$, is contained in Δ_0. As W is contained in $A \times B$, it must therefore be contained in a component of $\Delta_0 \cap (A \times B)$, hence, by prop. 2, in a variety Δ_C, where C is a component of $A \cap B$ which must contain Z since W contains Δ_Z; as this variety Δ_C, by what was proved above, is contained in $(A \times B) \cap \Lambda$, and as W is maximal in that intersection, this implies that we have $W = \Delta_C$. Conversely, if C is any component of $A \cap B$, containing Z, then Δ_C, by what we have proved, is contained in $(A \times B) \cap \Lambda$, hence in a component W of that intersection, which is itself, as we have proved, contained in $\Delta_0 \cap (A \times B)$; since Δ_C, by prop. 2, is maximal in the latter intersection, this gives $\Delta_C = W$.

COROLLARY 1. *Let A^r, B^s be two subvarieties of a variety U^n, and let C be a component of $A \cap B$. Then, if C is simple on U, its dimension is at least equal to $r + s - n$.*

Taking for the $F_i(X)$ any uniformizing set of linear forms for U along C, and defining Λ as in th. 1, we see, by th. 1, that Δ_C is a component of $(A \times B) \cap \Lambda$, hence, by prop. 1 of Chap. V, §1, that it has at least the dimension $r + s - n$.

COROLLARY 2. *Let the A_i, for $1 \leqq i \leqq m$, be m subvarieties of a variety U^n, respectively of dimension $n - r_i$; let C be a component of the intersection of the A_i. Then, if C is simple on U, its dimension is at least equal to $n - \sum_i r_i$.*

We proceed by induction on m; C being as stated, it is contained in some component D of $A_1 \cap A_2 \cap \cdots \cap A_{m-1}$. As C is simple on U, D, which contains C, is simple on U, and therefore, by the induction assumption, has a dimension $d \geqq n - \sum_{i=1}^{m-1} r_i$. Then C is in $D \cap A_m$, and is maximal in that intersection, since otherwise it would not be maximal in $A_1 \cap A_2 \cap \cdots \cap A_m$; therefore, by coroll. 1, it has at least the dimension $d - r_m$.

If A^r and B^s are two subvarieties of a variety U^n, a component C of $A \cap B$ will be called a *proper component of $A \cap B$ in U*, or *on U*, if it is simple on U and has the dimension $r + s - n$; one may omit the reference to the embedding variety U when it is clearly indicated by the context, and this applies in particular to proper components of the intersection of a variety V and of a linear variety L in a space S^n, as defined in Chap. V, where the reference should be understood to be to the space S^n itself.

More generally, if the A_i are subvarieties of a variety U^n, respectively of dimension $n - r_i$, then a component C of their intersection will be called a *proper component of $A_1 \cap A_2 \cap \cdots \cap A_m$ in U*, or *on U*, if it is simple on U and has the dimension $n - \sum_i r_i$. The existence of such a component implies that $\sum_i r_i$ is not greater than n, and also that the A_i are all simple on U.

THEOREM 2. *Let A and B be two subvarieties of a variety U^n in S^N, and let C be a proper component of $A \cap B$ on U. Let the $F_i(X)$, for $1 \leqq i \leqq n$, be a uniformizing set of linear forms for U along C, and let Λ be the variety defined in $S^N \times S^N$ by the set of equations $F_i(X - X') = 0$ $(1 \leqq i \leqq n)$. Then Δ_C is a proper component of $(A \times B) \cap \Lambda$ in $S^N \times S^N$; and the multiplicity $j[(A \times B) \cdot \Lambda, \Delta_C]$ depends only upon U, A, B and C, and not upon the choice of the uniformizing set of forms $F_i(X)$.*

The first point is contained in th. 1, when dimensions are taken into account. Now let r and s be the dimensions of A and of B, respectively; let the $F_i(X)$ and the $F'_i(X)$ be two uniformizing sets of linear forms for U along C, and let Λ and Λ' be the varieties respectively defined in $S^N \times S^N$ by the set of equations $\mathfrak{S}^n$ consisting of the n equations $F_i(X - X') = 0$ $(1 \leqq i \leqq n)$, and by the set of equations $F'_i(X - X') = 0$ $(1 \leqq i \leqq n)$. Let k be a common field of definition for U, A, B and C, containing all the coefficients in the $F_i(X)$ and in the $F'_i(X)$. Put $F_i(X) = \sum_{j=1}^{N} c_{ij}X_j$, for $1 \leqq i \leqq n$; and put $\bar{F}_i(X) = \sum_{j=1}^{N} u_{ij}X_j$, for $1 \leqq i \leqq n$, where $(u) = (u_{ij})$ is a set of Nn independent variables over k. The $\bar{F}_i(X)$ also are then a uniformizing set of linear forms for U along C; let $\bar{\Lambda}$ be the variety defined in $S^N \times S^N$ by the set of equations $\bar{\mathfrak{S}}^n$ consisting of the n equations $\bar{F}_i(X - X') = 0$ $(1 \leqq i \leqq n)$. Furthermore, let $\mathfrak{T}^{r+s-n}$ be a set of $r + s - n$ linear equations in the indeterminates (X, X'), generic over the field $k(u)$, so that the set (w) of the coefficients in these equations is a set of $(r + s - n)$ $(2N + 1)$ independent variables over $k(u)$; and let M be the linear variety defined by that set in $S^N \times S^N$. Then, by th. 1 of Chap. V, §1, there is a point in $\Delta_C \cap M$, which is algebraic over the field $K = k(w)$, and is a generic point of Δ_C over k, hence of the form (P, P), where P is a generic point of C over k, this implying that P is simple on U. Now let μ, μ' and $\bar{\mu}$ be the intersection-multiplicities of $A \times B$ and, respectively, Λ, Λ', and $\bar{\Lambda}$, along Δ_C; what we have to prove is that μ and μ' are equal, and this will be done by showing that both are equal to $\bar{\mu}$. By th. 4 of Chap. V, §2, and by the definition of multiplicities, μ and $\bar{\mu}$ are equal to the intersection-multiplicities at (P, P) of $A \times B$ and $\Lambda \cap M$, and of $A \times B$ and $\bar{\Lambda} \cap M$, respectively. As (u) and (w) are independent over k, (u) is a set of independent variables over the field $K = k(w)$, hence also over its algebraic closure $\bar{K}$; therefore $(c) = (c_{ij})$ is a specialization of the set $(u) = (u_{ij})$ over $\bar{K}$, so that the set $(\mathfrak{S}^n, \mathfrak{T}^{r+s-n})$, which is a minimal set of equations for $\Lambda \cap M$, is a specialization over $\bar{K}$ of the set $(\bar{\mathfrak{S}}^n, \mathfrak{T}^{r+s-n})$, which is a minimal set of equations for $\bar{\Lambda} \cap M$. This implies that a specialization over $(u) \rightarrow (c)$, with reference to $\bar{K}$, of a complete set of intersections of $A \times B$ and $\bar{\Lambda} \cap M$ gives, after the removal of pseudopoints if necessary, a complete set of intersections of $A \times B$ and $\Lambda \cap M$; as the point (P, P) occurs $\bar{\mu}$ times in the former set and μ times in the latter by th. 2 of Chap. V, §1, and as it is algebraic over K and therefore has no other specialization than itself over $\bar{K}$, it follows from this that we have $\mu \geqq \bar{\mu}$; and it also follows that μ and $\bar{\mu}$ must be equal if we show that no other point than (P, P), in the intersection of $A \times B$ and of $\bar{\Lambda} \cap M$, can have the specialization (P, P) over $(u) \rightarrow (c)$ with reference to $\bar{K}$. In fact, consider such a point, which, being in $A \times B$ and in $\bar{\Lambda} \cap M$, is a fortiori in $(U \times U) \cap \bar{\Lambda}$; by prop. 3, this point is then in Δ_0, and therefore can be written as (P', P'), where P' is in A and in B by th. 5 of Chap. IV, §3, and has the specialization P over $\bar{K}$ and a fortiori over $\bar{k}$. The locus of P' over $\bar{k}$ must then contain the locus C of P over $\bar{k}$; as it is contained in A and in B, and as C is maximal in $A \cap B$, it is no other than C itself. This implies that (P', P') is in Δ_C; as it is in M, it is therefore, by th. 1 of Chap. V, §1, a conjugate of (P, P) over K; as it has the specialization (P, P) over $\bar{K}$, it must be the same point as (P, P). This completes the proof of the equality $\mu = \bar{\mu}$. As the same proof can be applied to show that we have $\mu' = \bar{\mu}$, it follows from this that we have $\mu = \mu'$, as stated by our theorem.

As in th. 2, let A and B be two subvarieties of a variety U^n in S^N, and let C be a proper component of $A \cap B$ in U; then, if the $F_i(X)$, for $1 \leqq i \leqq n$, are any uniformizing set of linear forms for U along C, and if Λ is the variety defined in $S^N \times S^N$ by the set of equations $F_i(X - X') = 0$ $(1 \leqq i \leqq n)$, the integer $j[(A \times B)\cdot\Lambda, \Delta_C]$, which, by th. 2, depends only upon A, B, C and U, will be denoted by $i(A\cdot B, C; U)$, and will be called *the intersection-multiplicity of A and B along C in U*, or *the multiplicity of C* as a component of $A \cap B$ in U. We shall now justify our terminology by showing that this definition includes the definition of intersection-multiplicities in Chap. V, §§1–2, as a special case.

PROPOSITION 4. *Let W be a proper component, in a space S^n, of the intersection of a variety V and of a linear variety L; then we have* $i(V\cdot L, W; S^n) = j(V\cdot L, W)$.

As the X_i, for $1 \leqq i \leqq n$, are a uniformizing set of linear forms for S^n at every point, we can take for the variety Λ, in the definition of the symbol $i(V\cdot L, W; S^n)$, the variety defined in the space $S^n \times S^n$ by the equations $X_i - X'_i = 0$ $(1 \leqq i \leqq n)$, i.e. the diagonal Δ_0 of $S^n \times S^n$; that symbol, therefore, has the value

$$j[(V \times L)\cdot\Delta_0, \Delta_W];$$

this will be calculated by applying prop. 15 of Chap. V, §2, to the variety $V \times S^n$, and to the linear variety $(S^n \times L) \cap \Delta_0$, in the space $S^n \times S^n$. By prop. 2, we have $\Delta_L = (S^n \times L) \cap \Delta_0$; if dimensions are taken into account, this shows that $S^n \times L$ and Δ_0 are transversal to each other in $S^n \times S^n$. Moreover, by prop. 3, Δ_W is a component of $(V \times S^n) \cap \Delta_L$, and a proper one if dimensions are taken into account. That being so, put $\mu = j[(V \times S^n)\cdot\Delta_L, \Delta_W]$; this can be expressed by prop. 15 of Chap. V, §2, applied to $V \times S^n$, to

$$\Delta_L = (S^n \times L) \cap \Delta_0,$$

and to Δ_W; since, by coroll. 4 of th. 8, Chap. IV, §4, the only component of $(V \times S^n) \cap (S^n \times L)$ is $V \times L$, this shows that μ is the product of

$$j[(V \times S^n)\cdot(S^n \times L), V \times L]$$

and of $j[(V \times L)\cdot\Delta_0, \Delta_W]$. The second one of these two factors is equal to $i(V\cdot L, W; S^n)$, as we have seen; the first one, by prop. 17 of Chap. V, §2, is the product of $j(V\cdot S^n, V)$ and of $j(S^n\cdot L, L)$, which are both equal to 1 by prop. 16 of Chap. V, §2; we have thus proved that μ is equal to $i(V\cdot L, W; S^n)$. On the other hand, we can also write $\Delta_L = \Delta_0 \cap (S^n \times L)$, and again apply prop. 15 of Chap. V, §2, so as to obtain another expression for μ. Since, by prop. 2, the only component of $(V \times S^n) \cap \Delta_0$ is Δ_V, this shows that μ is the product of $j[(V \times S^n)\cdot\Delta_0, \Delta_V]$ and of $j[\Delta_V\cdot(S^n \times L), \Delta_W]$. The first one of these two factors is equal to 1; for, by coroll. 1 of th. 13, Chap. IV, §6, Δ_V is simple on $V \times S^n$, and, by that theorem, the tangent linear variety to $V \times S^n$ at any simple point of $V \times S^n$ is of the form $M \times S^n$; as we have, by prop. 2, $\Delta_M = \Delta_0 \cap (M \times S^n)$, Δ_0 is transversal to every variety of that form, and therefore, by prop. 16 of Chap. V, §1, we have $j[(V \times S^n) \cdot \Delta_0, \Delta_V] = 1$, as we have asserted. This shows that we have $\mu = j[\Delta_V \cdot (S^n \times L), \Delta_W]$; and this is equal to $j(V \cdot L, W)$ by prop. 18 of Chap. V, §2, applied to Δ_V and Δ_W, to their projections V and W on the second factor of the product-space $S^n \times S^n$, and to the linear varieties $S^n \times L$ and L. This completes our proof.

2. Properties of the symbol $i(A \cdot B, C; U)$. In the first place, the definition of the symbol $i(A \cdot B, C; U)$ shows that, whenever it is defined, it is a positive integer, and that it is commutative in A and B, i.e. that we have

$$i(A \cdot B, C; U) = i(B \cdot A, C; U);$$

for, since the symbol is defined as being equal to $j[(A \times B) \cdot \Lambda, \Delta_C]$, where Λ is as stated in th. 2 of §1, interchanging A and B in the symbol $i(A \cdot B, C; U)$ amounts to interchanging the two factors in the product-space $S^N \times S^N$, and this transforms $A \times B$ into $B \times A$, Λ and Δ_C into themselves, and the j-symbol into itself. We shall now, in this § and the next, extend to the i-symbol all the properties which have been proved for the j-symbol in Chap. V, §2 and §3.

THEOREM 3. *Let A and B be two subvarieties of a variety U; let C be a proper component of $A \cap B$ in U; let K be a common field of definition for U, A, B and C, and let σ be an isomorphism of K on a field K'. Then C^σ is a proper component of $A^\sigma \cap B^\sigma$ in U^σ, and we have $i(A^\sigma \cdot B^\sigma, C^\sigma; U^\sigma) = i(A \cdot B, C; U)$.*

The first assertion follows from coroll. 3 of th. 8, Chap. IV, §4, and from coroll. 2 of th. 12, Chap. IV, §6, if dimensions are considered. Now call n and N the dimensions of U and of its ambient space S^N; put $F_i(X) = \sum_{j=1}^N u_{ij}X_j$ and $F'_i(X) = \sum_{j=1}^N u'_{ij}X_j$ for $1 \leqq i \leqq n$, where (u) is a set of Nn independent variables over K, and (u') a set of Nn independent variables over K'; let Λ and Λ' be the varieties respectively defined in $S^N \times S^N$ by the sets of equations $F_i(X - X') = 0$ $(1 \leqq i \leqq n)$ and $F'_i(X - X') = 0$ $(1 \leqq i \leqq n)$. By prop. 8 of Chap. I, §3, σ can be extended to an isomorphism σ_1 of $K(u)$ on $K'(u')$, transforming (u) into (u'). Then, by coroll. 1 of th. 3, Chap. IV, §2, σ_1 transforms Λ into Λ'; by prop. 4 of Chap. IV, §2, it transforms A, B, C into A^σ, B^σ, C^σ, respectively, and therefore it transforms $A \times B$ into $A^\sigma \times B^\sigma$ by coroll. 1 of th. 5, Chap. IV, §3, and Δ_C into Δ_{C^σ} by coroll. 5 of th. 17, Chap. IV, §7. Our theorem now follows from the definitions and from prop. 12 of Chap. V, §2.

THEOREM 4. *Let U be a variety, defined over a field k; let A and B be two subvarieties of U, both algebraic over k; let C be a proper component of $A \cap B$ in U; and let p^a, p^b and p^c be the orders of inseparability of A, of B and of C, respectively, over k. Then $i(A \cdot B, C; U)$ is a multiple of p^{c-a-b}.*

The statement of our theorem depends upon the fact that, since A and B are algebraic over k, C also is algebraic over k; this is a consequence of th. 8 of Chap. IV, §4, applied to A, B, C and to the field $\bar{k}$. By definition, $i(A \cdot B, C; U)$ is equal to $j[(A \times B) \cdot \Lambda, \Delta_C]$, where Λ is defined as in th. 2 of §1 from a uniformizing set of linear forms $F_i(X)$ for U along C. The $F_i(X)$ can always be chosen in $k[X]$, e.g. from among the X_j; then Λ is defined over k. By its definition, the variety Δ_C is algebraic over k, and has the same order of inseparability p^c over k as C itself. The product $A \times B$ also is algebraic over k by th. 5 of Chap. IV, §3; and, by the definitions and by prop. 28 of Chap. I, §8, its order of inseparability over k is not greater than p^{a+b}. Our result now follows from this by prop. 13 of Chap. V, §2.

The following result is the associative property of intersections.

THEOREM 5. *Let A, B and C be subvarieties of a variety U; let D be a proper component of $A \cap B \cap C$ in U; let the X_λ be those components of $A \cap B$ which contain D, and let the Y_μ be those components of $B \cap C$ which contain D. Then, for every λ, X_λ is a proper component of $A \cap B$, and D a proper component of $X_\lambda \cap C$, on U; for every μ, Y_μ is a proper component of $B \cap C$, and D a proper component of $A \cap Y_\mu$, on U; and we have*

$$\textstyle\sum_\lambda i(A \cdot B, X_\lambda; U) \cdot i(X_\lambda \cdot C, D; U) = \sum_\mu i(A \cdot Y_\mu, D; U) \cdot i(B \cdot C, Y_\mu; U).$$

The assumption on D implies that it is simple on U; as the X_λ and the Y_μ contain D, they are also simple on U. Let n, q, r, s and N be the dimensions of U, of A, of B, of C, and of the ambient space S^N, respectively; our assumption on D implies that its dimension is $q + r + s - 2n$. The variety D must be maximal in $X_\lambda \cap C$, for otherwise it would not be maximal in $A \cap B \cap C$; by coroll. 1 of th. 1, §1, this implies that X_λ has at most the dimension $q + r - n$; on the other hand, by the same corollary applied to A, B and X_λ, X_λ has at least that dimension. This shows that, for every λ, the dimension of X_λ is $q + r - n$, hence that X_λ is proper in $A \cap B$, and D proper in $X_\lambda \cap C$, on U. A similar proof holds for the corresponding assertions on the Y_μ. Now let the $F_i(X)$, for $1 \leqq i \leqq n$, be a uniformizing set of linear forms for U along D, hence also, by prop. 25 of Chap. IV, §6, along the X_λ and the Y_μ; and let Λ be the variety defined in $S^N \times S^N$ by the set of linear equations

$$F_i(X - X') = 0 \qquad (1 \leqq i \leqq n).$$

Let k be a common field of definition for U, A, B and C, containing the coefficients in the $F_i(X)$. Then D is algebraic over k. Let P be a generic point of D over $\bar{k}$; and let W be the locus of (P, P, P) over $\bar{k}$ in $S^N \times S^N \times S^N$. The variety W is in $A \times B \times C$ by coroll. 5 of th. 6, Chap. IV, §3; moreover, considered as a subvariety of the product $(S^N \times S^N) \times S^N$, it has the projection Δ_D on the first factor $S^N \times S^N$ of that product, and therefore, by coroll. 5 of th. 6, Chap. IV, §3, it is contained in $\Delta_D \times S^N$ and a fortiori in $\Lambda \times S^N$; similarly, by considering it as a subvariety of $S^N \times (S^N \times S^N)$, we see that it is contained in $S^N \times \Lambda$; therefore it is contained in the intersection L of the linear varieties $\Lambda \times S^N$ and $S^N \times \Lambda$. If we denote by (X, X', X'') the indeterminates in the equations of varieties in $S^N \times S^N \times S^N$, then $\Lambda \times S^N$ and $S^N \times \Lambda$ can respectively be defined by the sets of equations $F_i(X - X') = 0$ $(1 \leqq i \leqq n)$ and $F_i(X' - X'') = 0$ $(1 \leqq i \leqq n)$; as these $2n$ equations are linearly independent, they are therefore a minimal set of equations for L; this implies that L has the dimension $3N - 2n$, and also that $\Lambda \times S^N$ and $S^N \times \Lambda$ are transversal to each other in $S^N \times S^N \times S^N$. As W is contained in $(A \times B \times C) \cap L$, it is contained in some component W' of that intersection. Then the variety W' is contained in $A \times B \times C$ and in $\Lambda \times S^N$; we now show that every component of

$$(A \times B \times C) \cap (\Lambda \times S^N)$$

which contains W', hence also W, must be one of the varieties $\Delta_{X_\lambda} \times C$. In fact, such a component, by coroll. 4 of th. 8, Chap. IV, §4, is of the form $Z \times C$, where Z is a component of $(A \times B) \cap \Lambda$; and coroll. 3 of th. 6, Chap. IV, §3, shows that Z must contain the projection Δ_D of W on the first factor of $(S^N \times S^N) \times S^N$; therefore, by th. 1 of §1, Z is one of the varieties Δ_{X_λ}. In the same manner, one shows that every component of $(A \times B \times C) \cap (S^N \times \Lambda)$ which contains W' must be one of the varieties $A \times \Delta_{Y_\mu}$. Since W' is algebraic over k, let (P', Q', R') be a generic point of W' over $\bar{k}$; what we have just proved implies that (P', Q') is in one at least of the varieties Δ_{X_λ}, so that we have $P' = Q'$, and similarly that (Q', R') is in one of the Δ_{Y_μ}, so that we have $Q' = R'$. Therefore W' is the locus of (P', P', P') over $\bar{k}$, so that it has the same projection, viz. the locus of P' over $\bar{k}$, on all three factors of the product $S^N \times S^N \times S^N$; as W' is in $A \times B \times C$, this projection, by coroll. 5 of th. 6, Chap. IV, §3, must then be in A, in B and in C, hence in $A \cap B \cap C$; as it contains the projection D of W on any one of the factors of $S^N \times S^N \times S^N$, it is therefore no other than D since D is maximal in $A \cap B \cap C$, so that, by prop. 1 of Chap. IV, §1, P' is a generic specialization of P over $\bar{k}$; by that same proposition, this proves that we have $W' = W$.

We have thus shown that W is a component of $(A \times B \times C) \cap L$, and, if dimensions are taken into account, a proper one in $S^N \times S^N \times S^N$; we have also proved that the components of $(A \times B \times C) \cap (\Lambda \times S^N)$ which contain W are all of the form $\Delta_{X_\lambda} \times C$; conversely, every variety of that form is a component of $(A \times B \times C) \cap (\Lambda \times S^N)$ by th. 1 of §1 and coroll. 4 of th. 8, Chap. IV, §4, and W is contained in all of them by coroll. 5 of th. 6, Chap. IV, §3. We can now calculate the multiplicity $\mu = j[(A \times B \times C) \cdot L, W]$ by applying prop. 15 of Chap. V, §2, to $A \times B \times C$, to $L = (\Lambda \times S^N) \cap (S^N \times \Lambda)$, and to W; taking into account what we have just proved, and putting

$$\alpha_\lambda = j[(A \times B \times C) \cdot (\Lambda \times S^N), \Delta_{X_\lambda} \times C], \qquad \beta_\lambda = j[(\Delta_{X_\lambda} \times C) \cdot (S^N \times \Lambda), W],$$

we thus get $\mu = \sum_\lambda \alpha_\lambda \beta_\lambda$. With respect to α_λ, prop. 17 of Chap. V, §2, shows that it is the product of $j[(A \times B) \cdot \Lambda, \Delta_{X_\lambda}]$, and of $j(C \cdot S^N, C)$; the first of these is, by definition, equal to $i(A \cdot B, X_\lambda; U)$, while the second is equal to 1 by prop. 16 of Chap. V, §2. On the other hand, we can calculate β_λ by applying prop. 18 of Chap. V, §2, to the variety $\Delta_{X_\lambda} \times C$ in the product-space $S^N \times (S^N \times S^N)$, to its projection $X_\lambda \times C$ on the second factor $S^N \times S^N$ of that product, to the linear variety Λ in that second factor, and to the proper component Δ_D of $(X_\lambda \times C) \cap \Lambda$ in $S^N \times S^N$; for the projection from $\Delta_{X_\lambda} \times C$ to $X_\lambda \times C$ is regular along every subvariety of $X_\lambda \times C$. That being so, we thus find that β_λ is equal to $j[(X_\lambda \times C)\cdot\Lambda, \Delta_D]$, i.e., by definition, to $i(X_\lambda \cdot C, D; U)$. This proves that the multiplicity $\mu = \sum_\lambda \alpha_\lambda\beta_\lambda$ is equal to the left-hand side of the formula in our theorem. Now we calculate μ by applying again prop. 15 of Chap. V, §2, to $A \times B \times C$ and to the variety L, which we write this time as

$$L = (S^N \times \Lambda) \cap (\Lambda \times S^N);$$

proceeding exactly in the same manner, we find μ to be equal to the right-hand side of the formula in our theorem. This completes our proof.

We shall now extend to the symbol $i(A \cdot B, C; U)$ the criterion of multiplicity 1 which, for the symbol $j(V \cdot L, W)$, was first given as a sufficient condition in prop. 16 of Chap. V, §2, and then in more precise form, as a necessary and sufficient condition, in prop. 21 of Chap. V, §3. We first introduce a new definition.

Let A^r and B^s be two subvarieties of a variety U^n; and let P be a point in $A \cap B$; then we say that A and B are *transversal* to each other *at P in U* (or *on U*) if P is simple on U, on A and on B, and if the tangent linear varieties to A and to B at P have an intersection of dimension $r + s - n$; the dimension of that intersection must in any case be at least equal to $r + s - n$ by coroll. 1 of th. 1, §1, applied to the tangent linear varieties to A and to B at P, and to the tangent linear variety to U at P in which they are both contained by prop. 23 of Chap. IV, §6. In making a statement about transversality, one may occasionally omit the reference to the embedding variety U when it is clearly indicated by the context; this applies in particular to our definition of transversality for linear varieties in Chap. IV, §5, where it is understood that the embedding variety is the ambient space. If two linear varieties L and M, in a space S^n or more generally in a linear variety N, are transversal to each other at some point, then they are so at every point of their intersection; and this is the case if and only if their intersection is proper in N; for linear varieties, therefore, a statement on transversality need not include a reference to the point at which the varieties are transversal; such a reference will never be omitted in any other case.

THEOREM 6. *Let A and B be two subvarieties of a variety U; let C be a component of $A \cap B$, and let P be a point of C, simple on U. Then, if A and B are transversal to each other at P on U, the component C of $A \cap B$ is proper on U and of multiplicity 1, has P as a simple point, and is the only component of $A \cap B$ which contains P; conversely, if these conditions are fulfilled, then A and B are transversal to each other at P on U.*

Let n, r, s and N be the dimensions of U, of A, of B, and of the ambient space S^N, respectively. Let the $F_i(X)$, for $1 \leqq i \leqq n$, be a uniformizing set of linear forms for U at P, and let Λ be the variety defined in $S^N \times S^N$ by the set of equations $F_i(X - X') = 0$ $(1 \leqq i \leqq n)$. The $F_i(X)$ are then also a uniformizing set of linear forms for U along C, so that Δ_C, by th. 1 of §1, is a component of $(A \times B) \cap \Lambda$; and, by the definition of a uniformizing set, they are also a uniformizing set of linear forms at P for the tangent linear variety L^n to U at P. Now assume that P is simple on A and on B, and let M^r and N^s be the tangent linear varieties to A and to B at P, which are both contained in L^n. Then we can apply th. 1 of §1 to L, M and N, to Λ, and to the zero-dimensional variety Δ_P reduced to the point (P, P); this shows that the intersection $(M \times N) \cap \Lambda$ is the variety $\Delta_{M \cap N}$, hence has the same dimension as $M \cap N$; therefore $(M \times N) \cap \Lambda$ is proper in $S^N \times S^N$, i.e. Λ is transversal to $M \times N$ in $S^N \times S^N$, if and only if $M \cap N$ has the dimension $r + s - n$. Now assume that this is so, i.e., by definition, that A and B are transversal to each other at P; as $M \times N$, by th. 13 of Chap. IV, §6, is the tangent linear variety to $A \times B$ at (P, P), we can now apply prop. 21 of Chap. V, §3, to $A \times B$, to Λ, to the component Δ_C of $(A \times B) \cap \Lambda$, and to the point (P, P); together with th. 1 of §1, applied to U, A, B, Λ, and to the zero-dimensional variety Δ_P reduced to (P, P), and with th. 2 of §1, applied to U, A, B, C and Λ, this proves our first assertion. Conversely, the same results show that, if C is proper in $A \cap B$ on U, has the multiplicity 1, and is the only component of $A \cap B$ containing P, then Δ_C is proper in $(A \times B) \cap \Lambda$ and of multiplicity 1, and is the only component of that intersection which contains (P, P); if, moreover, P is simple on C, then, by th. 14 of Chap. IV, §6, applied to Δ_C and to its projection C on S^N, the point (P, P) is simple on Δ_C. That being so, prop. 21 of Chap. V, §3, shows that (P, P) is simple on $A \times B$, hence that P is simple on A and on B by th. 13 of Chap. IV, §6, and that Λ is transversal in $S^N \times S^N$ to the tangent linear variety to $A \times B$ at (P, P). If we again call M^r and N^s the tangent linear varieties to A and to B at P, this means that Λ is transversal to $M \times N$ in $S^N \times S^N$, which implies, as we have shown above, that $M \cap N$ has the dimension $r + s - n$. This completes our proof.

Corollary. *Let A be a simple subvariety of a variety U. Then A is the only component of $A \cap U$, and a proper one in U; and we have $i(A \cdot U, A; U) = 1$.*

The first statement is obvious; the latter is a special case of th. 6.

3. Intersections in product-varieties. We shall now consider the properties of the i-symbol in a product-variety $U \times V$.

Theorem 7. *Let A and B be two subvarieties of a variety U; and let C and D be two subvarieties of a variety V. Then the proper components of $(A \times C) \cap (B \times D)$ in $U \times V$ are the varieties $X \times Y$, where X is any proper component of $A \cap B$ in U, and Y any proper component of $C \cap D$ in V; and, if $X \times Y$ is such a component, we have $i[(A \times C) \cdot (B \times D), X \times Y; U \times V] = i(A \cdot B, X; U) \cdot i(C \cdot D, Y; V)$.*

The first assertion follows from coroll. 4 of th. 8, Chap. IV, §4, and coroll. 1 of th. 13, Chap. IV, §6, if dimensions are taken into account. Now let n, m,

N and M be the dimensions of U, of V, and of the ambient spaces S^N and S^M for U and for V, respectively; and, denoting by (X, Y) the indeterminates for the space $S^N \times S^M$, let the $F_i(X)$, for $1 \leqq i \leqq n$, and the $G_j(Y)$, for $1 \leqq j \leqq m$, be uniformizing sets of linear forms for U along X, and for V along Y, respectively, so that, by th. 13 of Chap. IV, §6, these two sets of forms, taken together, are a uniformizing set of linear forms for $U \times V$ along $X \times Y$. Call (X, Y, X', Y') the indeterminates for the space $S^N \times S^M \times S^N \times S^M$, and let Λ be the variety defined in that space by the set of $n + m$ equations

$$F_i(X - X') = 0 \qquad (1 \leqq i \leqq n), \qquad G_j(Y - Y') = 0 \qquad (1 \leqq j \leqq m);$$

then, by definition, the multiplicity

$$i[(A \times C)\cdot(B \times D), X \times Y; U \times V]$$

is equal to $j[(A \times C \times B \times D)\cdot\Lambda, \Delta_{X \times Y}]$. In order to calculate this, we interchange the second and third factor in the product-space $S^N \times S^M \times S^N \times S^M$; this transforms $A \times C \times B \times D$ into $A \times B \times C \times D$, and $\Delta_{X \times Y}$ into $\Delta_X \times \Delta_Y$, as may be verified by considering generic points of these varieties over some common field of definition for A, B, C, D, X and Y. As to Λ, it is thereby transformed into the linear variety defined by the same equations as those written above for Λ, provided we write the indeterminates for $S^N \times S^N \times S^M \times S^M$ as (X, X', Y, Y'); by th. 5 of Chap. IV, §3, this shows that Λ is thus transformed into the product $\Lambda_1 \times \Lambda_2$ of the variety Λ_1 defined in $S^N \times S^N$ by the equations

$$F_i(X - X') = 0 \qquad (1 \leqq i \leqq n)$$

and of the variety Λ_2 defined in $S^M \times S^M$ by the equations

$$G_j(Y - Y') = 0 \qquad (1 \leqq j \leqq m).$$

The multiplicity $j[(A \times C \times B \times D)\cdot\Lambda, \Delta_{X \times Y}]$ is thus seen to be equal to $j[(A \times B \times C \times D)\cdot(\Lambda_1 \times \Lambda_2), \Delta_X \times \Delta_Y]$, which, by prop. 17 of Chap. V, §2, is the product of $j[(A \times B)\cdot\Lambda_1, \Delta_X]$ and of $j[(C \times D)\cdot\Lambda_2, \Delta_Y]$, i.e., by the definition of the i-symbol, of $i(A\cdot B, X; U)$ and of $i(C\cdot D, Y; V)$.

The next two results are auxiliary, prop. 5 being required for the proof of prop. 6, and prop. 6 being required for the proof of th. 8, and of th. 8 of Chap. VII, §5.

Proposition 5. *Let S^N and S^M be two spaces, V^m a variety in S^M, A a subvariety of $S^N \times V$, and $(\bar{x}, \bar{y})$ a point of A, simple on $S^N \times V$, with the projections $(\bar{x})$ on S^N and $(\bar{y})$ on V. Let the $G_j(Y)$, for $1 \leqq j \leqq m$, be a uniformizing set of linear forms for V at $(\bar{y})$; and let Λ_0 be the linear variety defined in $S^M \times S^M$ by the set of equations $G_j(Y - Y') = 0$ $(1 \leqq j \leqq m)$. Then the point $(\bar{x}, \bar{y}, \bar{y})$ is contained in one and only one component W of $(A \times V) \cap (S^N \times \Lambda_0)$, and this component is proper in $S^N \times S^M \times S^M$, and of multiplicity 1. Moreover, if k is a field of definition for A, and (x, y) a generic point of A over k, then this component W is the locus of (x, y, y) over k.*

The relation $k(x, y) = k(x, y, y)$ shows that, since (x, y) has the locus A over k, the point (x, y, y) has a locus over k, which we call W_0; this, considered as contained in the product $(S^N \times S^M) \times S^M$, has the projection A on the first factor $S^N \times S^M$ of this product, and its projection on the second factor S^M is the locus of (y) over k, i.e. the same as the projection of A on V; therefore, by coroll. 5 of th. 6, Chap. IV, §3, W_0 is contained in $A \times V$. Similarly, by considering W_0 as contained in $S^N \times (S^M \times S^M)$, we see that it is contained in $S^N \times \Delta_0$, where Δ_0 is the diagonal in $S^M \times S^M$, hence a fortiori in $S^N \times \Lambda_0$. On the other hand, the point $(\bar{x}, \bar{y}, \bar{y})$ is contained in $A \times V$ by th. 5 of Chap. IV, §3, since $(\bar{x}, \bar{y})$ is in A and therefore $(\bar{y})$ in V, and it is contained in $S^N \times \Lambda_0$ because it satisfies the equations for that variety; let W be a component of $(A \times V) \cap (S^N \times \Lambda_0)$, containing $(\bar{x}, \bar{y}, \bar{y})$. Then, if K is a common field of definition for A and V, containing k and the coefficients in the $G_j(Y)$, W is algebraic over K; let (x', y', y'') be a generic point of W over $\bar{K}$. As (x', y', y'') is in $A \times V$, the point (x', y') is in A, hence (y') in V, and (y'') is in V; as (x', y', y'') is in $S^N \times \Lambda_0$, the point (y', y'') is in Λ_0; as (y', y'') has the specialization $(\bar{y}, \bar{y})$ over $\bar{K}$, prop. 3 of §1 shows that we have $(y') = (y'')$. As (x', y') is a specialization of (x, y) over k, it follows from this, by coroll. 1 of th. 2, Chap. IV, §1, that W is contained in W_0; as W_0 is contained in $(A \times V) \cap (S^N \times \Lambda_0)$, and as W is maximal in that intersection, this implies $W = W_0$, which proves our first assertion. If dimensions are taken into account, one sees that the component W of $(A \times V) \cap (S^N \times \Lambda_0)$, which has the same dimension as A, is proper; it only remains for us to show that it has the multiplicity 1. If we assume, as we may, that we have taken for (x, y) a generic point of A, not only over k, but also over K, then $(\bar{y})$ is a specialization of (y) over K, and prop. 25 of Chap. IV, §6, shows that (y) is simple on V and that the $G_j(Y)$ are a uniformizing set of linear forms for V at (y). Then the $G_j(Y)$ are also a uniformizing set of linear forms at (y) for the tangent linear variety L^m to V at (y). Let M be the tangent linear variety to A at (x, y), which is contained in the tangent linear variety to $S^N \times V$ at (x, y), i.e., by th. 13 of Chap. IV, §6, in $S^N \times L$. What we have proved for V, A, $(\bar{x}, \bar{y})$, and Λ_0 can now be applied to L, M, (x, y), and Λ_0; this shows that (x, y, y) is contained in a proper component of the intersection of the linear varieties $M \times L$ and $S^N \times \Lambda_0$, hence that these two varieties are transversal to each other in $S^N \times S^M \times S^M$. As $M \times L$, by th. 13 of Chap. IV, §6, is the tangent linear variety to $A \times V$ at (x, y, y), this shows, by prop. 16 of Chap. V, §2, that we have $j[(A \times V) \cdot (S^N \times \Lambda_0), W] = 1$.

For convenience in stating and proving the next result, we introduce some notations, also of an auxiliary nature. Let Z be a variety in a product-space $S^N \times S^M$; let K be a field of definition for Z, and let (x, y) be a generic point of Z over K, with the projections (x) on S^N and (y) on S^M. Then Δ_Z is the locus of the point (x, y, x, y) over K in the product-space $S^N \times S^M \times S^N \times S^M$; if, in the latter product, we interchange the second and third factors, then Δ_Z is transformed into a variety which we shall denote by ∇_Z, and which is the locus of (x, x, y, y) over K in the space $S^N \times S^N \times S^M \times S^M$. Furthermore, if this variety ∇_Z is considered as being contained in the product $(S^N \times S^N \times S^M) \times S^M$, then its projection on the first factor $S^N \times S^N \times S^M$ of that product is a variety which we shall denote by Ω_Z, and which is the locus of (x, x, y) over K.

PROPOSITION 6. *Let U^n be a variety in S^N, and V^m a variety in S^M. Let A be a subvariety of $U \times V$, B a subvariety of U, and C a proper component of $A \cap (B \times V)$ in $U \times V$. Let the $F_i(X)$, for $1 \leqq i \leqq n$, be a uniformizing set of linear forms for U along the projection of C on U; and let Λ be the linear variety defined in $S^N \times S^N$ by the set of equations $F_i(X - X') = 0$ $(1 \leqq i \leqq n)$. Then the variety Ω_C is a proper component of $(B \times A) \cap (\Lambda \times S^M)$ in $S^N \times S^N \times S^M$, and we have $i[A \cdot (B \times V), C; U \times V] = j[(B \times A) \cdot (\Lambda \times S^M), \Omega_C]$.*

Let the $G_j(Y)$, for $1 \leqq j \leqq m$, be a uniformizing set of linear forms for V along the projection of C on V; then, by th. 13 of Chap. IV, §6, the $F_i(X)$ and the $G_j(Y)$, taken together, are a uniformizing set of linear forms for $U \times V$ along C. Therefore, by definition, the multiplicity $\mu = i[A \cdot (B \times V), C; U \times V]$ is equal to the multiplicity of Δ_C as a component of the intersection of $A \times B \times V$ and of the linear variety Λ_1 defined in the space $S^N \times S^M \times S^N \times S^M$ by the set of $n + m$ equations

$$F_i(X - X') = 0 \qquad (1 \leqq i \leqq n),$$
$$G_j(Y - Y') = 0 \qquad (1 \leqq j \leqq m).$$

Now, writing that space as the product $(S^N \times S^M) \times S^N \times S^M$, we interchange in that product the first and second factors, so as to transform our space into the product $S^N \times (S^N \times S^M) \times S^M$, and the variety $A \times B \times V$ into $B \times A \times V$; as to Λ_1, it is thereby transformed into a linear variety defined by the same set of equations as we have written for Λ_1, provided we write the indeterminates in the transformed space as (X', X, Y, Y'); by th. 5 of Chap. IV, §3, this shows that Λ_1 is thus transformed into the product $\Lambda \times \Lambda_0$ of Λ and of the linear variety Λ_0 defined in $S^M \times S^M$ by the set of equations $G_j(Y - Y') = 0$ $(1 \leqq j \leqq m)$. Now let k be a common field of definition for A, B and C; let (x, y) and (x') be independent generic points of A and of B, respectively, over k, and let $(\bar{x}, \bar{y})$ be a generic point of C over k. Then Δ_C is the locus of $(\bar{x}, \bar{y}, \bar{x}, \bar{y})$ over k, and therefore the above permutation of the first and second factors in $(S^N \times S^M) \times S^N \times S^M$ transforms $(\bar{x}, \bar{y}, \bar{x}, \bar{y})$ into $(\bar{x}, \bar{x}, \bar{y}, \bar{y})$, and Δ_C into ∇_C. The multiplicity μ, which has been found to have the value $j[(A \times B \times V) \cdot \Lambda_1, \Delta_C]$, is thus seen to be equal to $j[(B \times A \times V) \cdot (\Lambda \times \Lambda_0), \nabla_C]$. But, by coroll. 4 of th. 8, Chap. IV, §4, $\Lambda \times \Lambda_0$ is the intersection of the linear varieties $S^N \times S^N \times \Lambda_0$ and $\Lambda \times S^M \times S^M$, and, if dimensions are taken into account, this implies that the latter varieties are transversal to each other in $S^N \times S^N \times S^M \times S^M$. Moreover, by coroll. 4 of th. 8, Chap. IV, §4, every component of $(B \times A \times V) \cap (S^N \times S^N \times \Lambda_0)$ is of the form $B \times Z$, where Z is a component of $(A \times V) \cap (S^N \times \Lambda_0)$; and, if such a component contains ∇_C and therefore $(\bar{x}, \bar{x}, \bar{y}, \bar{y})$, then Z must contain $(\bar{x}, \bar{y}, \bar{y})$ and therefore, by prop. 5, is the locus W of (x, y, y) over k. That being so, we can now calculate the multiplicity $j[(B \times A \times V)\cdot(\Lambda \times \Lambda_0), \nabla_C]$ by applying prop. 15 of Chap. V, §2, to $B \times A \times V$, to the intersection $\Lambda \times \Lambda_0$ of $S^N \times S^N \times \Lambda_0$ and of $\Lambda \times S^M \times S^M$, and to ∇_C; that multiplicity is thus shown to be the product of $j[(B \times A \times V)\cdot(S^N \times S^N \times \Lambda_0), B \times W]$ and of

$$j[(B \times W)\cdot(\Lambda \times S^M \times S^M), \nabla_C].$$

The first one of these two factors, by prop. 17 of Chap. V, §2, is the product of $j(B\cdot S^N, B)$, which is 1 by prop. 16 of Chap. V, §2, and of

$$j[(A \times V)\cdot(S^N \times \Lambda_0), W],$$

which is 1 by prop. 5. Therefore μ is equal to

$$j[(B \times W)\cdot(\Lambda \times S^M \times S^M), \nabla_C].$$

This can now be transformed by prop. 18 of Chap. V, §2, applied to the variety $B \times W$ and its subvariety ∇_C in the product-space $(S^N \times S^N \times S^M) \times S^M$, to their projections on the first factor $S^N \times S^N \times S^M$ of that product, and to the linear variety $\Lambda \times S^M$ in that first factor; for $B \times W$ and ∇_C are the loci of (x', x, y, y) and of $(\bar{x}, \bar{x}, \bar{y}, \bar{y})$, respectively, over k, so that their projections on $S^N \times S^N \times S^M$ are the loci of (x', x, y) and of $(\bar{x}, \bar{x}, \bar{y})$, respectively, over k, i.e. are the varieties $B \times A$ and Ω_C; moreover, it follows from the definitions that the projection from $B \times W$ to $B \times A$ is everywhere regular. That being so, prop. 18 of Chap. V, §2, applied as we have said, shows that μ is equal to $j[(B \times A)\cdot(\Lambda \times S^M), \Omega_C]$, as asserted by our proposition.

THEOREM 8. *Let U and V be two varieties, A a subvariety of $U \times V$, A' its projection on U, and B a subvariety of U. Let C be a subvariety of A, simple on $U \times V$, with the projection C' on U, and such that the projection from A to A' is regular along C'. Then C is a proper component of $A \cap (B \times V)$ on $U \times V$ if and only if C' is a proper component of $A' \cap B$ on U, and, if that is so, we have* $i(A'\cdot B, C'; U) = i[A\cdot(B \times V), C; U \times V]$.

The assumptions imply that A and C have the same dimensions as A' and as C', respectively, and also, by coroll. 1 of th. 13, Chap. IV, §6, that C' is simple on U. Since the projection from A to A' is regular along C', hence a fortiori along every subvariety D' of A' containing C', there is a one-to-one correspondence between such varieties D' and the subvarieties D of A which contain C, in such a way that, if D and D' correspond to each other, D' is the projection of D on U; that being so, D is contained in $B \times V$ if and only if D' is contained in B. This implies that C is maximal in $A \cap (B \times V)$ if and only if C' is maximal in $A' \cap B$; if dimensions are taken into account, this proves our first assertion. Now, assuming C' to be a proper component of $A' \cap B$ in U, so that C is a proper component of $A \cap (B \times V)$ in $U \times V$, we apply prop. 6, which, with the same notations as in that proposition, shows that $i[A\cdot(B \times V), C; U \times V]$ is equal to $j[(B \times A)\cdot(\Lambda \times S^M), \Omega_C]$. Let k be a common field of definition for A, B and C; let (x, y) and (x') be independent generic points of A and of B, respectively, over k, and let $(\bar{x}, \bar{y})$ be a generic point of C over k. Then $B \times A$ is the locus of (x', x, y) over k, so that, if we consider it as being contained in the product-space $(S^N \times S^N) \times S^M$, its projection on the first factor $S^N \times S^N$ of that product is the locus of (x', x) over k, i.e. the variety $B \times A'$; similarly, Ω_C is, by definition, the locus of $(\bar{x}, \bar{x}, \bar{y})$ over k, so that its projection on $S^N \times S^N$ is the locus of $(\bar{x}, \bar{x})$ over k, i.e. the variety $\Delta_{C'}$. Moreover, by assumption, the y_j, for $1 \leqq j \leqq M$, are in the specialization-ring of $(\bar{x})$ in $k(x)$, hence a fortiori in the specialization-ring of $(\bar{x}, \bar{x})$ in $k(x', x)$; therefore the projection from $B \times A$ to $B \times A'$ is regular along $\Delta_{C'}$. We can now apply prop. 18 of Chap. V, §2, to the variety $B \times A$ in the product-space $(S^N \times S^N) \times S^M$, to its projection $B \times A'$ on the first factor $S^N \times S^N$ of that product, to the linear variety Λ in $S^N \times S^N$, and to the subvariety $\Delta_{C'}$ of $B \times A'$, which, by th. 2 of §1, is a proper component of $(B \times A') \cap \Lambda$; this shows that $j[(B \times A)\cdot(\Lambda \times S^M), \Omega_C]$ is equal to $j[(B \times A')\cdot\Lambda, \Delta_{C'}]$, i.e., by definition, to $i(B\cdot A', C; U)$; in view of the commutativity of the i-symbol, this completes our proof.

Theorem 9. *Let U be a simple subvariety of a variety V; let A be a subvariety of U, B a subvariety of V, and C a proper component of $A \cap B$ in V. Then, if C is simple on U, Δ_C is a proper component of $(A \times B) \cap \Delta_U$ in $U \times V$, and we have $i(A\cdot B, C; V) = i[(A \times B)\cdot\Delta_U, \Delta_C; U \times V]$. Moreover, if that is so, and if the X_λ are all those components of $U \cap B$ which contain C, then, for every λ, X_λ is a proper component of $U \cap B$ in V, and C a proper component of $A \cap X_\lambda$ in U, and we have $i(A\cdot B, C; V) = \sum_\lambda i(U\cdot B, X_\lambda; V)\cdot i(A\cdot X_\lambda, C; U)$.*

By coroll. 1 of th. 13, Chap. IV, §6, the variety Δ_C is simple on $U \times V$; by prop. 2 of §1, it is a component of $\Delta_U \cap (A \times B)$. But, by coroll. 4 of th. 8, Chap. IV, §4, we have $A \times B = (A \times V) \cap (U \times B)$. Therefore Δ_C is a component of $\Delta_U \cap (A \times V) \cap (U \times B)$, and a proper one in $U \times V$ if dimensions are taken into account, the dimension of C being determined by the assumption that C is a proper component of $A \cap B$ in V; to this we can now apply th. 5 of §2. By prop. 3 of §1, Δ_A is the only component of $\Delta_U \cap (A \times V)$; and $A \times B$ is the only component of $(A \times V) \cap (U \times B)$; therefore, applying th. 5 of §2 to Δ_C as we have said, we get a formula in which either side consists of one term only, the left-hand side being the product of $i[\Delta_U\cdot(A \times V), \Delta_A; U \times V]$ and of $i[\Delta_A\cdot(U \times B), \Delta_C; U \times V]$, and the right-hand side being the product of $i[\Delta_U\cdot(A \times B), \Delta_C; U \times V]$ and of $i[(A \times V)\cdot(U \times B), A \times B; U \times V]$. The two factors of the left-hand side can be transformed by th. 8, which, applied to the first one and to projections on U, shows that it is equal to $i(U\cdot A, A; U)$, i.e. to 1 by the coroll. of th. 6, §2, and, applied to the second one and to projections on V, shows that it is equal to $i(A\cdot B, C; V)$; therefore the left-hand side is equal to $i(A\cdot B, C; V)$. On the other hand, of the two factors of the right-hand side, the second one, by th. 7, is the product of $i(A\cdot U, A; U)$ and of $i(V\cdot B, B; V)$, and is therefore equal to 1 by the coroll. of th. 6, §2. In view of the commutativity of the i-symbol, this completes the proof of the first equality in our theorem. The second equality will now be proved by applying th. 5 of §2 to the proper component Δ_C of $(A \times V) \cap \Delta_U \cap (U \times B)$; in this application of th. 5, the left-hand side is exactly the same as before, hence equal to $i(A \cdot B, C; V)$. The X_λ being as stated in our theorem, prop. 3 of §1 shows that the components of $\Delta_U \cap (U \times B)$ which contain Δ_C are the varieties Δ_{X_λ}; therefore th. 5 of §2 shows that, for every λ, Δ_{X_λ} is a proper component of $\Delta_U \cap (U \times B)$ in $U \times V$, and Δ_C a proper component of $(A \times V) \cap \Delta_{X_\lambda}$; and the right-hand side of the formula in that theorem, applied as we have said, is equal to

$$\textstyle\sum_\lambda i[(A \times V) \cdot \Delta_{X_\lambda}, \Delta_C; U \times V] \cdot i[\Delta_U \cdot (U \times B), \Delta_{X_\lambda}; U \times V].$$

Both factors in each term of that sum can now be calculated by means of th. 8; this theorem, applied to the first factor and to projections on U, shows that C is a proper component of $A \cap X_\lambda$ on U, and shows that factor to be equal to $i(A \cdot X_\lambda, C; U)$; similarly, since Δ_{X_λ} contains Δ_C and therefore is simple on $U \times V$, th. 8 can be applied to the second factor and to projections on V, showing that X_λ is a proper component of $U \cap B$ in V, and showing that factor to be equal to $i(U \cdot B, X_\lambda; V)$. This completes our proof.

THEOREM 10. *Let A and B be two subvarieties of a variety U, and let C be a proper component of $A \cap B$ on U. Let $\bar{U}$ be a birational correspondence, biregular along C, between U and a variety U'; and let A', B', C' be the subvarieties of U', respectively corresponding to A, B and C by the birational correspondence $\bar{U}$. Then C' is a proper component of $A' \cap B'$ on U', and we have*

$$i(A' \cdot B', C'; U') = i(A \cdot B, C; U).$$

The statement of our theorem depends upon the fact that, $\bar{U}$ being biregular along C, it is also biregular along A and along B; this is a consequence of coroll. 4 of th. 17, Chap. IV, §7, which also shows that the variety $C' = \bar{U}(C)$ is contained both in $A' = \bar{U}(A)$ and in $B' = \bar{U}(B)$; moreover, by the same corollary, if D' is a component of $A' \cap B'$, containing C', then $\bar{U}$ is biregular along D', and the variety $D = \bar{U}^{-1}(D')$ contains C and is contained in A and in B, and therefore is the same as C; this implies that the variety $D' = \bar{U}(D)$ is then the same as C', which shows that C' is a component of $A' \cap B'$. Moreover, by th. 17 of Chap. IV, §7, C' is simple on U'; if dimensions are taken into account, this completes the proof of our first assertion, since the dimensions of U', A', B', and C' are the same as those of U, A, B, and C, respectively. Now, let $\bar{A}$, $\bar{B}$, and $\bar{C}$ be the subvarieties of $\bar{U}$ with the projections A, B and C, respectively, on U; by th. 17 of Chap. IV, §7, $\bar{C}$ is then simple on $\bar{U}$, and, by coroll. 1 of th. 13, Chap. IV, §6, it is simple on $U \times U'$; we can therefore apply th. 8 to U and U', to the subvariety $\bar{A}$ of $U \times U'$, to the subvariety B of U, and to the proper component C of $A \cap B$, which is the projection on U of the subvariety $\bar{C}$ of $\bar{A}$; this shows that $\bar{C}$ is a proper component of $\bar{A} \cap (B \times U')$ in $U \times U'$, and that $i(A \cdot B, C; U)$ is equal to $i[\bar{A} \cdot (B \times U'), \bar{C}; U \times U']$. We now apply th. 9 to the variety $V = U \times U'$, to its subvariety $\bar{U}$, to the subvariety $\bar{A}$ of $\bar{U}$, and to the intersection of $\bar{A}$ and of $B \times U'$. A component of $\bar{U} \cap (B \times U')$, containing $\bar{C}$, must be a subvariety $\bar{D}$ of $\bar{U}$, the projection D of which on U contains C and is contained in B; by coroll. 4 of th. 17, Chap. IV, §7, this, in view of the assumption that $\bar{U}$ is biregular along C, implies that we have $\bar{C} \subset \bar{D} \subset \bar{B}$, hence $\bar{D} = \bar{B}$ since $\bar{B}$ is contained in $\bar{U} \cap (B \times U')$ and $\bar{D}$ is maximal in that intersection. If we now apply th. 9 as we have said, the left-hand side of the last formula in that theorem becomes, in the present case, $i[\bar{A} \cdot (B \times U'), \bar{C}; U \times U']$, which is equal to $i(A \cdot B, C; U)$ as we have seen; and the right-hand side now consists of one term only, which is the product of $i[\bar{U} \cdot (B \times U'), \bar{B}; U \times U']$ and of $i(\bar{A} \cdot \bar{B}, \bar{C}; \bar{U})$, the fact that these two symbols are defined being also a consequence of th. 9 as applied here. The first one of these two factors can be calculated by th. 8, applied to projections on U; this shows that it is equal to $i(U \cdot B, B; U)$, hence to 1 by the coroll. of th. 6, §2. We have thus proved that $i(A \cdot B, C; U)$ is equal to $i(\bar{A} \cdot \bar{B}, \bar{C}; \bar{U})$. If we interchange U and U', this shows that $i(A' \cdot B', C'; U')$ also is equal to $i(\bar{A} \cdot \bar{B}, \bar{C}; \bar{U})$, which completes the proof of our theorem.

In the next theorems, we shall consider products of the form $P \times V$, where P is a point and V a variety; if V is defined over a field k, hence also over $k(P)$, and if Q is a generic point of V over $k(P)$, the variety $P \times V$ is the locus of $P \times Q$ over $k(P)$. Before proving the theorems we have in view, we give a preliminary result which will be used in their proofs.

PROPOSITION 7. *Let U^n be a variety in S^N, V^m a variety in S^M, and W a subvariety of the product $U \times V$. Let $P = (x)$ be a simple point of U; let the $F_i(X)$, for $1 \leqq i \leqq n$, be a uniformizing set of linear forms for U at P; let L be the linear variety defined in S^N by the set of linear equations $F_i(X - x) = 0$ $(1 \leqq i \leqq n)$. Then a variety $\bar{Z}$ contained in $W \cap (P \times V)$ is a component of $W \cap (P \times V)$ if and only if it is a component of $W \cap (L \times S^M)$; it is a proper component of $W \cap (P \times V)$ in $U \times V$ if and only if it is a proper component of $W \cap (L \times S^M)$ in $S^N \times S^M$ and is simple on $U \times V$; and, when that is so, we have*

$$i[W \cdot (P \times V), \bar{Z}; U \times V] = j[W \cdot (L \times S^M), \bar{Z}].$$

As L contains P, a variety contained in $W \cap (P \times V)$ is a fortiori contained in $W \cap (L \times S^M)$; therefore, if it is maximal in the latter intersection, it must also be maximal in the former. Conversely, let $\bar{Z}$ be a component of $W \cap (P \times V)$; $\bar{Z}$ must be contained in some component $\bar{Z}'$ of $W \cap (L \times S^M)$. The projection on S^N of the variety $\bar{Z}'$ in $S^N \times S^M$ is then contained in the projection of W on S^N, hence in U, and also in L, hence in $U \cap L$; and it contains the projection of $\bar{Z}$ on S^N, which is reduced to the point P since $\bar{Z}$ is in $P \times V$. As P is a proper intersection of U and L by prop. 7 of Chap. V, §1, this implies that the projection of $\bar{Z}'$ on S^N is also reduced to P; as the projection of $\bar{Z}'$ on S^M is contained in the projection of W on S^M, hence in V, this shows that $\bar{Z}'$ is contained in $P \times V$, hence in $W \cap (P \times V)$; as it contains $\bar{Z}$ which is maximal in the latter intersection, it follows from this that we have $\bar{Z} = \bar{Z}'$, which completes the proof of our first assertion. The second assertion follows from this by taking dimensions into account. As to the assertion concerning multiplicities, we shall prove it by applying th. 9 to the subvariety $U \times V$ of $S^N \times S^M$, and to the proper component $\bar{Z}$ of $W \cap (L \times S^M)$ in $S^N \times S^M$. By coroll. 4 of th. 8, Chap. IV, §4, every component of $(U \times V) \cap (L \times S^M)$ must be of the form $X \times V$, where X is a component of $U \cap L$; if such a component contains $\bar{Z}$, then X must contain the projection P of $\bar{Z}$ on S^N, and therefore must be reduced to P since P is proper in $U \cap L$. That being so, the left-hand side of the second formula in th. 9, applied as we have said, is equal to

$$i[W \cdot (L \times S^M), \bar{Z}; S^N \times S^M],$$

hence to $j[W \cdot (L \times S^M), \bar{Z}]$ by prop. 4 of §1. As to the right-hand side of that formula, it consists here of one term only, which is the product of

$$i[(U \times V) \cdot (L \times S^M), P \times V; S^N \times S^M]$$

and of $i[W \cdot (P \times V), \bar{Z}; U \times V]$; the first one of these factors, by th. 7, is the product of $i(U \cdot L, P; S^N)$, i.e. of $j(U \cdot L, P)$, which is equal to 1 by prop. 7 of Chap. V, §1, and of $i(V \cdot S^M, V; S^M)$, which is equal to 1 by the coroll. of th. 6 §2. This completes our proof.

THEOREM 11. *Let U and V be two varieties, defined over a field k. Let W be a simple subvariety of $U \times V$, algebraic over k; and let p^f be its order of inseparability over k. Then, if P is a generic point of U over k, $W \cap (P \times V)$ is empty if the projection of W on U is other than U, and is not so if that projection is U. In the latter case, every component of $W \cap (P \times V)$ is proper on $U \times V$, and is of the form $P \times Z$, where Z is a subvariety of V, algebraic over the field $K = k(P)$; and then, if p^g is the order of inseparability of Z over K, the multiplicity*

$$i[W \cdot (P \times V), P \times Z; U \times V]$$

is equal to p^{g-f}. Moreover, every generic point of such a component $P \times Z$ over $\bar{K}$ is a generic point of W over $\bar{k}$; and, if the W^σ are all the conjugates of W over k, every component of any one of the intersections $W^\sigma \cap (P \times V)$ is a conjugate of $P \times Z$ over K, and conversely every such conjugate is a component of one and only one of these intersections.

If there exists a point in $W \cap (P \times V)$, such a point has the projection P on U; therefore its locus over $\bar{k}$, which is contained in W, has the projection U on U, so that the projection of W on U must then contain U, hence must be U. Conversely, if W has the projection U on U, then, by th. 6 of Chap. IV, §3, W has a generic point over $\bar{k}$ of the form $P \times Q$, which is in $P \times V$. This being assumed to be the case, consider a component of $W \cap (P \times V)$, which, by coroll. 6 of th. 6, Chap. IV, §3, must be of the form $P \times Z$. Let n, m, r, N and M be the dimensions of U, of V, of W, and of the ambient spaces S^N and S^M for U and for V, respectively. Let the $F_i(X)$, for $1 \leqq i \leqq n$, be a uniformizing set of linear forms for U at P, with coefficients in k; put $P = (x)$, and $v_i = F_i(x)$ for $1 \leqq i \leqq n$; then, by prop. 24 of Chap. IV, §6, P is separably algebraic over $k(v)$. As the v_i are in the field $K = k(P)$, $\bar{K}$ is thus the algebraic closure, not only of K, but also of the fields $k(v)$ and $\bar{k}(v)$; and (v) must have the dimension n over k, so that it is a set of independent variables over k. Let now L be the linear variety defined in S^N by the set of linear equations $F_i(X - x) = 0$ $(1 \leqq i \leqq n)$, which can also be written as $F_i(X) - v_i = 0$ $(1 \leqq i \leqq n)$. As $P \times Z$ is a component of $W \cap (P \times V)$, prop. 7 shows that it is also a component of $W \cap (L \times S^M)$. As $L \times S^M$ is the linear variety defined in $S^N \times S^M$ by the set of equations $F_i(X) - v_i = 0$ $(1 \leqq i \leqq n)$, where the v_i are independent variables over k, we can make use of prop. 2 of Chap. V, §1, which shows here that $P \times Z$ has the dimension $r - n$, and that every generic point of $P \times Z$ over the algebraic closure $\bar{K}$ of $\bar{k}(v)$ is a generic point of W over $\bar{k}$, hence is simple on $U \times V$. Thus $P \times Z$ is a proper component of $W \cap (P \times V)$ in $U \times V$, hence, by prop. 7, of $W \cap (L \times S^M)$ in $S^N \times S^M$; also by prop. 7, $i[W\cdot(P \times V), P \times Z; U \times V]$ is equal to $j[W\cdot(L \times S^M), P \times Z]$, hence, by prop. 14 of Chap. V, §2, to the product of p^{-f} and of the order of inseparability of $P \times Z$ over $k(v)$; the latter order of inseparability is equal to p^g by the definitions and by prop. 25 of Chap. I, §8, since $k(P)$ is separably algebraic over $k(v)$. This completes the proof of the assertion in our theorem about the multiplicity of $P \times Z$. Now consider a generic point of $P \times Z$ over $\bar{K}$, which must be of the form $P \times Q$, where Q is a generic point of Z over $\bar{K}$; by what we have proved, this point must have the dimension $r - n$ over $\bar{K}$, hence over $\bar{k}(P)$, so that it has the dimension r over $\bar{k}$ and is therefore, by th. 2 of Chap. IV, §1, a generic point of W over $\bar{k}$. Also, if σ is any automorphism of $\bar{k}$ over k, and if $P \times Z'$ is any component of $W^\sigma \cap (P \times V)$, a generic point of $P \times Z'$ over $\bar{K}$ must be of the form $P \times Q'$, and must be a generic point of W^σ over $\bar{k}$. Then, by th. 3 of Chap. IV, §2, σ can be extended to an isomorphism of $\bar{k}(P, Q)$ on $\bar{k}(P, Q')$, transforming P into P and Q into Q'; this can be further extended to an isomorphism between the algebraic closures of these two fields, which induces on the field $\bar{K}$ an automorphism σ_1 over $K = k(P)$, and transforms $P \times Q$ into $P \times Q'$; by th. 3 of Chap. IV, §2, this shows that $P \times Z'$ is the transform of $P \times Z$ by σ_1. Conversely, if σ_1 is any automorphism of $\bar{K}$ over K, it induces on $\bar{k}$ an automorphism σ over k; and coroll. 3 of th. 8, Chap. IV, §4, combined with prop. 4 of Chap. IV, §2, shows that the transform of $P \times Z$ by σ_1 is then a component of $W^\sigma \cap (P \times V)$. Finally, if $P \times Q'$ is, as above, a generic point of such a component over $\bar{K}$, then, by what we have proved, $P \times Q'$ is contained in one and only one of the conjugates of W over k, viz. in its locus over $\bar{k}$. This completes our proof.

THEOREM 12. *Let U and V be two varieties; let W be a simple subvariety of $U \times V$, with the projection U on U, and of the same dimension as U. Let k be a common field of definition for U, V and W; and let P be a generic point of U over k. Then $W \cap (P \times V)$ is not empty; if $P \times Q$ is any point in it, $P \times Q$ is algebraic over $k(P)$, and is a generic point of W over k; the points in $W \cap (P \times V)$ are all the conjugates of $P \times Q$ over $k(P)$; they are all proper in $W \cap (P \times V)$ on $U \times V$, and have the multiplicity $[k(P, Q):k(P)]_i$. Moreover, if $(Q^{(1)}, \cdots, Q^{(d)})$ is a complete set of conjugates of Q over $k(P)$, and if $P' \times Q'$ is a point of W such that* *it is a proper intersection, of multiplicity* μ, *of* W *and of* $P' \times V$ *on* $U \times V$, *then, in every specialization* $(Q'^{(1)}, \cdots, Q'^{(d)})$ *of* $(Q^{(1)}, \cdots, Q^{(d)})$ *over* $P \to P'$ *with reference to* k, *the point* Q' *occurs exactly* μ *times among the points* $Q'^{(\lambda)}$.

The first part of our theorem is an immediate consequence of th. 11, applied to the present case; one should only observe that the variety denoted by Z in th. 11 is here reduced to the point $P \times Q$, so that its order of inseparability over $k(P)$ is that of $k(P, Q)$ over $k(P)$, which is equal to $[k(P, Q):k(P)]_i$ since $k(P, Q)$ is now algebraic over $k(P)$. As to the second part, let S^N and S^M be the ambient spaces for U and for V, respectively; and, n being the dimension of U, let the $F_i(X)$, for $1 \leqq i \leqq n$, be a uniformizing set of linear forms for U at P', with coefficients in k; moreover, put $P = (x)$, $P' = (x')$, $v_i = F_i(x)$ and $v_i' = F_i(x')$ for $1 \leqq i \leqq n$. Let L and L' be the linear varieties respectively defined in S^N by the two sets of linear equations

$$F_i(X - x) = 0 \qquad (1 \leqq i \leqq n)$$

and

$$F_i(X - x') = 0 \qquad (1 \leqq i \leqq n),$$

which sets can also be written as

$$F_i(X) - v_i = 0 \qquad (1 \leqq i \leqq n)$$

and as

$$F_i(X) - v_i' = 0 \qquad (1 \leqq i \leqq n),$$

respectively. Then these sets of equations define in the space $S^N \times S^M$ the linear varieties $L \times S^M$ and $L' \times S^M$. Prop. 7 now shows that the point (P', Q') is a proper intersection, of multiplicity μ, of W and of $L' \times S^M$ in $S^N \times S^M$. By the coroll. of th. 3, Chap. V, §1, applied to W, to the $F_i(X)$, to the generic point (P, Q) of W over k, and to the point (P', Q'), it follows from this that (v) is a set of independent variables over k, and that μ is the multiplicity of (P', Q') as a specialization of (P, Q) over $(v) \to (v')$ with reference to k. Similarly, since P', by prop. 7 of Chap. V, §1, is a proper intersection, of multiplicity 1, of U and of L' in S^N, the same corollary, applied to U, to the $F_i(X)$, to the generic point P of U over k, and to P', shows that P' is a proper specialization of P, of multiplicity 1, over $(v) \to (v')$, with reference to k. Now let $(P^{(1)}, \cdots, P^{(\delta)})$ be a complete set of conjugates of P over $k(v)$, where we may assume that we have $P^{(1)} = P$; then, by prop. 11 of Chap. I, §4, a complete set of conjugates of (P,Q) over $k(v)$ will consist of the $\delta \cdot d$ points $(P^{(\nu)}, Q^{(\nu\lambda)})$ for $1 \leqq \nu \leqq \delta$, $1 \leqq \lambda \leqq d$, where $(Q^{(\nu 1)}, \cdots, Q^{(\nu d)})$ is the transform of $(Q^{(1)}, \cdots, Q^{(d)})$ by some automorphism of the algebraic closure of $k(v)$ over $k(v)$ which maps P on $P^{(\nu)}$; as we have $P^{(1)} = P$, we may therefore assume that we have $Q^{(1\lambda)} = Q^{(\lambda)}$ for $1 \leqq \lambda \leqq d$. Consider now an arbitrary specialization $(P', Q'^{(1)}, \cdots, Q'^{(d)})$ of $(P, Q^{(1)}, \cdots, Q^{(d)})$ over $P \to P'$, with reference to k; and extend this to a specialization over k of the set of all $(P^{(\nu)}, Q^{(\nu\lambda)})$, which consists of $\delta \cdot d$ points or pseudopoints

$(P'^{(\nu)}, Q'^{(\nu\lambda)})$; we must have $P'^{(1)} = P'$, and $Q'^{(1\lambda)} = Q'^{(\lambda)}$ for $1 \leqq \lambda \leqq d$. The relations $v_i = F_i(x)$, $v'_i = F_i(x')$ imply, by prop. 13 of Chap. II, §4, that (v') is the uniquely determined specialization of (v) over $P \to P'$ with reference to k. Therefore the set of all $(P'^{(\nu)}, Q'^{(\nu\lambda)})$, being a specialization of the set of all $(P^{(\nu)}, Q^{(\nu\lambda)})$ over $P \to P'$ with reference to k, is a fortiori a specialization of that set over $(v) \to (v')$ with reference to k, so that, by what we have proved above, (P', Q') must occur exactly μ times among the $(P'^{(\nu)}, Q'^{(\nu\lambda)})$; for similar reasons, P' must occur exactly once among the $P'^{(\nu)}$. As we have $P'^{(1)} = P'$, it follows from this that we have $P'^{(\nu)} \neq P'$ for $\nu \neq 1$; hence we cannot have $(P'^{(\nu)}, Q'^{(\nu\lambda)}) = (P', Q')$ except for $\nu = 1$. Therefore Q' must occur exactly μ times among the $Q'^{(1\lambda)}$, i.e. among the $Q'^{(\lambda)}$, as asserted by our theorem.

We conclude this chapter with some applications of th. 12, which give sufficient conditions for a projection to be regular along a variety[1]:

THEOREM 13. *Let W be a variety in a product $U \times V$, such that its projection on U is U and that we have $[W:U] = 1$. Let Z' be a simple subvariety of U, such that there exists a component Z of $W \cap (Z' \times V)$, of the same dimension as Z', with the projection Z' on U. Then the projection from W to U is regular along Z'.*

Let k be a common field of definition for U, W and Z; let $P \times Q$ and $P' \times Q'$ be generic points of W and of Z, respectively, over k; then the projections P and P' of these points on U are generic points of U and of Z', respectively, over k. Let now S^M be the ambient space for V; $P' \times Q'$ is contained in $W \cap (P' \times S^M)$, hence in some component of that intersection, which is defined over the algebraic closure $\bar{K}$ of the field $K = k(P')$, since W and $P' \times S^M$ are defined over K; a generic point of that component over $\bar{K}$ can then be written as $P' \times Q''$ since it is in $P' \times S^M$. Then $P' \times Q'$ is a specialization of $P' \times Q''$ over $\bar{K}$ and a fortiori over $\bar{k}$, and is therefore in the locus $\bar{Z}$ of $P' \times Q''$ over $\bar{k}$; this implies that Z, which is the locus of $P' \times Q'$ over k and therefore also over $\bar{k}$, is contained in $\bar{Z}$. On the other hand, as $P' \times Q''$ is in W, $\bar{Z}$ is contained in W, hence also in $U \times V$; and the projection of $\bar{Z}$ on U is the locus Z' of P' over $\bar{k}$, so that $\bar{Z}$ is contained in $Z' \times V$, hence in $W \cap (Z' \times V)$; as Z is maximal in that intersection and is contained in $\bar{Z}$, this shows that $\bar{Z}$ is the same as Z and has therefore the same dimension as Z', so that Q'' is algebraic over $\bar{k}(P')$. This implies that the locus of $P' \times Q''$ over $\bar{K}$ is reduced to that point, which must be the same as $P' \times Q'$ since $P' \times Q'$ is in that locus. Therefore $P' \times Q'$ is a component of $W \cap (P' \times S^M)$; moreover, as Z' is simple on U, P' is simple on U, so that $P' \times Q'$ is simple on $U \times S^M$ by th. 13 of Chap. IV, §6; if dimensions are taken into account, this shows that $P' \times Q'$ is a proper component of $W \cap (P' \times S^M)$ on $U \times S^M$. We can now apply th. 12 to the subvariety W of $U \times S^M$, to the proper intersection $P' \times Q'$ of W and $P' \times S^M$ on $U \times S^M$, and to a complete set of conjugates of Q over $k(P)$; as $[W:U] = 1$ and therefore $k(P, Q) = k(P)$,

[1] This is equivalent to a special case of Zariski's "main theorem" on birational correspondences; cf. Chap. IX, §3.

such a complete set consists of one point only, viz. of Q itself. It follows from this that Q' is the only specialization of Q over $P \to P'$ with reference to k; this implies that every coordinate of Q is finite over $P \to P'$ with reference to k, and therefore, by th. 5 of Chap. V, §3, that every coordinate of Q is in the specialization-ring of P' in $k(P)$. This means that the projection from W to U is regular at P', hence, by definition, along Z'.

COROLLARY 1. *Let W^r be a variety in a product $U \times V$, with the projection W' on U, and such that we have $[W:W'] = 1$. Let Z'^{r-1} be a simple subvariety of W'. Then, if there is a subvariety Z of W with the projection Z' on U, the projection from W to W' is regular along Z'.*

Our assumptions imply that W' has the same dimension r as W; then Z' is not the same as W', so that W is not contained in $Z' \times V$. If Z is as stated, it is contained in W and in $Z' \times V$, hence in a component Z_1 of $W \cap (Z' \times V)$, and has at least the dimension $r - 1$. Then Z_1 is contained in W; as it cannot be W, it has at most the dimension $r - 1$; as it contains Z which has at least that dimension, it is Z itself. Our assertion now follows from th. 13, applied to the subvariety W of the product $W' \times V$, and to the varieties Z' and Z.

COROLLARY 2. *Let T be a birational correspondence between two varieties U^n and V^n; let U'^{n-1} be a simple subvariety of U^n, and V'^{n-1} a simple subvariety of V^n, such that there is a subvariety T' of T with the projections U' on U, and V' on V. Then U' and V' are regularly corresponding subvarieties of U and of V by T.*

This is an immediate consequence of coroll. 1 and of the definitions.

CHAPTER VII
THE GEOMETRY ON ABSTRACT VARIETIES

1. The Zariski topology. In Chap. IV, §4, we considered only unions and intersections of varieties, and of bunches of varieties, in finite number. The operation of intersection can be extended to infinite families, as shown by the following:

PROPOSITION 1. *Let* $(\mathcal{B}_\alpha)_{\alpha \in A}$ *be any family of bunches of varieties in* S^n, *indexed by a set* A. *Then there is a finite subset* J *of* A, *such that:*

$$\bigcap_{\alpha \in A} \{\mathcal{B}_\alpha\} = \bigcap_{\alpha \in J} \{\mathcal{B}_\alpha\}.$$

To each bunch $\mathcal{B}$ in S^n, we attach the sequence

$$\nu(\mathcal{B}) = (\nu_0, \nu_1, \cdots, \nu_n),$$

where ν_d is the number of components of $\mathcal{B}$ of dimension $n - d$; we order such sequences lexicographically, i.e. we put

$$(\nu_0, \cdots, \nu_n) < (\nu_0', \cdots, \nu_n')$$

if and only if, for some d, we have $\nu_i = \nu_i'$ $(0 \leqq i < d)$ and $\nu_d < \nu_d'$. Also, call $\delta(\mathcal{B})$ the largest of the dimensions of the components of $\mathcal{B}$, so that $\nu_i = 0$ for $i < n - \delta(\mathcal{B})$ and $\nu_i \neq 0$ for $i = n - \delta(\mathcal{B})$. It is easily seen, by induction on $\delta(\mathcal{B})$, that $\mathcal{B}' \subset \mathcal{B}$, $\mathcal{B}' \neq \mathcal{B}$ imply $\nu(\mathcal{B}') < \nu(\mathcal{B})$. Now, for each finite subset I of A, call $\mathcal{B}_I$ the intersection of the bunches $\mathcal{B}_\alpha$ for $\alpha \in I$, and let J be such a subset for which $\nu(\mathcal{B}_J)$ has its lowest value; then, for each $I \supset J$, we have $\mathcal{B}_I = \mathcal{B}_J$. This implies that $\mathcal{B}_J \subset \mathcal{B}_\alpha$ for all $\alpha \in A$, so that J has the required property.

Therefore we can define a topology in S^n by taking as closed sets the sets attached to the bunches of varieties in S^n; this will be called *the Zariski topology in* S^n. In view of prop. 1 and of coroll. 2 of th. 8, Chap. IV, §4, we can also, if k is any field, define a topology in S^n by taking as closed sets the sets attached to the normally algebraic bunches of varieties over k; this will be called *the* k-*topology in* S^n. Sets which are closed in the Zariski topology (resp. in the k-topology) will be called *closed* (resp. k-*closed*). If V is any subvariety of S^n, we define *the Zariski topology on* V as that induced by the Zariski topology in S^n; and, if k is any field of definition of V, we define *the* k-*topology on* V as that induced by the k-topology in S^n; thus the closed (resp. k-closed) subsets of V are those which are such in the ambient space. *Open* (resp. k-*open*) sets are, as usual, the complements of closed (resp. k-closed) sets. Clearly these topologies do not satisfy the Hausdorff separation axiom, as the intersection of two non-empty open sets is never empty. One should also note that, if V and W are two varieties, neither of which is reduced to a point, the Zariski topology on $V \times W$ is *not* the product of the Zariski topologies on V and on W; in fact, in the latter, there are no other closed sets than the finite unions of sets $X \times Y$, where X is closed in V and Y closed in W, and there are always subvarieties of $V \times W$ which are not of that form (for instance, any variety of dimension 1 on $V \times W$ whose projections on V and on W are both of dimension 1).

From now on, we shall use freely the usual topological terms (closure, neighborhood, etc.), always with reference to the Zariski topology; similarly, when the reference is to the k-topology, we shall speak of k-closure, k-neighborhood, etc. Every k-closed set is closed and is K-closed whenever $K \supset k$; one expresses this by saying that the Zariski topology is "finer" than all k-topologies, and the K-topology is finer than the k-topology for $K \supset k$. On the other hand, if a set is closed, there are fields k such that it is k-closed; for instance, every common field of definition for its components has that property; but there is not always a smallest field k such that a given closed set is k-closed; for instance, if k is of characteristic $p > 1$ and x is a generic point of S^1 over k, $\{x\}$ is K-closed for every $K = k(x^{p^n})$, but is not k-closed. Prop. 1 implies the "compactoid" property for the topologies in question.

THEOREM 1. *Let k be a field, X any subset of S^n and $\bar{X}$ its k-closure. Then $\bar{X}$ is the set of the common zeros in S^n of all the polynomials in $k[X]$ which are 0 at every point of X.*

Let $\mathfrak{A}$ be the set of all those polynomials; this is an ideal in $k[X]$, and the set X' of the common zeros of the polynomials in $\mathfrak{A}$ is also the set of the common zeros of the polynomials in any basis of $\mathfrak{A}$; therefore, by th. 7, Chap. IV, §4, X' is k-closed, so that it contains $\bar{X}$. Now write $\bar{X} = \{\mathfrak{B}\}$, where $\mathfrak{B}$ is a bunch of varieties; we can write $\mathfrak{B}$ as the union of bunches $\mathfrak{B}_\mu (1 \leqq \mu \leqq m)$, where each $\mathfrak{B}_\mu$ is the union of a variety V_μ, algebraic over k, and of all the conjugates of V_μ over k. For each μ, let x_μ be a generic point of V_μ over $\bar{k}$, and let $\mathfrak{P}_\mu$ be the prime ideal in $k[X]$ determined by x_μ over k; by definition, the common zeros of all the polynomials in $\mathfrak{P}_\mu$ are the finite specializations of x_μ over k, i.e., by th. 4 of Chap. IV, §2, the points of $\mathfrak{B}_\mu$. Let y be a point in $S^n - \bar{X}$; for every μ, y is not in $\mathfrak{B}_\mu$, so that there is a polynomial P_μ in $\mathfrak{P}_\mu$ such that $P_\mu(y) \neq 0$. Then the polynomial $\prod_\mu P_\mu(X)$ is 0 at every point of $\mathfrak{B}$, hence everywhere on X, and is not 0 at y; therefore y is not in X'. This proves that $X' \subset \bar{X}$.

COROLLARY 1. *A set F in S^n is k-closed if and only if it is the set of common zeros of all the polynomials in some ideal in $k[X_1, \cdots, X_n]$.*

The condition is necessary, by th. 1; it is sufficient, by th. 7 of Chap. IV, §4. Had we proved this first, prop. 1 would have followed at once from it and from Hilbert's theorem.

COROLLARY 2. *If k is a field, and x a point of S^n, the k-closure of $\{x\}$ is the* *union of the locus of x over $\bar{k}$ and of all its conjugates over k; in particular, it is the locus of x over k if x has a locus over k.*

This follows at once from th. 1 and from th. 4 of Chap. IV, §2.

COROLLARY 3. *If V is a variety, defined over a field k, every non-empty k-open subset of $\{V\}$ contains all the generic points of V over k.*

In fact, if this were not so, some generic point of V over k would be contained in some k-closed subset of $\{V\}$, other than $\{V\}$, and this would contradict coroll. 2.

COROLLARY 4. *If V is a variety, the closure of every non-empty open subset of $\{V\}$ is $\{V\}$.*

Let X be such a subset of $\{V\}$; let k be a field of definition of V such that X is k-open and that its closure $\bar{X}$ is k-closed; then, by coroll. 3 and coroll. 2, we must have $\bar{X} \supset \{V\}$; as $\{V\}$ is closed, this proves our assertion.

PROPOSITION 2. *If k is any field, every k-closed set contains all the finite specializations over k of every one of its points. Conversely, a closed set is k-closed if it contains all the generic specializations of all its points over k.*

In view of prop. 12 of Chap. IV, §4, all we have to prove is that, if X is a closed set and contains all generic specializations of some point x over k, it contains all specializations of x over k. In fact, let X' be the locus of x over $\bar{k}$, and X'' a conjugate of X' over k; by th. 4 of Chap. IV, §2, our assumption about X implies that X contains all the generic points of X'' over $\bar{k}$; in particular, if K is a field containing $\bar{k}$, such that X is K-closed, X contains all generic points of X'' over K, and therefore, by coroll. 2 of th. 1, it contains X''. Thus X contains all conjugates of X' over k; by th. 4 of Chap. IV, §2, this completes the proof.

COROLLARY 1. *Let k be a field, and K a field containing k; let F be a closed set, whose components are all defined over K. Then F is k-closed if and only if it is invariant under all isomorphisms of K over k.*

Put $F = \{\mathfrak{B}\}$, and call $V_1, \cdots, V_q$ the components of $\mathfrak{B}$; our condition means that, if σ is any isomorphism of K over k (i.e., any isomorphic mapping of K into the universal domain which leaves invariant all the elements of k), then $\mathfrak{B}$ is again the union of the varieties V_i^σ. Let σ be such an isomorphism, and assume F to be k-closed; σ can be extended to an isomorphism of $\bar{K}$ over k, and this induces on $\bar{k}$ an automorphism τ of $\bar{k}$ over k; as the V_i are algebraic over k, the V_i^σ are no other than the V_i^τ; by the definition of a k-closed set, every automorphism of $\bar{k}$ over k induces on the V_i a permutation among themselves; therefore it leaves F invariant. Conversely, assume that F satisfies the condition in our corollary, and let x' be a generic specialization over k of a point x of a component X of F; then the isomorphism of $k(x)$ onto $k(x')$ over k which maps x onto x' can be extended to an isomorphism σ of $K(x)$ onto a field $K^\sigma(x')$;

then, by coroll. 2 of th. 3, Chap. IV, §2, x' is on X^σ, hence on $F^\sigma = F$. Therefore F satisfies the condition in the second part of prop. 2.

COROLLARY 2. *Let V, W be two varieties, defined over k; let X be a k-closed subset of $V \times W$. Then the set Y of the points P of V, such that $P \times W \subset X$, is k-closed.*

Let Q be a generic point of W over k; let X_Q be the set of those points P of V such that (P, Q) is in X; this is the projection on V of the set $X \cap (V \times Q)$ and is obviously $k(Q)$-closed; Y is contained in X_Q for every Q, and therefore in the intersection Y' of all the sets X_Q when Q runs through the set of all generic points of W over k. Conversely, let P be in Y'; then $X \cap (P \times W)$ contains all points (P, Q), where Q is any generic point of W over k, and in particular it contains all generic points of $P \times W$ over $k(P)$; as it is a $k(P)$-closed set, coroll. 2 of th. 1 shows that it is $P \times W$, i.e. that P is in Y. Thus we have $Y = Y'$; but Y' is closed by its definition, and then coroll. 1 of prop. 2 shows that it is k-closed.

PROPOSITION 3. *Let U be a subvariety of a product $V \times W$; let U' be its projection on V; let k be a field of definition for U, V, W; let X be the set-theoretic projection on $\{V\}$ of the point-set $\{U\}$, considered as a subset of $\{V \times W\} = \{V\} \times \{W\}$. Then X contains a non-empty k-open subset of $\{U'\}$.*

Call S^n, S^m the ambient spaces of V, W; let (x, y) be a generic point of U over k, with $x = (x_1, \cdots, x_n)$ and $y = (y_1, \cdots, y_m)$. By prop. 12 of Chap. II, §3, y has a finite specialization y' over $k(x)$ which is algebraic over $k(x)$; (x, y') is then a specialization of (x, y) over k, i.e. a point of U, whose dimension over k is the same as that of x. Call d_j the degree of y'_j over $k(x)$; then y'_j satisfies an equation

$$\sum_{\nu=0}^{d_j} P_{j\nu}(x) \cdot (y'_j)^{d_j - \nu} = 0$$

where the $P_{j\nu}$ are in $k[X]$ and $P_{j0}(x) \neq 0$ for all j. Now let F be the set of common zeros of the ideal generated by a basis of the defining ideal for U' and by the polynomial $\prod_{j=1}^m P_{j0}(X)$; this is a closed proper subset of $\{U'\}$, so that $X' = \{U'\} - F$ is open and not empty. Let x' be any point of X'; then, by prop. 22 of Chap. II, §5, all the y'_j are finite over $x \to x'$ with reference to k; therefore, if y'' is a specialization of y' over $x \to x'$, with reference to k, it is finite. Then (x', y'') is a finite specialization of (x, y'), hence also of (x, y), with reference to k, and is therefore a point of U. This proves that X' is contained in X. Now let Z be the union of the open subsets of $\{U'\}$ which are contained in X; Z is open, and we have just proved that it is not empty; coroll. 1 of prop. 2 shows that it is k-open; this completes the proof.

From now on, *we shall identify varieties and bunches of varieties with the closed point-sets attached to them,* and consequently we shall discard the notation $\{V\}$,

$\{\mathfrak{B}\}$, which, in view of this, becomes superfluous. If U is a subvariety of a product $V \times W$, its projection U' on V in the sense of Chap. IV, §3, will be called its *geometric projection* whenever it is necessary to distinguish it from the *set-theoretic projection* of U on V; prop. 3 shows that the former is the closure of the latter; the latter will always be called the set-theoretic projection, but the former will often be called simply *the projection* when no confusion is to be feared. This is the only change of terminology required by our new identification.

2. Mappings and morphisms. We first make some additions to the language introduced in Chap. IV, §7.

Let U be a subvariety of a product $V \times W$, with the (geometric) projection V on V, and such that $[U:V] = 1$, i.e. that the projection from U to V is regular in the sense of Chap. IV, §7. Call $\mathfrak{X}$ the set of all those subvarieties of V along which the projection from U to V is regular. For any $X \in \mathfrak{X}$, th. 15 of Chap. IV, §7, shows that there is a uniquely determined subvariety Z of U with the projection X on V; call Y the (geometric) projection of Z on W, and put

$$Y = f_U(X).$$

Thus we have defined a mapping f_U of $\mathfrak{X}$ into the set of all subvarieties of W; more precisely, if we put $W' = f_U(V)$, i.e. if W' is the (geometric) projection of U on W, f_U maps $\mathfrak{X}$ into the set of all subvarieties of W'. In particular, if $\mathfrak{D}(U)$ is the set of all points of V at which the projection from U to V is regular, f_U induces a mapping, which we also denote by f_U, of $\mathfrak{D}(U)$ into W (the latter being identified, as we have said, with the set of its points), and more precisely into W'. By abuse of language, we shall call f_U *the mapping of V into W associated with U*; and, if X is a subvariety of V, we shall say that f_U is *defined at X* whenever X is in $\mathfrak{X}$, i.e. whenever the projection from U to V is regular along X. By *a mapping of a variety V into a variety W*, we shall always understand a mapping f_U associated with some subvariety U of $V \times W$ such that U has the projection V on V and that $[U:V] = 1$. If $U = V \times P$, where P is some point of W, f_U is defined for every subvariety X of V, and, for every such X, we have $f_U(X) = P$; this will be called *the constant mapping of V into W with the* (constant) *value P*; for this to be so, it is necessary and sufficient that $f_U(V)$ should be P. On the other hand, if $V = W$ and if U is the diagonal of $V \times V$, prop. 1 of Chap. VI, §1, shows that, for every subvariety X of V, f_U is defined and that we have $f_U(X) = X$; this is called *the identity mapping of V*. More generally, if $V \subset W$, and if we take for U the diagonal Δ_V of $V \times V$, considered as a subvariety of $V \times W$, the mapping f_U is called *the injection mapping of V into W*; it is everywhere defined, and we have $f_U(X) = X$ for every point or subvariety X of V.

Let again U be a subvariety of $V \times W$, with the geometric projection V on V, and such that $[U:V] = 1$; call f the mapping of V into W associated with U; and let $\mathfrak{D}$ be the set of the points of V at which f is defined, i.e. at which the projection from U to V is regular. Then, for every $P \in \mathfrak{D}$, $(P, f(P))$ is the uniquely determined point of U with the projection P on V; if k is any common field of definition for V, W and U, then prop. 28 of Chap. IV, §7, shows that $k(f(P)) \subset k(P)$. In particular, if M is a generic point of V over k, prop. 14 of Chap. II, §4, shows that f is defined at M; then the dimension of $(M, f(M))$ over k is the same as that of M over k, which is the dimension of V, and also that of U; therefore $(M, f(M))$ is then a generic point of U over k. Now call F the closure of the set of all points $(P, f(P))$, with $P \in \mathfrak{D}$, and let K be a common field of definition for V, W, U and all components of F, so that F is K-closed; taking M generic on U over K, we see that F must contain the K-closure of $(M, f(M))$ over K, which is U by coroll. 2 of th. 1, §1; on the other hand, all points $(P, f(P))$ are in U, so that $F \subset U$. This shows that U is the closure of the set of all points $(P, f(P))$, for $P \in \mathfrak{D}$, or, in other words, of the set-theoretical graph of the mapping of $\mathfrak{D}$ into W induced by f. By abuse of language, we will say that *U is the graph of the mapping f of V into W*. If f is a mapping of V into W, its graph will usually be denoted by Γ_f; by a *field of definition for f*, we understand any common field of definition for V, W and Γ_f.

In order to formulate our next result, we shall agree that, if Ω is any open subset of a variety V, the Zariski topology on Ω will be that induced by the Zariski topology on V, or, what amounts to the same, on the ambient space of V; if V is defined over k, and Ω is k-open on V, we define similarly the k-topology on Ω.

THEOREM 2. *Let f be a mapping of a variety V into a variety W; and let k be a field of definition for f. Then the set $\mathfrak{D}$ of the points of V where f is defined is non-empty and k-open on V; and f induces on $\mathfrak{D}$ a continuous and k-continuous mapping of $\mathfrak{D}$ into W.*

Let S^n, S^m be the ambient spaces for V and W; let (x, y) be a generic point over k of the graph Γ_f of f, with $y = (y_1, \cdots, y_m)$. Let x' be a point of V at which f is defined; by definition, this means that the y_j are all in the specialization-ring of x' in $k(x)$, i.e. that we can write $y_j = P_j(x)/Q_j(x)$ with P_j, Q_j in $k[X]$ and $Q_j(x') \neq 0$, for $1 \leqq j \leqq m$. If we put $A = \prod_j Q_j$, this shows that, for every j, $A(x)y_j$ is in the ring $k[x]$ generated over k by the x_i, and that $A(x') \neq 0$. Conversely, if A is in $k[X]$ and such that $A(x') \neq 0$ and that $A(x)y_j \in k[x]$ for every j, f is defined at x'. Now call $\mathfrak{A}$ the set of all polynomials A in $k[X]$, such that $A(x)y_j \in k[x]$ for every j; this is clearly an ideal in $k[X]$, containing the prime ideal $\mathfrak{P}$ which defines V over k, since we have $A(x) = 0$ for every $A \in \mathfrak{P}$; this implies that the set of zeros of $\mathfrak{A}$, i.e. the set of the common zeros of all polynomials in $\mathfrak{A}$, is contained in V. Now, from what we have proved, it follows that a point x' is in $V - \mathfrak{D}$ if and only if it is a zero of $\mathfrak{A}$; this shows that $V - \mathfrak{D}$ is k-closed, i.e. that $\mathfrak{D}$ is k-open. As we already know that $\mathfrak{D}$ contains all generic points of V over k, it is not empty. This proves the first part of our theorem.

As to the second part, let Z be any closed subset of W. Let X be the closure of the set-theoretic projection on V of the closed subset

$$T = \Gamma_f \cap (V \times Z)$$

of $V \times W$; this is the union of the geometric projections on V of the components of T. If a point P of $\mathfrak{D}$ is not in X, then $f(P)$ is not in Z, for otherwise $(P, f(P))$ would be both in Γ_f and in $V \times Z$. Now let P be in $\mathfrak{D} \cap X$; as it is in X, it is in the geometric projection Y' on V of some component Y of T. As P is in $\mathfrak{D}$, the projection from Γ_f to V is regular at P. Call M a generic point of Y' over a common field of definition K for f and Y'; as P is a specialization of M over K, f is defined at M, by the coroll. of th. 15, Chap. IV, §7, and $(M, f(M))$ is a generic point of Y over K; also, $(P, f(P))$ is a specialization of $(M, f(M))$ over K; therefore $(P, f(P))$ is in Y, hence in $V \times Z$, so that $f(P)$ is in Z. We have thus shown that, if P is in $\mathfrak{D}$, $f(P)$ is in Z if and only if P is in X. As $\mathfrak{D} \cap X$ is closed in $\mathfrak{D}$ by definition, this proves the continuity of f. The k-continuity, for any field of definition k for f, also follows from what we have just proved, in view of the fact that, if F is any k-closed subset of $V \times W$, the closure of its set-theoretic projection on V is also k-closed (this is for instance a consequence of coroll. 1 of prop. 2, §1). This completes the proof of our theorem. It is convenient to formulate as a separate corollary the characterization of $\mathfrak{D}$ which we have obtained by means of the ideal $\mathfrak{A}$:

COROLLARY 1. *Notations and assumptions being as in th. 2, let (x) be a generic point of V over k; put $f(x) = (y_1, \cdots, y_m)$, and call $\mathfrak{A}$ the ideal of all the polynomials A in $k[X]$ such that $A(x)y_j \in k[x]$ for all j. Then the set of zeros of $\mathfrak{A}$ is the set of the points of V where f is not defined.*

COROLLARY 2. *Notations and assumptions being as in th. 2 and in coroll. 1, f is everywhere defined on V if and only if the ring $k[y]$ is contained in the ring $k[x]$.*

This follows from coroll. 1 if we observe that, by Hilbert's theorem, $\mathfrak{A}$ has no zero if and only if it contains 1.

COROLLARY 3. *Assumptions and notations being as in th. 2, let X be a subvariety of V; then f is defined at X if and only if $\mathfrak{D} \cap X$ is not empty; and, when that is so, $f(X)$ is the closure of the set of all points $f(P)$ for $P \in \mathfrak{D} \cap X$.*

The first assertion follows at once from the definitions. Now let f be defined at X; call Y the closure of the set of points $f(P)$ for $P \in \mathfrak{D} \cap X$, and let K be a common field of definition for f, X and every component of Y, so that Y is K-closed. Let P be a generic point of X over K; then, by th. 15 of Chap. IV, §7, and its corollary, $(P, f(P))$ is a generic point over K of the uniquely determined subvariety Z of Γ_f with the geometric projection X on V, and $f(X)$ is the geometric projection of Z on W, which is the locus of $f(P)$ over K. As Y contains $f(P)$, it must contain its K-closure, which is $f(X)$ by coroll. 2 of th. 1, §1. On the other hand, if P' is any point of $\mathfrak{D} \cap X$, then, by prop. 28 of Chap. IV, §7, $f(P')$ is the uniquely determined specialization of $f(P)$ over $P \to P'$, with reference to K; therefore it is in $f(X)$, so that $Y \subset f(X)$.

From now on, notations being as in coroll. 3 of th. 2, the variety $f(X)$, when f is defined at X, will be called *the geometric image of X by f*; coroll. 3 of th. 2

shows that it is the closure of the set-theoretic image of $\mathfrak{D} \cap X$ by f. An everywhere defined mapping will be called a *morphism*; if $x = (x_1, \cdots, x_n)$ is a generic point of V over k, and if f is a mapping of V into a variety W in S^m, with the field of definition k, then, by coroll. 2 of th. 2, f is a morphism if and only if $f(x)$ can be written as

$$f(x) = (P_1(x), \cdots, P_m(x)),$$

where the P_j are polynomials in $k[X]$.

Let f be a mapping of a variety V into a variety W, with the field of definition k. If f is defined at a point P of V, $f(P)$ is called *the value of f at P*; we have already observed that $k(f(P))$ is then contained in $k(P)$; if P' is a finite specialization of P over k, hence also a point of V, and if f is defined at P', then, by prop. 29 of Chap. IV, §7, and prop. 13 of Chap. II, §4, $f(P')$ is the uniquely determined specialization of $f(P)$ over $P \to P'$ with reference to k. If M is a generic point of V over k, then $(M, f(M))$ is a generic point over k of the graph Γ_f of f. Conversely, let V and W be two varieties, both defined over k; let M be a generic point of V over k, and let N be a point of W such that

$$k(N) \subset k(M);$$

then the locus of (M, N) over k is the graph of a mapping f of V into W, with the field of definition k; f is uniquely determined by these conditions, and will be called the mapping of V into W, with the field of definition k, such that $f(M) = N$.

Let f be a mapping of V into W, and let V' be a subvariety of V; instead of saying that f is defined at V', we will frequently say that it is *defined along V'*. Assume that f is defined along V'; then, by th. 15 of Chap. IV, §7, there is a uniquely determined subvariety of Γ_f with the geometric projection V' on V, and it is the graph of a mapping f' of V' into W; if k is a common field of definition for f and V', and if M' is a generic point of V' over k, f' may also be described as the mapping of V' into W, with the field of definition k, such that $f'(M') = f(M')$. We say that f' is *the mapping of V' into W induced by f on V'*. If $\mathfrak{D}$ and $\mathfrak{D}'$ are the sets of points where f and f', respectively, are defined, then the coroll. of th. 15, Chap. IV, §7, shows that $\mathfrak{D}' \supset \mathfrak{D} \cap V'$; f' coincides with f on $\mathfrak{D} \cap V'$, since, for every point P in that set, $(P', f'(P'))$ is in $\Gamma_{f'}$, hence also in Γ_f. It may happen that $\mathfrak{D}'$ is not the same as $\mathfrak{D} \cap V'$; for instance, if f is the mapping of S^2 into S^1 given by $f(x_1, x_2) = x_1/x_2$, it is not defined at $(0, 0)$, and it induces on the variety $X_1 = 0$ the constant mapping 0, which is everywhere defined.

Let again f be a mapping of V into W; let W' be a subvariety of W. The geometric image $f(V)$ of V by f is contained in W' if and only if the graph Γ_f of f is contained in $V \times W'$; in that case, Γ_f is also the graph of a mapping of V into W', defined at the same points of V as f and having the same values at all those points; by abuse of language, that mapping is usually identified with f.

If f is a mapping of a product $V_1 \times \cdots \times V_n$ into a variety W, and if

$$P_1 \times \cdots \times P_n$$

is a point of that product where f is defined, then we usually write

$$f(P_1, \cdots, P_n),$$

instead of $f(P_1 \times \cdots \times P_n)$, for the value of f at that point. On the other hand, take $m + 1$ varieties $V, W_1, \cdots, W_m$, and, for each j, a mapping f_j of V into W_j; one sees at once that there is a mapping f of V into

$$W_1 \times \cdots \times W_m,$$

defined at those points of V where all the f_j are defined and at no other point of V, with the value

$$f(P) = f_1(P) \times \cdots \times f_m(P),$$

wherever it is defined. This will be denoted by $f = (f_1, \cdots, f_m)$.

Proposition 4. *Let f be a mapping of a product $U \times V$ into a variety W; let k be a field of definition for U, V, W and f; let (M, N) be a generic point of $U \times V$ over k. Then there is a mapping f_M of V into W, with the field of definition $k(M)$, such that $f_M(N) = f(M, N)$; if N' is any point of V, f is defined at (M, N') if and only if f_M is defined at N', and, when that is so, we have*

$$f(M, N') = f_M(N').$$

The first assertion is obvious from what has been said above; the second one is an easy consequence of the definitions and of prop. 17, Chap. II, §4.

Theorem 3. *Let U, V, W be three varieties; let f be a mapping of U into V, and g a mapping of V into W. Let $\mathfrak{D}_f$, $\mathfrak{D}_g$ be the point-sets where f and g, respectively, are defined; let k be a field of definition for f and g. Then the set $\mathfrak{D}'$ of the points P of $\mathfrak{D}_f$ such that $f(P) \in \mathfrak{D}_g$ is k-open on U; it is non-empty if and only if g is defined at the variety $f(U)$. Furthermore, when that is so, the closure of the set of the points $(P, g(f(P)))$ on $U \times W$, for $P \in \mathfrak{D}'$, is the graph of a mapping h of U into W, defined everywhere on $\mathfrak{D}'$ and such that $h(P) = g(f(P))$ for every $P \in \mathfrak{D}'$; and k is a field of definition for h.*

By coroll. 3 of th. 2, $f(U)$ is the closure of the set of points $f(P)$ for $P \in \mathfrak{D}_f$; this implies that $f(U)$ is contained in the closed set $V - \mathfrak{D}_g$, i.e. that $f(U) \cap \mathfrak{D}_g$ is empty, if and only if all the points $f(P)$, for $P \in \mathfrak{D}_f$, are in $V - \mathfrak{D}_g$, i.e. if and only if $\mathfrak{D}'$ is empty. The same corollary shows that $f(U) \cap \mathfrak{D}_g$ is empty if and only if g is not defined at $f(U)$. As $\mathfrak{D}'$ is the complement in $\mathfrak{D}_f$ of the set of points $P \in \mathfrak{D}_f$ such that $f(P)$ is in $V - \mathfrak{D}_g$, and as the latter set is closed, th. 2 shows that $\mathfrak{D}'$ is k-open in $\mathfrak{D}_f$, hence also in U. This proves the first part of our theorem. Now let x be a generic point of U over k, and put $y = f(x)$; y is generic on $f(U)$ over k. Let g be defined at y; put $z = g(y) = g(f(x))$. As we have $k(z) \subset k(y) \subset k(x)$, there is a mapping h

of U into W, with the field of definition k, such that $z = h(x)$. Let x' be any point of $\mathfrak{D}'$, and put

$$y' = f(x'), \qquad z' = g(y');$$

then y' is the uniquely determined specialization of y over $x \to x'$, with reference to k, and z' is the uniquely determined specialization of z over $y \to y'$, with reference to k; this implies that (x', z') is a specialization of (x, z) over k, i.e. a point of the graph Γ_h of h. Call R the set of points $(x', g(f(x')))$ for $x' \in \mathfrak{D}'$; we have thus shown that R, hence also its closure $\bar{R}$, are contained in Γ_h. Let now K be a field containing k, such that $\bar{R}$ is K-closed; let Z be the locus of (x, y, z) over k, and let $(\bar{x}, \bar{y}, \bar{z})$ be a generic point of Z over K; as this is a generic specialization of (x, y, z) over k, we have $\bar{y} = f(\bar{x})$, $\bar{z} = g(\bar{y})$, so that $(\bar{x}, \bar{z})$ is in R; by coroll. 2 of th. 1, §1, this implies that $\bar{R}$ contains the locus of $(\bar{x}, \bar{z})$ over K, which is Γ_h. So we have $\bar{R} = \Gamma_h$.

Finally, let again x' be a point of $\mathfrak{D}'$, and put $y' = f(x')$, $z' = g(y')$; to complete the proof of our theorem, it will be enough to show that h is defined at x'; for then $h(x')$ will be the uniquely determined specialization of z over $x \to x'$, with reference to k; as we already know that z' is such a specialization, this will imply $h(x') = z'$. Let S^n, S^m be the ambient spaces for V and for W; put $y = (y_1, \cdots, y_n)$, $z = (z_1, \cdots, z_m)$. For each i, we can write y_i in the form $y_i = P_i(x)/Q_i(x)$ with P_i, Q_i in $k[X]$ and $Q_i(x') \neq 0$; then we have

$$y' = (y'_1, \cdots, y'_n),$$

where the y'_i are given by $y'_i = P_i(x')/Q_i(x')$. Let $\bar{y}$ be a generic point of V over k, and put $\bar{z} = g(\bar{y}) = (\bar{z}_1, \cdots, \bar{z}_m)$, $z' = (z'_1, \cdots, z'_m)$; if, for some given value of j, we write $\bar{z}_j = F(\bar{y})/G(\bar{y})$, with F, G in $k[Y]$ and $G(y') \neq 0$, we have $G(y) \neq 0$ (since y' is a specialization of y over k), so that the j-th coordinates of z and of z' are respectively given by

$$z_j = F(y)/G(y), \qquad z'_j = F(y')/G(y').$$

That being so, there are polynomials Φ, Ψ in $k[X]$, and an integer N, such that, if we put

$$Q(X) = \prod_{i=1}^{n} Q_i(X)^N,$$

we have:

$$Q(X) \cdot F(P_1(X)/Q_1(X), \cdots, P_n(X)/Q_n(X)) = \Phi(X),$$

$$Q(X) \cdot G(P_1(X)/Q_1(X), \cdots, P_n(X)/Q_n(X)) = \Psi(X).$$

Then we have $\Psi(x)z_j = \Phi(x)$ and $\Psi(x') \neq 0$, hence also $\Psi(x) \neq 0$, which shows that z_j is in the specialization-ring of x' in $k(x)$. As this is true for every j, we have thus proved that the mapping h defined above is defined at x'.

It should be observed that, with the notations of th. 3, h may be defined at other points than those of $\mathfrak{D}'$; for instance, if g is a constant mapping, h is also constant and has the same value; in that case, g and h are everywhere defined, while $\mathfrak{D}'$ coincides with $\mathfrak{D}_f$ and may be a proper subset of U.

The assumptions being those of th. 3, *we shall write* $h = g \circ f$. With this notation, we have the following obvious corollary to th. 3:

COROLLARY. *Let U, V, W be three varieties; let f be a morphism of U into V, and g a morphism of V into W. Then $g \circ f$ is a morphism of U into W.*

Th. 3 makes it possible to use the functional notation in algebraic geometry, very much in the usual manner; a trivial induction shows that it can be used to superpose functions of any number of variables in any number. As it would be tedious to make a formal and completely general statement of what is meant here, it will be enough to indicate our meaning by an example. Let U_1, U_2, V_0, V_1, V_2, W be varieties; let φ, f, g, F be mappings, as follows: φ, of U_2 into V_0; f, of $U_1 \times V_0$ into V_1; g, of U_1 into V_2; F, of $V_1 \times V_2$ into W; let k be a common field of definition for all of these. If u_1 is any point of U_1, and u_2 any point of U_2, we shall say that the functional symbol

$$F(f(u_1, \varphi(u_2)), g(u_1))$$

is defined and has the value w if the following holds true: (a) φ is defined at u_2; (b) f is defined at $(u_1, \varphi(u_2))$; (c) g is defined at u_1; (d) F is defined at

$$(f(u_1, \varphi(u_2)), g(u_1))$$

and has the value w at that point. Thus, in th. 3, $\mathfrak{D}'$ is the set of points for which the functional symbol $g(f(P))$ is defined. By repeated application of th. 3 in the present instance (and, in general, by induction), it is easily seen that, if there is any point (u_1, u_2) of $U_1 \times U_2$ such that the functional symbol written above is defined, then it is also defined whenever (u_1, u_2) is a generic point of $U_1 \times U_2$ over k. Moreover, if we assume that this is so, then there is a mapping G of $U_1 \times U_2$ into W, with the field of definition k, such that

$$G(u_1, u_2) = F(f(u_1, \varphi(u_2)), g(u_1))$$

whenever the right-hand side is defined; this means that G is defined (at least) at every point (u_1, u_2) of $U_1 \times U_2$ for which the functional symbol in the right-hand side is defined, and has the same value as the latter at every such point. From what has been said, it will be clear that, in order to verify the above relation for *all* such points, it is enough to verify it for *one generic point* of $U_1 \times U_2$ over k. Similar conclusions obviously hold for relations containing functional symbols on both sides. Of course, if all the mappings appearing in a "functional symbol" are morphisms, then the functional symbol is everywhere defined and determines a morphism.

We can now apply the foregoing definitions and results to birational correspondences. Let T be a birational correspondence between two varieties V and W; let k be a field of definition for V, W and T; let (M, N) be a generic point of T over k, so that we have $k(M) = k(N)$. Then, according to our definitions, there is a mapping f of V into W and a mapping g of W into V, both with the field of definition k, such that $N = f(M)$ and $M = g(N)$; the graph of f is T, and the graph of g is the locus of (N, M) over k on $W \times V$; $g \circ f$ and $f \circ g$ are both defined, and are the identity mappings of V and of W, respectively. Under these circumstances, we say that f and g are *inverse* to each other, and we write $g = f^{-1}$. When the graph of a mapping f of V into W is a birational correspondence between V and W, we shall say that f is a *birational mapping of V into W.*

PROPOSITION 5. *Let V and W be two varieties; let f be a mapping of V into W, and g a mapping of W into V, such that $g \circ f$ and $f \circ g$ are both defined and are the identity mappings of V and of W, respectively. Then f is a birational mapping of V into W, and g is its inverse.*

Let k be a common field of definition for f and g; let M be a generic point of V over k; put $N = f(M)$; then g is defined at N, and we have $g(N) = M$; this implies $k(N) \subset k(M)$, $k(M) \subset k(N)$, and hence $k(N) = k(M)$; if m, n are the dimensions of V and of W, M and N are then both of dimension m over k, which implies that $n \geqq m$. Exchanging f and g, we find similarly that $m \geqq n$. This gives $m = n$, so that N is a generic point of W over k. The graph of f, i.e. the locus of (M, N) over k, is then a birational correspondence between V and W, as asserted.

We shall now investigate the structure of the set of points where a birational mapping T between V and W is biregular. Let f be the mapping of V into W with the graph T; according to our definitions (those of Chap. IV, §7, and those of this Chapter), T is biregular at a point P of V if f is defined at P and if f^{-1} is defined at $f(P)$; when that is so, we shall also say that f is *biregular at P*; then, of course, we have $f^{-1}(f(P)) = P$, and f^{-1} is biregular at $f(P)$.

PROPOSITION 6. *Let f be a birational mapping of V into W, with the field of definition k and the graph T. Let $\mathfrak{D}_V$ and $\mathfrak{D}_W$ be the sets of points where f and f^{-1}, respectively, are biregular; let $\mathfrak{E}$ be the set of points $(P, f(P))$ for $P \in \mathfrak{D}_V$. Then $\mathfrak{D}_V$, $\mathfrak{D}_W$ and $\mathfrak{E}$ are non-empty k-open subsets of V, of W and of T, respectively; and the mappings which, to every P in $\mathfrak{D}_V$, assign the points $f(P)$ and $(P, f(P))$ are one-to-one, bicontinuous and k-bicontinuous mappings of $\mathfrak{D}_V$ onto $\mathfrak{D}_W$ and onto $\mathfrak{E}$, respectively.*

Let $\mathfrak{D}'$, $\mathfrak{D}''$ be the sets of points where f and f^{-1}, respectively, are defined; $\mathfrak{D}_V$ is the set of the points P in $\mathfrak{D}'$ such that $f(P)$ is in $\mathfrak{D}''$; by th. 2, this implies that $\mathfrak{D}_V$ is k-open; similarly, $\mathfrak{D}_W$ is k-open. The assertions about the mapping of $\mathfrak{D}_V$ into $\mathfrak{D}_W$ induced by f follow at once from th. 2. Now let F be the mapping of V into T such that $F(P) = (P, f(P))$ for every P where f is defined; this is a birational mapping, and it is biregular at every point of $\mathfrak{D}'$; therefore it induces a one-to-one, bicontinuous and k-bicontinuous mapping of $\mathfrak{D}'$ onto its set-theoretic image $\mathfrak{E}'$ by F; in view of our definitions for the topologies of open sets, this implies that the mapping of $\mathfrak{D}_V$ onto $\mathfrak{E}$ induced by it on $\mathfrak{D}_V$ has the same properties and that $\mathfrak{E}$ is k-open on $\mathfrak{E}'$, hence on T.

With the notations of prop. 6, we will say that the birational mapping f is *coherent* if $\mathfrak{E} = T$; in other words, f is coherent if f is defined at P, and f^{-1} at Q, whenever (P, Q) is a point of the graph of f. Prop. 6, applied to that case, gives the following:

COROLLARY. *Let f be a coherent birational mapping of a variety V into a variety W, with the field of definition k and the graph T. Let $\mathfrak{D}_V$ and $\mathfrak{D}_W$ be the set-theoretic projections of T on V and on W. Then $\mathfrak{D}_V$ is the same as the set of points of V where f is defined, and also as the set of points of V where f is biregular; and the projection from $V \times W$ to V induces on T a one-to-one, bicontinuous and k-bicontinuous mapping of T onto $\mathfrak{D}_V$.*

The following proposition gives a criterion for coherent birational mappings:

PROPOSITION 7. *Let T be a subvariety of a product $V \times W$, with the geometric projections V on V and W on W; let S^n, S^m be the ambient spaces for V and for W; let k be a field of definition for V, W and T, and let (x, y) be a generic point of T over k. Let $\mathfrak{P}$ be the ideal defining T in $k[X, Y]$; let $\mathfrak{A}$ be the ideal of the polynomials A in $k[X]$, such that $A(x)y_j$ is in $k[x]$ for every j; let $\mathfrak{B}$ be the ideal of the polynomials B in $k[Y]$, such that $B(y)x_i$ is in $k[y]$ for every i. Then T is the graph of a coherent birational mapping of V into W if and only if*

$$\mathfrak{P} + \mathfrak{A}\cdot k[X, Y] = \mathfrak{P} + \mathfrak{B}\cdot k[X, Y] = k[X, Y].$$

By $\mathfrak{A}\cdot k[X, Y]$, we denote, of course, the ideal generated in $k[X, Y]$ by the polynomials in $\mathfrak{A}$; this consists of all polynomials which can be written as

$$\sum A_\nu(X)P_\nu(Y),$$

where the A_ν are in $\mathfrak{A}$ and the P_ν in $k[Y]$, so that it could also be denoted by $\mathfrak{A}\cdot k[Y]$; a similar remark applies to $\mathfrak{B}\cdot k[X, Y]$. By Hilbert's theorem, the ideal $\mathfrak{P} + \mathfrak{A}\cdot k[X, Y]$ is the same as $k[X, Y]$ if and only if it has no zero, i.e. if and only if there is no point (x', y') of T such that x' is a zero of $\mathfrak{A}$. In particular, if that is so, x is not a zero of $\mathfrak{A}$, so that there is a polynomial A in $\mathfrak{A}$ such that $A(x) \neq 0$; then, writing the $A(x)y_j$ in the form $F_j(x)$, with $F_j \in k[X]$, we get $y_j = F_j(x)/A(x)$, so that $k(x, y) = k(x)$. The assumption on $\mathfrak{B}$ implies similarly that $k(x, y) = k(y)$; as our assumptions imply that x is generic on V, and y on W, over k, this shows that T is the graph of a birational mapping of V into W. That being so, coroll. 1 of th. 2 shows at once that this mapping is coherent; this proves that the condition in our theorem is sufficient. Its necessity is an immediate consequence of the same corollary.

If a birational mapping f of V into W is such that f and f^{-1} are both morphisms, then we say that f is an *isomorphism* of V onto W; we call it a *k-isomorphism* if, at the same time, k is a field of definition for f. Then, by prop. 6, f determines a one-to-one, bicontinuous and k-bicontinuous correspondence between V and W. If f is an isomorphism, f and f^{-1} are biregular everywhere (this is sometimes expressed by saying that f is everywhere biregular on V and on W, or, by abuse of language, that it is "everywhere biregular"). If (x, y) is a generic point of the graph of f over k, then, by coroll. 2 of th. 2, f is an isomorphism if and only if $k[x] = k[y]$.

3. Abstract varieties. Topologists and differential geometers have frequently defined manifolds by means of overlapping neighborhoods, of homeomorphisms between parts of these, and by the identification of corresponding points in these homeomorphisms. We shall imitate this procedure in order to extend the concept of variety.

Let A be any set; let the V_α, for $\alpha \in A$, be varieties, in the same or in different spaces. We shall say that $(f_{\beta\alpha})$ is a *consistent set of birational mappings between the* V_α if, for every pair (α, β), $f_{\beta\alpha}$ is a birational mapping of V_α into V_β, and if, for all α, β, γ, these satisfy the relation $f_{\gamma\alpha} = f_{\gamma\beta} \circ f_{\beta\alpha}$. This can also be written as $f_{\beta\alpha} = f_{\gamma\beta}^{-1} \circ f_{\gamma\alpha}$; for $\beta = \alpha$, it shows that $f_{\alpha\alpha}$, for every α, is the identity mapping on V_α; then, for $\gamma = \alpha$, it shows that $f_{\beta\alpha} = f_{\alpha\beta}^{-1}$ for all α, β.

Now let A be a *finite* set of indices; let the V_α, for $\alpha \in A$, be varieties, in the same or in different spaces; let $(f_{\beta\alpha})$, for α, β in A, be a *consistent* set of *coherent* birational mappings between the V_α. If we call $T_{\beta\alpha}$ the graph of $f_{\beta\alpha}$, and $\mathfrak{D}_{\beta\alpha}$ the set of points of V_α where $f_{\beta\alpha}$ is defined, then, by prop. 6 of §2 and its corollary, $\mathfrak{D}_{\beta\alpha}$ is the set-theoretic projection of $T_{\beta\alpha}$ on V_α, and $f_{\beta\alpha}$ determines a one-to-one mapping of $\mathfrak{D}_{\beta\alpha}$ onto $\mathfrak{D}_{\alpha\beta}$. Let $\mathfrak{S}$ be the "set-theoretic sum" of the varieties V_α; this can be defined as the set of all pairs (α, P_α), where $\alpha \in A$ and P_α is a point of V_α. For two elements (α, P_α), (β, P_β) of that set, we shall write $(\alpha, P_\alpha) \sim (\beta, P_\beta)$ whenever (P_α, P_β) is in the graph $T_{\beta\alpha}$ of $f_{\beta\alpha}$. This is an equivalence relation:

(a) it is reflexive, since $f_{\alpha\alpha}$ is the identity on V_α;

(b) it is symmetric, since $f_{\beta\alpha} = f_{\alpha\beta}^{-1}$;

(c) it is transitive; in fact, if (P_α, P_β) is in $T_{\beta\alpha}$ and (P_β, P_γ) in $T_{\gamma\beta}$, then $f_{\beta\alpha}$ is defined at P_α, $f_{\gamma\beta}$ at P_β, and we have $P_\beta = f_{\beta\alpha}(P_\alpha)$, $P_\gamma = f_{\gamma\beta}(P_\beta)$; therefore the functional symbol $f_{\gamma\beta}(f_{\beta\alpha}(P_\alpha))$ is defined and has the value P_γ. As $f_{\gamma\alpha} = f_{\gamma\beta} \circ f_{\beta\alpha}$, this implies, by th. 3 of § 2, that $f_{\gamma\alpha}$ is defined at P_α and has the value P_γ at that point.

The set-theoretic quotient of $\mathfrak{S}$ by the equivalence relation we have just defined will be called the *abstract variety* determined by the V_α and the $f_{\beta\alpha}$, and will be denoted by $\mathbf{V} = [V_\alpha, f_{\beta\alpha}]_{\alpha,\beta\in A}$; it can be described as the set derived from the set-theoretic sum of the varieties V_α by "identifying" a point P_α of V_α with a point P_β of V_β whenever we have $P_\beta = f_{\beta\alpha}(P_\alpha)$; more precisely, if $\mathfrak{D}_{\beta\alpha}$ is the open subset of V_α where $f_{\beta\alpha}$ is defined, we are identifying the subset $\mathfrak{D}_{\beta\alpha}$ of V_α with the subset $\mathfrak{D}_{\alpha\beta}$ of V_β, for each pair (α, β), by means of the one-to-one mapping of $\mathfrak{D}_{\beta\alpha}$ onto $\mathfrak{D}_{\alpha\beta}$ induced by $f_{\beta\alpha}$. The varieties V_α are called the *representatives* of $\mathbf{V}$; the equivalence classes which are the elements of $\mathbf{V}$ are called its *points*; if (α, P_α) is an element of the equivalence class which defines a point $\mathbf{P}$ of $\mathbf{V}$, we shall say that $\mathbf{P}$ has *the representative* P_α in V_α. From now on, abstract varieties, and points on such varieties, will usually be denoted by bold-face capitals.

An abstract variety with only one representative is necessarily of the form $[V, i_V]$, where i_V is the identity mapping of V, and will be called an *affine variety.* We can identify $[V, i_V]$ with V in an obvious manner; this makes the "varieties" in the sense of Chap. IV a special case of our abstract varieties; of course one has then to take care that all definitions given for abstract varieties coincide with the former ones in the case of affine varieties. Eventually the word "abstract" will be dropped altogether; after this is done, it will still be possible, by using the word "affine", to distinguish, whenever necessary, the varieties in the sense of Chap. IV from the more general ones we have just defined.

Let $\boldsymbol{V} = [V_\alpha, f_{\beta\alpha}]_{\alpha,\beta\in A}$ be an abstract variety; we say that n is the dimension of $\boldsymbol{V}$ if it is the dimension of its representatives V_α. By a *field of definition for* $\boldsymbol{V}$, we understand any common field of definition for all the V_α and $f_{\beta\alpha}$. If k is such a field, and if P_α, P_β are two representatives for a point $\boldsymbol{P}$ of $\boldsymbol{V}$, then the relation $P_\beta = f_{\beta\alpha}(P_\alpha)$ holds and implies that $k(P_\alpha) = k(P_\beta)$; we may therefore define $k(\boldsymbol{P})$ as being the field $k(P_\alpha)$ if P_α is any representative of $\boldsymbol{P}$. The smallest common field of definition for the V_α and the $f_{\beta\alpha}$ is the smallest field of definition for $\boldsymbol{V}$.

Let again $\boldsymbol{V} = [V_\alpha, f_{\beta\alpha}]_{\alpha,\beta\in A}$ be an abstract variety, defined over a field k. Let W_α be a subvariety of V_α, defined over a field K containing k; let M_α be a generic point of W_α over K; let B be the set of all indices $\beta \in A$ such that $f_{\beta\alpha}$ is defined at W_α, or, what amounts to the same, at M_α; put

$$M_\beta = f_{\beta\alpha}(M_\alpha), \qquad W_\beta = f_{\beta\alpha}(W_\alpha)$$

for $\beta \in B$. Then, for every pair β, γ in B, we have $M_\gamma = f_{\gamma\beta}(M_\beta)$, and therefore, since W_β, W_γ are the loci of M_β, M_γ over k, $W_\gamma = f_{\gamma\beta}(W_\beta)$. From th. 17 of Chap. IV, §7, it follows, in view of the definitions in §2, that the mapping $g_{\gamma\beta}$ of W_β into W_γ induced by $f_{\gamma\beta}$ is birational. As all the W_β, $g_{\gamma\beta}$ have K as a field of definition, and as M_β is generic on W_β over K, the formula

$$g_{\delta\beta}(M_\beta) = g_{\delta\gamma}(g_{\gamma\beta}(M_\beta)),$$

where β, γ, δ are any three indices in B, shows that the set $(g_{\gamma\beta})$ is consistent. As the graph of $g_{\gamma\beta}$ is contained in the graph of $f_{\gamma\beta}$, $f_{\gamma\beta}$ is defined at P_β if (P_β, P_γ) is any point of the graph of $g_{\gamma\beta}$; therefore, as we have seen in §2, $g_{\gamma\beta}$ is also defined there. Thus the $g_{\gamma\beta}$ are coherent, and we may use them to define an abstract variety $\boldsymbol{W} = [W_\beta, g_{\gamma\beta}]_{\beta,\gamma\in B}$, defined over K. For any $\beta \in B$, let P_β be a point in W_β; if an element λ of A is such that $f_{\lambda\beta}$ is defined at P_β, then, by prop. 29 of Chap. IV, §7, $f_{\lambda\beta}$ is also defined at M_β, and therefore $f_{\lambda\alpha} = f_{\lambda\beta} \circ f_{\beta\alpha}$ is defined at M_α, so that we have $\lambda \in B$, and then $g_{\lambda\beta}$, being the mapping induced by $f_{\lambda\beta}$ on W_β, is defined at P_β and coincides there with $f_{\lambda\beta}$. Conversely, if λ is in B and such that $g_{\lambda\beta}$ is defined at P_β, then $(P_\beta, g_{\lambda\beta}(P_\beta))$ is in the graph of $g_{\lambda\beta}$, hence in the graph of $f_{\lambda\beta}$, so that $f_{\lambda\beta}$ is defined at P_β. In other words, the elements λ of A such that $f_{\lambda\beta}(P_\beta)$ is defined are the same as the elements λ of B such that $g_{\lambda\beta}(P_\beta)$ is defined, and, for every such λ, those symbols have the same value. This means that the equivalence class which defines the point $\boldsymbol{P}$ of $\boldsymbol{V}$ with the representative P_β on V_β is the same as the equivalence class which defines the point of $\boldsymbol{W}$ with the representative P_β on W_β; thus $\boldsymbol{W}$, as a point-set, is contained in $\boldsymbol{V}$. Moreover, an index λ in A belongs to B if and only if some point of $\boldsymbol{W}$ has a representative in V_λ; and, when that is so, W_λ is the set of the representatives in V_λ of all those points of $\boldsymbol{W}$ which have such a representative; furthermore, the graph of $g_{\gamma\beta}$, for β and γ in B, is the set of all points (P_β, P_γ) of $W_\beta \times W_\gamma$ such that $(\beta, P_\beta) \sim (\gamma, P_\gamma)$. This shows that B, the W_β, and the $g_{\gamma\beta}$, are uniquely determined by the point-set $\boldsymbol{W}$ (which is why it was not necessary to make a distinction between an abstract variety and the set of its points).

Under the circumstances described above, we say that $\boldsymbol{W}$ is a *subvariety of* $\boldsymbol{V}$; if $\boldsymbol{M}$ is the point of $\boldsymbol{V}$ with the representative M_β in V_β for every $\beta \in B$, we say that $\boldsymbol{M}$ is *a generic point of* $\boldsymbol{W}$ *over* K, and that $\boldsymbol{W}$ is *the locus of* $\boldsymbol{M}$ *over* K *in* $\boldsymbol{V}$.

Let again $\boldsymbol{V} = [V_\alpha, f_{\beta\alpha}]_{\alpha,\beta\in A}$ be an abstract variety, defined over k; let $\boldsymbol{M}$ be a generic point of $\boldsymbol{V}$ over k, with the representatives M_α. Let (P_α) be a specialization over k, finite or not, of the set of points (M_α); let B be the set of those α for which P_α is finite; and assume first that B is not empty. Then, for each β in B, P_β is a point of V_β; moreover, for β, γ in B, (P_β, P_γ) is a finite specialization of (M_β, M_γ) over k, i.e. a point of the graph of $f_{\gamma\beta}$, so that the (β, P_β), for $\beta \in B$, all belong to one and the same equivalence class, which defines a point $\boldsymbol{P}$ of $\boldsymbol{V}$. Conversely, if $\boldsymbol{P}$ has a representative in V_λ, then λ must be in B, and this representative must be P_λ; for in that case $f_{\lambda\beta}$ must be defined at P_β for every $\beta \in B$, and then M_λ has the uniquely determined specialization $f_{\lambda\beta}(P_\beta)$ over $M_\beta \to P_\beta$, with reference to k, so that we must have $P_\lambda = f_{\lambda\beta}(P_\beta)$. In other words, those among the P_α which are finite are precisely the representatives of $\boldsymbol{P}$. Under these circumstances, we shall say that (P_α) is *a specialization of* (M_α) *over* k, *attached to* $\boldsymbol{P}$. If a point $\boldsymbol{P}$ of $\boldsymbol{V}$ has the representative P_λ in V_λ, then every specialization (P_α) of (M_α) over $M_\lambda \to P_\lambda$, with reference to k, is attached to $\boldsymbol{P}$.

Now, let $\boldsymbol{P}$ and $\boldsymbol{P}'$ be two points of $\boldsymbol{V}$; assume that, for some α, they both have representatives P_α, P'_α in V_α, and that P'_α is a specialization of P_α over k. Let B be the set of those β for which $\boldsymbol{P}$ has a representative P_β in V_β, and let B' be the similarly defined set for $\boldsymbol{P}'$. For every $\beta \in B'$, $f_{\beta\alpha}$ is defined at P'_α, hence also at P_α by prop. 29 of Chap. IV, §7; therefore we have $B \supset B'$; also, for every $\beta \in B'$, P'_β is the uniquely determined specialization of $M_\beta = f_{\beta\alpha}(M_\alpha)$ over $M_\alpha \to P'_\alpha$, with reference to k; now, if P''_β is any specialization of P_β over $P_\alpha \to P'_\alpha$, with reference to k, then (P'_α, P''_β) is a specialization of (P_α, P_β), hence also of (M_α, M_β) over k, so that we must have $P''_\beta = P'_\beta$. In particular, this shows that P'_β is a specialization of P_β over k for every $\beta \in B'$. When that is so, we shall say that $\boldsymbol{P}'$ is *a specialization of* $\boldsymbol{P}$ *over* k *on* $\boldsymbol{V}$. In that case, if (P_α) is any specialization of (M_α) over k, attached to $\boldsymbol{P}$, and if, for some $\beta \in B'$, (P'_α) is a specialization of (P_α) over $P_\beta \to P'_\beta$, with reference to k, then (P'_α) is a specialization of (M_α) over k, attached to $\boldsymbol{P}'$; thus the existence of such specializations (P_α), (P'_α) of (M_α) is a necessary and sufficient condition for $\boldsymbol{P}'$ to be a specialization of $\boldsymbol{P}$ over k on $\boldsymbol{V}$.

Just as in the case of specializations of sets of quantities, or of points in n-space, specializations of points of abstract varieties are transitive; by this we mean that, if P, P' and P'' are points of V, such that P' is a specialization of P, and P'' a specialization of P', over k on V, then P'' is a specialization of P over k on V. Our definition of subvarieties shows at once that, if a subvariety W of V has the generic point P over a field K, then it is the set of all the points of V which are specializations of P over K on V. From this, one concludes easily that, if Q and Q' are points of such a subvariety W of V, then Q' is a specialization of Q over K on W if and only if it is a specialization of Q over K on V. In particular, if $K(Q)$ is a regular extension of K, so that Q has a locus over K both on V and on W, these loci are the same; this can be expressed by saying that every subvariety of W is a subvariety of V.

Let again $V = [V_\alpha, f_{\beta\alpha}]_{\alpha,\beta\in A}$ be an abstract variety; let k be any field of definition for V, and let M be a generic point of V over k, with the representatives M_α; by coroll. 4 of th. 1, Chap. IV, §1, the set of all the specializations of (M_α) over k does not depend upon the choice of M and k. We shall say that the abstract variety is *complete* if every specialization (P_α) of (M_α) over k is such that at least one P_α is finite, i.e. if every such specialization is attached to some point of V; this definition does not depend upon the choice of k and M. If V is not complete, we introduce a new element, which we call *the pseudopoint of* V and which we denote by ∞_V (this is similar to "the point at infinity" in the so-called Alexandroff compactification of a non-compact locally compact space in general topology); and we say that every specialization (P_α) of (M_α) over k, such that no P_α is finite, is *attached to* ∞_V or that it is *improper*; we say that such a specialization is *proper* if it is attached to some point of V, i.e. if some P_α is finite. If we agree to write $(P_\alpha) \sim (P'_\alpha)$ for two specializations of (M_α) over k if and only if $P_\alpha = P'_\alpha$ for every α such that P_α or P'_α is finite, then the quotient of the set of all specializations of (M_α) over k by this equivalence relation can be identified in an obvious manner with the set consisting of all the points of V and, if V is not complete, of its pseudopoint.

Notations being as above, if P is a point of V, and if some specialization of (M_α) over k, attached to P, has an improper specialization over k, then we say that ∞_V *is a specialization of* P *over* k, and more precisely that it is an *improper specialization* of P over k; whenever a point P' of V is a specialization of P over k, this specialization will be called *proper*. If B is the set of those $\beta \in A$ for which P has a representative P_β in V_β, and if the set $(P_\beta)_{\beta\in B}$ has a specialization $(P'_\beta)_{\beta\in B}$ over k such that no P'_β is finite, then V is not complete and ∞_V is a specialization of P over k; in fact, if $(P_\alpha)_{\alpha\in A}$ is a specialization of (M_α) over k attached to P, we have seen that P_α cannot be finite for α not in B; therefore, if we extend the specialization $(P'_\beta)_{\beta\in B}$ of $(P_\beta)_{\beta\in B}$ to a specialization $(P'_\alpha)_{\alpha\in A}$ of $(P_\alpha)_{\alpha\in A}$ over k, the latter is improper. In particular, this shows that, if P is on a subvariety W of V, also defined over k, it has an improper specialization over k on V if and only if it has such a specialization on W. Applying this to a generic point of W over k, we conclude that, if W is not complete, V cannot be complete. In other words:

THEOREM 4. *Every subvariety of a complete abstract variety is complete.*

In view of what we have just proved, one may, whenever $\boldsymbol{W}$ is a non-complete subvariety of an abstract variety $\boldsymbol{V}$, identify the pseudopoint $\boldsymbol{\infty}_{\boldsymbol{W}}$ of $\boldsymbol{W}$ with the pseudopoint $\boldsymbol{\infty}_{\boldsymbol{V}}$ of $\boldsymbol{V}$; after that is done, the specializations of a point $\boldsymbol{P}$ of $\boldsymbol{W}$ over a common field of definition of $\boldsymbol{V}$ and of $\boldsymbol{W}$ are the same on $\boldsymbol{V}$ and on $\boldsymbol{W}$, so that one may frequently, when speaking of a specialization, omit any mention of the ambient variety.

The simplest example of a complete abstract variety is given by the *projective line*. This is the abstract variety $\boldsymbol{D}$ given by two representatives $D_1 = D_2 = S^1$, f_{21} being the mapping of S^1 into S^1 whose graph has the equation $X_1X_2 = 1$; f_{11} and f_{22} are of course the identity mapping of S^1, and f_{12} is the inverse of f_{21} (which coincides with f_{21}); it is easily seen that f_{21} is coherent, and the consistency of the set $(f_{\beta\alpha})$ is obvious; $\boldsymbol{D}$ is defined over the prime field k_0. A generic point of $\boldsymbol{D}$ over k_0 has the representatives $M_1 = t$, $M_2 = t^{-1}$, where t is any transcendental quantity over k_0; a specialization of (M_1, M_2) over k_0 must be $(0, \infty)$ or $(\infty, 0)$ or of the form (x, x^{-1}) where x is any quantity other than 0; this shows that $\boldsymbol{D}$ is complete, and also that the points of $\boldsymbol{D}$ can be put into a one-to-one correspondence with the "generalized quantities" of Chap. II, §1, by assigning to the generalized quantity x the point $\boldsymbol{P}$ with the representative x on D_1 whenever x is finite, and the point with the representative 0 on D_2 if $x = \infty$; we shall say that x is *the coordinate of the point* $\boldsymbol{P}$ *of* $\boldsymbol{D}$, and we shall frequently denote the point $\boldsymbol{P}$ by the symbol (x).

We shall now give a criterion for a variety to be complete; in order to do this conveniently, we need the following definition. Let P be a polynomial in $k[X] = k[X_1, \cdots, X_n]$; we shall say that a term with a non-zero coefficient in P is *the dominating term of* P if it is a multiple (in $k[X]$) of all the terms in P, i.e. if, for every i, the exponent of X_i in that term is equal to the degree of P in X_i; we shall say that a polynomial P is *dominated* if it has a dominating term, and we shall say that it is *monic* if it is dominated and the coefficient of its dominating term is 1.

PROPOSITION 8. *Let* $\boldsymbol{V} = [V_\alpha, f_{\beta\alpha}]_{\alpha,\beta\in A}$ *be an abstract variety; let k be a field of definition for* $\boldsymbol{V}$, *and* $\boldsymbol{M}$ *a generic point of* $\boldsymbol{V}$ *over k. For each α, let S^{n_α} be the ambient space of V_α, and let*

$$M_\alpha = (x_\alpha) = (x_{\alpha 1}, \cdots, x_{\alpha n_\alpha})$$

be the representative of $\boldsymbol{M}$ *in V_α. Then* $\boldsymbol{V}$ *is complete if and only if, for every set $(i) = (i_\alpha)_{\alpha\in A}$ of integers such that $1 \leqq i_\alpha \leqq n_\alpha$ for every α, there is a monic polynomial $P_{(i)}$ in $k[(X_\alpha)_{\alpha\in A}]$ such that $P_{(i)}((x_{\alpha,i_\alpha})_{\alpha\in A}) = 0$.*

In fact, the assertion that $\boldsymbol{V}$ is complete is equivalent by definition to the following: (a) if $(\bar{x}_{\alpha i})$ is any specialization over k of the set $(x_{\alpha i})$ of all the coordinates of all the M_α, then there is α such that $\bar{x}_{\alpha i}$ is finite for $1 \leqq i \leqq n_\alpha$; this is equivalent to: (b) if $(\bar{x}_{\alpha i})$ is such a specialization, then, for every set (i_α) of integers such that $1 \leqq i_\alpha \leqq n_\alpha$ for every α, there is α such that $\bar{x}_{\alpha,i_\alpha}$

is finite; and this is equivalent to: (c) for every set (i_α), the set $(\infty, \cdots, \infty)$ is not a specialization of $((x_{\alpha, i_\alpha})_{\alpha \in A})$ over k; in fact, if $(\infty, \cdots, \infty)$ were such a specialization, it could be extended to a specialization of $(x_{\alpha i})$ which would contradict (b), and on the other hand it is obvious that (c) implies (b). Now, for a given set (i_α), assume first that some x_{α, i_α} is 0; then, for that set, (c) is satisfied, and $P = X_\alpha$ is a monic polynomial which is 0 at (x_{α, i_α}). Assume now that no x_{α, i_α} is 0, and put $y_\alpha = 1/x_{\alpha, i_\alpha}$ for every α; then, by the definition of a specialization, (x_{α, i_α}) has the specialization $(\infty, \cdots, \infty)$ over k if and only if every polynomial Q in $k[Y]$ such that $Q(y) = 0$ satisfies $Q(0) = 0$; in other words, (c) will hold for that set (i_α) if and only if there is Q in $k[Y]$ such that $Q(y) = 0$ and $Q(0) = 1$. Then take $P(X) = \prod_\alpha (X_\alpha)^{N_\alpha} \cdot Q((X_\alpha^{-1}))$, where the N_α are large enough to make this a polynomial; this is monic and such that $P((x_{\alpha, i_\alpha})) = 0$. Conversely, if $P(X)$ is such a monic polynomial, and $M(X)$ is its dominating term, put $Q(Y) = M(Y) \cdot P((Y_\alpha^{-1}))$; then we have $Q(y) = 0$ and $Q(0) = 1$. This completes the proof of our proposition.

Now we shall extend the definition of a specialization to a set of points or pseudopoints on abstract varieties in any number. To simplify notations, we shall explain our definition in the case of two abstract varieties $\boldsymbol{V}$ and $\boldsymbol{W}$. Let k be a field of definition for $\boldsymbol{V}$ and $\boldsymbol{W}$; let $\boldsymbol{M}, \boldsymbol{N}$ be generic points of $\boldsymbol{V}$ and of $\boldsymbol{W}$ over k, with the representatives M_α $(\alpha \in A)$ and N_λ $(\lambda \in L)$, respectively. Let $\boldsymbol{P}, \boldsymbol{P}'$ be points or pseudopoints of $\boldsymbol{V}$; let $\boldsymbol{Q}, \boldsymbol{Q}'$ be points or pseudopoints of $\boldsymbol{W}$. Then we say that $(\boldsymbol{P}', \boldsymbol{Q}')$ is a specialization of $(\boldsymbol{P}, \boldsymbol{Q})$ over k on $(\boldsymbol{V}, \boldsymbol{W})$ if and only if there exist specializations (P_α) and (P'_α) of (M_α) over k, and specializations (Q_λ) and (Q'_λ) of (N_λ) over k, respectively attached to $\boldsymbol{P}, \boldsymbol{P}', \boldsymbol{Q}, \boldsymbol{Q}'$, such that $((P'_\alpha), (Q'_\lambda))$ is a specialization of $((P_\alpha), (Q_\lambda))$ over k. One sees at once that, if this is so, $\boldsymbol{P} = \boldsymbol{\infty}_V$ implies $\boldsymbol{P}' = \boldsymbol{\infty}_V$, and $\boldsymbol{Q} = \boldsymbol{\infty}_W$ implies $\boldsymbol{Q}' = \boldsymbol{\infty}_W$. One can also verify immediately that, if the specializations $\boldsymbol{P}'$ of $\boldsymbol{P}$, and $\boldsymbol{Q}'$ of $\boldsymbol{Q}$, are both proper, and if $\boldsymbol{P}'$ has the representative P'_β on V_β and $\boldsymbol{Q}'$ the representative Q'_μ on W_μ, then the pair of points $(\boldsymbol{P}', \boldsymbol{Q}')$ is a specialization of the pair of points $(\boldsymbol{P}, \boldsymbol{Q})$ over k if and only if $\boldsymbol{P}$ has a representative P_β on V_β, $\boldsymbol{Q}$ a representative Q_μ on W_μ, and (P'_β, Q'_μ) is a specialization of (P_β, Q_μ) over k. Now assume that $\boldsymbol{P}, \boldsymbol{Q}$ belong respectively to subvarieties $\boldsymbol{V}', \boldsymbol{W}'$ of $\boldsymbol{V}, \boldsymbol{W}$, also defined over k. Then, if pseudopoints are identified as previously stated, one sees at once, just as in the case of a single variety, that the specializations of $(\boldsymbol{P}, \boldsymbol{Q})$ over k are the same on $(\boldsymbol{V}, \boldsymbol{W})$ and on $(\boldsymbol{V}', \boldsymbol{W}')$; this frequently makes it unnecessary to specify the ambient varieties in the mention of a specialization. Of course all this can be extended at once to specializations of any number of points on any number of varieties.

In particular, let $(x) = (x_1, \cdots, x_n)$ and $(x') = (x'_1, \cdots, x'_n)$ be two sets of generalized quantities; for each i, let $\boldsymbol{P}_i, \boldsymbol{P}'_i$ be the points of the projective line $\boldsymbol{D}$ with the coordinates x_i, x'_i. Then it is easily seen that (x') is a specialization of (x) over k if and only if $(\boldsymbol{P}'_1, \cdots, \boldsymbol{P}'_n)$ is a specialization of $(\boldsymbol{P}_1, \cdots, \boldsymbol{P}_n)$ over k on $(\boldsymbol{D}, \cdots, \boldsymbol{D})$ according to our latest definition. Thus the specialization of sets of generalized quantities is a special case of the specialization of sets of points on abstract varieties.

The principle of the extension of specializations can also be verified at once in the following form: let the V_i and the W_j be abstract varieties in any number; for each i, let P_i, P'_i be points or pseudopoints of V_i, such that $(P'_1, \cdots, P'_n)$ is a specialization of $(P_1, \cdots, P_n)$ over k on $(V_1, \cdots, V_n)$; for each j, let Q_j be a point or pseudopoint of W_j; then there exists a set (Q'_j), where, for each j, Q'_j is a point or pseudopoint of W_j, such that $(P'_1, \cdots, P'_n, Q'_1, \cdots, Q'_m)$ is a specialization of $(P_1, \cdots, P_n, Q_1, \cdots, Q_m)$ over k on $(V_1, \cdots, V_n, W_1, \cdots, W_m)$.

4. The topology of abstract varieties. Almost all the definitions and results in Chap. IV, Chap. VI, and §§1–2 of the present Chapter, which do not depend explicitly upon the use of coordinates can now be extended, in most cases quite trivially, to abstract varieties. Whenever possible, this is to be done according to the following "metamathematical" recipe.

If P, P', $\cdots$, and W, W', $\cdots$ are points and subvarieties of an abstract variety V, and if they all have representatives on one and the same representative V_α of V, we shall say that V_α, together with these representatives, constitutes a "simultaneous representation" of V and of these points and varieties. Now suppose that the assumptions made about some points and subvarieties of an abstract variety V imply that they must have at least one simultaneous representation; then we say that an assertion about such a representation has *local character* if its truth for one such representation implies its truth for all the others. For instance, let P be a point of a subvariety W of V; as W has a representative W_α on every representative V_α of V on which P has a representative P_α, there is always a simultaneous representation for V, W and P; by coroll. 1 of th. 17, Chap. IV, §7, the assertion "P_α is a simple point of W_α" has local character. Now, whenever an assertion of local character contains a term which has not yet been defined for abstract varieties, we shall agree to take it as the definition of that term; for instance, we say that P is a *simple point* of a subvariety W of V if, for some representation, P_α is a simple point of W_α. On the other hand, if a proposition which has been proved previously has local character, and if all the terms in it have already been defined for abstract varieties, then we may conclude at once that it remains true in the abstract case. For instance, take coroll. 1 of th. 1, Chap. VI, §1, which we reformulate for abstract varieties: "Let A^r, B^s be subvarieties of an abstract variety U^n; let C be a component of $A \cap B$, simple on U; then C has at least the dimension $r + s - n$." In this proposition, the terms "C is a component of $A \cap B$" and "C is simple on U" can obviously be defined according to our principle, and then the same principle shows at once that the proposition holds true in the abstract case. Our principle will be referred to, from now on, as "*the principle of localization.*" In applying it, it is useful to remember that, if a subvariety W of an abstract variety V has a representative in the representative V_α of V, then the same holds true for every subvariety of V which contains W, for every generic point P of W over a common field of definition for V and W, and also, if k is a field of definition for V, for the transform of such a point P under any isomorphism of $k(P)$ onto some field K' over k.

No further explanation is now needed concerning the extension to abstract varieties of the results of Chap. IV, §1; of course the results concerning polynomials, polynomial ideals and equations cannot be so extended. As to Chap. IV, §2, the principle of localization shows how to extend the definition of the symbol W^σ if W is a subvariety of an abstract variety V, V being defined over k and W over a field $K \supset k$, and if σ is an isomorphism of K over k. More generally, if $V = [V_\alpha, f_{\beta\alpha}]_{\alpha,\beta\in A}$ is any abstract variety, K a field of definition for V, and σ an isomorphism of K on a field K', we define V^σ as $[V_\alpha^\sigma, f_{\beta\alpha}^\sigma]_{\alpha,\beta\in A}$, which is obviously an abstract variety; in particular, if V is defined over $\bar{k}$, we say that it is *algebraic over* k, and then its transforms V^σ by the automorphisms σ of $\bar{k}$ over k are called its *conjugates*. In applying the principle of localization, one should keep in mind that, if V is an abstract variety, defined over k, and W a subvariety of V, defined over $K \supset k$, then any representative V_α of V which contains a representative W_α of W contains the representative W_α^σ of W^σ if σ is any isomorphism of K over k; in particular, if W is algebraic over k and has the representative W_α in V_α, all the conjugates of W over k have representatives in V_α, viz., the conjugates of W_α over k.

There is now no difficulty in extending most of Chap. IV, §2, to the abstract case; concerning prop. 6, 7 and 8, we merely remark that, in view of th. 17 of Chap. IV, §7, the definition of "the specialization-ring of W in $k(P)$" in the latter part of §2 of Chap. IV can be extended at once to the abstract case by means of the principle of localization. As to the extension of th. 4 of Chap. IV, §2, it will have to read as follows (keeping in mind that we have defined "a specialization over k of a point P on an abstract variety V" only if V is defined over k):

PROPOSITION 9. *Let V be an abstract variety, defined over a field k; let P be a point of V, and W its locus over $\bar{k}$. Then every generic specialization of P over k on V is a generic point over $\bar{k}$ of a conjugate of W over k, and is a point of only one such conjugate; conversely, every generic point over $\bar{k}$ of a conjugate of W over k is a generic specialization of P over k on V. Moreover, every proper specialization of P over k on V is a point of a conjugate of W over k, and every such point is a specialization of P over k.*

We could now extend to the abstract case the results of Chap. IV, §4, keeping in mind that the operations of union and intersection are meaningful only for point-sets contained in one and the same abstract variety, just as in Chap. IV they were applied only to subsets of one and the same space S^n. It will be more convenient, however, to formulate those results directly in the language of the Zariski topology.

As in §1, we say that a subset of an abstract variety V is *closed* if and only if it is the union of subvarieties of V in finite number. If k is a field of definition for

$\boldsymbol{V}$, we say that the union of any subvariety of $\boldsymbol{V}$, algebraic over k, and of all its conjugates over k is *k-closed*; and we say that a subset of $\boldsymbol{V}$ is *k-closed* if and only if it is a finite union of sets of the type we have just described. That this actually defines topologies on $\boldsymbol{V}$ is an immediate consequence of the following:

THEOREM 5. *Let $\boldsymbol{X}$ be a subset of an abstract variety $\boldsymbol{V} = [V_\alpha, f_{\beta\alpha}]_{\alpha,\beta \in A}$, defined over k. For each $\alpha \in A$, let X_α be the set of those points in V_α which are representatives in V_α of some point of $\boldsymbol{X}$. Then $\boldsymbol{X}$ is closed (resp. k-closed) if and only if all the X_α are closed (resp. k-closed).*

That the X_α are closed (resp. k-closed) if $\boldsymbol{X}$ is so follows at once from the definitions. Now assume that all the X_α are closed. For each α, let the $W_{\alpha i}$ be all the components of X_α; for each pair (α, i), let $\boldsymbol{W}_i^{(\alpha)}$ be the subvariety of $\boldsymbol{V}$ with the representative $W_{\alpha i}$ in V_α, and call $\boldsymbol{X}'$ the union of all the $\boldsymbol{W}_i^{(\alpha)}$; we shall prove that $\boldsymbol{X} = \boldsymbol{X}'$. Firstly, if $\boldsymbol{P}$ is any point of $\boldsymbol{X}$, and P_α a representative of $\boldsymbol{P}$, P_α must be in some $W_{\alpha i}$, so that $\boldsymbol{P}$ is in some $\boldsymbol{W}_i^{(\alpha)}$, hence in $\boldsymbol{X}'$; so we have $\boldsymbol{X} \subset \boldsymbol{X}'$. In order to show that $\boldsymbol{X}' \subset \boldsymbol{X}$, we have to show that, if W_α is any component of X_α and $\boldsymbol{W}$ is the subvariety of $\boldsymbol{V}$ with the representative W_α in V_α, $\boldsymbol{W}$ is contained in $\boldsymbol{X}$. This is the same as to say that if, for any β, $\boldsymbol{W}$ has a representative W_β in V_β, then W_β is contained in X_β. In fact, let K be a common field of definition, containing k, for all the $W_{\alpha i}$; let $\boldsymbol{M}$ be a generic point of $\boldsymbol{W}$ over K, with the representatives M_α, M_β in V_α, V_β. As M_α is in X_α, $\boldsymbol{M}$ is in $\boldsymbol{X}$, hence M_β in X_β; as X_β is K-closed, it must therefore, by coroll. 2 of th. 1, §1, contain the locus of M_β over K, which is W_β. This completes the proof that $\boldsymbol{X} = \boldsymbol{X}'$. But it is clear that $\boldsymbol{X}'$ is closed; and its definition shows that it is k-closed if all the X_α are so; this proves our theorem. Also, with these same notations, if we have $X_\alpha = V_\alpha$ for some α, then V_α is the unique component of X_α, and our proof shows that $\boldsymbol{V}$ is contained in $\boldsymbol{X}' = \boldsymbol{X}$, so that we have $\boldsymbol{X} = \boldsymbol{V}$; conversely, if $\boldsymbol{X} = \boldsymbol{V}$, we have $X_\alpha = V_\alpha$ for every α. It is convenient to formulate this as a separate corollary:

COROLLARY 1. *Notations being as in th. 5, assume that $\boldsymbol{X}$ is closed. Then, for each α, we have $\boldsymbol{X} = \boldsymbol{V}$ if and only if $X_\alpha = V_\alpha$.*

COROLLARY 2. *Let $\boldsymbol{V}$ be an abstract variety, defined over k, and $\boldsymbol{P}$ a point of $\boldsymbol{V}$. Then the k-closure of $\boldsymbol{P}$ in $\boldsymbol{V}$ is the union of the locus of $\boldsymbol{P}$ over $\bar{k}$ on $\boldsymbol{V}$ and of all the conjugates of that locus over k; it is also the set of all proper specializations of $\boldsymbol{P}$ over k on $\boldsymbol{V}$. In particular, if $\boldsymbol{P}$ has a locus $\boldsymbol{W}$ over k, $\boldsymbol{W}$ is the k-closure of $\boldsymbol{P}$ on $\boldsymbol{V}$.*

The first assertion follows at once from th. 5 and from coroll. 2 of th. 1, §1; the next one follows from this and from prop. 9; the last one is a special case of the first one.

COROLLARY 3. *Every family of closed subsets of an abstract variety has a finite subfamily with the same intersection.*

This follows at once from the same property for the affine case (prop. 1 of §1) and from th. 5; it implies the "compactoid" property for the Zariski topology.

COROLLARY 4. *Let V be an abstract variety, and let $W_1, \cdots, W_h, W'$ be subvarieties of V. Then W' is contained in the union of the W_i if and only if it is contained in one of them.*

Let K be a common field of definition for all these varieties; let P be a generic point of W' over K. If W' is contained in the union of the W_i, P must be in one of them, which must then contain the K-closure of P, i.e. W' by coroll. 2.

As in the affine case, the maximal subvarieties of V contained in a closed subset of V are called its *components*; coroll. 4 of th. 5 shows that, if X is the union of the subvarieties W_i of V, its components are those among the W_i which are not contained in any other one; from this it follows at once that, if X is k-closed, all its components are algebraic over k, and every conjugate over k of a component of X is a component of X.

If W is any subvariety of V, our definitions show that the Zariski topology on W is that induced on W by the Zariski topology on V, and that the same holds for the k-topologies if V and W are both defined over k.

All topological terms can now be used in the manner explained in §1. In particular, a subset of an abstract variety V, defined over k, will be called *open* (resp. *k-open*) *on* V if and only if its complement on V is closed (resp. k-closed). With the notations of th. 5, a subset X of V is open (resp. k-open) on V if and only if X_α is open (resp. k-open) on V_α for every α; moreover, by coroll. 1 of that theorem, X is open and non-empty if and only if every X_α is open in V_α and some X_α is not empty, and in that case no X_α can be empty.

The coroll. 3 and 4 of th. 1, §1, can be extended at once to the abstract case, either by reproducing their proof (making use of coroll. 2 of th. 5 instead of coroll. 2 of th. 1, §1), or by applying th. 5. Similarly, combining prop. 2 of §1 and its coroll. 1 with th. 5, one gets the corresponding results for the abstract case; one has only, in the formulation of these results, to replace "set" by "subset of an abstract variety V, defined over k" and "finite specialization" by "proper specialization".

Let X be a closed subset of an abstract variety V, defined over k; let the W_i be its components; if σ is an isomorphism of some common field of definition K for the W_i, containing k, on some field K', we denote by X^σ the union of the subvarieties W_i^σ of V^σ, which is a closed subset of V^σ. In particular, if X is k-closed, it follows at once from coroll. 1 of prop. 2, §1, applied to the abstract case in the manner just explained, that X^σ depends only upon the isomorphism induced by σ on k. In other words, if X is k-closed, and if τ is an isomorphism of k onto some field k', and σ is any extension of τ to $\bar{k}$, X^σ depends only upon X and τ, and not upon the choice of σ when these are given; therefore, under these circumstances, we may write X^τ instead of X^σ.

Finally, we note the following proposition, even though a much more comprehensive result is to be proved soon:

PROPOSITION 10. *Let $V = [V_\alpha, f_{\beta\alpha}]_{\alpha,\beta\in A}$ be an abstract variety, defined over k. Then, for each α, the set $D^{(\alpha)}$ of those points of V which have a representative in V_α is k-open in V.*

As before, call $\mathfrak{D}_{\alpha\beta}$, for each pair (α, β), the set of those points of V_β where $f_{\alpha\beta}$ is biregular; we have seen in §3 that this is also the set of the representatives in V_β of those points of $\boldsymbol{V}$ which have representatives both in V_α and in V_β, or in other words of those points of $\boldsymbol{D}^{(\alpha)}$ which have a representative in V_β. As the $\mathfrak{D}_{\alpha\beta}$ are k-open, th. 5 shows that $\boldsymbol{D}^{(\alpha)}$ is k-open. The mapping which, to every $\boldsymbol{P} \in \boldsymbol{D}^{(\alpha)}$, assigns the representative of $\boldsymbol{P}$ in V_α, is clearly a one-to-one mapping of $\boldsymbol{D}^{(\alpha)}$ onto V_α.

5. Products and projections. For $1 \leqq i \leqq n$, let f_i be a mapping of a variety V_i into a variety W_i; let k be a common field of definition for all the f_i. Put $V = V_1 \times \cdots \times V_n$, $W = W_1 \times \cdots \times W_n$; let $M = (M_1, \cdots, M_n)$ be a generic point of V over k; and let f be the mapping of V into W, with the field of definition k, such that

$$f(M) = (f_1(M_1), \cdots, f_n(M_n)).$$

If $P = (P_1, \cdots, P_n)$ is any point of V, one sees at once that f is defined at P if and only if f_i is defined at P_i for every i, and that $f(P)$ is then given by

$$f(P) = (f_1(P_1), \cdots, f_n(P_n)).$$

This implies that f is independent of the choice of k and M. When f is so defined, we shall write $f = f_1 \times \cdots \times f_n$.

With that notation, we define as follows the product of abstract varieties. In order to avoid multiple indices, we shall consider only the product of two factors. Let $\boldsymbol{V} = [V_\alpha, f_{\beta\alpha}]_{\alpha,\beta \in A}$, $\boldsymbol{W} = [W_\lambda, g_{\mu\lambda}]_{\lambda,\mu \in L}$ be two abstract varieties. One sees at once that the $f_{\beta\alpha} \times g_{\mu\lambda}$, for (α, λ) and (β, μ) in $A \times L$, are a consistent set of coherent mappings between the varieties $V_\alpha \times W_\lambda$; therefore these data define an abstract variety $\boldsymbol{Z}$ with the representatives $V_\alpha \times W_\lambda$. A point (P_α, Q_λ) of $V_\alpha \times W_\lambda$ and a point (P_β, Q_μ) of $V_\beta \times W_\mu$ are representatives of one and the same point $\boldsymbol{R}$ of $\boldsymbol{Z}$ if and only if P_α, P_β are representatives of the same point $\boldsymbol{P}$ of $\boldsymbol{V}$ and Q_λ, Q_μ are representatives of the same point $\boldsymbol{Q}$ of $\boldsymbol{W}$; when that is so, we write $\boldsymbol{R} = \boldsymbol{P} \times \boldsymbol{Q}$; it is obvious that this establishes a one-to-one correspondence between the points of $\boldsymbol{Z}$ and the pairs $(\boldsymbol{P}, \boldsymbol{Q})$ of a point $\boldsymbol{P}$ of $\boldsymbol{V}$ and a point $\boldsymbol{Q}$ of $\boldsymbol{W}$. The variety $\boldsymbol{Z}$ will be called *the product-variety of* $\boldsymbol{V}$ and $\boldsymbol{W}$ and will be written $\boldsymbol{V} \times \boldsymbol{W}$. In other words, we write:

$$\boldsymbol{V} \times \boldsymbol{W} = [V_\alpha \times W_\lambda, f_{\beta\alpha} \times g_{\mu\lambda}]_{(\alpha,\lambda),(\beta,\mu) \in A \times L}.$$

All this can be extended in an obvious manner to the product of any number of factors. A field k is a field of definition for a product if and only if it is a common field of definition for its factors.

Notations being as above, let k be a field of definition for $\boldsymbol{V}$ and $\boldsymbol{W}$, hence also for $\boldsymbol{V} \times \boldsymbol{W}$. Let $\boldsymbol{P}$, $\boldsymbol{P}'$ be points of $\boldsymbol{V}$, and let $\boldsymbol{Q}$, $\boldsymbol{Q}'$ be points of $\boldsymbol{W}$; then it follows at once from the definitions of §3 that $\boldsymbol{P}' \times \boldsymbol{Q}'$ is a specialization of $\boldsymbol{P} \times \boldsymbol{Q}$ over k on $\boldsymbol{V} \times \boldsymbol{W}$ if and only if the pair $(\boldsymbol{P}', \boldsymbol{Q}')$ is a specialization of the pair $(\boldsymbol{P}, \boldsymbol{Q})$ over k on $(\boldsymbol{V}, \boldsymbol{W})$. On the other hand, the same definitions show that $\boldsymbol{\infty}_{\boldsymbol{V}\times\boldsymbol{W}}$ is a specialization of $\boldsymbol{P} \times \boldsymbol{Q}$ over k on $\boldsymbol{V} \times \boldsymbol{W}$ if and only if the pair $(\boldsymbol{P}, \boldsymbol{Q})$ has a specialization $(\boldsymbol{P}'', \boldsymbol{Q}'')$ over k on $(\boldsymbol{V}, \boldsymbol{W})$ for which

$P'' = \infty_V$ or $Q'' = \infty_W$. Thus the set of all specializations (proper or improper) of $P \times Q$ over k is not the one-to-one image of the set of all specializations of the pair (P, Q), but it may be considered as the quotient of the latter by an obvious equivalence relation; this is why we refrain, in our notation, from identifying the pair (P, Q) with the point $P \times Q$ of $V \times W$. Similar results hold of course for products of varieties in any number. In particular:

THEOREM 6. *A product-variety is complete if and only if all its factors are so.*

Let V and W be as above; let the V'_i be subvarieties of V (possibly of dimension 0, so that we need not distinguish between points and varieties); let the W'_j be subvarieties of W, and let the Z_h be subvarieties of $V \times W$; we shall say that all these varieties have a "simultaneous representation" if there is a pair (α, λ) such that all the V'_i have a representative in V_α, all the W'_j have a representative in W_λ, and all the Z_h have a representative in $V_\alpha \times W_\lambda$. The "principle of localization" can now be applied to products, in a manner quite similar to that explained at the beginning of §4.

For instance, let Z be a subvariety of $V \times W$; let k be a common field of definition for V, W and Z; let $P \times Q$ be a generic point of Z over k; then, if P has a representative P_α in V_α, and Q has a representative Q_λ in W_λ, Z has a representative $Z_{\alpha\lambda}$ in $V_\alpha \times W_\lambda$, namely the locus of (P_α, Q_λ) over k; this shows that these points and varieties can be simultaneously represented. Let Z' be the locus of P over k on V; according to the principle of localization, Z' will be called *the geometric projection of* Z *on* V; the principle of localization shows that it is the closure of the set-theoretic projection. If Z', Z'' are the geometric projections of Z on V and on W, respectively, then Z has a representative in $V_\alpha \times W_\lambda$ if and only if Z' has a representative Z_α in V_α, and Z'' has a representative Z''_λ in W_λ; and then Z'_α, Z''_λ are the projections, on V_α and on W_λ respectively, of the representative of Z in $V_\alpha \times W_\lambda$; these facts, which follow at once from the consideration of a generic point of Z over a field of definition for Z, are frequently useful in applying the principle of localization to product-varieties. Notations being as above, assume now that Z has the same dimension as Z', i.e. that $k(P, Q)$ is algebraic over $k(P)$; as these fields are the same as $k(P_\alpha, Q_\lambda)$ and $k(P_\alpha)$, respectively, the principle of localization shows that the degree $d = [k(P, Q):k(P)]$ does not depend upon the choice of k and of $P \times Q$, and that this degree may be denoted by $[Z:Z']$, a notation which we shall adopt henceforward. For the same reason, we write $[Z:Z'] = 0$ whenever $\dim(Z) > \dim(Z')$.

The principle of localization, applied to most of the results of Chap. IV, §§3 and 7, gives at once the corresponding results for the abstract case. This holds in particular for prop. 26 of Chap. IV, §7; we shall now reformulate that proposition in the abstract case, with an addition which will be needed later on.

PROPOSITION 11. *Let* A *be a subvariety of a product* $V \times W$, *with the geometric projection* A' *on* V; *let* n *and* $n + r$ *be the dimensions of* A' *and* A, *respectively. Let* B *be a subvariety of* A, *with the geometric projection* B' *on* V. *Then every com-*

ponent of $\boldsymbol{A} \cap (\boldsymbol{B}' \times \boldsymbol{W})$ *which has the projection* $\boldsymbol{B}'$ *on* $\boldsymbol{V}$ *has at least the dimension* $r + \dim(\boldsymbol{B}')$, *and* $\boldsymbol{B}$ *is contained in such a component. Moreover, let* $\boldsymbol{F}$ *be the closure of the union of all the subvarieties* $\boldsymbol{B}'$ *of* $\boldsymbol{A}'$ *such that some component of* $\boldsymbol{A} \cap (\boldsymbol{B}' \times \boldsymbol{W})$ *has the geometric projection* $\boldsymbol{B}'$ *on* $\boldsymbol{V}$ *and has a dimension* $>r + \dim(\boldsymbol{B}')$; *then we have* $\boldsymbol{F} \neq \boldsymbol{A}'$.

In view of what we have said, only the last assertion needs proving. Without changing the contents of our assertions, we may replace $\boldsymbol{V}$ by $\boldsymbol{A}'$, i.e. we may assume that $\boldsymbol{A}' = \boldsymbol{V}$. By th. 5 of §4 and its coroll. 1, and by the principle of localization, it is enough to consider the case in which $\boldsymbol{V}$ is an affine variety, which we identify with its one and only representative. Let W_λ be a representative of $\boldsymbol{W}$ such that $\boldsymbol{A}$ has a representative A_λ in $\boldsymbol{V} \times W_\lambda$; let X_λ be the union of all the subvarieties $\boldsymbol{B}'$ of $\boldsymbol{V}$ such that some component of $A_\lambda \cap (\boldsymbol{B}' \times W_\lambda)$ has the geometric projection $\boldsymbol{B}'$ on $\boldsymbol{V}$ and has a dimension $>r + \dim(\boldsymbol{B}')$; the principle of localization shows at once that the set in prop. 11 whose closure is $\boldsymbol{F}$ is the union of all the X_λ, so that $\boldsymbol{F}$ is the union of the closures of the X_λ; it is therefore enough to show that none of these closures is $\boldsymbol{V}$, or in other words it is enough to treat the case in which both $\boldsymbol{V}$ and $\boldsymbol{W}$ are affine varieties. Now let k be a field of definition for $\boldsymbol{V}$, $\boldsymbol{W}$ and $\boldsymbol{A}$; let (x, y) be a generic point of $\boldsymbol{A}$ over k, with the projections (x) on $\boldsymbol{V}$ and (y) on $\boldsymbol{W}$. As (y) has the dimension r over $k(x)$, there is, for every choice $(y_{j_0}, \cdots, y_{j_r})$ of $r + 1$ quantities among the coordinates of (y), a polynomial P in $k[X, Y_0, \cdots, Y_r]$ such that

$$P(x, y_{j_0}, \cdots, y_{j_r}) = 0$$

and $P(x, Y) \neq 0$; for each such choice, select one such polynomial P, and, considering P as a polynomial in $Y_0, \cdots, Y_r$ with coefficients in $k[X]$, select one coefficient $Q(X)$ of P, such that $Q(x) \neq 0$. As there are finitely many possible choices for $y_{j_0}, \cdots, y_{j_r}$, this gives finitely many polynomials $Q(X)$; call $\Phi(X)$ their product. Now let $\boldsymbol{B}'$ be a subvariety of $\boldsymbol{V}$, and assume that there is a component $\boldsymbol{B}$ of $\boldsymbol{A} \cap (\boldsymbol{B}' \times \boldsymbol{W})$ with the projection $\boldsymbol{B}'$ on $\boldsymbol{V}$ and of dimension $>r + \dim(\boldsymbol{B}')$. Let K be a field of definition for $\boldsymbol{B}$, containing k; let (x', y') be a generic point of $\boldsymbol{B}$ over K. The assumption on the dimension of $\boldsymbol{B}$ implies that (y') has at least the dimension $r + 1$ over $K(x')$, so that, for some choice of $j_0, \cdots, j_r$, the quantities $y'_{j_0}, \cdots, y'_{j_r}$ are algebraically independent over $K(x')$. If P is the polynomial corresponding to that choice of $j_0, \cdots, j_r$, we have $P(x', y') = 0$, since (x', y') is a point of $\boldsymbol{A}$; this is a contradiction unless we have $P(x', Y) = 0$, and in particular $Q(x') = 0$ and therefore $\Phi(x') = 0$. This shows that $\boldsymbol{B}'$ is contained in the set of those points (x') of $\boldsymbol{V}$ for which $\Phi(x') = 0$; as this is a closed set, it must therefore contain the closure of the union of all the $\boldsymbol{B}'$; as $\Phi(x) \neq 0$, this set is not $\boldsymbol{V}$, which completes the proof of our proposition.

The concept of completeness, for which there was no analogue in the affine case, has now a number of important consequences; for instance, for subvarieties of products of complete abstract varieties, the set-theoretic projection is always the same as the geometric projection. One obtains a somewhat more general result by introducing the following concept. Let A be a subvariety of the product $V \times W$ of two abstract varieties V and W; let A' be its geometric projection on V, and P' a point of A'; call k a common field of definition for V, W and A, and $P \times Q$ a generic point of A over k. Then we say that A is *complete over* P' if every specialization of Q over $P \rightarrow P'$, with reference to k, is proper, i.e. if (P', ∞_W) is not a specialization of (P, Q) over k on (V, W); of course this must always be so if W is complete. One sees at once, in the usual manner, that this definition does not depend upon the choice of k and of $P \times Q$ when V, W, A and P' are given. If B is a subvariety of A, and if A is complete over a point P' of the geometric projection B' of B on V, then B is also complete over P'. If V', W' are subvarieties of V, W, such that A is contained in $V' \times W'$, A is complete over a point P' of A' on $V' \times W'$ if and only if it is so on $V \times W$, which is why no reference to the ambient varieties had to be included in our definition. In particular, we may take for V', W' the geometric projections of A on V and on W; therefore, in order to give a criterion for A to be complete over P', it will be enough to consider the case in which the geometric projections of A on V and on W are V and W. That criterion, which contains prop. 8 of §3 as a special case (the case in which V is reduced to a point) is as follows:

PROPOSITION 12. *Let A be a subvariety of a product $U \times V$ of two abstract varieties U and $V = [V_\alpha, f_{\beta\alpha}]_{\alpha,\beta \in A}$, with the geometric projections U on U and V on V; let k be a field of definition for U, V and A, and let $P \times M$ be a generic point of A over k. For each $\alpha \in A$, let S^{n_α} be the ambient space for V_α, and let*

$$M_\alpha = (x_\alpha) = (x_{\alpha 1}, \cdots, x_{\alpha n_\alpha})$$

be the representative of M in V_α. Then A is complete over a point P' of U if and only if, for every set $(i) = (i_\alpha)$ of integers such that $1 \leqq i_\alpha \leqq n_\alpha$ for every α, there is a monic polynomial $P_{(i)}$ in $(X_\alpha)_{\alpha \in A}$, with coefficients in the specialization-ring of P' in $k(P)$, such that $P_{(i)}((x_{\alpha, i_\alpha})_{\alpha \in A}) = 0$.

By the principle of localization, it is enough to prove this when U is an affine variety, with a single representative U. The proof is now exactly similar to that of prop. 8 of §3.

COROLLARY. *Notations being as in prop. 12, the set of those points of U over which A is complete is k-open on U; if at the same time A has the same dimension as U, that set is not empty.*

In view of th. 5 of §4 and its coroll. 1, it is again enough to consider the case when U is affine, with the single representative U; let S^m be the ambient space for U, and put $P = (u) = (u_1, \cdots, u_m)$ and $K = k(u)$. For each set $(i) = (i_\alpha)$, consider the set of all dominated polynomials in $(X_\alpha)_{\alpha \in A}$, with coefficients in $k[U] = k[U_1, \cdots, U_m]$, which vanish when (u) is substituted for (U) and (x_{α, i_α}) is substituted for (X_α); for each such polynomial, consider the coefficient $Q(U)$ of its dominating term; one sees at once that these coefficients

$Q(U)$, together with 0, make up a polynomial ideal $\mathfrak{Q}_{(i)}$ in $k[U]$. Prop. 12 can now be expressed by saying that A is complete over a point (u') of U if and only if, for every set (i), there is a polynomial Q in $\mathfrak{Q}_{(i)}$ such that $Q(u') \neq 0$. In other words, if $F_{(i)}$ is the set of the common zeros of all the polynomials in $\mathfrak{Q}_{(i)}$, the union of the $F_{(i)}$, for all sets (i), is the set of those points of U over which A is not complete. Therefore the complement of that set in U is k-open. On the other hand, prop. 27 of Chap. IV, §7, shows that A is complete over all generic points of U over k if it has the same dimension as U. This completes our proof.

Let again A be a subvariety of a product $V \times W$, with the geometric projection A' on V; let B' be a subvariety of A'; the coroll. of prop. 12 shows that, if A is complete over some point of B', it is complete over all generic points of B' with reference to any common field of definition for V, W, A and B'; when that is so, we say that A is *complete over* B'.

Proposition 13. *Let A be a subvariety of a product $V \times W$, with the geometric projection A' on V; let B' be a subvariety of A' over which A is complete. Then there is a component of $A \cap (B' \times W)$ which has the geometric projection B' on V.*

Let k be a common field of definition for V, W, A and B'; let $P \times Q$ and P' be generic points of A and of B', respectively, over k; let Q' be any specialization of Q over $P \rightarrow P'$, with reference to k. The assumption that A is complete over B' implies that Q' is proper; therefore $P' \times Q'$ is a point of A. Let B be the locus of $P' \times Q'$ over $\bar{k}$; this has the projection B' on V and is contained in $A \cap (B' \times W)$; therefore any component of the latter intersection which contains B will satisfy the conditions in prop. 13.

Theorem 7. *Let A be a subvariety of a product $V \times W$, with the geometric projection A' on V. If A is complete over every point of A', then A' is also the set-theoretic projection of A on V. For A to be complete over every point of A', it is sufficient that either W or A should be complete.*

Let k be a common field of definition for V, W and A; let $P \times Q$ be a generic point of A over k. If P' is any point of A', Q has a specialization Q' over $P \rightarrow P'$, with reference to k, and this must be proper if A is complete over P'; then P' is the projection on V of the point $P' \times Q'$ of A; this proves the first assertion. Now assume that A is not complete over P'; this means that Q has an improper specialization over $P \rightarrow P'$, with reference to k; in other words, when that is so, W is not complete, and (P', ∞_W) is a specialization of (P, Q) over k; but then $P \times Q$ has the specialization $\infty_{V \times W}$ over k, which means that A is not complete.

Corollary. *If W is complete, the set-theoretic projection on V of every closed subset of $V \times W$ is closed.*

The first assertion of th. 7 can be generalized as follows:

PROPOSITION 14. *Let A be a subvariety of a product $V \times W$, with the geometric projection A' on V; for each $d \geqq 0$, let X_d be the set of those points P of V such that $A \cap (P \times W)$ has at least one component of dimension $\geqq d$, so that X_0 is the set-theoretic projection of A on V and, if $n = \dim(W)$, X_n is the set of those P for which $P \times W \subset A$. Then X_n is closed, and, if A is complete over every point of A', all the X_d are closed, and k-closed if k is a field of definition for V, W and A.*

Consider first the assertion about X_n; this has been proved in the affine case as coroll. 2 of prop. 2, §1. Using th. 5 of §4, one sees at once that it is enough to prove it when V is an affine variety, with the single representative V. Let W_λ be a representative of W such that A has a representative A_λ in $V \times W_\lambda$; if P is a point on V, one sees at once, by considering generic points over $k(P)$, that $P \times W$ is contained in A if and only if $P \times W_\lambda$ is contained in A_λ; our assertion now follows from the corresponding one in the affine case.

Now we shall use induction on the dimension of A' in order to prove our assertion about the X_d, since everything is trivial if A' is reduced to a point. Let n and $n + r$ be the dimensions of A' and of A, respectively; prop. 11 shows that we have $X_0 = \cdots = X_r$ and that there is a closed subset Y of A', other than A', containing all the X_s for $s \geqq r + 1$. By th. 7, X_0 is closed. Call B_i the components of $A \cap (Y \times W)$, and let the B_i' be their geometric projections on V; as the latter are contained in Y, their dimensions are all $\leqq n - 1$; as the B_i are contained in A, B_i is complete over every point of B_i' for every i; by the induction assumption, our proposition is true for the B_i. But, if P is in Y, $A \cap (P \times W)$ is the same as the union of the sets $B_i \cap (P \times W)$; our assertion that the X_s are closed for $s \geqq r + 1$ follows now at once from the induction assumption. As to their being k-closed, this follows from coroll. 1 of prop. 2, §1, applied to the abstract case as we have explained.

COROLLARY. *Notations being as in prop. 14, assume that A is complete over every point of A'. Then a subvariety B' of A' is contained in X_d if and only if there is a subvariety B of A with the projection B' on V and with a dimension $\geqq d + \dim(B')$.*

Assume that there is such a B; call K a common field of definition for V, W, A and B, and $P \times Q$ a generic point of B over K; then Q has at least the dimension d over $K(P)$, so that, taking its locus over the algebraic closure of $K(P)$, we see that P is in X_d. As X_d is K-closed by prop. 14, this implies that $B' \subset X_d$. Conversely, if $B' \subset X_d$, call K a field of definition for V, W, A and B', and P a generic point of B' over K; there is a component of $A \cap (P \times W)$ with a dimension $\geqq d$; call $P \times Q$ a generic point of such a component over the algebraic closure of $K(P)$, and take for B the locus of $P \times Q$ over $\bar{K}$; this has the required properties.

6. Mappings of abstract varieties. Practically all the definitions and results of Chap. IV, §7, and of §2 of this Chapter (except of course for those which depend explicitly upon the use of coordinates) can be extended to the abstract case by means of the principle of localization.

In particular, let $\mathbf{V} = [V_\alpha, f_{\beta\alpha}]_{\alpha,\beta\in A}$, $\mathbf{W} = [W_\lambda, g_{\mu\lambda}]_{\lambda,\mu\in L}$ be two abstract varieties; let $\mathbf{U}$ be a subvariety of $\mathbf{V} \times \mathbf{W}$ with the projection $\mathbf{V}$ on $\mathbf{V}$ and such that $[\mathbf{U}:\mathbf{V}] = 1$; let L' be the set of those $\lambda \in L$ for which the projection of $\mathbf{U}$ on $\mathbf{W}$ has a representative in W_λ. Then, for every pair $(\alpha, \lambda) \in A \times L'$, $\mathbf{U}$ has a representative $U_{\alpha\lambda}$ in $V_\alpha \times W_\lambda$, and this is the graph of a mapping $\varphi_{\lambda\alpha}$ of V_α into W_λ; moreover, as one sees at once by considering generic points of these varieties over some common field of definition k for $\mathbf{V}$, $\mathbf{W}$ and $\mathbf{U}$, we have $\varphi_{\mu\beta} = g_{\mu\lambda} \circ \varphi_{\lambda\alpha} \circ f_{\alpha\beta}$ whenever (α, λ) and (β, μ) are in $A \times L'$. Now let $\mathbf{P}$ be a point of $\mathbf{V}$; assume that, for some pair (α, λ) in $A \times L'$, $\mathbf{P}$ has a representative P_α in V_α, and $\varphi_{\lambda\alpha}$ is defined at P_α; put $Q_\lambda = \varphi_{\lambda\alpha}(P_\alpha)$, and call $\mathbf{Q}$ the point of $\mathbf{W}$ with the representative Q_λ in W_λ. Then, for every pair (β, μ) such that $\mathbf{P}$ has a representative P_β in V_β and $\mathbf{Q}$ has a representative Q_μ in W_μ, $\varphi_{\mu\beta}$ is defined at P_β and has the value $\varphi_{\mu\beta}(P_\beta) = Q_\mu$ at that point. When that is so, we say, according to the principle of localization, that the mapping φ of $\mathbf{V}$ into $\mathbf{W}$ with the graph $\mathbf{U}$ is defined at $\mathbf{P}$ and has at $\mathbf{P}$ the value $\mathbf{Q} = \varphi(\mathbf{P})$.

Notations being as above, let $\Omega_{\lambda\alpha}$, for each pair $(\alpha, \lambda) \in A \times L'$, be the subset of V_α where $\varphi_{\lambda\alpha}$ is defined; and, for each α, call Ω_α the union of all the sets $\Omega_{\lambda\alpha}$ for $\lambda \in L'$. Then Ω_α is the set of those points of V_α which are representatives in V_α of points of $\mathbf{V}$ where φ is defined. Now, combining th. 2 of §2 with th. 5 of §4, we see that the subset of $\mathbf{V}$ where φ is defined is k-open on $\mathbf{V}$. This is the extension to the abstract case of the first part of th. 2 of §2. The extension of all the other definitions and results in §2 can now be carried out quite similarly. Two abstract varieties $\mathbf{V}$, $\mathbf{W}$ are called *isomorphic* if there exists an isomorphism f of $\mathbf{V}$ onto $\mathbf{W}$, i.e. a birational mapping f of $\mathbf{V}$ into $\mathbf{W}$ such that both f and f^{-1} are everywhere defined; they are said to be *isomorphic over* k if they are both defined over k and if there is an isomorphism f of $\mathbf{V}$ onto $\mathbf{W}$ which is also defined over k, or, as we shall also say, a *k-isomorphism of $\mathbf{V}$ onto $\mathbf{W}$*. By th. 2 of §2, such an isomorphism f determines a one-to-one, bicontinuous and k-bicontinuous mapping of $\mathbf{V}$ onto $\mathbf{W}$; and one sees at once, by using prop. 5 of §2, coroll. 3 of th. 2, §2, and the principle of localization, that f induces an isomorphism of each subvariety $\mathbf{V}'$ of $\mathbf{V}$ onto the corresponding subvariety $f(\mathbf{V}')$ of $\mathbf{W}$, which is a K-isomorphism if K is a field of definition for $\mathbf{V}'$, containing k.

As in §2, if f is a mapping of $\mathbf{V}$ into $\mathbf{W}$, and if f is defined at a subvariety $\mathbf{X}$ of $\mathbf{V}$, we call $f(\mathbf{X})$ *the geometric image of* $\mathbf{X}$ *by* f; it is again the closure of the set-theoretic image of $\mathbf{X}$ by f, which is the set of all points $f(\mathbf{P})$ when $\mathbf{P}$ is any point of $\mathbf{X}$ at which f is defined. If $\mathbf{X}$ is complete and f is a morphism, we have a more precise result:

THEOREM 8. *Let* $\mathbf{V}$ *and* $\mathbf{W}$ *be abstract varieties,* $\mathbf{X}$ *a complete subvariety of* $\mathbf{V}$, *and f a morphism of $\boldsymbol{V}$ into $\boldsymbol{W}$. Then the set-theoretic image of $\boldsymbol{X}$ by f is the same as its geometric image and is a complete variety.*

Let k be a common field of definition for $\boldsymbol{V}$, $\boldsymbol{W}$, $\boldsymbol{X}$ and f; let $\boldsymbol{M}$ be a generic point of $\boldsymbol{X}$ over k; then f is defined at $\boldsymbol{M}$, and the geometric image $f(\boldsymbol{X})$ of $\boldsymbol{X}$ is the locus of the point $\boldsymbol{N} = f(\boldsymbol{M})$ over k. Let $\boldsymbol{Q}$ be a point or pseudopoint of the variety $f(\boldsymbol{X})$, i.e. a specialization of $\boldsymbol{N}$ over k on $\boldsymbol{X}$, or, what amounts to the same, on $\boldsymbol{W}$. This can be extended to a specialization $(\boldsymbol{Q}, \boldsymbol{P})$ of $(\boldsymbol{N}, \boldsymbol{M})$ over k on $(\boldsymbol{W}, \boldsymbol{V})$. As $\boldsymbol{X}$ is complete, the specialization $\boldsymbol{P}$ of $\boldsymbol{M}$ over k on $\boldsymbol{V}$, or, what amounts to the same, on $\boldsymbol{X}$, must be proper; in other words, $\boldsymbol{P}$ is a point of $\boldsymbol{X}$. As f is a morphism, it is defined at $\boldsymbol{P}$, so that $\boldsymbol{N}$ has no other specialization than $f(\boldsymbol{P})$ on $\boldsymbol{W}$, with reference to k, over the specialization $\boldsymbol{P}$ of $\boldsymbol{M}$ on $\boldsymbol{V}$. Therefore we have $\boldsymbol{Q} = f(\boldsymbol{P})$, which shows that $\boldsymbol{Q}$ is proper, i.e. that it is a point of $f(\boldsymbol{X})$, and that it is in the set-theoretic image of $\boldsymbol{X}$ by f. This proves our theorem.

In particular, th. 8 shows that, if two varieties are isomorphic, and one of them is complete, the other is complete.

PROPOSITION 15. *Let $\boldsymbol{\Omega}$ be a non-empty k-open subset of an abstract variety $\boldsymbol{V}$, defined over k. There is an abstract variety $\boldsymbol{W}$ and a coherent birational mapping φ of $\boldsymbol{W}$ into $\boldsymbol{V}$, both defined over k, such that φ is everywhere biregular on $\boldsymbol{W}$, that $\boldsymbol{\Omega}$ is the subset of $\boldsymbol{V}$ where φ^{-1} is biregular, and that φ induces a one-to-one mapping of $\boldsymbol{W}$ onto $\boldsymbol{\Omega}$. Moreover, $\boldsymbol{W}$ and φ are uniquely determined by these conditions, up to a k-isomorphism.*

The last assertion means that, if $\boldsymbol{W}'$ and φ' also satisfy the same conditions, then there is an isomorphism ψ of $\boldsymbol{W}$ onto $\boldsymbol{W}'$, defined over k, such that

$$\varphi' = \varphi \circ \psi^{-1}.$$

That is obvious; in fact, if $\boldsymbol{W}'$ and φ' are such, $\psi = \varphi'^{-1} \circ \varphi$ is a birational mapping of $\boldsymbol{W}$ into $\boldsymbol{W}'$, with the inverse $\psi^{-1} = \varphi^{-1} \circ \varphi'$, and the assumptions imply that these are everywhere defined. Now, in order to construct $\boldsymbol{W}$ and φ, put

$$\boldsymbol{V} = [V_\alpha, f_{\beta\alpha}]_{\alpha,\beta\in A}, \qquad \boldsymbol{F} = \boldsymbol{V} - \boldsymbol{\Omega},$$

and call F_α, for each α, the set of those points of V_α which are representatives of points of $\boldsymbol{F}$. Let S^{n_α} be the ambient space for V_α; then, by coroll. 1 of th. 1, §1, F_α is the set of common zeros in S^{n_α} of an ideal $\mathfrak{A}_\alpha$ in $k[X_1, \cdots, X_{n_\alpha}]$. As F_α is contained in V_α, $\mathfrak{A}_\alpha$ contains the ideal $\mathfrak{P}_\alpha$ which defines V_α over k; we can then select a basis for $\mathfrak{A}_\alpha$, consisting of a basis for $\mathfrak{P}_\alpha$ and the polynomials $P_{\alpha 1}, \cdots, P_{\alpha N_\alpha}$, none of which is in $\mathfrak{P}_\alpha$; then F_α can also be described as the set of those points of V_α which are common zeros for all the $P_{\alpha i}$. Now let $\boldsymbol{M}$ be a generic point of $\boldsymbol{V}$ over k; let

$$M_\alpha = (x_\alpha) = (x_{\alpha 1}, \cdots, x_{\alpha n_\alpha})$$

be its representative in V_α; then we have $P_{\alpha i}(x_\alpha) \neq 0$ for $1 \leqq i \leqq N_\alpha$. Call

B the set of all pairs (α, i) with $\alpha \in A$ and $1 \leqq i \leqq N_\alpha$; for each such pair, put

$$N_{\alpha i} = (x_{\alpha 1}, \cdots, x_{\alpha n_\alpha}, P_{\alpha i}(x_\alpha)^{-1});$$

call $W_{\alpha i}$ the locus of $N_{\alpha i}$ over k in the space $S^{n_\alpha+1}$; and, for (α, i) and (β, j) in B, call $g_{\beta j, \alpha i}$ the mapping of $W_{\alpha i}$ into $W_{\beta j}$ whose graph is the locus of $(N_{\alpha i}, N_{\beta j})$ over k. One verifies at once that this is a consistent set of coherent birational mappings between the $W_{\alpha i}$, so that we may define an abstract variety $\boldsymbol{W}$ by putting

$$\boldsymbol{W} = [W_{\alpha i}, g_{\beta j, \alpha i}]_{(\alpha, i), (\beta, j) \in B}.$$

This is defined over k; call $\boldsymbol{N}$ the generic point of $\boldsymbol{W}$ over k which has the representative $N_{\alpha i}$ in $W_{\alpha i}$ for every $(\alpha, i) \in B$. Then the locus of $\boldsymbol{N} \times \boldsymbol{M}$ over k on $\boldsymbol{W} \times \boldsymbol{V}$ is the graph $\boldsymbol{\Gamma}_\varphi$ of a birational mapping φ of $\boldsymbol{W}$ into $\boldsymbol{V}$. Let $\boldsymbol{N}'$ be any point of $\boldsymbol{W}$; let $(\alpha, i) \in B$ be such that $\boldsymbol{N}'$ has a representative $N'_{\alpha i}$ in $W_{\alpha i}$; then $N'_{\alpha i}$ must be of the form $((x'_\alpha), P_{\alpha i}(x'_\alpha)^{-1})$, where (x'_α) is a point of V_α such that $P_{\alpha i}(x'_\alpha) \neq 0$. The graph $\boldsymbol{\Gamma}_\varphi$ of φ has in $W_{\alpha i} \times V_\alpha$ a representative which is the locus of $(N_{\alpha i}, M_\alpha)$ over k; this is the graph of a mapping $\varphi_{\alpha i}$ of $W_{\alpha i}$ into V_α which obviously is everywhere defined on $W_{\alpha i}$, and has at $N'_{\alpha i}$ the value $\varphi_{\alpha i}(N'_{\alpha i}) = M'_\alpha = (x'_\alpha)$; this proves that φ is defined at $\boldsymbol{N}'$, and that its value at $\boldsymbol{N}'$ is the point $\boldsymbol{M}' = \varphi(\boldsymbol{N}')$ with the representative M'_α on V_α. As we have $P_{\alpha i}(x') \neq 0$, M'_α is in $V_\alpha - F_\alpha$, and therefore $\boldsymbol{M}'$ is in $\boldsymbol{\Omega} = \boldsymbol{V} - \boldsymbol{F}$. This implies in particular that, if $\boldsymbol{N}' \times \boldsymbol{M}'$ is any point of $\boldsymbol{\Gamma}_\varphi$, $\boldsymbol{M}'$ is not in $\boldsymbol{F}$; therefore φ^{-1} cannot be defined at any point of $\boldsymbol{F}$. Now let $\boldsymbol{M}'$ be any point of $\boldsymbol{\Omega}$, with a representative $M'_\alpha = (x'_\alpha)$ in V_α; then M'_α is not in F_α, so that we must have $P_{\alpha i}(x'_\alpha) \neq 0$ for some i; but then $\varphi_{\alpha i}^{-1}$ is defined at M'_α, so that φ^{-1} is defined at $\boldsymbol{M}'$. The fact that φ induces a one-to-one mapping of $\boldsymbol{W}$ onto $\boldsymbol{\Omega}$ is clear from what we have just said; it is also a special case of prop. 6 of §2, which, as we have explained, can be applied without change to the abstract case; that proposition also shows that the mapping in question is bicontinuous and k-bicontinuous if, as usual, we define the topologies on $\boldsymbol{\Omega}$ as those induced by the corresponding ones on $\boldsymbol{V}$.

As long as one is concerned only with those properties of abstract varieties which are preserved under isomorphisms, one may therefore, with the notations of prop. 15, identify the k-open subset $\boldsymbol{\Omega}$ of $\boldsymbol{V}$ with the variety $\boldsymbol{W}$, defined over k, which has been constructed above, or with any variety isomorphic to $\boldsymbol{W}$ over k; or, what amounts to the same, one may consider any non-empty k-open subset of an abstract variety $\boldsymbol{V}$, defined over k, as being again such a variety. This will be done from now on. It is easily seen that $\boldsymbol{\Omega}$ cannot be complete unless $\boldsymbol{V}$ is so and $\boldsymbol{\Omega} = \boldsymbol{V}$. As observed above, the Zariski topology and the k-topology on $\boldsymbol{\Omega}$, when $\boldsymbol{\Omega}$ is considered as an abstract variety, are the same as those induced on $\boldsymbol{\Omega}$ by the corresponding topologies on $\boldsymbol{V}$. If f is any mapping of $\boldsymbol{V}$ into some abstract variety $\boldsymbol{U}$, and $\mathfrak{D}_f$ is the open set where f is defined, then, with the notations of prop. 15, $f \circ \varphi$ is a mapping of $\boldsymbol{W}$ into $\boldsymbol{U}$, defined at those points of W whose image by φ is in $\mathfrak{D}_f$ and at no other point of W; for, if it is defined at a point N' of W, $f = (f \circ \varphi) \circ \varphi^{-1}$ is defined at the point $\varphi(N')$. Identifying now $\mathbf{\Omega}$ with W by means of φ in the manner we have described, we say that $f \circ \varphi$ is the mapping *induced by f on* $\mathbf{\Omega}$; the set where it is defined is $\mathbf{\Omega} \cap \mathfrak{D}_f$.

We can now supplement prop. 10 of §4 as follows:

PROPOSITION 16. *Let $V = [V_\alpha, f_{\beta\alpha}]_{\alpha,\beta \in A}$ be an abstract variety, defined over k. Then there is, for each α, a birational mapping φ_α of V_α into V, defined over k, whose value at every point P_α of V_α is the point P of V with the representative P_α in V_α; φ_α determines an isomorphism of V_α onto the k-open subset $D^{(\alpha)}$ of V, consisting of those points of V which have a representative in V_α; and we have*

$$f_{\beta\alpha} = \varphi_\beta^{-1} \circ \varphi_\alpha$$

for all α, β in A.

If M is a generic point of V over k, with the representatives M_α, we have $k(M) = k(M_\alpha)$ for all α; therefore, for each α, there is a birational mapping φ_α of V_α into V, with the field of definition k, such that $\varphi_\alpha(M_\alpha) = M$; this is defined everywhere on V_α, and its inverse φ_α^{-1} is defined everywhere on $D^{(\alpha)}$ and nowhere else; as φ_α obviously induces a one-to-one correspondence between the points of V_α and those of $D^{(\alpha)}$, prop. 15 shows that it determines an isomorphism between these varieties. All our other assertions are now obvious.

Prop. 16 can be expressed by saying that V has the covering $(D^{(\alpha)})_{\alpha \in A}$ by finitely many k-open subsets $D^{(\alpha)}$, each of which is k-isomorphic to an affine variety V_α. One says that an abstract variety is "affinely representable" if it is isomorphic to an affine variety; sometimes, however, these same words are used in the sense "isomorphic to an open subset of an affine variety"; in using them, one should be careful to avoid confusion.

The procedure which has been used to define abstract varieties can now be generalized as follows:

PROPOSITION 17. *Let L be a finite set, and let, for each $\lambda \in L$,*

$$V_\lambda = [V_{\lambda\alpha}, f_{\lambda\beta\alpha}]_{\alpha,\beta \in A_\lambda}$$

be an abstract variety, defined over a field k. Let $(\varphi_{\mu\lambda})$ be a consistent set of coherent birational mappings between the V_λ. Then there is an abstract variety W, defined over k, with a covering (D_λ) by k-open sets D_λ, and, for each λ, a birational mapping φ_λ of V_λ into W, with the field of definition k, such that

$$\varphi_{\mu\lambda} = \varphi_\mu^{-1} \circ \varphi_\lambda$$

for all λ, μ, and that, for each λ, φ_λ determines an isomorphism of V_λ onto D_λ. Moreover, W, the D_λ and the φ_λ are uniquely determined, up to a k-isomorphism of W.

The last assertion means that, if W', the D'_λ and the φ'_λ also satisfy the same conditions, then there is a k-isomorphism ψ of $\boldsymbol{W}$ onto $\boldsymbol{W}'$, mapping $\boldsymbol{D}_\lambda$ onto $\boldsymbol{D}'_\lambda$ for each λ and such that $\varphi'_\lambda = \psi \circ \varphi_\lambda$ for each λ. That is obvious; in fact, the relation $\varphi'^{-1}_\mu \circ \varphi'_\lambda = \varphi^{-1}_\mu \circ \varphi_\lambda$ shows that the birational mapping $\varphi'_\lambda \circ \varphi^{-1}_\lambda$ is independent of the choice of λ; if this is called ψ, its definition shows at once that it is defined everywhere in $\boldsymbol{D}_\lambda$ for every λ, hence everywhere on $\boldsymbol{W}$; similarly its inverse is defined everywhere on $\boldsymbol{W}'$, so that it is an isomorphism; the assumptions on φ_λ, φ'_λ imply then that it maps $\boldsymbol{D}_\lambda$ onto $\boldsymbol{D}'_\lambda$ for every λ. Now call B the set of all pairs (λ, α) with $\lambda \in L$, $\alpha \in A_\lambda$. Applying prop. 16 to $\boldsymbol{V}_\lambda$, we see that, for each pair (λ, α) in B, there is a birational mapping $\psi_{\lambda\alpha}$ of $V_{\lambda\alpha}$ into $\boldsymbol{V}_\lambda$, with the field of definition k, which maps every point $P_{\lambda\alpha}$ of $V_{\lambda\alpha}$ onto the point of $\boldsymbol{V}_\lambda$ with the representative $P_{\lambda\alpha}$ in $V_{\lambda\alpha}$. For each pair of elements (λ, α), (μ, β) of B, put

$$g_{\mu\beta,\lambda\alpha} = \psi^{-1}_{\mu\beta} \circ \varphi_{\mu\lambda} \circ \psi_{\lambda\alpha},$$

which implies in particular, for $\lambda = \mu$, that we have $g_{\lambda\beta,\lambda\alpha} = \psi^{-1}_{\lambda\beta} \circ \psi_{\lambda\alpha}$, and therefore, by prop. 16, $g_{\lambda\beta,\lambda\alpha} = f_{\lambda\beta\alpha}$, whenever α, β are in A_λ. It is now a matter of routine to verify that these are coherent birational mappings between the $V_{\lambda\alpha}$; and they are obviously consistent. Therefore the formula

$$\boldsymbol{W} = [V_{\lambda\alpha}, g_{\mu\beta,\lambda\alpha}]_{(\lambda,\alpha),(\mu,\beta)\in B}$$

defines an abstract variety. Applying prop. 16 to $\boldsymbol{W}$, call $\theta_{\lambda\alpha}$ the birational mapping of $V_{\lambda\alpha}$ into $\boldsymbol{W}$ which maps every point $P_{\lambda\alpha}$ of $V_{\lambda\alpha}$ onto the point of $\boldsymbol{W}$ which has the representative $P_{\lambda\alpha}$ on $V_{\lambda\alpha}$. By prop. 16, we have

$$g_{\mu\beta,\lambda\alpha} = \theta^{-1}_{\mu\beta} \circ \theta_{\lambda\alpha},$$

hence, for $\lambda = \mu$, $f_{\lambda\beta\alpha} = \theta^{-1}_{\lambda\beta} \circ \theta_{\lambda\alpha}$. From this, one concludes at once that the mapping $\theta_{\lambda\alpha} \circ \psi^{-1}_{\lambda\alpha}$ of $\boldsymbol{V}_\lambda$ into $\boldsymbol{W}$ is independent of the choice of α in A_λ; and, if we call it φ_λ, it is again a routine matter to verify that this is an isomorphism of $\boldsymbol{V}_\lambda$ onto a k-open subset $\boldsymbol{D}_\lambda$ of $\boldsymbol{W}$ and that $\boldsymbol{W}$, the φ_λ and the $\boldsymbol{D}_\lambda$ have all the properties stated in prop. 17.

Here again, we can express prop. 17 by saying that $\boldsymbol{W}$ has the covering $(\boldsymbol{D}_\lambda)$ by k-open subsets, respectively isomorphic to the varieties $\boldsymbol{V}_\lambda$. Conversely, it is obvious that every finite k-open covering of an abstract variety can be described by means of coherent birational mappings between the open sets of that covering.

The following result is occasionally useful in applying "projective" methods to abstract varieties:

PROPOSITION 18. *Let* $\boldsymbol{V} = [V_\alpha, f_{\beta\alpha}]_{\alpha,\beta\in A}$ *be an abstract variety, defined over* k. *Then there is a subvariety* $\boldsymbol{W}$ *of a product* $\boldsymbol{D} \times \boldsymbol{D} \times \cdots \times \boldsymbol{D}$ *and a birational mapping* f *of* $\boldsymbol{W}$ *into* $\boldsymbol{V}$, *both defined over* k, *such that, if* $\boldsymbol{\Omega}$ *is the* k*-open subset of* $\boldsymbol{W}$ *where* f *is defined, the set-theoretic projections of the graph of* f *on* $\boldsymbol{V}$ *and on* $\boldsymbol{W}$ *are* $\boldsymbol{V}$ *and* $\boldsymbol{\Omega}$, *respectively.*

Let S^{m_α} be the ambient space for V_α; let $\boldsymbol{M}$ be a generic point of $\boldsymbol{V}$ over k, with the representative

$$M_\alpha = (x_\alpha) = (x_{\alpha 1}, \cdots, x_{\alpha m_\alpha})$$

on V_α for each $\alpha \in A$. For $\alpha \in A$, $1 \leqq i \leqq m_\alpha$, let $N_{\alpha i}$ be the point of D with the coordinate $x_{\alpha i}$; put $N = \prod_{\alpha, i} N_{\alpha i}$, this being a point on the product U of m factors, all equal to D, with $m = \sum_\alpha m_\alpha$. We take for W the locus of N over k on that product, and for f the mapping of W into V whose graph Γ_f is the locus of $N \times M$ over k. For each set $(i) = (i_\alpha)$ of integers, such that $1 \leqq i_\alpha \leqq m_\alpha$ for every α, call $F_{(i)}$ the closed subset of U consisting of all the points $P = \prod_{\alpha, i} P_{\alpha i}$ such that, for every α, P_{α, i_α} is the point of D with the coordinate ∞; call F the union of all the sets $F_{(i)}$, and Ω the complement of $W \cap F$ in W. It is now a routine matter to verify that W, f and Ω have all the properties stated in our proposition.

7. Intersection-multiplicities. By using the principle of localization, it is an easy matter to extend to abstract varieties all the main results of Chap. VI, viz. (as has already been mentioned in §4) coroll. 1 and 2 of th. 1, Chap. VI, §1, and further all the theorems of Chap. VI, §§2–3, together with their corollaries. Only one point requires some comment, namely the fact that the transversality of varieties (as defined in Chap. VI, §2) has local character in the sense of §4. That could easily be verified by a straightforward calculation, based on the results of Chap. IV, §§6–7; but it can also be derived as follows from th. 6 of Chap. VI, §2. Let A, B be two subvarieties of an abstract variety U; let P be a point of $A \cap B$. Then, if U_α is any representative of U on which P has a representative P_α, A and B have representatives A_α, B_α on U_α. Now denote by (T_α) the assertion "A_α and B_α are transversal to each other at P_α", and by (S_α) the assertion "there is only one component C_α of $A_\alpha \cap B_\alpha$ which contains P_α; this component is proper and of multiplicity 1 on U_α, and it has P_α as a simple point". By th. 6 of Chap. VI, §2, the assertions (T_α) and (S_α) are equivalent; since it is clear that (S_α) has local character, i.e. that it is equivalent to (S_β) for every β such that P has a representative on U_β, (T_α) must also have local character. Transversality can therefore be defined for abstract varieties, simply by means of the principle of localization; when this is done, th. 6 of Chap. VI, §2, can be extended in the usual manner.

It will be convenient to reformulate as follows, in the language of this Chapter, th. 13 of Chap. VI, §3, and its corollaries:

THEOREM 9. *Let V, W be two abstract varieties, and f a mapping of V into W, with the graph Γ_f. Let A be a simple subvariety of V, and assume that there is a component of $\Gamma_f \cap (A \times W)$ which has the same dimension as A and has the projection A on V. Then f is defined along A, and Γ_f is complete over A.*

In fact, the first assertion is nothing else than th. 13 of Chap. VI, §3, and the second one follows then at once from the definitions.

COROLLARY 1. *Let f be a mapping of V^n into W, and assume that its graph Γ_f is complete over a simple subvariety A^{n-1} of V^n; then f is defined along A.*

In fact, by prop. 13 of §5, the assumption implies that there is a component $\mathbf{X}$ of $\mathbf{\Gamma}_f \cap (\mathbf{A} \times \mathbf{W})$ with the projection $\mathbf{A}$ on $\mathbf{V}$; then the dimension of $\mathbf{X}$ is at least $n - 1$, and it is $<n$ since $\mathbf{X}$ is contained in $\mathbf{\Gamma}_f$ and other than $\mathbf{\Gamma}_f$.

COROLLARY 2. *Let f be a mapping of $\mathbf{V}^n$ into a complete abstract variety $\mathbf{W}$. Then every component of the set of the points where f is not defined is either multiple on $\mathbf{V}$ or has a dimension $\leqq n - 2$.*

COROLLARY 3. *Let f be a birational mapping of $\mathbf{V}^n$ into $\mathbf{W}^n$, with the graph $\mathbf{\Gamma}_f$. Let $\mathbf{X}^{n-1}$ be a subvariety of $\mathbf{\Gamma}_f$, with the geometric projections $\mathbf{V}'$ on $\mathbf{V}$ and $\mathbf{W}'$ on $\mathbf{W}$, and assume that $\mathbf{V}'$, $\mathbf{W}'$ are both of dimension $n - 1$ and are simple on $\mathbf{V}$ and on $\mathbf{W}$, respectively. Then f is biregular along $\mathbf{V}'$, and f^{-1} is so along $\mathbf{W}'$.*

The results of Chap. VI, §§2–3, extended as we have just said to abstract varieties, and one more result which will be proved presently as th. 10, constitute the fundamental properties of intersection-multiplicities which it was the main purpose of this book to formulate and establish. Th. 10, which will now be proved, could not have been considered within the framework of Chap. VI, because it depends upon the concept of completeness. We begin with a special case, which is at the same time a generalization of prop. 11 of Chap. V, §1.

PROPOSITION 19. *Let $\mathbf{W}$ be a subvariety of the product $S^n \times \mathbf{V}$ of S^n and of an abstract variety $\mathbf{V} = [V_\alpha, f_{\beta\alpha}]_{\alpha,\beta\in A}$, with the geometric projection W'^r on S^n; let L^{n-r} be a linear variety in S^n, and P a proper point of intersection of W' and L in S^n, such that $\mathbf{W}$ is complete over P and that $\mathbf{W} \cap (P \times \mathbf{V})$ contains only finitely many points $P \times \mathbf{Q}_\rho$. Then, if, for any ρ, $\mathbf{Q}_\rho$ has a representative $Q_{\rho\alpha}$ in V_α, and if S^{m_α} is the ambient space of V_α, $\mathbf{W}$ has a representative W_α in $S^n \times V_\alpha$, and $P \times Q_{\rho\alpha}$ is a proper point of intersection of W_α and $L \times S^{m_\alpha}$ in $S^n \times S^{m_\alpha}$, whose multiplicity μ_ρ is independent of α; furthermore, we have:*

$$\sum_\rho \mu_\rho = [\mathbf{W}:W']\cdot j(W'\cdot L, P).$$

Since $\mathbf{W}$ is complete over P, $\mathbf{W} \cap (P \times \mathbf{V})$ is not empty; in view of this and of prop. 11 of §5, our assumption about that set implies that $\mathbf{W}$ has the same dimension as W'. If $\mathbf{Q}_\rho$ has a representative $Q_{\rho\alpha}$ in V_α, $\mathbf{W}$ has a representative W_α in $S^n \times V_\alpha$; as $P \times \mathbf{Q}_\rho$ is a component of $\mathbf{W} \cap (P \times \mathbf{V})$, $P \times Q_{\rho\alpha}$ is a component of $W_\alpha \cap (P \times V_\alpha)$. Let Z be a component of $W_\alpha \cap (L \times S^{m_\alpha})$ containing $P \times Q_{\rho\alpha}$; let Z' be its geometric projection on S^n. As the geometric projection of W_α on S^n is W', Z' is contained in $W' \cap L$; as Z' contains P, this implies that $Z' = P$, so that Z is contained in $W_\alpha \cap (P \times S^{m_\alpha})$, which is the same as $W_\alpha \cap (P \times V_\alpha)$, and is therefore reduced to $P \times Q_{\rho\alpha}$. If dimensions are taken into account, this shows that $P \times Q_{\rho\alpha}$ is a proper point of intersection of W_α and $L \times S^{m_\alpha}$ in $S^n \times S^{m_\alpha}$.

Now let k be a common field of definition for $\mathbf{V}$, $\mathbf{W}$ and L. Let B be the set of those $\beta \in A$ for which $\mathbf{W}$ has a representative W_β in $S^n \times V_\beta$. Then, if $\bar{P} \times \bar{\mathbf{Q}}$ is any generic point of $\mathbf{W}$ over k, $\bar{\mathbf{Q}}$ has a representative $\bar{Q}_\beta$ in V_β for every $\beta \in B$. Put

$$P = (x) = (x_1, \cdots, x_n), \quad \bar{P} = (\bar{x}) = (\bar{x}_1, \cdots, \bar{x}_n),$$

$$\bar{Q}_\beta = (\bar{y}_\beta) = (\bar{y}_{\beta 1}, \cdots, \bar{y}_{\beta m_\beta}),$$

and finally

$$(\bar{y}) = ((\bar{y}_\beta)_{\beta \in B}) = (\bar{y}_{\beta j})_{\beta \in B, 1 \leqq j \leqq m_\beta}.$$

As the W_β are all the representatives of $\boldsymbol{W}$, the points $(\bar{x}, \bar{y}_\beta)$ are all the representatives of $\bar{P} \times \bar{\boldsymbol{Q}}$; then, in the sense of the definitions of §3, every specialization $((x', y'_\beta)_{\beta \in B})$ of the set of quantities $((\bar{x}, \bar{y}_\beta)_{\beta \in B})$ over k is attached to a point or pseudopoint of $\boldsymbol{W}$; when that is so, we say that the specialization (x', y') of $(\bar{x}, \bar{y})$ is attached to that same point or pseudopoint. By the definition of the completeness over a point, every specialization of $(\bar{x}, \bar{y})$ over k, of the form (x, y), must be proper since $\boldsymbol{W}$ is complete over $P = (x)$; such a specialization is then attached to a point of $\boldsymbol{W}$ which has the projection P on S^n and is therefore one of the points $P \times \boldsymbol{Q}_\rho$; this means that, for some $\beta \in B$, we have

$$(y_\beta) = Q_{\rho\beta}.$$

Let $\mathfrak{S}^r$ be a minimal set of equations for L; let $\bar{L}^{n-r}$ be a linear variety defined in S^n by a generic set of equations $\bar{\mathfrak{S}}^r$ over k; we may write these equations as $\sum_{j=1}^n u_{ij}X_j - v_i = 0 \ (1 \leqq i \leqq r)$, where (u) is a set of rn independent variables over k and (v) is a set of r independent variables over the field $K = k(u)$. By th. 1 of Chap. V, §1, $W' \cap \bar{L}$ is not empty, and, if $\bar{P}$ is any point in it, it is a generic point of W' over K, algebraic over $K(v)$; then, by th. 6 of Chap. IV, §3, and prop. 27 of Chap. IV, §7, there is a generic point $\bar{P} \times \bar{\boldsymbol{Q}}$ of $\boldsymbol{W}$ with the projection $\bar{P}$ on W', and, if we put $d = [\boldsymbol{W}:W']$, we have $d = [K(\bar{P}, \bar{\boldsymbol{Q}}):K(\bar{P})]$.

Let $(\bar{P}^{(1)}, \cdots, \bar{P}^{(\delta)})$ be a complete set of conjugates of $\bar{P}$ over $K(v)$; by the definitions in Chap. V, §1, this is a complete set of intersections of W' and $\bar{L}$; for each λ, put $\bar{P}^{(\lambda)} = (\bar{x}^{(\lambda)})$; let σ_λ be an automorphism over $K(v)$ of the algebraic closure of $K(v)$ which maps $\bar{P}$ on $\bar{P}^{(\lambda)}$. As above, call $\bar{Q}_\beta = (\bar{y}_\beta)$ the representatives of $\bar{\boldsymbol{Q}}$, put $(\bar{y}) = ((\bar{y}_\beta)_{\beta \in B})$, and call $(\bar{y}^{(1)}, \cdots, \bar{y}^{(d)})$ a complete set of conjugates of $(\bar{y})$ over $K(\bar{x})$, which consists of d sets $(\bar{y}^{(\nu)})$ since d is the degree of $K(\bar{P}, \bar{\boldsymbol{Q}})$ over $K(\bar{P})$, i.e. of $K(\bar{x}, \bar{y})$ over $K(\bar{x})$. Also, for every λ, call $(\bar{y}^{(\lambda\nu)})$ the image of $(\bar{y}^{(\nu)})$ under σ_λ. Then, by prop. 11 of Chap. I, §4, the δd sets of quantities $(\bar{x}^{(\lambda)}, \bar{y}^{(\lambda\nu)})$ are a complete set of conjugates of $(\bar{x}, \bar{y})$ over $K(v)$. Consider now any simultaneous specialization

$$(x^{(\lambda)}, y^{(\lambda\nu)})_{1 \leqq \lambda \leqq \delta, 1 \leqq \nu \leqq d}$$

of all the quantities in that complete set over $\bar{\mathfrak{S}}^r \to \mathfrak{S}^r$, with reference to k. Put $\mu = j(W' \cdot L, P)$; by the definition of the latter symbol, there are exactly μ values of λ for which $(x^{(\lambda)}) = (x)$; by reordering the $\bar{P}^{(\lambda)}$ if necessary, we may assume that this is so for $1 \leqq \lambda \leqq \mu$, and for no other value of λ. Then, for each one of the μd pairs (λ, ν) such that $1 \leqq \lambda \leqq \mu$, $(x, y^{(\lambda\nu)})$ is a specialization of $(\bar{x}^{(\lambda)}, \bar{y}^{(\lambda\nu)})$ over k; as the latter set is a conjugate of $(\bar{x}, \bar{y})$ over $K(v)$, it is a generic specialization of $(\bar{x}, \bar{y})$ over k, so that $(x, y^{(\lambda\nu)})$ is a specialization of $(\bar{x}, \bar{y})$ over k; as we have seen above, it must therefore be attached to one of the points $P \times \mathbf{Q}_\rho$. If now we call μ'_ρ the number of pairs (λ, ν) such that $1 \leqq \lambda \leqq \mu$ and that $(x, y^{(\lambda\nu)})$ is attached to $P \times \mathbf{Q}_\rho$, we have $\mu d = \sum \mu'_\rho$. Our proposition will be proved if we show that the μ'_ρ are the same as the μ_ρ.

In fact, for any given ρ, let $\alpha \in A$ be such that $\mathbf{Q}_\rho$ has a representative $Q_{\rho\alpha}$ in V_α; since $P \times \mathbf{Q}_\rho$ is in $\mathbf{W}$, this implies that α is in B. The set $(x, y^{(\lambda\nu)})$ is attached to $\mathbf{Q}_\rho$ if and only if $(y_\alpha^{(\lambda\nu)}) = Q_{\rho\alpha}$; therefore, if we consider the δd sets of quantities $(\bar{x}^{(\lambda)}, \bar{y}_\alpha^{(\lambda\nu)})$, which, as above, make up a complete set of conjugates of $(\bar{x}, \bar{y}_\alpha)$ over $K(v)$, and its specialization

$$(x^{(\lambda)}, y_\alpha^{(\lambda\nu)})_{1 \leqq \lambda \leqq \delta, 1 \leqq \nu \leqq d},$$

μ'_ρ is the number of pairs (λ, ν) for which we have $(x^{(\lambda)}) = (x)$ and $(y_\alpha^{(\lambda\nu)}) = Q_{\rho\alpha}$. By th. 3 of Chap. V, §1, the δd sets $(\bar{x}^{(\lambda)}, \bar{y}_\alpha^{(\lambda\nu)})$ are a complete set of intersections of W_α and $\bar{L} \times S^{m_\alpha}$ in $S^n \times S^{m_\alpha}$; therefore, those among the $(x^{(\lambda)}, y_\alpha^{(\lambda\nu)})$ which are finite are a complete set of intersections of W_α and $L \times S^{m_\alpha}$; by the definition of the symbol $j(W_\alpha \cdot (L \times S^{m_\alpha}), P \times Q_{\rho\alpha})$, it must therefore be equal to μ'_ρ, hence independent of α since μ'_ρ is so. This completes the proof.

THEOREM 10. *Let $\mathbf{U}$, $\mathbf{V}$ be two abstract varieties and $\mathbf{A}$ a subvariety of their product $\mathbf{U} \times \mathbf{V}$, with the geometric projection $\mathbf{A}'$ on $\mathbf{U}$. Let $\mathbf{B}$ be a subvariety of $\mathbf{U}$; let $\mathbf{C}'$ be a proper component of $\mathbf{A}' \cap \mathbf{B}$ on $\mathbf{U}$, such that $\mathbf{A}$ is complete over $\mathbf{C}'$; let the $\mathbf{C}_\rho$, for $1 \leqq \rho \leqq r$, be those components of $\mathbf{A} \cap (\mathbf{C}' \times \mathbf{V})$ which have the projection $\mathbf{C}'$ on $\mathbf{U}$, and assume that every $\mathbf{C}_\rho$ has the same dimension as $\mathbf{C}'$ and is simple on $\mathbf{U} \times \mathbf{V}$. Then the $\mathbf{C}_\rho$ are proper components of $\mathbf{A} \cap (\mathbf{B} \times \mathbf{V})$ on $\mathbf{U} \times \mathbf{V}$, and we have*

$$[\mathbf{A}:\mathbf{A}'] \cdot i(\mathbf{A}' \cdot \mathbf{B}, \mathbf{C}'; \mathbf{U}) = \sum_\rho [\mathbf{C}_\rho : \mathbf{C}'] \cdot i(\mathbf{A} \cdot (\mathbf{B} \times \mathbf{V}), \mathbf{C}_\rho; \mathbf{U} \times \mathbf{V}).$$

By prop. 11 of §5, the assumptions imply that $\mathbf{A}$ has the same dimension as $\mathbf{A}'$; the assertion about the $\mathbf{C}_\rho$ being proper follows from this at once. If $\mathbf{C}'$ has a representative in some representative of $\mathbf{U}$, the projections on $\mathbf{U}$ of all the varieties under consideration have representatives in it; and the principle of localization shows at once that it is enough to consider that representative for $\mathbf{U}$; in other words, it is enough to prove our theorem in the case in which $\mathbf{U}$ is an affine variety with the single representative U. For the sake of consistency, we shall write A', B, C' instead of $\mathbf{A}'$, $\mathbf{B}$, $\mathbf{C}'$.

Let S^N be the ambient space for U, and n the dimension of U. Call k a common field of definition for U, $\mathbf{V}$, $\mathbf{A}$, B, C' and the $\mathbf{C}_\rho$. As explained in Chap. VI, §1, take a uniformizing set of linear forms $F_i(X) (1 \leqq i \leqq n)$ for U along C', with coefficients in k; let Λ be the linear variety defined in $S^N \times S^N$ by the set of equations $F_i(X - X') = 0$ $(1 \leqq i \leqq n)$. Then, if we call μ the intersection-multiplicity of A' and B along C' on U, we have, by the definition of Chap. VI, §1:

$$\mu = i(A' \cdot B, C'; U) = j((B \times A') \cdot \Lambda, \Delta_{C'}).$$

Furthermore, call d the dimension of C', and let L_0 be a linear variety defined in $S^N \times S^N$ by a generic set of d linear equations over k; applying th. 4 of Chap. V, §2, we see, firstly, that $\Delta_{C'} \cap L_0$ contains a generic point of $\Delta_{C'}$ over k, i.e. a point of the form $P' \times P'$, where P' is a generic point of C' over k; and, secondly, by that theorem and by the definition of the intersection-multiplicity in Chap. V, §2, we see that μ is the same as the intersection-multiplicity of $B \times A'$ and of the linear variety $L = \Lambda \cap L_0$ at $P' \times P'$. On the other hand, if M and $N \times \boldsymbol{Q}$ are independent generic points of B and of $\boldsymbol{A}$ over k, then $N \times \boldsymbol{Q}$ is a generic point of $\boldsymbol{A}$ over the field $K = k(M)$, so that $[\boldsymbol{A}:A']$ is the same as

$$[K(N \times \boldsymbol{Q}):K(N)],$$

i.e. as $[k(M \times N \times \boldsymbol{Q}):k(M \times N)]$, hence also as $[(B \times \boldsymbol{A}):(B \times A')]$. The left-hand side of the formula in our theorem can therefore be written as follows:

$$[(B \times \boldsymbol{A}):(B \times A')]\cdot j((B \times A')\cdot L, P' \times P').$$

Now we show that this can be calculated by means of prop. 19, i.e. that the assumptions in that proposition are fufilled if we substitute $B \times \boldsymbol{A}$ for $\boldsymbol{W}$, $B \times A'$ for W' and $P' \times P'$ for P. In fact, the assumption that $\boldsymbol{A}$ is complete over C' is the same as to say that it is so over P', so that $B \times \boldsymbol{A}$ is complete over $P' \times P'$. Now consider the set $(B \times \boldsymbol{A}) \cap (P' \times P' \times \boldsymbol{V})$; it consists of all the points $P' \times P' \times \boldsymbol{Q}'$, where $P' \times \boldsymbol{Q}'$ is any point of $\boldsymbol{A}$ with the projection P' on U. Call $\boldsymbol{D}$ the locus of $P' \times \boldsymbol{Q}'$ over $\bar{k}$; this is a subvariety of $\boldsymbol{A}$ with the projection C' on U, and is therefore contained in one of the $\boldsymbol{C}_\rho$; as it has at least the dimension d, and the $\boldsymbol{C}_\rho$ have the dimension d, $\boldsymbol{D}$ must be one of the $\boldsymbol{C}_\rho$, so that $P' \times \boldsymbol{Q}'$ is in $\boldsymbol{C}_\rho \cap (P' \times \boldsymbol{V})$ for some ρ. Now prop. 27 of Chap. IV, §7, shows that, for each ρ, $\boldsymbol{C}_\rho \cap (P' \times \boldsymbol{V})$ consists of finitely many points $P' \times \boldsymbol{Q}'_{\rho\lambda}$, which are all generic points of $\boldsymbol{C}_\rho$ over k and are all conjugates of each other over $k(P')$. This shows that $B \times \boldsymbol{A}$, $B \times A'$, L, $P' \times P'$ and the points $P' \times P' \times \boldsymbol{Q}'_{\rho\lambda}$ satisfy all the assumptions in prop. 19. Therefore the left-hand side of the formula in th. 10 is equal to a sum $\sum_{\rho,\lambda} \mu_{\rho\lambda}$, where each $\mu_{\rho\lambda}$ is defined as follows. Let α be such that $\boldsymbol{Q}'_{\rho\lambda}$ has a representative $Q'_{\rho\lambda\alpha}$ in V_α ; then, if A_α is the representative of $\boldsymbol{A}$ in $U \times V_\alpha$, and if S^{m_α} denotes again the ambient space for V_α, we have

$$\mu_{\rho\lambda} = j((B \times A_\alpha)\cdot(L \times S^{m_\alpha}), P' \times P' \times Q'_{\rho\lambda\alpha}).$$

Observe now that $\boldsymbol{Q}'_{\rho\lambda}$ has a representative in V_α if and only if $\boldsymbol{C}_\rho$ has a representative $C_{\rho\alpha}$ in $U \times V_\alpha$, and that, when that is so, the term depending upon $\boldsymbol{C}_\rho$, in the right-hand side of the formula in th. 10, can be rewritten as $[C_{\rho\alpha}:C']\cdot\mu'_\rho$, with

$$\mu'_\rho = i(A_\alpha\cdot(B \times V_\alpha), C_{\rho\alpha} ; U \times V_\alpha),$$

so that our theorem will be proved if we show that this is equal to $\sum_\lambda \mu_{\rho\lambda}$ for every ρ. Now μ'_ρ can be expressed by means of prop. 6 of Chap. VI, §3; in fact, call $\Omega_{\rho\alpha}$ the locus of $P' \times P' \times Q'_{\rho\lambda\alpha}$ over k, which does not depend upon λ since all the $Q'_{\rho\lambda\alpha}$, for given values of ρ and α, are conjugates of each other over $k(P')$; then that proposition shows that we have:

$$\mu'_\rho = j((B \times A_\alpha)\cdot(\Lambda \times S^{m_\alpha}), \Omega_{\rho\alpha}).$$

In order to compare this with $\sum_\lambda \mu_{\rho\lambda}$, we apply the associativity property of intersections, or rather the special case of it which is contained in prop. 15, Chap. V, §2. In fact, $L \times S^{m_\alpha}$ is the intersection of $\Lambda \times S^{m_\alpha}$ and $L_0 \times S^{m_\alpha}$; also, any component X of $(B \times A_\alpha) \cap (\Lambda \times S^{m_\alpha})$ must be algebraic over k, so that, if it contains $P' \times P' \times Q'_{\rho\lambda\alpha}$, it must contain the locus $\Omega_{\rho\alpha}$ of that point over k; as $\Omega_{\rho\alpha}$, by prop. 6 of Chap. VI, §3, is a proper component of that intersection, we have then $X = \Omega_{\rho\alpha}$. Now prop. 15 of Chap. V, §2, gives

$$\mu_{\rho\lambda} = \mu'_\rho\cdot j(\Omega_{\rho\alpha}\cdot(L_0 \times S^{m_\alpha}), P' \times P' \times Q'_{\rho\lambda\alpha}).$$

Our result follows now at once from prop. 11 of Chap. V, §1, applied to the variety $\Omega_{\rho\alpha}$ in $(S^N \times S^N) \times S^{m_\alpha}$, to its projection $\Delta_{C'}$ on $S^N \times S^N$, to the linear variety L_0 in the same space, and to the point $P' \times P'$ in $\Delta_{C'} \cap L_0$; in applying that proposition, one need only observe that, by prop. 27 of Chap. IV, §7, $\Omega_{\rho\alpha}$ is finite over $P' \times P'$, that the $P' \times P' \times Q'_{\rho\lambda\alpha}$ are all the points of $\Omega_{\rho\alpha}$ with the projection $P' \times P'$ on $S^N \times S^N$, and that $P' \times P'$ is of multiplicity 1 in the intersection of $\Delta_{C'}$ and L_0, by the definition of intersection-multiplicities, since L_0 was taken generic in $S^N \times S^N$.

One should observe that th. 8 of Chap. VI, §3, is no more than a special case of th. 10 above.

CHAPTER VIII

THE CALCULUS OF CYCLES

1. Chains and cycles. Now that we have obtained all the local properties of intersection-multiplicities which we intended to assemble, it remains for us to translate them into a practical calculus. This will be done in this Chapter by means of the concept of cycle. It should be kept in mind, however, that the results "in the large" which are now to be given are necessarily less precise than the earlier ones on which they rest, since they require global and not merely local assumptions; for the sake of simplicity, too, we shall often make more restrictive assumptions than would actually have been needed for the validity of our theorems.

Let U be an abstract variety. By a *chain of dimension r on U*, or a *U-chain of dimension r*, or an *r-chain on U*, we understand an element of the free abelian group generated by the subvarieties of U of dimension r; the elements of the subgroup generated by the simple subvarieties of U of dimension r will be called the *cycles of dimension r on U*, or the *U-cycles of dimension r*, or the *r-cycles on U*. Superscripts will occasionally be used to denote the dimension of cycles, just as has been done for varieties. If n is the dimension of U, and a subvariety, chain or cycle on U has the dimension r, we shall also say that it has the *codimension* $n - r$ *on* U. For formal reasons, we do not restrict our definitions to the case $0 \leqq r \leqq n$; as there are of course no subvarieties of U of dimension r for $r < 0$ or for $r > n$, the group of r-chains on U, for $r < 0$ or $r > n$, has no other element than 0. The group of n-chains on U is generated by U and consists of the elements $a \cdot U$, where a is any integer. Cycles of codimension 1 on U are called *U-divisors*.

If X is a chain on U, and A a subvariety of U, the coefficient of A in X will be denoted by $\gamma_A(X)$, so that we can always write any r-chain X on U as $X = \sum_A \gamma_A(X) \cdot A$, where the sum is extended to all subvarieties of U of dimension r; by the definition of a chain, the right-hand side has only finitely many non-zero terms. Those varieties A for which $\gamma_A(X) \neq 0$ are called *the components of X*; their union is a closed subset of U which is called *the support of X* and will be denoted by $|X|$; it has the same components as X.

A chain X is called *positive* if $\gamma_A(X) \geqq 0$ for all A, or, what amounts to the same, if it can be written as the sum $\sum_i A_i$ of finitely many varieties, distinct or not; when that is so, we write $X \succ 0$; and, if X, Y are two chains of the same dimension, we write $X \succ Y$ and $Y \prec X$ if $X - Y \succ 0$. If $X_1, \cdots, X_h$ are r-chains on U, the support of $\sum_i X_i$ is contained in the union of the $|X_i|$; it coincides with that union if $X_i \succ 0$ for all i. If X, Y are r-chains such that $0 \prec X \prec Y$, then $|X|$ is contained in $|Y|$.

Let U' be a non-empty open subset of U, which, by prop. 15 of Chap. VII, §6, may be identified with a variety. If A is any subvariety of U, put $A' = 0$ if

$A \cap U' = \emptyset$, i.e. if A is contained in the closed set $U - U'$; otherwise put $A' = A \cap U'$. In the latter case, prop. 15 shows at once that A' is a subvariety of U'; more precisely, if k is a common field of definition for U and A, such that U' is k-open, and if P is a generic point of A over k, A' is the locus of P over k on U'; this also shows that A is then the closure of A' on U, so that the mapping $A \rightarrow A'$ is a one-to-one correspondence between the subvarieties of U, not contained in $U - U'$, and the subvarieties of U'. For every r, the mapping $A \rightarrow A'$ can now be extended to a homomorphism of the group of r-chains on U into the group of r-chains on U', which will be called the *restriction from U to U'*; it is surjective, and its kernel consists of the U-chains whose support is contained in $U - U'$. The restriction to U' of a U-cycle is a U'-cycle.

Let U be an abstract variety, defined over a field k. Let V be a subvariety of U, algebraic over k, with the generic point P over $\bar{k}$; let p^m be the order of inseparability of V over k, which has the value $[k(P):k]_\iota$. Let X be the U-chain such that $\gamma_A(X) = 0$ unless A is one of the conjugates of V over k, and that $\gamma_A(X) = p^m$ whenever A is one of these conjugates. In other words, if $V, V', V'', \cdots$ are all the distinct conjugates of V over k, we have

$$X = p^m(V + V' + V'' + \cdots).$$

Then this cycle X will be called *the prime rational chain over k with the component V*, or also *the prime rational chain over k with the generic point P over k*. By prop. 9 of Chap. VII, §4, its support $|X|$ is the k-closure of P, and also the k-closure of V; the same proposition shows that a point P' of $|X|$ is a generic point of X over k if and only if it is a generic specialization of P over k, or also if and only if its dimension over k is at least equal to the dimension of X, in which case it is necessarily equal to it.

As two varieties which are conjugate over k have the same conjugates and the same order of inseparability over k, our definition shows that two prime rational chains over k coincide whenever they have at least one component in common. Therefore, if the X_i are distinct prime rational r-chains over k and the a_i are integers, $\sum_i a_i \cdot X_i$ cannot be 0 unless all the a_i are 0. This means that the subgroup of the group of r-chains on U generated by the prime rational r-chains over k can be identified with the free abelian group generated by the latter chains. The elements of that group are called *the rational r-chains over k on U*. A chain X is rational over k if and only if the following conditions are satisfied: (a) $\gamma_A(X) = 0$ *unless A is algebraic over k*; (b) *if A is algebraic over k and A' is any conjugate of A over k, then $\gamma_{A'}(X) = \gamma_A(X)$*; (c) *if A is algebraic over k, $\gamma_A(X)$ is a multiple of the order of inseparability of A over k.* If a chain is rational over k, its support is k-closed; the converse is not true. If U' is a k-open subset of U, and X is a U-chain, rational over k, then the restriction X' of X to U' is rational over k; if no component of X is contained in $U - U'$, then X is rational over k if and only if X' is so; also, if (U'_α) is a covering of U by k-open subsets U'_α, one sees at once that a U-chain is rational over k if and only if all its restrictions to the U'_α are so.

If X is a U-chain, and σ is an isomorphism of some common field of definition for U and all the components of X onto some other field, then X^σ is defined in an obvious manner and is a U^σ-chain. If X is rational over k, or, more generally, if it satisfies the two conditions (a) and (b) stated above, one sees, just as in the case of k-closed sets, that X is invariant under any isomorphism σ which induces the identity on k, and therefore that X^σ, for any σ, depends only upon the isomorphism of k induced by σ on k; in fact, it is easily seen, by means of coroll. 1 of prop. 2, Chap. VII, §1, that conditions (a) and (b) are necessary and sufficient for a chain X to be invariant under all isomorphisms over k of a common field of definition, containing k, for U and the components of X; in other words, X has that property if and only if there is an integer m such that $p^m \cdot X$ is rational over k. Now, if X is such a chain, and if τ is any isomorphism of k on some field k', we define X^τ as being the same as X^σ if σ is any isomorphism of $\bar{k}$ on $\bar{k}'$, coinciding with τ on k.

Let k be a field of definition for U, and K a field containing k; if two subvarieties of U, both algebraic over k, are conjugate over K, they are obviously so over k; this, together with prop. 26 of Chap. I, §8, shows that, if a chain is rational over k, it is so over K. If a U-chain X is given, there are always fields over which it is rational; for instance, every common field of definition for U and for all the components of X has that property; but there is not always a smallest field over which it is rational. For instance, let $M = (x_1, x_2)$ be a generic point of S^2 over k, and assume that the characteristic p of k is >1; then the 0-cycle $p \cdot M$ on S^2 is rational over $k(x_1, x_2^p)$ and over $k(x_1^p, x_2)$, but not over the intersection $k(x_1^p, x_2^p)$ of these fields. Nevertheless, there are cases when there is a smallest field over which a given chain is rational; the simplest one is that of a chain consisting of a single component V with the coefficient 1, as shown by the following proposition:

Proposition 1. *Let U be a variety, defined over a field k; let V be a subvariety of U. Then the chain V is rational over k if and only if k is a field of definition for V.*

If the variety V is defined over k, it is obvious that the chain V is rational over k. Conversely, assume that the chain V is rational over k; then V is defined over $\bar{k}$, has no conjugate over k other than itself, and has the order of inseparability 1 over k. By prop. 5 of Chap. IV, §2, the smallest field of definition k_1 for V, containing k, must then be purely inseparable over k. On the other hand, if M is a generic point of V over $\bar{k}$, th. 8 of Chap. I, §8, shows that $k(M)$ is separably generated over k; then prop. 23 of Chap. I, §7, together with coroll. 3 of th. 1, Chap. IV, §1, applied to any representative of V, shows that k_1 is separable over k. Therefore $k_1 = k$.

Because of this result, we will, from now on, identify varieties with the corresponding chains, and we will use the words "*rational over* k" interchangeably with "defined over k," not only for those varieties which can be used to define a chain (i.e. subvarieties of some ambient variety having k as its field of definition), but for all varieties (affine or abstract) and mappings. When a variety or mapping is rational over k (in this sense), as well as when a chain is rational over k, we shall say that k is a *field of rationality* for that variety, mapping or chain. For mappings, this has the advantage of avoiding the clash of words between "a mapping defined at a point" and "a mapping having k as field of definition" (some authors avoid this by saying that a mapping is "holomorphic at a point" instead of "defined at a point"). Little confusion is to be feared here with the use made of the word "rational" by classical geometers (they applied it to curves, surfaces and sometimes varieties, defined over a field k, usually the field of complex numbers, and such that, if $\boldsymbol{P}$ is a generic point of the variety over k, $k(\boldsymbol{P})$ is a purely transcendental extension of k; such a variety could more suitably be called *"pure over k,"* and one could call it *"semi-pure over k"* if $k(\boldsymbol{P})$ is contained in a purely transcendental extension of k).

Prop. 1 shows that, if $\boldsymbol{U}$ is defined over k, and $\boldsymbol{V}$ is a subvariety of $\boldsymbol{U}$, $\boldsymbol{V}$, as a $\boldsymbol{U}$-chain, has a smallest field of rationality containing k, viz. the smallest field of definition for $\boldsymbol{V}$ containing k. In order to treat more general cases, we shall need the following lemmas:

LEMMA 1. *Let V be a variety, algebraic over a field k; let K be a field containing k. Then there is a finitely generated extension K' of k, contained in K and such that V has the same order of inseparability over K' as over K.*

We may clearly assume that V is an affine variety; let q be its order of inseparability over k, and let (x) be a generic point of V over $\bar{K}$. By prop. 26 of Chap. I, §8, the order of inseparability Q of V over K is $\leqq q$; we shall use induction on q/Q; if $q/Q = 1$, we take $K' = k$. Assume now that $q/Q > 1$; let (u) be a set of independent variables over k in $k(x)$, such that $\bar{k}(x)$ is separably algebraic over $\bar{k}(u)$; let (v) be a set of elements of $k(x)$, such that $k(u, v)$ is the field of the separably algebraic elements over $k(u)$ in $k(x)$; then q is the degree of $k(x)$ over $k(u, v)$, and we can find q linearly independent elements $y_1, \cdots, y_q$ over $k(u, v)$ in $k(x)$. As (x) is generic over $\bar{K}$ on V, (u) is still a set of independent variables over K in $K(x)$; $K(u, v)$ is separably algebraic over $K(u)$; $K(x)$ is purely inseparable over $K(u, v)$; as $\bar{K}(x)$ is separably algebraic over $\bar{K}(u)$, Q is the degree of $K(x)$ over $K(u, v)$. As $Q < q$, there is a linear relation between the y_i, with coefficients in $K(u, v)$; writing the latter in the form $R_i(u, v)$, where the R_i are rational fractions, and calling K_1 the extension of K generated by all the coefficients in the R_i, we see that the y_i are not linearly independent over $K_1(u, v)$; by prop. 6 of Chap. I, §2, this implies that the degree Q_1 of $K_1(x)$ over $K_1(u, v)$ is $< q$. As above we see that Q_1 is the order of inseparability of $K_1(x)$ over K_1; as $Q_1/Q < q/Q$, we can apply the induction assumption to K and K_1, so that there is a finitely generated extension K' of K_1 such that V has the same order of inseparability over K as over K'. This completes the proof.

LEMMA 2. *Let Z be a k-closed set in the affine space S^n; let K be a field containing k. Then the ideal of the polynomials in $K[X]$ which are 0 on Z has a basis in*

$k[X]$ *if and only if all the components of* Z *have the same order of inseparability over* K *as over* k.

For every field L between k and K, call $\mathfrak{a}_L$ the ideal of the polynomials in $L[X]$ which are 0 on Z. Using lemma 1 of Chap. I, §6, one sees at once that, when L is such a field, $\mathfrak{a}_K$ has a basis in $k[X]$ if and only if it has a basis in $L[X]$ and $\mathfrak{a}_L$ has a basis in $k[X]$. Also, prop. 26 of Chap. I, §8, shows that, if a component of Z has the same order of inseparability q over K as over k, then its order of inseparability over L is also q. Therefore, if we denote by $p(Z, K, k)$ the assertion in the lemma, we see that $p(Z, K, k)$ is true whenever $p(Z, K, L)$ and $p(Z, L, k)$ are true. Now, by lemma 2 of Chap. I, §7, there is a finitely generated extension L' of k such that $\mathfrak{a}_K$ has a basis in $L'[X]$; and, by lemma 1 above, there is a finitely generated extension L of L', contained in K, such that every component of Z has the same order of inseparability over L as over K; then $p(Z, K, L)$ is true, so that it is enough to prove $p(Z, L, k)$. In other words, it will be enough to prove our lemma under the additional assumption that K is finitely generated over k. That being assumed, let (u) be a maximal set of independent variables over k in K, so that K is an algebraic extension of $k(u)$; let L be the field of all separably algebraic elements over $k(u)$ in K; then L is separably generated over k, and K is purely inseparable and of finite degree over L. By coroll. 1 of th. 3, Chap. I, §6, and prop. 26 of Chap. I, §8, every variety V, algebraic over k, has the same order of inseparability over $k(u)$ as over k; by prop. 25 of Chap. I, §8, its order of inseparability over L is still the same. Therefore $p(Z, L, k)$ will be proved if we show that $\mathfrak{a}_L$ has a basis in $k[X]$.

In fact, let P be a polynomial in $\mathfrak{a}_L$, and write it as $P = \sum_\lambda \omega_\lambda P_\lambda$, where the P_λ are in $k[X]$ and the ω_λ are in L and linearly independent over k. By prop. 19 of Chap. I, §7, and prop. 19 of Chap. II, §4, (ω_λ) has generic specializations $(\omega_\lambda^{(\rho)})$ over k, such that $\det(\omega_\lambda^{(\rho)}) \neq 0$. Let V be any component of Z, and (x) a generic point of V over $\bar{L}$; by prop. 4 of Chap. II, §2, we can extend, for each ρ, the generic specialization (ω_λ) of $(\omega_\lambda^{(\rho)})$ over k to a generic specialization $(\omega_\lambda, x^{(\rho)})$ of $(\omega_\lambda^{(\rho)}, x)$ over k. By prop. 2 of Chap. VII, §1, $(x^{(\rho)})$ is in Z. As P is 0 on Z, we get $P(x^{(\rho)}) = 0$, i.e. $\sum_\lambda \omega_\lambda P_\lambda(x^{(\rho)}) = 0$, which implies $\sum_\lambda \omega_\lambda^{(\rho)} P_\lambda(x) = 0$. As this holds for every ρ, we see that all the $P_\lambda(x)$ must be 0, and therefore all the P_λ must be 0 on V. As this holds for every component V of Z, it shows that the P_λ are 0 on Z, i.e. that they are in $\mathfrak{a}_k$; therefore any basis for $\mathfrak{a}_k$ is one for $\mathfrak{a}_L$.

Our lemma will now be fully proved if we prove $p(Z, K, L)$. In other words, it will be enough to prove the lemma under the additional assumption that K is a purely inseparable extension of k, of finite degree over k. Then it follows at once from prop. 3 of Chap. II, §1, and from prop. 2 of Chap. VII, §1, that a set is k-closed if and only if it is K-closed. Let $Z_1, \cdots, Z_h$ be all the distinct sets among the k-closures of the components of Z; thus, each Z_i is the union of a component of Z and of all its conjugates over k, and no component of Z_i is contained in any component of Z_j for $i \neq j$. Write $\mathfrak{a}$ instead of $\mathfrak{a}_k$, $\mathfrak{A}$ instead of $\mathfrak{a}_K$, and put $\mathfrak{A}' = \mathfrak{a} \cdot K[X]$, this meaning the ideal generated in $K[X]$ by all the polynomials in $\mathfrak{a}$, so that $\mathfrak{A}' = \mathfrak{A}$ if and only if $\mathfrak{A}$ has a basis in $k[X]$. For each i, let $\mathfrak{a}_i$, $\mathfrak{A}_i$, $\mathfrak{A}'_i$ be the ideals defined by means of Z_i just as $\mathfrak{a}$, $\mathfrak{A}$, $\mathfrak{A}'$ have been defined by means of Z; then $\mathfrak{a}_i$ is the prime ideal determined over k by any generic point over $\bar{k}$ of any component of Z_i, and $\mathfrak{A}_i$ is the prime ideal determined by the same point over K. Clearly $\mathfrak{A}$ and $\mathfrak{a}$ are the intersections of the $\mathfrak{A}_i$ and of the $\mathfrak{a}_i$, respectively; from this it follows at once that $\mathfrak{A}'$ is contained in the intersection $\mathfrak{A}''$ of the $\mathfrak{A}'_i$. Conversely, take any P in $\mathfrak{A}''$, and write it as $P = \sum_\lambda \omega_\lambda P_\lambda$, where the P_λ are in $k[X]$ and the ω_λ are in K and linearly independent over k. As P is in $\mathfrak{A}'_i$, lemma 1 of Chap. I, §6, shows that the P_λ are in $\mathfrak{a}_i$; as this is so for every i, the P_λ are in $\mathfrak{a}$, so that P is in $\mathfrak{A}'$. Thus we have proved that $\mathfrak{A}' = \mathfrak{A}''$, i.e. that $\mathfrak{A}'$ is the intersection of the $\mathfrak{A}'_i$. Therefore, if $\mathfrak{A}'_i = \mathfrak{A}_i$ for every i, we have $\mathfrak{A}' = \mathfrak{A}$. Conversely, assume that, for some i, we have $\mathfrak{A}'_i \neq \mathfrak{A}_i$, so that we can choose a polynomial P in $\mathfrak{A}_i$ and not in $\mathfrak{A}'_i$. For every $j \neq i$, Z_i is not contained in Z_j, and therefore, by th. 1 of Chap. VII, §1, we can choose in $k[X]$ a polynomial Q_j which is 0 on Z_j and not on Z_i, i.e. which is in $\mathfrak{a}_j$ and not in $\mathfrak{a}_i$; call Q the product of all the Q_j for $j \neq i$. Write $P = \sum_\lambda \omega_\lambda P_\lambda$, where the P_λ are in $k[X]$ and the ω_λ are in K and linearly independent over k. As P is not in $\mathfrak{A}'_i$, some P_λ is not in $\mathfrak{a}_i$; then, as $\mathfrak{a}_i$ is prime in $k[X]$, and as no Q_j is in $\mathfrak{a}_i$, some QP_λ is not in $\mathfrak{a}_i$; by lemma 1 of Chap. I, §6, applied to QP, this implies that QP is not in $\mathfrak{A}'_i$, and therefore also not in $\mathfrak{A}'$. On the other hand, the definition of QP shows that it is in $\mathfrak{A}$. Thus we have proved that $\mathfrak{A}' = \mathfrak{A}$ if and only if $\mathfrak{A}'_i = \mathfrak{A}_i$ for all i. From this it follows at once that $p(Z, K, k)$ is true if and only if $p(Z_i, K, k)$ is true for every i. Thus we are reduced to proving our lemma under the additional assumption that Z is the union of a variety V, algebraic over k, and of all its conjugates over k, so that $\mathfrak{A}$ and $\mathfrak{a}$ are the prime ideals determined over K and over k respectively by a generic point (x) of V over $\bar{k}$. That being assumed, we know, by th. 3 of Chap. I, §6, that $\mathfrak{A}$ has a basis in $k[X]$ if and only if K and $k(x)$ are linearly disjoint over k. When that is so, then, by prop. 26 of Chap. I, §8, V and its conjugates over k have the same order of inseparability over K as over k. On the other hand, assume that K and $k(x)$ are not linearly disjoint over k, so that there is a relation $\sum_\lambda \omega_\lambda z_\lambda = 0$, where the z_λ are in $k(x)$ and not all 0 and the ω_λ are in K and linearly independent over k. Let (y) be a set of independent variables over k in $k(x)$, such that $\bar{k}(x)$ is separably algebraic over $\bar{k}(y)$. By coroll. 1 of th. 3, Chap. I, §6, the ω_λ are in $K(y)$ and are linearly independent over $k(y)$; therefore $K(y)$ and $k(x)$ are not linearly disjoint over $k(y)$; by prop. 6 of Chap. I, §2, this implies that we have

$$[K(x):K(y)] < [k(x):k(y)].$$

But, by prop. 11 of Chap. I, §4, $[K(x):K(y)]_s$ and $[k(x):k(y)]_s$ are both equal to $[K(x):k(y)]_s$; therefore the above inequality implies that

$$[K(x):K(y)]_i < [k(x):k(y)]_i\,;$$

as these are the orders of inseparability of $K(x)$ over K and of $k(x)$ over k, respectively, this completes the proof of our lemma.

THEOREM 1. *Let* $\boldsymbol{U}$ *be a variety, defined over a field* k; *let* $\boldsymbol{Z}$ *be a* $\boldsymbol{U}$*-chain, and assume, if the characteristic* p *of* k *is* > 1, *that the coefficients in* $\boldsymbol{Z}$ *of all the components of* $\boldsymbol{Z}$ *are prime to* p. *Then there is a smallest field of rationality* K_0 *for* $\boldsymbol{Z}$, *containing* k; *and an isomorphism of* K_0 *onto some field* K'_0 *over* k *leaves* $\boldsymbol{Z}$ *invariant if and only if it is the identity.*

Let $\boldsymbol{Z}$ be a $\boldsymbol{U}$-chain; let the U_α be the representatives of $\boldsymbol{U}$, which we may identify with their images in $\boldsymbol{U}$ by prop. 16 of Chap. VII, §6. Then, if we call Z_α, for every α, the restriction of $\boldsymbol{Z}$ to U_α, $\boldsymbol{Z}$ is rational over a field if and only if all the Z_α are so, and it is invariant under an isomorphism if and only if all the Z_α are so. It is therefore enough to consider the case of a chain Z on an affine variety U, defined over k. But then Z determines, in an obvious sense, a chain, and actually a cycle, in the ambient space S^n for U, and the fields of rationality for the former are clearly the same as the fields of rationality containing k for the latter. Thus it is enough to prove our theorem for S^n-cycles. Now, Z being such a cycle, we can write $Z = \sum n \cdot Z_n$, where the sum is taken over all integers n and where Z_n denotes, for every n, the sum of those components of Z which have the coefficient n in Z; the definition of a rational cycle shows at once that Z is rational over a field k if and only if all the $n \cdot Z_n$ are so, and that, if n is prime to p, $n \cdot Z_n$ is rational over k if and only if Z_n is so. Thus it is enough to prove our theorem for an S^n-cycle Z which is the sum of distinct varieties $V_1, \cdots, V_h$.

Let K be a common field of definition for all the V_i; this is a field of rationality for Z. Let $\mathfrak{A}$ be the ideal of the polynomials in $K[X]$ which are 0 on $|Z|$, i.e. on the union of the V_i. Let k be any field of rationality for Z, contained in K; then $|Z|$ is k-closed, and lemma 2 shows that $\mathfrak{A}$ has a basis in $k[X]$. Conversely, if that is so, th. 1 of Chap. VII, §1, shows that $|Z|$ is k-closed, and then lemma 2 shows that all the V_i have the order of inseparability 1 over k, so that Z is rational over k. Now let k be the smallest field such that $\mathfrak{A}$ has a basis in $k[X]$; there is such a field, by lemma 2 of Chap. I, §7, and, by what we have just proved, it is a field of rationality for Z, and the smallest one contained in K. Let k' be any field of rationality for Z; call K' the compositum of K and k'; then, just as before, there is a smallest field of rationality k'' for Z contained in K'; this must be contained both in k and in k', which contradicts the definition of k unless $k \subset k'$. Therefore k is the smallest field whose existence was asserted by our theorem. As Z determines k uniquely, an isomorphism of a field of rationality of Z which leaves Z invariant must map k onto itself; also, it must map onto itself the ideal of the polynomials in $k[X]$ which are 0 on Z; that being so, the last assertion in our theorem follows at once from the last assertion in lemma 2 of Chap. I, §7.

As shown by the example given above, the condition in th. 1, concerning the coefficients of the components of $\boldsymbol{Z}$, is necessary for the validity of the theorem. It will be shown later that, even without that condition, the conclusions of th. 1 remain true for all $\boldsymbol{U}$-divisors. Another result of more limited scope is as follows:

PROPOSITION 2. *Let* $\boldsymbol{U}$ *be a variety, defined over a field* k; *let* K *be a field containing* k, *and* $\boldsymbol{P}$ *a point of* $\boldsymbol{U}$. *Then the prime rational chains with the generic point* $\boldsymbol{P}$ *over* k *and over* K, *respectively, are the same if and only if* K *and* $k(\boldsymbol{P})$ *are linearly disjoint over* k.

Call $\boldsymbol{X}_k$, $\boldsymbol{X}_K$ these two chains; by prop. 2 of Chap. I, §2, they have the same dimension if and only if K and $k(\boldsymbol{P})$ are independent over k; so we may assume, from now on, that this is so; then $\boldsymbol{P}$ has the same locus $\boldsymbol{V}$ over $\bar{K}$ as over $\bar{k}$, and the components of $\boldsymbol{X}_k$ and $\boldsymbol{X}_K$ are the conjugates of $\boldsymbol{V}$ over k and over K, respectively, with coefficients equal to the orders of inseparability of $\boldsymbol{V}$ over k and over K. By the principle of localization, it is enough to consider the case of chains on an affine variety; as in the proof of th. 1, it is therefore enough to consider S^n-cycles. Put $\boldsymbol{P} = (x)$; the supports of $\boldsymbol{X}_K$ and $\boldsymbol{X}_k$ are the K-closure and the k-closure of (x), i.e. the sets of zeros of the prime ideals $\mathfrak{P}$ and $\mathfrak{p}$ respectively determined by (x) over K and over k. By th. 3 of Chap. I, §6, K and $k(x)$ are linearly disjoint over k if and only if $\mathfrak{P}$ has a basis in $k[X]$. Assume that this is so; then $\boldsymbol{X}_K$ and $\boldsymbol{X}_k$ have the same support, i.e. the same components, and lemma 2 above (or prop. 26 of Chap. I, §8) shows that these have the same coefficient in both, so that $\boldsymbol{X}_K = \boldsymbol{X}_k$. Conversely, if $\boldsymbol{X}_K = \boldsymbol{X}_k$, the support of $\boldsymbol{X}_K$ is k-closed, and then lemma 2 shows that $\mathfrak{P}$ has a basis in $k[X]$. This completes the proof.

COROLLARY. *Let* $\boldsymbol{U}$ *be a variety, defined over* k; *let* K *be a field containing* k, *and* $\boldsymbol{X}$ *a prime rational chain over* K *on* $\boldsymbol{U}$. *Then* $\boldsymbol{X}$ *is prime rational over every field between* k *and* K *over which it is rational*; *among such fields, there is a smallest one* K_0; *and an automorphism of* K *over* k *leaves* $\boldsymbol{X}$ *invariant if and only if it induces the identity on* K_0.

Let $\boldsymbol{P}$ be a generic point of $\boldsymbol{X}$ over K; let K_1 be a field between k and K, and call $\boldsymbol{X}_1$ the prime rational chain with the generic point $\boldsymbol{P}$ over K_1. Then $|\boldsymbol{X}|$ and $|\boldsymbol{X}_1|$ are the K-closure and the K_1-closure of $\boldsymbol{P}$, respectively, so that $|\boldsymbol{X}| \subset |\boldsymbol{X}_1|$. On the other hand, if $\boldsymbol{X}$ is rational over K_1, $|\boldsymbol{X}|$ must be K_1-closed, so that it is then the same as $|\boldsymbol{X}_1|$. Then, since $\boldsymbol{X}$ is rational over K_1 and $\boldsymbol{X}_1$ is prime rational over K_1, we have $\boldsymbol{X} \succ \boldsymbol{X}_1$; similarly, since $\boldsymbol{X}_1$ is rational over K and $\boldsymbol{X}$ is prime rational over K, we have $\boldsymbol{X}_1 \succ \boldsymbol{X}$. This gives $\boldsymbol{X} = \boldsymbol{X}_1$. By prop. 2, this shows that the fields K_1 between k and K over which $\boldsymbol{X}$ is rational are those for which K and $K_1(\boldsymbol{P})$ are linearly disjoint over K_1; if (x) is any representative of $\boldsymbol{P}$, and $\mathfrak{P}$ is the ideal determined by (x) over K, th. 3 of Chap. I, §6, shows that these are the fields such that $\mathfrak{P}$ has a basis in $K_1[X]$. Our corollary follows now at once from lemma 2 of Chap. I, §7.

2. Chains and cycles of dimension 0. If $\boldsymbol{X}$ is a chain of dimension 0 (or, more briefly, a 0-chain) on a variety $\boldsymbol{U}$, the sum of the coefficients in $\boldsymbol{X}$ of the components of $\boldsymbol{X}$ will be called the *degree* of $\boldsymbol{X}$ and will be denoted by $\deg(\boldsymbol{X})$. A positive 0-chain of degree m is thus the sum of m points of $\boldsymbol{U}$, distinct or not.

Let $\boldsymbol{X}$ be a 0-chain on $\boldsymbol{U}$, with the components $\boldsymbol{P}_i$, and write it as

$X = \sum_i c_i P_i$; let k be a field of definition for U, and let (P'_i) be a specialization of the set of points (P_i) over k on $(U, \cdots, U)$, such that all the P'_i are points of U; then we say that the chain $X' = \sum_i c_i P'_i$ is *a specialization of X over k on U*. This can be extended in an obvious manner to any number of 0-chains, on one or more varieties. If X is a positive chain of degree m, every specialization of X is a positive chain of degree m; and, if we write $X = \sum_{i=1}^m P_i$, a chain $X' = \sum_{i=1}^m P'_i$ is a specialization of X over k on U if and only if there is a permutation $(i_1, \cdots, i_m)$ of $(1, \cdots, m)$ such that $(P'_{i_1}, \cdots, P'_{i_m})$ is a specialization of $(P_1, \cdots, P_m)$ over k on $(U, \cdots, U)$. If X is any 0-chain and if we write it as $X = Y - Z$, where Y and Z are positive chains with no component in common, then a 0-chain X' is a specialization of X over k if and only if it can be written as $X' = Y' - Z'$, where (Y', Z') is a specialization of the pair of chains (Y, Z) over k on (U, U).

If U is a variety, defined over a field k, we say that a positive 0-chain of degree m on U is *generic over k* if it has m distinct components and these are independent generic points of U over k; then it is a 0-cycle on U, since generic points are simple. By th. 1 of §1, such a cycle has a smallest field of rationality containing k; this is given by the following proposition:

PROPOSITION 3. *Let U be a variety, defined over k; let $M_1, \cdots, M_m$ be m independent generic points of U over k. Let $\mathfrak{g}$ be the group of those automorphisms of $k(M_1, \cdots, M_m)$ over k which induce a permutation of the M_i among themselves. Then the field K of the elements of $k(M_1, \cdots, M_m)$ which are invariant under $\mathfrak{g}$ is the smallest field of rationality, containing k, for the cycle $X = \sum_{i=1}^m M_i$, and X is prime rational over K.*

By Galois theory, $k(M_1, \cdots, M_m)$ is a Galois extension of K with the Galois group $\mathfrak{g}$; therefore the M_i are separably algebraic over K and they are the conjugates of one another over K, so that X is prime rational over K. Let K' be a field of rationality for X between k and K; then all the M_i must be separably algebraic over K', so that K is separably algebraic over K'. If σ is any automorphism of $\bar{K}'$ over K', it must leave X invariant, and therefore must belong to $\mathfrak{g}$, so that it induces the identity on K; by Galois theory, this implies that $K = K'$.

If U is a variety, defined over a field k, and P any point of U, the prime rational chain with the generic point P over k on U is of dimension 0 if and only if P is algebraic over k; then it is the sum of the distinct conjugates of P over k, each one being taken a number of times equal to $[k(P):k]_i$; with the language of Chap. I, §4, we can say that it is the sum of the points in a *complete set of conjugates of P over k*; its degree is equal to $[k(P):k]$.

Chains of dimension 0 provide a convenient language for expressing some basic facts about symmetric functions. Let U be a variety, and consider the product $U^{(m)} = U \times \cdots \times U$ of m factors, all equal to U; then every permutation $(i_1, \cdots, i_m)$ of $(1, \cdots, m)$ determines an automorphism p of $U^{(m)}$, i.e. an isomorphism of $U^{(m)}$ onto itself, given by

$$p(P_1 \times \cdots \times P_m) = P_{i_1} \times \cdots \times P_{i_m}$$

for every point $P_1 \times \cdots \times P_m$ of $U^{(m)}$; such an automorphism p will be called a *permutation* of the m factors of the product $U^{(m)}$. A mapping f of $U^{(m)}$ into a variety V will be called *symmetric* if $f = f \circ p$ for every permutation p of the factors of $U^{(m)}$. Now, f being such a mapping, let X be a positive 0-chain of degree m on U; this can be written as $X = \sum_{i=1}^{m} P_i$, in one and only one way up to a permutation of the terms in the right-hand side; then, if $f(P_1, \cdots, P_m)$ is defined for one such expression of X, it is defined also for all the others and has the same value; in that case, we shall say that $f(X)$ is defined and has that value. These definitions can be extended in an obvious manner to products of any number of factors such as $U^{(m)}$; for instance, if a mapping of a product $U^{(m)} \times V^{(n)}$ into W is invariant under any permutation of the factors in $U^{(m)}$ and under any permutation of the factors in $V^{(n)}$, it will be called symmetric with respect to both these sets of factors; and then the notation $f(X, Y)$ will be given a meaning, just as above, whenever X is a positive 0-chain of degree m on U and Y is a positive 0-chain of degree n on V. In particular, let f be a symmetric mapping of the $(m + n)$-fold product $U^{(m+n)}$ into W; then it is a fortiori symmetric with respect to the first m factors and also with respect to the last n factors; therefore, if X, Y are positive 0-chains on U, with the degrees m and n respectively, $f(X + Y)$ has then a meaning, in our notation, if and only if $f(X, Y)$ has a meaning, and then both these symbols have the same value.

THEOREM 2. *Let the U_ν, for $1 \leqq \nu \leqq n$, be varieties; let f be a mapping of the product $U = \prod_\nu U_\nu^{(m_\nu)}$ into a variety V, where, for each ν, $U_\nu^{(m_\nu)}$ denotes the product of m_ν factors equal to U_ν; assume that f is symmetric with respect to all the factors in each one of the partial products $U_\nu^{(m_\nu)}$. For each ν, let X_ν be a positive 0-cycle of degree m_ν on U_ν; and assume that $f(X_1, \cdots, X_n)$ is defined. Then $f(X_1, \cdots, X_n)$ is rational over every common field of rationality for the U_ν, V, f and the X_ν.*

If k is such a field, $f(X_1, \cdots, X_n)$ is algebraic over k and is invariant under every automorphism of $\bar{k}$ over k, so that it must be purely inseparable over k; this proves the theorem for the case of characteristic 0. From now on, we assume that the characteristic p is > 1; we begin with some lemmas.

LEMMA 3. *Let k be a field, and z an element of an extension $K = k(x_1, \cdots, x_n)$ of k. Then z is in $k(x_1^p, \cdots, x_n^p)$ if and only if $Dz = 0$ for every derivation D in K over k.*

The condition is obviously necessary. Put now $y_i = x_i^p$, and assume that z is in $K = k(x)$ and not in $L = k(y)$; as z^p is in L, prop. 15 of Chap. I, §5, shows that there is a derivation D_0 in the field $K_0 = L(z)$ over L, such that $D_0 z = 1$. Now we use induction on i to define the fields K_i and the derivations D_i, for $1 \leqq i \leqq n$, as follows; we put $K_i = K_{i-1}(x_i)$; if $K_i = K_{i-1}$, we put $D_i = D_{i-1}$; and, if $K_i \neq K_{i-1}$, we take for D_i the derivation in K_i which coincides with D_{i-1} on K_{i-1} and is such that $D_i x_i = 0$; prop. 15 of Chap. I, §5, shows in fact that there is such a derivation, since the irreducible equation for x_i over K_{i-1} is

$X^p = y_i$, and $D_{i-1}y_i = 0$ by the definition of D_0. Then D_n is a derivation of K over k, and is not 0 at z.

LEMMA 4. *Let U be a variety in S^n, and f a symmetric mapping of $U^{(q)}$ into S^1, where $q = p^\nu$ for some integer $\nu \geqq 1$. Let k be a field of rationality for U and f, and let $M = (x_1, \cdots, x_n)$ be a generic point of U over k. Then, if $f(q \cdot M)$ is defined, it is in $k(x_1^q, \cdots, x_n^q)$.*

We proceed by induction on ν, and begin with the case $\nu = 1$, i.e. $q = p$. The assumption that $f(p \cdot M)$ is defined means that f is defined at the point $M \times \cdots \times M$ of $U^{(p)}$; if the $M_\lambda = (x^{(\lambda)})$, for $1 \leqq \lambda \leqq p$, are independent generic points of U over k, we can therefore write f in the form

$$P(x^{(1)}, \cdots, x^{(p)})/Q(x^{(1)}, \cdots, x^{(p)}),$$

where P and Q are polynomials with coefficients in k, and $Q(x, \cdots, x) \neq 0$. Now let Q' be the product of the $p!$ polynomials in the np indeterminates $X_i^{(\lambda)}$ which can be derived from Q by all permutations of $(X^{(1)}), \cdots, (X^{(p)})$ among themselves; put $Q'' = Q'^p$ and $P'' = PQ''/Q$; it is obvious that $Q''(x^{(1)}, \cdots, x^{(p)})$ is symmetric in the $(x^{(\lambda)})$ and that $Q''(x, \cdots, x)$ is not 0 and is in $k(x_1^p, \cdots, x_n^p)$; therefore it is enough to prove our conclusion for $P''(x^{(1)}, \cdots, x^{(p)})$, or in other words, changing the notation again, to prove it under the assumption that f can be written as $P(x^{(1)}, \cdots, x^{(p)})$, where P is a polynomial in the $X_i^{(\lambda)}$ with coefficients in k. By lemma 3, all that we need show is that $DP(x, \cdots, x) = 0$ for every derivation D of $k(x)$ over k. Now let $P_{i\lambda}(X^{(1)}, \cdots, X^{(p)})$, for $1 \leqq i \leqq n$, $1 \leqq \lambda \leqq p$, be the partial derivative $\partial P/\partial X_i^{(\lambda)}$; we have:

$$DP(x, \cdots, x) = \sum_{\lambda=1}^{p} \sum_{i=1}^{n} P_{i\lambda}(x, \cdots, x) \cdot Dx_i .$$

Call σ_λ the isomorphism of $k(x)$ onto $k(x^{(\lambda)})$ over k which maps (x) onto $(x^{(\lambda)})$; this transforms D into a derivation D_λ of $k(x^{(\lambda)})$ over k, which is given by $D_\lambda x_i^{(\lambda)} = (Dx_i)^{\sigma_\lambda}$ for every i. Let (u) be a maximal set of independent variables over k in $k(x)$, such that $k(x)$ is separably algebraic over $k(u)$, and, for each μ, call $(u^{(\mu)})$ the image of (u) under σ_μ; then the $(u^{(\mu)})$, taken for all $\mu \neq \lambda$, are a maximal set of independent variables over $k(x^{(\lambda)})$ in the field

$$K = k(x^{(1)}, \cdots, x^{(p)}),$$

and K is separably algebraic over the field generated by these variables over $k(x^{(\lambda)})$; therefore we can extend D_λ to K, in one and only one way, by putting $D_\lambda u_j^{(\mu)} = 0$ for all j and all $\mu \neq \lambda$, and then we have $D_\lambda x_i^{(\mu)} = 0$ for all i and all $\mu \neq \lambda$. Now write that $P(x^{(1)}, \cdots, x^{(p)})$ is symmetric; this means that, if $(\rho_1, \cdots, \rho_p)$ is any permutation of $(1, \cdots, p)$, we have

$$P(x^{(\rho_1)}, \cdots, x^{(\rho_p)}) = P(x^{(1)}, \cdots, x^{(p)}).$$

Apply D_λ to this formula; if μ is such that $\rho_\mu = \lambda$, we get:

$$\sum_i P_{i\mu}(x^{(\rho_1)}, \cdots, x^{(\rho_p)}) \cdot (Dx_i)^{\sigma_\lambda} = \sum_i P_{i\lambda}(x^{(1)}, \cdots, x^{(p)}) \cdot (Dx_i)^{\sigma_\lambda}.$$

Specializing $(x^{(1)}, \cdots, x^{(p)})$ to $(x, \cdots, x)$ in this, we get:

$$\sum_i P_{i\mu}(x, \cdots, x) \cdot Dx_i = \sum_i P_{i\lambda}(x, \cdots, x) \cdot Dx_i .$$

This holds for all λ, μ, and shows that all the p terms in the right-hand side of the formula for $DP(x, \cdots, x)$ are equal; therefore $DP(x, \cdots, x) = 0$, as asserted.

Now put $q' = q/p$ and $U' = U^{(p)}$, so that we may write $U^{(q)}$ as the product $U'^{(q')}$ of q' factors equal to U'; then f can also be considered, in an obvious sense, as a symmetric mapping f' of $U'^{(q')}$ into S^1. Call N the point $M \times \cdots \times M$ of U', and call M' a generic point of U' over k; as f' is defined, by assumption, at the point $N \times \cdots \times N$ of $U'^{(q')}$, it is also defined at the point $M' \times \cdots \times M'$, since the former is a specialization of the latter over k. The induction assumption shows now that, if the x'_ρ are all the coordinates of M', $f'(M', \cdots, M')$ is in the field generated over k by the $(x'_\rho)^{q'}$; this is the same as to say that, if we put $k' = k^{1/q'}$, $f'(M', \cdots, M')$ can be written as $z^{q'}$, with z in $k'(M')$; let g be the mapping of U' into S^1, rational over k', such that $g(M') = z$. As f' is defined at $N \times \cdots \times N$, prop. 15 of Chap. II, §4, shows that $f'(M', \cdots, M')$ is in the specialization-ring of $N \times \cdots \times N$ in $k(M' \times \cdots \times M')$, or, what is the same thing, of N in $k(M')$. As $z^{q'}$ is in that ring, z is finite over the specialization N of M', with reference to k, or, what amounts to the same by prop. 3 of Chap. II, §1, with reference to k'; as N is simple on U' by th. 13 of Chap. IV, §6, it follows from this, by th. 5 of Chap. V, §3, that z is in the specialization-ring of N in $k'(M')$, or in other words that the mapping g is defined at N. Now, by the case $\nu = 1$ of our lemma, we know that $g(N)$ is in $k'(x_1^p, \cdots, x_n^p)$. As $f(q \cdot M)$ is the same as $f'(N, \cdots, N)$, hence also, by the definition of g, the same as $g(N)^{q'}$, this completes our proof.

The next lemma is only a special case of th. 2, with which it is convenient to deal first.

LEMMA 5. *Let $\boldsymbol{U}$ be a variety, and f a symmetric mapping of $\boldsymbol{U}^q$ into a variety $\boldsymbol{V}$, where $q = p^\nu$ for some integer $\nu \geqq 1$; let k be a field of rationality for $\boldsymbol{U}$, $\boldsymbol{V}$ and f; let $\boldsymbol{P}$ be a simple point of $\boldsymbol{U}$, purely inseparable of degree q over k. Then, if $f(q \cdot \boldsymbol{P})$ is defined, it is rational over k.*

By the principle of localization, it is enough to consider the case when $\boldsymbol{U}$ and $\boldsymbol{V}$ are affine varieties. Then, if S^m is the ambient space for $\boldsymbol{V}$, f determines a mapping of $\boldsymbol{U}^{(q)}$ into S^m which has the same graph and is defined at the same points, so that we may in fact assume that $\boldsymbol{V} = S^m$. Writing f as $(f_1, \cdots, f_m)$, where the f_i are mappings into S^1, we see that we may consider the f_i separately, so that it is enough to consider the case $\boldsymbol{V} = S^1$. Now let $M = (x_1, \cdots, x_n)$ be a generic point of $\boldsymbol{U}$ over k; if $f(q \cdot \boldsymbol{P})$ is defined, $f(q \cdot M)$ is defined, and, by lemma 4, it is in $k(x_1^q, \cdots, x_n^q)$. As in the proof of lemma 4, we can express this by saying that $f(q \cdot M)$ can be written as $g(M)^q$, where g is a mapping of $\boldsymbol{U}$ into S^1, rational over the field $k' = k^{1/q}$. Again as in the proof of lemma 4, we observe that $g(M)$ is finite over $M \to \boldsymbol{P}$, with reference to k'; as $\boldsymbol{P}$ is simple on $\boldsymbol{U}$, this implies, by th. 5 of Chap. V, §3, that g is defined at $\boldsymbol{P}$, so that $g(\boldsymbol{P})$ is in $k'(\boldsymbol{P})$. As $f(q \cdot \boldsymbol{P})$ is then the same as $g(\boldsymbol{P})^q$, it must therefore be in the field $k(a_1^q, \cdots, a_n^q)$, where the a_i are the coordinates of $\boldsymbol{P}$. As the a_i are purely inseparable over k and of degree $\leqq q$ over k, all the a_i^q are in k, which completes the proof of lemma 5.

Now we come back to the notations and assumptions in theorem 2. Write each $\boldsymbol{X}_\nu$ as a sum of prime rational cycles over k, say $\boldsymbol{X}_\nu = \boldsymbol{X}_{\nu 1} + \cdots + \boldsymbol{X}_{\nu r_\nu}$; as we observed earlier, $f(\boldsymbol{X}_1, \cdots, \boldsymbol{X}_n)$ is the same as

$$f(\boldsymbol{X}_{11}, \cdots, \boldsymbol{X}_{1r_1}, \cdots, \boldsymbol{X}_{n1}, \cdots, \boldsymbol{X}_{nr_n}),$$

so that it will be enough to prove our theorem under the assumption that all the $\boldsymbol{X}_\nu$ are prime rational over k. This will be done by induction on the number of factors in the product $\boldsymbol{U}$, or, what amounts to the same, on the sum $m = \sum_\nu m_\nu$ of the degrees of the $\boldsymbol{X}_\nu$. We distinguish two cases, according as $n \geqq 2$ or $n = 1$.

Assume first that $n \geqq 2$, and take an r such that $1 \leqq r \leqq n - 1$. Call $\boldsymbol{U}'$, $\boldsymbol{U}''$ the products of the $\boldsymbol{U}_\nu^{(m_\nu)}$ for $1 \leqq \nu \leqq r$ and for $r + 1 \leqq \nu \leqq n$, respectively, so that $\boldsymbol{U} = \boldsymbol{U}' \times \boldsymbol{U}''$. Put

$$\mathbf{X}_\nu = \sum_{i=1}^{m_\nu} \boldsymbol{P}_{\nu i}, \qquad \boldsymbol{Q}_\nu = \boldsymbol{P}_{\nu 1} \times \cdots \times \boldsymbol{P}_{\nu m_\nu}, \qquad \boldsymbol{Q} = \boldsymbol{Q}_1 \times \cdots \times \boldsymbol{Q}_n,$$

and call $\boldsymbol{Q}'$, $\boldsymbol{Q}''$ the projections of $\boldsymbol{Q}$ on $\boldsymbol{U}'$ and on $\boldsymbol{U}''$. Also , let $\boldsymbol{N}$ be a generic point of $\boldsymbol{U}$ over $k(\boldsymbol{Q})$, with the projections $\boldsymbol{N}'$, $\boldsymbol{N}''$ on $\boldsymbol{U}'$, $\boldsymbol{U}''$. By assumption, the mapping f is defined at $\boldsymbol{Q}$, hence also, by th. 2 of Chap VII, §2, at the subvariety $\boldsymbol{Q}' \times \boldsymbol{U}''$ of $\boldsymbol{U}$, and therefore at the generic point $\boldsymbol{Q}' \times \boldsymbol{N}''$ of $\boldsymbol{Q}' \times \boldsymbol{U}''$ over $k(\boldsymbol{Q})$. For a similar reason, f is defined at $\boldsymbol{U}' \times \boldsymbol{N}''$; it induces on it a mapping f', rational over $k(\boldsymbol{N}'')$, which is given by its value $f(\boldsymbol{N}' \times \boldsymbol{N}'')$ at the generic point $\boldsymbol{N}' \times \boldsymbol{N}''$ of $\boldsymbol{U}' \times \boldsymbol{N}''$ over $k(\boldsymbol{N}'')$; moreover, since f is defined at $\boldsymbol{Q}' \times \boldsymbol{N}''$, f' is also defined there and has there the same value as f. Since $r < n$, we can apply the induction assumption to f'; this shows that the value of f' at $\boldsymbol{Q}' \times \boldsymbol{N}''$, which is equal to $f(\boldsymbol{Q}' \times \boldsymbol{N}'')$, is rational over $k(\boldsymbol{N}'')$. Now call p the projection of $\boldsymbol{Q}' \times \boldsymbol{U}''$ onto $\boldsymbol{U}''$, which is obviously an isomorphism of $\boldsymbol{Q}' \times \boldsymbol{U}''$ onto $\boldsymbol{U}''$; and call g the mapping of $\boldsymbol{U}''$ into $\boldsymbol{V}$, rational over k, which is given by $g(\boldsymbol{N}'') = f(\boldsymbol{Q}' \times \boldsymbol{N}'')$. The mapping f'' of $\boldsymbol{Q}' \times \boldsymbol{U}''$ into $\boldsymbol{V}$ induced by f on $\boldsymbol{Q}' \times \boldsymbol{U}''$ is then the same as $g \circ p$, since these two mappings are rational over $k(\boldsymbol{Q}')$ and coincide at the generic point $\boldsymbol{Q}' \times \boldsymbol{N}''$ of $\boldsymbol{Q}' \times \boldsymbol{U}''$ over that field; as p is an isomorphism, we have also $g = f'' \circ p^{-1}$. As f is defined at $\boldsymbol{Q}$, f'' is also defined there, so that g is defined at $\boldsymbol{Q}''$; as $n - r < n$, we can apply the induction assumption to g; this shows that $g(\boldsymbol{Q}'')$, which is the same as $f(\boldsymbol{Q}' \times \boldsymbol{Q}'')$, is rational over k.

Take now the case $n = 1$; then we have $m = m_1$. Call $\boldsymbol{P}$ a component of $\boldsymbol{X}_1$; as $\boldsymbol{X}_1$ is prime rational, we can write it as $\boldsymbol{X}_1 = q\sum_{i=1}^d \boldsymbol{P}_i$, where $\boldsymbol{P}_1, \cdots, \boldsymbol{P}_d$ are all the distinct conjugates of $\boldsymbol{P}$ over k and where $q = [k(\boldsymbol{P}):k]_i$. We again distinguish two cases, according as $d \geqq 2$ or $d = 1$. The case $d = 1$ has been treated above, as lemma 5. Assume now that $d \geqq 2$; let k' be the field of all separably algebraic elements over k in $k(\boldsymbol{P}_1, \cdots, \boldsymbol{P}_d)$, so that all the $\boldsymbol{P}_i$ are purely inseparable over k'; by prop. 12 of Chap. I, §4, the chains $\boldsymbol{Y}_i = q \cdot \boldsymbol{P}_i$ are rational over k'. Since $f(\boldsymbol{X})$ is the same as $f(\boldsymbol{Y}_1, \cdots, \boldsymbol{Y}_d)$, and since we have shown that the induction assumption implies the validity of our theorem, for the given value of m, in the case $n \geqq 2$, we see that $f(\boldsymbol{X})$ is rational over k', so that it is separably algebraic over k. On the other hand, we have already observed that it is purely inseparable over k. This completes the proof of th. 2.

The assumption made in th. 2, that all the $\boldsymbol{X}_\nu$ are cycles (and not merely chains), means that all the components of $\boldsymbol{X}_\nu$ are simple on $\boldsymbol{U}_\nu$ for each ν. One can show by examples that some assumption about these components is needed for the conclusion to hold; but a much weaker one would suffice. All that was needed, in fact, was the following property, which was used in the proof of lemma 5: let $\boldsymbol{P}$ be any one of the components of $\boldsymbol{X}_\nu$; let K be any field of definition for $\boldsymbol{U}_\nu$, containing k, and let $\boldsymbol{M}$ be a generic point of $\boldsymbol{U}_\nu$ over K; then every element z of $K(\boldsymbol{M})$ such that z^p is in the specialization-ring of $\boldsymbol{P}$ in $K(\boldsymbol{M})$ must be in that specialization-ring; in other words, if f is a function on $\boldsymbol{U}_\nu$ (in the sense of Chap. IX, § 2) and if f^p is defined at $\boldsymbol{P}$, f itself must be defined there.

3. Fundamental operations on chains and cycles. If $\boldsymbol{U}$, $\boldsymbol{V}$ are two varieties, then $\boldsymbol{A} \times \boldsymbol{B}$ may be considered as a binary operation between subvarieties $\boldsymbol{A}$ of $\boldsymbol{U}$ and $\boldsymbol{B}$ of $\boldsymbol{V}$, which can then be extended by linearity to $\boldsymbol{U}$-chains and $\boldsymbol{V}$-chains. This means that, if $\boldsymbol{X}$ is an r-chain on $\boldsymbol{U}$, given by $\boldsymbol{X} = \sum_\alpha a_\alpha \boldsymbol{A}_\alpha$, where the $\boldsymbol{A}_\alpha$ are subvarieties of $\boldsymbol{U}$ of dimension r and the a_α are integers, and $\boldsymbol{Y}$ is an s-chain on $\boldsymbol{V}$, similarly given by $\boldsymbol{Y} = \sum_\beta b_\beta \boldsymbol{B}_\beta$, then we denote by $\boldsymbol{X} \times \boldsymbol{Y}$ the $(r + s)$-chain

$$\boldsymbol{X} \times \boldsymbol{Y} = \sum_{\alpha,\beta} a_\alpha b_\beta \cdot (\boldsymbol{A}_\alpha \times \boldsymbol{B}_\beta)$$

on $\boldsymbol{U} \times \boldsymbol{V}$. This operation has obviously the property of right-hand and left-hand distributivity with respect to the addition of chains, and the property of associativity; it can be extended in an obvious manner to products of more than two factors. From coroll. 1 of th. 13, Chap. IV, §6, it follows at once that, if $\boldsymbol{X}$ is a $\boldsymbol{U}$-cycle and $\boldsymbol{Y}$ a $\boldsymbol{V}$-cycle, $\boldsymbol{X} \times \boldsymbol{Y}$ is a cycle on $\boldsymbol{U} \times \boldsymbol{V}$. On the other hand, it follows at once from coroll. 1 of th. 5, Chap. IV, §3, and from prop. 28 of Chap. I, §8, that, if k is a field of rationality for the varieties $\boldsymbol{U}$ and $\boldsymbol{V}$, for the $\boldsymbol{U}$-chain $\boldsymbol{X}$, and for the $\boldsymbol{V}$-chain $\boldsymbol{Y}$, then $\boldsymbol{X} \times \boldsymbol{Y}$ also is rational over k. If $\boldsymbol{U}'$, $\boldsymbol{V}'$ are non-empty open subsets of $\boldsymbol{U}$, $\boldsymbol{V}$, and if $\boldsymbol{X}'$, $\boldsymbol{Y}'$ are the restrictions of a $\boldsymbol{U}$-chain $\boldsymbol{X}$ to $\boldsymbol{U}'$, and of a $\boldsymbol{V}$-chain $\boldsymbol{V}$ to $\boldsymbol{V}'$, respectively, then $\boldsymbol{X}' \times \boldsymbol{Y}'$ is the restriction of $\boldsymbol{X} \times \boldsymbol{Y}$ to $\boldsymbol{U}' \times \boldsymbol{V}'$.

We can apply this to a result which is related to those of §2:

PROPOSITION 4. *Let $\boldsymbol{U}$ be a variety; call $\boldsymbol{U}^{(n)}$, for each n, the product of n factors equal to n. Let $\boldsymbol{X} = \sum_{i=1}^m \boldsymbol{P}_i$ be a positive 0-chain of degree m on $\boldsymbol{U}$; for $1 \leqq n \leqq m$, let $\boldsymbol{X}_n$ be the 0-chain on $\boldsymbol{U}^{(n)}$ defined by*

$$\boldsymbol{X}_n = \sum(\boldsymbol{P}_{i_1} \times \cdots \times \boldsymbol{P}_{i_n}),$$

where the sum is taken over all the $m(m-1)\cdots(m-n+1)$ *ordered sets of distinct indices* $(i_1, \cdots, i_n)$. *Then all the* X_n *are rational over every common field of rationality for* U *and* X.

For $n \geqq 2$, put $Y_n = (X_{n-1} \times X) - X_n$; then we have $Y_n = \sum_{\nu=1}^{n-1} Z_{n\nu}$, with

$$Z_{n\nu} = \sum (P_{i_1} \times \cdots \times P_{i_{n-1}}) \times P_{i_\nu},$$

where the sum is taken over all the $m(m-1)\cdots(m-n+2)$ ordered sets of distinct indices $(i_1, \cdots, i_{n-1})$; and it follows at once, from the definition of a rational chain, that $Z_{n\nu}$ is rational over a field k if and only if X_{n-1} is so. We now get our result immediately by induction on n.

We introduce now another operation on chains, the *algebraic projection*. Let A be a subvariety of a product $U \times V$, with the geometric projection A' on U; then we put $\mathrm{pr}_U A = 0$ if $\dim(A') < \dim(A)$, i.e. if $[A:A'] = 0$; on the other hand, if A' has the same dimension as A, i.e. if $[A:A'] \neq 0$, we put $\mathrm{pr}_U A = [A:A'] \cdot A'$; and we extend this operation by linearity to all chains on $U \times V$, so that, for each r, it determines a homomorphism of the group of r-chains on $U \times V$ into the group of r-chains on U. By coroll. 1 of th. 13, Chap. IV, §6, if X is a cycle on $U \times V$, its algebraic projection $\mathrm{pr}_U X$ on U is a U-cycle. It is an immediate consequence of coroll. 1 of th. 6, Chap. IV, §3, and of prop. 27 of Chap. I, §8, that the U-chain $\mathrm{pr}_U X$ is rational over every common field of rationality for U, V and the chain X on $U \times V$. If U' is a non-empty open subset of U, and X' is the restriction to $U' \times V$ of a chain X on $U \times V$, then $\mathrm{pr}_{U'} X'$ is the restriction of $\mathrm{pr}_U X$ to U'.

These definitions can be extended in an obvious manner to algebraic projections on partial products of products of more than two factors. For instance, if X is a chain on a product $U \times V \times W$, we may, in an obvious sense, consider the chain $\mathrm{pr}_{U\times W} X$ on $U \times W$; this could also be defined as the algebraic projection on $U \times W$, in the sense explained above, of the image of X by the obvious isomorphism of $U \times V \times W$ onto $(U \times W) \times V$. Care should of course be taken to choose notations so as to avoid confusions; for instance, if X is a chain on a product $U \times U \times U$, its algebraic projections on the three factors of that product may be denoted by $\mathrm{pr}_1(X)$, $\mathrm{pr}_2(X)$, $\mathrm{pr}_3(X)$, and the algebraic projections on the partial products of two factors may similarly be denoted by $\mathrm{pr}_{12} X$, etc.

THEOREM 3. *Let* U, V, W *be varieties.* (i) *Let* k *be a field of rationality for* U *and* V; *let* $P \times Q$ *be a point of* $U \times V$, *and let* X, Y *be the prime rational chains, on* $U \times V$ *and on* U *respectively, with the generic points* $P \times Q$ *and* P *over* k; *then* $\mathrm{pr}_U X = [k(P, Q):k(P)] \cdot Y$ *if* X *and* Y *have the same dimension, and* $\mathrm{pr}_U X = 0$ *otherwise.* (ii) *If* f *is a morphism of a subvariety* A *of* U *into* V, *the projection from* $U \times V$ *to* U *induces on the graph* Γ_f *of* f *an isomorphism of* Γ_f *onto* A *which maps each* Γ_f*-chain* X *onto the* A*-chain* $\mathrm{pr}_U X$. (iii) *If* X *is a* U*-chain and* Y *a* 0*-chain on* V, *then* $\mathrm{pr}_U(X \times Y) = \deg(Y) \cdot X$. (iv) *If* X *is a chain on* $U \times V \times W$, *then* $\mathrm{pr}_U(\mathrm{pr}_{U\times V} X) = \mathrm{pr}_U X$. (v) *If* X *is a* U*-chain and* Y *a* $(V \times W)$*-chain, then* $\mathrm{pr}_{U\times V}(X \times Y) = X \times \mathrm{pr}_V Y$.

As to (i), let W and W' be the loci of $P \times Q$ and of P over $\bar{k}$; then the components of X and of Y are the conjugates of W and those of W', respectively, over k, the latter being the geometric projections of the former on U; thus we have $\mathrm{pr}_U X = 0$ unless X and Y have the same dimension, i.e. unless $k(P, Q)$ is algebraic over $k(P)$. Also, if X and Y have the same dimension, $\mathrm{pr}_U X$ has the same components as Y; as it is rational over k, it must therefore be of the form $a \cdot Y$, where a is an integer. Comparing the coefficients of W' in $\mathrm{pr}_U X$ and in Y, we get:

$$a = \nu \cdot [\bar{k}(P, Q) : \bar{k}(P)] \cdot [k(P, Q) : k]_\iota / [k(P) : k]_\iota ,$$

where ν is the number of distinct conjugates of W over k which have the geometric projection W' on U. The points of $|X|$ which have the projection P on U are the points $P \times Q^{(i)}$, where the $Q^{(i)}$ are the conjugates of Q over $k(P)$; the number of such points is $[k(P, Q) : k(P)]_s$. Similarly, the number of distinct points of W with the projection P on U is $[\bar{k}(P, Q) : \bar{k}(P)]_s$; also, if W_1 is a conjugate of W over k with the geometric projection W' on U, W_1 has a generic point over $\bar{k}$ of the form $P \times Q_1$, so that the number of points of W_1 with the projection P on U is $[\bar{k}(P, Q_1) : \bar{k}(P)]_s$; as Q_1 must then be a conjugate of Q over $k(P)$, there is an isomorphism σ of $\bar{k}(P, Q)$ onto $\bar{k}(P, Q_1)$ over $k(P)$, so that all these numbers are equal. This gives:

$$\nu = [k(P, Q) : k(P)]_s / [\bar{k}(P, Q) : \bar{k}(P)]_s .$$

Furthermore, prop. 27 of Chap. I, §8, applied to $k(P, Q)$ and $k(P)$, gives:

$$[k(P, Q) : k]_\iota / [k(P) : k]_\iota = [k(P, Q) : k(P)]_i / [\bar{k}(P, Q) : \bar{k}(P)]_i .$$

Combining those three formulas, we get $a = [k(P, Q) : k(P)]$, which proves (i). As to our other assertions, it is enough, by linearity, to consider the cases when the chains under consideration are varieties; then they are immediate consequences of the definitions. For instance, in order to prove (iv), take a common field of rationality k for U, V, W and X; take a generic point $P \times Q \times R$ of X over k; call X', X'' the loci of $P \times Q$ and of P over k, and call r, r', r'' the dimensions of X, X', X'', so that we have in any case $r \geqq r' \geqq r''$. Then $\mathrm{pr}_U X$ is 0 if $r'' < r$, and it is $[k(P, Q, R) : k(P)] \cdot X''$ if $r'' = r$. On the other hand, $\mathrm{pr}_U(\mathrm{pr}_{U \times V} X)$ is 0 if $r' < r$ or $r'' < r'$, and, if $r'' = r' = r$, it is equal to

$$[k(P, Q) : k(P)] \cdot [k(P, Q, R) : k(P, Q)] \cdot X'';$$

thus, in all cases, those chains are equal. The proofs for the other assertions may be left to the reader.

The first two fundamental operations, $X \times Y$ and $\mathrm{pr}_U X$, have been defined for chains. The last one, the intersection-product, will be defined only for cycles; as before, we begin with the case of two cycles, each of which is a variety. Let A^r, B^s be two simple subvarieties of a variety U^n; then we put

$$A \cdot B = \sum_C i(A \cdot B, C; U) \cdot C$$

where the sum is taken over all the components C of $A \cap B$ for which the intersection-multiplicity $i(A \cdot B, C; U)$ is defined, i.e. for all the components C of $A \cap B$ which are simple on U and have the dimension $r + s - n$; the latter condition may also be expressed by saying that the codimension of C on U should be the sum of the codimensions of A and of B. If now $X = \sum_\alpha a_\alpha A_\alpha$ and $Y = \sum_\beta b_\beta B_\beta$ are two cycles on U, with the components A_α, B_β respectively, then we put

$$X \cdot Y = \sum_{\alpha,\beta} a_\alpha b_\beta \cdot (A_\alpha \cdot B_\beta),$$

where the $A_\alpha \cdot B_\beta$ are as defined above, and we call this *the intersection-product of X and Y on U*; it is a U-cycle, whose codimension on U is the sum of those of X and of Y. Occasionally it is desirable to have for this a notation which shows the ambient variety U; in such cases, it will be written as $\{X \cdot Y\}_U$.

The intersection-product is obviously commutative and distributive with respect to the addition of cycles. Also, in view of th. 10, Chap. VI, §3, if U' is a non-empty subset of U, and if X', Y' are the restrictions to U' of the U-cycles X, Y, then $X' \cdot Y'$ is the restriction of $X \cdot Y$ to U'. In particular, if U' is the set of simple points on U, the restriction from U to U' induces, for every r, an isomorphism of the group of r-cycles on U onto the group of r-cycles on U'; then $X \cdot Y$ is uniquely determined by $X' \cdot Y'$; in this sense, it would have been enough to define the intersection-product on varieties without multiple points; some of the following results could be reformulated accordingly, without any substantial loss in generality.

Our definition of the intersection-product takes no account of components which are either multiple on the ambient variety or simple on it but not proper; the most important properties of that operation, however, are valid only under suitable restrictions about such components; in order to express them conveniently, we introduce the following definitions. Let $X_1, \cdots, X_m$ be U-cycles with the respective codimensions $r_1, \cdots, r_m$ on U; then a component of $|X_1| \cap \cdots \cap |X_m|$ will be called *proper* if it is simple on U and has on U the codimension $\sum_i r_i$; we say that the cycles X_i *intersect properly* on U if every component of $|X_1| \cap \cdots \cap |X_m|$ which is simple on U is proper on U. It may happen that $X_1, \cdots, X_m$ intersect properly on U and that $X_1, \cdots, X_{m-1}$ do not (for instance, if A and B are two subvarieties of U with no point in common, the three cycles A, A, B intersect properly, but the two cycles A, A do not). On the other hand, if $X_1, \cdots, X_{m-1}$ intersect properly on U, then $X_1, \cdots, X_m$ intersect properly on U if and only if X_m intersects properly every component of $|X_1| \cap \cdots \cap |X_{m-1}|$ which is simple on U. If U' is a non-empty open subset of U, and if the X_i intersect properly on U, then their restrictions to U' intersect properly on U'; the converse is not true in general, but it is true if U' is the set of simple points on U. More generally, let (U'_α) be a family of open subsets of U, whose union contains the set of simple points of U; then the X_i intersect properly on U if and only if their restrictions to U'_α do so for every α.

PROPOSITION 5. *Let U be a variety, X a U-divisor and Y a U-cycle; then X and Y intersect properly on U if and only if no component of Y is contained in a component of X. In particular, two U-divisors intersect properly if and only if they have no component in common.*

Call C a component of $|X| \cap |Y|$, simple on U; call A a component of X, and B a component of Y, both containing C; then C is a component of $A \cap B$. Call r the codimension of Y on U; by coroll. 1 of th. 1, Chap. VI, §1, C has at most the codimension $r + 1$ on U, i.e. at most the codimension 1 on B. If it has the codimension 1 on B, it is proper; otherwise it has the codimension 0 on B, which means that $C = B$, i.e. that $B \subset A$.

PROPOSITION 6. *Let $X_1, \cdots, X_m$ be U-cycles; let W be a component of $|X_1| \cap \cdots \cap |X_r|$ for some $r < m$, and assume that W contains a proper component of $|X_1| \cap \cdots \cap |X_m|$ on U; then W is a proper component of $|X_1| \cap \cdots \cap |X_r|$ on U.*

Let Z be a proper component of $|X_1| \cap \cdots \cap |X_m|$, contained in W; by definition, Z is simple on U, so that W is simple on U. Let d be the codimension of W on U, and let d_i, for each i, be that of X_i. For each i, let A_i be a component of X_i, containing Z; let Z' be a component of $W \cap A_{r+1} \cap \cdots \cap A_m$, containing Z; as Z' is contained in the intersection of the $|X_i|$, we must have $Z' = Z$; by coroll. 2 of th. 1, Chap. VI, §1, the codimension of Z, which is equal to $\sum_i d_i$ by assumption, must be at most equal to $d + d_{r+1} + \cdots + d_m$; therefore we have $d \geqq d_1 + \cdots + d_r$; as coroll. 2 of th. 1, Chap. VI, §1, also shows that d is at most equal to $d_1 + \cdots + d_r$, this proves our assertion.

The main properties of the intersection-product are contained in the theorems that follow; they are essentially translations of the properties of intersection-multiplicities obtained in Chap. VI and VII.

THEOREM 4. (i) *If X is a cycle on a variety U, X and U intersect properly, and $X \cdot U = X$.* (ii) *If X and Y are U-cycles, then $|X \cdot Y|$ is contained in $|X| \cap |Y|$; if X, Y are positive and intersect properly on U, then $X \cdot Y > 0$, and $|X \cdot Y|$ is the union of the proper components of $|X| \cap |Y|$.* (iii) *If k is a common field of rationality for U and the U-cycles X, Y, the cycle $X \cdot Y$ is rational over k.* (iv) *If X, Y, Z are properly intersecting cycles on U, then $(X \cdot Y) \cdot Z = X \cdot (Y \cdot Z)$.*

The assertion (i) follows at once from the definitions and the corollary of th. 6, Chap. VI, §2, and (ii) from the definitions. As to (iii), it follows at once from the definitions, and from th. 3 of Chap. VI, §2, that, if σ is any isomorphism of $\bar{k}$ onto some field, $(X \cdot Y)^\sigma$ is the same as the intersection-product $X^\sigma \cdot Y^\sigma$, taken on U^σ; in particular, every automorphism of $\bar{k}$ over k leaves $X \cdot Y$ invariant; that being so, (iii) is an immediate consequence of th. 4 of Chap. VI, §2. As to (iv), let X, Y, Z have the components A_α, B_β, C_γ, respectively; the definitions show at once that X, Y, Z intersect properly on U if and only if A_α, B_β, C_γ do so for every triplet (α, β, γ); therefore it is enough, by linearity, to prove (iv) in the case of three properly intersecting varieties A, B, C. Then th. 5 of Chap. VI, §2, shows that every component D of $A \cap B \cap C$, simple on U, is a component of $(A \cdot B) \cdot C$ and of $A \cdot (B \cdot C)$ and has the same coefficient in both. On the other hand, let D' be a component of $(A \cdot B) \cdot C$; this is contained in $A \cap B \cap C$, hence in some component D of $A \cap B \cap C$; as the definitions imply that D' is simple on U, D must be simple on U, hence proper by our assumption on A, B, C, which implies that it has the same dimension as D'; thus we have $D' = D$. This completes the proof, since it shows that $(A \cdot B) \cdot C$ and $A \cdot (B \cdot C)$ have the same components, each with the same coefficient.

Th. 4 (i) can be expressed by saying that U is the unit-element for the intersection-product, and th. 4 (iv) is the associative property for that operation, under the restriction which is needed to guarantee its validity. As usual for associative operations, we define the intersection-product $X_1 \cdot X_2 \cdots X_m$ by induction on m, as being equal to $(X_1 \cdot X_2 \cdots X_{m-1}) \cdot X_m$; then we have the following corollary to th. 4:

COROLLARY. *Let $X_1, \cdots, X_m$ be U-cycles, intersecting properly on U; then all the products consisting of the factors $X_1 . \cdots, X_m$, in any order and any arrangement, are equal to $X_1 \cdot X_2 \cdots X_m$; if, moreover, all the X_i are positive, then $X_1 \cdot X_2 \cdots X_m$ is positive, and its components are the proper components of $|X_1| \cap \cdots \cap |X_m|$ on U.*

For each i, let the $A_{i\alpha}$ be all the components of X_i; the X_i intersect properly if and only if $A_{1\alpha_1}, \cdots, A_{m\alpha_m}$ do so for every choice of $\alpha_1, \cdots, \alpha_m$, so that it is enough to prove our corollary for the case when the X_i are varieties, or, more generally, for the case when they are all positive; let that be assumed from now on. As explained above, we may assume that U has no multiple point, for otherwise we replace it by the open set U' of the simple points on U, and we replace the X_i by their restrictions to U'. That being also assumed, the last assertion in our corollary says that $|X_1 \cdot X_2 \cdots X_m|$ is the intersection of the $|X_i|$.

We prove our corollary, first, under the additional assumption that, for every set of distinct indices $i_1, \cdots, i_r$, the cycles $X_{i_1}, \cdots, X_{i_r}$ intersect properly on U; we can then proceed by induction on m. In fact, for $m = 2$, the assertion amounts to th. 4 (ii), and, for $m = 3$, it is an immediate consequence of th. 4 (ii) and th. 4 (iv); the proof for every m follows from this by induction, in the same manner as for all operations which are commutative and associative. Now consider the general case; call Y any component of some product consisting of the factors $X_1, \cdots, X_m$; using th. 4 (ii), one sees at once by induction on m that Y must be contained in all the $|X_i|$, hence in some component Z of $|X_1| \cap \cdots \cap |X_m|$. Our assumptions imply that Z is proper, i.e. that its codimension on U is the sum of those of the X_i; by the definition of the intersection-product, the codimension of Y on U is also equal to that sum; therefore we have $Y = Z$, so that our assertion will be proved if we show that every component Z of $|X_1| \cap \cdots \cap |X_m|$ has the same coefficient in all the products consisting of the factors $X_1, \cdots, X_m$, and that this coefficient is >0. Now, for each set of distinct indices $i_1, \cdots, i_r$, call $F_{(i)}$ the union of those components of $|X_{i_1}| \cap \cdots \cap |X_{i_r}|$ which do not contain any component of $|X_1| \cap \cdots \cap |X_m|$; call U' the complement on U of the union of all the closed sets $F_{(i)}$; and, for every i, call X'_i the restriction of X_i to U'. If Z is any component of $|X_1| \cap \cdots \cap |X_m|$, and if Z' is the restriction of Z to U', the coefficient of Z in any product consisting of the factors $X_1, \cdots, X_m$ is the same as the coefficient of Z' in the product similarly made up of the factors $X'_1, \cdots, X'_m$. But, by prop. 6, if $i_1, \cdots, i_r$ are distinct indices, the cycles $X'_{i_1}, \cdots, X'_{i_r}$ intersect properly on U'; by what we have already proved, this implies that our corollary is valid for the X'_i on U'. This completes the proof.

We come now to the properties of the intersection-product which involve the operations $X \times Y$ and $\mathrm{pr}_U X$.

THEOREM 5. *If X, X' are cycles on a variety U, and Y, Y' are cycles on a variety V, then $(X \times Y)\cdot(X' \times Y') = (X\cdot X') \times (Y\cdot Y')$.*

If our four cycles are varieties, this is an immediate consequence of the definitions and of th. 7, Chap. VI, §3. The general case follows at once from this by linearity.

In the next theorems, we shall be concerned with intersection-products of the form $X\cdot(P \times V)$, where X is a cycle on a product $U \times V$ and P is a point of U, or more generally $X\cdot(Y \times V)$, Y being a cycle on U; in applying these theorems, it is useful to know when such intersections are proper. The following propositions give some information in that respect.

PROPOSITION 7. *Let A be a subvariety of a product $U \times V$, with the geometric projection A' on U, and let B be a subvariety of A'. Then no proper component of $A \cap (B \times V)$ can have the geometric projection B on U unless $A' = U$.*

Let C be a component of $A \cap (B \times V)$ with the projection B on U; call n, $n + r$ and m the dimensions of A', of A and of B, respectively. By prop. 11 of Chap. VII, §5, C has at least the dimension $r + \dim(B)$; on the other hand, if it is proper, it must have the dimension $n + r + \dim(B) - \dim(U)$; in that case, we must have $n \geqq \dim(U)$, which implies $A' = U$.

COROLLARY. *Let X be a cycle on $U \times V$, such that no component of X has the geometric projection U on U. Then, if P is any point of U, $|X| \cap (P \times V)$ has no proper component.*

Assume first that X is a subvariety of U; then, if P is in the geometric projection of X on U, our assertion is a special case of prop. 7; if not, $X \cap (P \times V)$ is empty, since the geometric projection contains the set-theoretic projection. The general case follows from this by linearity.

PROPOSITION 8. *Let X be a cycle of codimension r on a product $U \times V$; let k be a common field of rationality for U, V and X. Let Ω be the set of the simple points P of U such that $P \times V$ intersects X properly on $U \times V$. Then Ω contains a non-empty k-open subset of U; it is k-open if V is complete and has no multiple subvariety of codimension $<r$.*

It will be enough to show that Ω contains a non-empty open set in the first case, and that it is open in the second case; for then coroll. 1 of prop. 2, Chap. VII, §1, applied in the first case to the union of all the open subsets of U contained in Ω, and in the second case to Ω itself, will show that these are k-open. That being so, one sees at once that it is enough to consider the case when X is a subvariety of $U \times V$. If the geometric projection X' of X on U is not U, Ω contains the complement on U of the union of X' and of the set M of the multiple points of U. If $X' = U$, then prop. 11 of Chap. VII, §5, shows that there is a closed subset F of U, other than U, such that, if P is in $U - F$, every component of $X \cap (P \times V)$ has the dimension $\dim(X) - \dim(U)$ and is therefore proper if it is simple on $U \times V$; thus, in this case, Ω contains the complement of $M \cup F$. As M is closed by th. 12 of Chap. IV, §6, this proves the first part of our proposition. Now assume that V is complete; then, by prop. 14 of Chap. VII, §5, and th. 7 of Chap. VII, §5, the set F' of the points P such that some component of $X \cap (P \times V)$ has a codimension $<r$ in $P \times V$ is closed; if we assume that V has no multiple subvariety of codimension $<r$, every such component is simple on $P \times V$, hence on $U \times V$ by coroll. 1 of th. 13, Chap. IV, §6, if P is simple on U; therefore, when that is so, no point of F' can be in Ω. Then Ω is the complement of $M \cup F'$ in U, which completes the proof.

THEOREM 6. *Let U and V be two varieties, both defined over a field k, and let P be a generic point of U over k.* (i) *Let Q be a simple point of V, X the prime rational $(U \times V)$-cycle with the generic point $P \times Q$ over k, and $X(P)$ the prime rational V-cycle with the generic point Q over $k(P)$; then $X \cdot (P \times V) = P \times X(P)$.* (ii) *If X is any $(U \times V)$-cycle, rational over k, then $X \cdot (P \times V)$ is of the form $P \times X(P)$, where $X(P)$ is a V-cycle, rational over $k(P)$; and $X(P)$ is 0 if and only if no component of X has the geometric projection U on U.* (iii) *Conversely, if $X(P)$ is any V-cycle, rational over $k(P)$, there is one and only one $(U \times V)$-cycle X, rational over k, such that $X \cdot (P \times V) = P \times X(P)$ and that the geometric projection on U of every component of X is U; if $X(P)$ is positive, this cycle X is positive.*

Put $K = k(P)$. If Q, X and $X(P)$ are as in (i), $|X|$ and $|P \times X(P)|$ are respectively the k-closure and the K-closure of $P \times Q$ on $U \times V$, so that $|P \times X(P)|$ is contained in $|X| \cap (P \times V)$; conversely, if $P \times Q'$ is any point of the latter set, prop. 9 of Chap. VII, §4, shows that it is a specialization of $P \times Q$ over k, which is the same as to say that Q' is a specialization of Q over $k(P)$, so that Q' is in $|X(P)|$. If dimensions are taken into account, this shows that $X \cdot (P \times V)$ has the same support as $P \times X(P)$; then th. 11 of Chap. VI, §3 (extended to abstract varieties by the principle of localization as explained in Chap. VII, §7) shows that every component of these cycles has the same coefficient in both, which completes the proof of (i). As to (ii), the coroll. of prop. 7 shows that, if no component of X has the geometric projection U on U, $X \cdot (P \times V)$ is 0. Consider now the case when X is a prime rational cycle over k on $U \times V$ and has a component W with the geometric projection U on U; then, by th. 6 of Chap. IV, §3, there is a generic point of W over $\bar{k}$ of the form $P \times Q$, where Q is a simple point of V since otherwise, by th. 13 of Chap. IV, §6, and its coroll. 1, W would not be simple on $U \times V$. Then $P \times Q$ is a generic point of X over k, and (i) shows that $X \cdot (P \times V)$ is defined and of the form $P \times X(P)$. Now let X' be another prime rational cycle over k on $U \times V$, of the same dimension as X, and such that the geometric projection of its components on U is U; then it has a generic point over k of the form $P \times Q'$; as before, $X' \cdot (P \times V)$ is defined and of the form $P \times X'(P)$. By (i), $X(P)$ and $X'(P)$ are prime rational cycles over $k(P)$; therefore they cannot have any component in common unless they coincide, and they coincide if and only if Q' is a generic specialization of Q over $k(P)$; but then $P \times Q'$ is a generic specialization of $P \times Q$ over k, so that $X' = X$. Take now any rational cycle X over k on $U \times V$, and write it as $X = \sum_i a_i X_i + Y$, where the X_i are distinct prime rational cycles over k whose components have the projection U on U, while Y is a cycle, no component of which has the projection U on U; also, put $X_i \cdot (P \times V) = P \times X_i(P)$ for each i. Then $X \cdot (P \times V)$ is the same as $P \times \sum_i a_i X_i(P)$; as no two $X_i(P)$ can have a component in common, this cannot be 0 unless all the a_i are 0; this completes the proof of (ii). As to (iii), take first the case when $X(P)$ is prime rational over $k(P)$; then (i) shows how to construct X as a prime rational cycle over k. This construction can be extended at once by linearity to any rational cycle $X(P)$ over $k(P)$, and gives a positive cycle X if $X(P) > 0$; the unicity of X, when $X(P)$ is given, is just another statement for what has been proved in (ii).

Corollary. *Let U, V, W be three varieties, and X a cycle on $U \times V \times W$. Let k be a common field of rationality for U, V, W and X, and let P be a generic point of U over k. Then* $\mathrm{pr}_{U\times V}[X \cdot (P \times V \times W)] = (\mathrm{pr}_{U\times V} X) \cdot (P \times V)$.

As P is also generic on U over $\bar{k}$, and as every component of X is rational over $\bar{k}$, it is enough, by linearity, to prove our assertion in the case when X is a variety; also, we may assume that the geometric projection of X on U is U, since otherwise, by the corollary of prop. 7, both sides are 0. That being so, X has a generic point over k, of the form $P \times Q \times R$. By th. 6 (i), $X \cdot (P \times V \times W)$ is the prime rational cycle with the generic point $P \times Q \times R$ over $k(P)$; also, if we call X' the locus of $P \times Q$ over k, $X' \cdot (P \times V)$ is the prime rational cycle with the generic point $P \times Q$ over $k(P)$. By definition, $\mathrm{pr}_{U\times V} X$ is equal to $[k(P, Q, R):k(P, Q)] \cdot X'$ if $k(P, Q, R)$ is algebraic over $k(P, Q)$, and it is 0 otherwise; our assertion is now contained in th. 3 (i).

We will generalize as follows the notation in th. 6. We observe first that, if U and V are two varieties, and P is any point of U, the projection on V induces on the subvariety $P \times V$ of $U \times V$ an isomorphism of that variety onto V; moreover, if Y is any chain on $P \times V$ and Y' is its image on V by that isomorphism, we have $Y = P \times Y'$ and $Y' = \mathrm{pr}_V Y$; also, if P is simple on U, Y' is a V-cycle if and only if Y is a $(U \times V)$-cycle. Now let X be any cycle on $U \times V$; in view of the remarks we have just made, we can define, for every simple point P of U, a V-cycle $X(P)$ by means of the formula

$$X \cdot (P \times V) = P \times X(P).$$

Loosely speaking, one might describe the cycles $X(P)$ as an "algebraic family" of V-cycles (a designation which would be misleading, however, except under suitable additional conditions). The coroll. of prop. 7 shows that the components of X whose geometric projection on U is not U make no contribution to $X(P)$; thus, in considering a "family" $X(P)$, one may always, without restricting the generality, assume that all the components of X have the projection U on U.

More precise results will now be given in the case when the cycles $X(P)$ have the dimension 0. In order to state them, we introduce the following definition. Let X be a chain on a product $U \times V$, and let P be a point of U; then we say that X is *complete over* P if every component of X whose geometric projection on U contains P is complete over P; we say that X is *everywhere complete over* U if it is complete over every point of U. Thus, if V is complete, every chain on $U \times V$ is everywhere complete over U. More generally, if W is a subvariety of $U \times V$, complete over every point of its geometric projection on U, every $(U \times V)$-chain X such that $|X| \subset W$ is everywhere complete over U.

THEOREM 7. *Let U^n and V be two varieties, and X^n a positive cycle on $U \times V$. Let k be a common field of rationality for U, V and X; let P be a generic point of U over k; let P' be a simple point of U such that X and $P' \times V$ intersect properly on $U \times V$ and that no point of $|X| \cap (P' \times V)$ is multiple on $U \times V$. Put $X(P) = \sum_{i=1}^{d} Q_i$ and $X(P') = \sum_{i=1}^{d'} Q'_i$. Then we have $\mathrm{pr}_U X = d \cdot U$ and $d' \leqq d$; and every specialization of $(Q_1, \cdots, Q_d)$ over $P \rightarrow P'$ with reference to k differs at most by a permutation from the set $(Q'_1, \cdots, Q'_{d'}, \infty_V, \cdots, \infty_V)$, where the pseudopoint ∞_V of V is repeated $d - d'$ times.*

Let $(Q''_1, \cdots, Q''_d)$ be a specialization of $(Q_1, \cdots, Q_d)$ over $P \rightarrow P'$ with reference to k; by prop. 7 of Chap. II, §3, there is a generic specialization $(P^*, Q^*_1, \cdots, Q^*_d)$ of $(P, Q_1, \cdots, Q_d)$ over k such that $(P', Q''_1, \cdots, Q''_d)$ is a specialization of $(P^*, Q^*_1, \cdots, Q^*_d)$ over $\bar{k}$. Call σ the isomorphism of $k(P, Q_1, \cdots, Q_d)$ onto $k(P^*, Q^*_1, \cdots, Q^*_d)$ over k which maps P onto P^* and Q_i onto Q^*_i for $1 \leqq i \leqq d$; transforming both sides of the formula $X \cdot (P \times V) = P \times X(P)$ by σ, we see that $X(P^*) = \sum_{i=1}^{d} Q^*_i$. Replacing now P by P^*, we see that it is enough to prove our theorem for specializations over $\bar{k}$; as all the components of X are rational over $\bar{k}$, this shows, by linearity, that it is enough to prove our theorem in the case when X is a variety. That being now assumed, take first the case when the geometric projection of X

on U is not U; then we have $d = 0$, and the corollary of prop. 7 shows that $X(P)$ and $X(P')$ are both 0, so that our assertions are true in this case. Now assume that X is a variety of dimension n with the geometric projection U on U; by th. 6 of Chap. IV, §3, X has a generic point over k of the form $P \times Q$. Then X is also the prime rational cycle with the generic point $P \times Q$ over k; therefore, by th. 6 (i), $X(P)$ is the prime rational cycle on V with the generic point Q over $k(P)$; as Q is algebraic over $k(P)$, this means that $(Q_1, \cdots, Q_d)$ is a complete set of conjugates of Q over $k(P)$; in particular, we must have $d = [k(P, Q):k(P)]$, hence $\mathrm{pr}_U X = d \cdot U$. As X and $P' \times V$ intersect properly on $U \times V$, and as no point of $X \cap (P' \times V)$ is multiple on V, the components of $X \cap (P' \times V)$ are all proper, so that they are the same as those of $X \cdot (P' \times V)$; th. 12 of Chap. VI, §3, shows now that every one of the Q'_i must occur, in any specialization $(Q''_1, \cdots, Q''_d)$ of $(Q_1, \cdots, Q_d)$ over $P \rightarrow P'$ with reference to k, a number of times equal to its coefficient in $X(P')$. Now assume that some Q''_i is not a component of $X(P')$; (P', Q''_i) is a specialization of (P, Q_i), hence also of (P, Q), over k; if Q''_i were not the pseudopoint of V, $P' \times Q''_i$ would be a point of $X \cap (P' \times V)$, hence a component of $X \cdot (P' \times V)$, against our assumption; therefore we must have $Q''_i = \infty_V$. This completes our proof.

Corollary. *Let U^n and V be two varieties, and X^n a cycle on $U \times V$. Let P' be a simple point of U such that X is complete over P' and intersects $P' \times V$ properly on $U \times V$ and that no point of $|X| \cap (P' \times V)$ is multiple on $U \times V$; let k be a common field of rationality for U, V and X, and let P be a generic point of U over k. Then $X(P')$ is the uniquely determined specialization of $X(P)$ over $P \rightarrow P'$ with reference to k, and their common degree is the integer d determined by* $\mathrm{pr}_U X = d \cdot U$.

For a positive cycle X, this is a special case of th. 7; the general case follows from this at once by writing $X = X' - X''$, where X' and X'' are positive cycles without any common component.

The last assertion in the corollary of th. 7 is the so-called "principle of the conservation of number."

Theorem 8. *Let U^n and V be two varieties; let X^r be a $(U \times V)$-cycle, everywhere complete over U, and let Y^s be a U-cycle, such that X and $Y \times V$ intersect properly on $U \times V$. Assume that there is no multiple subvariety of $U \times V$, contained in $|X| \cap |Y \times V|$, whose geometric projection on U is of dimension $\geqq r + s - n$ and is simple on U. Then the cycles* $\mathrm{pr}_U X$ *and Y intersect properly on U; and we have*

$$\mathrm{pr}_U[X \cdot (Y \times V)] = (\mathrm{pr}_U X) \cdot Y.$$

By linearity, it is enough to consider the case when X, Y are varieties. Call X' the geometric projection of X on U, and assume first that X' has a dimension $r' < r$, i.e. that $\mathrm{pr}_U X = 0$; this is so, in particular, if $r > n$. Then, if Z is any component of $X \cap (Y \times V)$, and if Z' is its geometric projection on U, Z must also be a component of $X \cap (Z' \times V)$, and prop. 11 of Chap. VII, §5, shows that $\mathrm{pr}_U Z = 0$; this proves the theorem in this case. From now on, assume that the dimension of X' is r; we prove first that X' and Y intersect properly on U. In fact, let Z' be a component of $X' \cap Y$, simple on U; by prop. 13 of Chap. VII, §5, there is a component Z of $X \cap (Z' \times V)$ with the projection Z' on U; by our assumptions on X and Y, this cannot be multiple on $U \times V$, since Z', by coroll. 1 of th. 1, Chap. VI, §1, has at least the dimension $r + s - n$; therefore Z is simple on $U \times V$. As Z is contained in $X \cap (Y \times V)$, it is contained in some component W of that intersection; then W is simple on $U \times V$, hence proper by our assumptions on X and Y, so that it has the dimension $r + s - n$; this implies that the dimension of Z and that of Z' are at most $r + s - n$, so that Z' is proper. Now we prove that every component of $\mathrm{pr}_U[X \cdot (Y \times V)]$ is a proper component of $X' \cap Y$. In fact, let Z be a proper component of $X \cap (Y \times V)$, with the projection Z' on U; if the dimension of Z' is $< r + s - n$, $\mathrm{pr}_U Z$ is 0; if it is $r + s - n$, call W' a component of $X' \cap Y$ containing Z; by coroll. 1 of th. 13, Chap. IV, §6, Z' must be simple on U, so that W' is also simple on U; by what we have proved, the dimension of W' must then be $r + s - n$, which implies that $Z' = W'$. In order to complete the proof, it only remains for us to show that every proper component of $X' \cap Y$ has the same coefficient in both sides of the final formula in our theorem. This is now an immediate consequence of th. 10, Chap. VII, §7; in order to apply that theorem here, one need only observe that, under our present assumptions, if Z' is a proper component of $X' \cap Y$ and Z is a component of $X \cap (Z' \times V)$ with the projection Z' on U, Z must be a proper component of $X \cap (Y \times V)$.

COROLLARY 1. *Let U be a variety, A a simple subvariety of U, V a variety without multiple point, and f a morphism of A into V. Then a U-cycle Y intersects A properly on U if and only if $Y \times V$ and the graph Γ_f of f intersect properly on $U \times V$; and, when that is so, $A \cdot Y$ is the image of $\Gamma_f \cdot (Y \times V)$ by the isomorphism of Γ_f onto A induced on Γ_f by the projection from $U \times V$ to U, and we have*

$$A \cdot Y = \mathrm{pr}_U[\Gamma_f \cdot (Y \times V)].$$

It follows at once from the definitions that Γ_f is everywhere complete over U; that being so, all our assertions are immediate consequences of th. 3 (ii) and of th. 8, except for the fact that Γ_f and $Y \times V$ intersect properly provided A and Y do so; in proving this, we may assume that Y is a simple subvariety of U. Let Z be a component of $\Gamma_f \cap (Y \times V)$, simple on $U \times V$; by th. 3 (ii), its projection Z' on U has the same dimension as Z. Call n, r, s the dimensions of U, A and Y, respectively; if A and Y intersect properly on U, Z', which is simple on U, can have at most the dimension $r + s - n$; therefore Z has at most that dimension, which shows that it is proper. One may observe that our corollary could also have been derived from th. 8 of Chap. VI, §3 (which, as we noted at the end of Chap. VII, is a special case of th. 10 of that Chapter, and therefore also of th. 8 above).

COROLLARY 2. *Let f be a morphism of a variety U into a variety V without multiple point; let Γ_f be its graph. Then a Γ_f-chain is a Γ_f-cycle if and only if it is a $(U \times V)$-cycle; and the relations $X' = \mathrm{pr}_U X$, $X = \Gamma_f \cdot (X' \times V)$, between U-cycles X' and Γ_f-cycles X, imply each other and determine isomorphisms between the groups of cycles on U and on Γ_f.*

The first assertion is an immediate consequence of the coroll. of th. 14, Chap. IV, §6, and of coroll. 1 of th. 13, Chap. IV, §6. The others follow at once from th. 3 (ii), coroll. 1 above, and th. 4 (i).

COROLLARY 3. *Let f be an isomorphism of a variety U onto a variety V; let Γ_f be its graph. Then, if X is a U-cycle and Y is the corresponding V-cycle in the isomorphism f, there is a Γ_f-cycle Z such that*

$$Z = \Gamma_f \cdot (X \times V) = \Gamma_f \cdot (U \times Y), \qquad X = \mathrm{pr}_U Z, \qquad Y = \mathrm{pr}_V Z;$$

conversely, if Z is any Γ_f-cycle, the latter formulas determine corresponding cycles X, Y on U and on V, such that all these formulas are valid.

If U, V are without multiple points, this is an immediate consequence of coroll. 2, applied to the morphisms f, f^{-1} of U into V and of V into U. In the general case, call U', V' the open subsets of U and of V consisting respectively of the simple points on these two varieties; then f induces an isomorphism f' of U' onto V', whose graph is $\Gamma_f \cap (U' \times V')$. In view of the remarks which were previously made about the restriction of cycles to the sets of simple points on their ambient varieties, it is now clear that the validity of our corollary for U', V' and f' implies that it holds also for U, V and f.

4. Images and counterimages of cycles. In what follows, we shall chiefly be concerned with cycles of the form $\mathrm{pr}_V[Z \cdot (X \times V)]$, where Z is a cycle on a product $U \times V$, and X is a U-cycle. The special case in which X is a point of U has already been considered above in th. 6 and th. 7 of §3; in agreement with the notation introduced there, we write:

$$Z(X) = \mathrm{pr}_V[Z \cdot (X \times V)].$$

This notation is not always in agreement with the notation introduced in Chap. IV, §7, concerning birational correspondences (the two notations do agree, however, in the case of an everywhere biregular birational correspondence, i.e. of the graph of an isomorphism). It should be understood that our new notation supersedes the former one, which will not be used again.

In this §, if Z is any cycle on the product $U \times V$, we will denote by Z' the image of Z by the isomorphism of $U \times V$ onto $V \times U$ which maps each point $P \times Q$ of $U \times V$ onto the point $Q \times P$ of $V \times U$; with this notation, we have, if Y is any V-cycle:

$$Z'(Y) = \mathrm{pr}_U[Z' \cdot (Y \times U)] = \mathrm{pr}_U[Z \cdot (U \times Y)].$$

The most important case is that in which Z is the graph Γ_f of a mapping f of U into V; this is simple on $U \times V$, i.e. it is a $(U \times V)$-cycle, if and only if the geometric image of U by f is simple on V. In that case, we call $\mathbf{\Gamma}_f(X)$ *the algebraic image of X by f, and* $\mathbf{\Gamma}'_f(Y)$ *the algebraic counterimage of Y by f*; the former is a V-cycle of the same dimension as X, and the latter is a U-cycle which has on U the same codimension as Y has on V. If f is an isomorphism of U onto V, it follows at once from coroll. 3 of th. 8, §3, that $\mathbf{\Gamma}_f(X)$ is the same as the image of X under the isomorphism of U-cycles onto V-cycles induced by f, and that $\mathbf{\Gamma}'_f(Y)$ is the same as the image of Y under the isomorphism of V-cycles onto U-cycles induced by f^{-1}; in particular, if that is so, and if X, Y are simple subvarieties of U and of V, $\mathbf{\Gamma}_f(X)$ is the same as the geometric image $f(X)$ of X by f, and $\mathbf{\Gamma}'_f(Y)$ the same as the geometric image $f^{-1}(Y)$.

In what follows, we will usually write $f(X)$ instead of $\mathbf{\Gamma}_f(X)$, and $f^{-1}(Y)$ instead of $\mathbf{\Gamma}'_f(Y)$, for the algebraic image and the algebraic counterimage of a cycle. In other words, we write:

$$f(X) = \mathbf{\Gamma}_f(X) = \mathrm{pr}_V[\mathbf{\Gamma}_f\cdot(X \times V)], \qquad f^{-1}(Y) = \mathbf{\Gamma}'_f(Y) = \mathrm{pr}_U[\mathbf{\Gamma}_f\cdot(U \times Y)].$$

Care should be taken to avoid confusion with the geometric image; in the case of the notation $f(X)$, confusion could arise whenever X is a variety; in the case of $f^{-1}(Y)$, it can arise only when Y is a variety and f is a birational mapping and not an isomorphism. To avoid such conflicts, we will refrain from using the notation $f(X)$ any more for geometric images from now on. One may observe that, if f is a morphism of U into a variety V without multiple point, and if we denote by φ the isomorphism of $\mathbf{\Gamma}_f$ onto U induced on $\mathbf{\Gamma}_f$ by the projection from $U \times V$ to U, then, by th. 3 (ii) of §3 and by coroll. 2 of th. 8, §3, we could also define the algebraic image by $f(X) = \mathrm{pr}_V[\varphi^{-1}(X)]$; when written in this form, the definition can be extended at once to any U-chain X.

PROPOSITION 9. *Let U, V be two varieties; let X, Y, Z be cycles on U, on V, and on $U \times V$, respectively, such that Z is everywhere complete over U and intersects $X \times Y$ properly on $U \times V$; put $T = Z\cdot(X \times Y)$, and call t the dimension of T. Then we have $\mathrm{pr}_U T = X\cdot Z'(Y)$ provided there is no multiple subvariety of $U \times V$, contained in $|Z| \cap |X \times Y|$, whose geometric projection on U is simple on U and of dimension $\geqq t$.*

The cycles $X \times V$ and $U \times Y$ intersect properly on $U \times V$, and the intersection of their supports is $|X \times Y|$; therefore our assumption that Z and $X \times Y$ intersect properly implies that Z, $X \times V$ and $U \times Y$ intersect properly. By th. 4 (iv) of §3, this gives

$$T = [Z\cdot(U \times Y)]\cdot(X \times V);$$

moreover, $Z\cdot(U \times Y)$ and $X \times V$ also intersect properly on $U \times V$. Now we have, by definition

$$X\cdot Z'(Y) = \mathrm{pr}_U[Z\cdot(U \times Y)]\cdot X.$$

As Z is everywhere complete over U, the same is true of all the cycles whose support is contained in $|Z|$, and in particular of $Z\cdot(U \times Y)$. Now we get our proposition by applying th. 8 of §3 to the above formula.

In the applications of prop. 9, $\boldsymbol{Z}$ will usually be the graph $\boldsymbol{\Gamma}_f$ of a mapping f; $\boldsymbol{\Gamma}_f$ is everywhere complete over $\boldsymbol{U}$ if f is a morphism, or also if $\boldsymbol{V}$ is complete. We shall say that a morphism f of $\boldsymbol{U}$ into $\boldsymbol{V}$ is *proper* if $\boldsymbol{\Gamma}_f$ is everywhere complete over $\boldsymbol{V}$.

THEOREM 9. *Let f be a proper morphism of a variety $\boldsymbol{U}$ into a variety $\boldsymbol{V}$ without multiple point; let $\boldsymbol{X}$ be a $\boldsymbol{U}$-cycle and $\boldsymbol{Y}$ a $\boldsymbol{V}$-cycle, such that $\boldsymbol{\Gamma}_f$ and $\boldsymbol{X} \times \boldsymbol{Y}$ intersect properly on $\boldsymbol{U} \times \boldsymbol{V}$; put $\boldsymbol{T} = \boldsymbol{\Gamma}_f \cdot (\boldsymbol{X} \times \boldsymbol{Y})$, and call t the dimension of $\boldsymbol{T}$. Then we have*

$$\mathrm{pr}_{\boldsymbol{U}}\boldsymbol{T} = \boldsymbol{X} \cdot f^{-1}(\boldsymbol{Y}), \qquad \mathrm{pr}_{\boldsymbol{V}}\boldsymbol{T} = f(\boldsymbol{X}) \cdot \boldsymbol{Y} = f[\boldsymbol{X} \cdot f^{-1}(\boldsymbol{Y})],$$

provided there is no multiple subvariety of $\boldsymbol{U}$, contained in $|\boldsymbol{X}|$, whose geometric image by f is contained in $|\boldsymbol{Y}|$ and of dimension $\geqq t$.

The first formula, and the first part of the second one, are special cases of prop. 9, obtained by applying prop. 9 to $\boldsymbol{Z} = \boldsymbol{\Gamma}_f$ and to $\boldsymbol{Z} = \boldsymbol{\Gamma}_f'$, respectively. Then coroll. 2 of th. 8, §3, shows that $\boldsymbol{T} = \boldsymbol{\Gamma}_f \cdot (\mathrm{pr}_{\boldsymbol{U}}\boldsymbol{T} \times \boldsymbol{V})$; applying $\mathrm{pr}_{\boldsymbol{V}}$ to both sides, we get the last part of the second formula.

The projection from a product $\boldsymbol{U} \times \boldsymbol{V}$ to the first factor $\boldsymbol{U}$ is a morphism of $\boldsymbol{U} \times \boldsymbol{V}$ into $\boldsymbol{U}$; it is proper if and only if $\boldsymbol{V}$ is complete. If we apply th. 9 to this morphism, we get exactly the statement of th. 8 of §3, with the additional assumptions that $\boldsymbol{U}$ should be without multiple point and $\boldsymbol{V}$ should be complete; the first one does not substantially affect the generality of that result, as one sees by restricting all $\boldsymbol{U}$-cycles in th. 8 to the set $\boldsymbol{U}'$ of the simple points on $\boldsymbol{U}$, and all $(\boldsymbol{U} \times \boldsymbol{V})$-cycles to $\boldsymbol{U}' \times \boldsymbol{V}$; the second one, however, is a good deal more restrictive than the assumption, made in th. 8, that $\boldsymbol{X}$ should be everywhere complete over $\boldsymbol{U}$; incidentally, even the latter was more than would have been strictly needed for the proof of that theorem. These are examples of what may be lost in precision, for the sake of simplicity, in the formulation of global theorems of intersection-theory.

Another special case of th. 9 deserves to be formulated separately, viz., the case of the injection mapping j into $\boldsymbol{V}$ of a subvariety $\boldsymbol{U}$ of $\boldsymbol{V}$; as defined in Chap. VII, §2, this is the mapping of $\boldsymbol{U}$ into $\boldsymbol{V}$ with the graph $\boldsymbol{\Delta}_{\boldsymbol{U}}$, which maps each point and subvariety of $\boldsymbol{U}$ onto itself; it is obviously a proper morphism of $\boldsymbol{U}$ into $\boldsymbol{V}$. We shall identify $\boldsymbol{U}$-chains, in an obvious manner, with the $\boldsymbol{V}$-chains whose support is contained in $\boldsymbol{U}$; also, if $\boldsymbol{X}$ is such a chain, we shall denote by $\boldsymbol{X}^{(\boldsymbol{U})}$ the $\boldsymbol{U}$-cycle $\boldsymbol{X}^{(\boldsymbol{U})} = \sum_{\boldsymbol{A}} \gamma_{\boldsymbol{A}}(\boldsymbol{X}) \cdot \boldsymbol{A}$, where the sum is extended only to the simple subvarieties $\boldsymbol{A}$ of $\boldsymbol{U}$, and by $\boldsymbol{X}^{(\boldsymbol{V})}$ the $\boldsymbol{V}$-cycle $\boldsymbol{X}^{(\boldsymbol{V})} = \sum_{\boldsymbol{B}} \gamma_{\boldsymbol{B}}(\boldsymbol{X}) \cdot \boldsymbol{B}$, where the sum is extended to the simple subvarieties $\boldsymbol{B}$ of $\boldsymbol{V}$. With this notation, we have the following theorem:

THEOREM 10. *Let $\boldsymbol{U}$ be a simple subvariety of a variety $\boldsymbol{V}$, and let j be the injection mapping of $\boldsymbol{U}$ into $\boldsymbol{V}$. Then we have $j(\boldsymbol{X}) = \boldsymbol{X}^{(\boldsymbol{V})}$ for every $\boldsymbol{U}$-cycle $\boldsymbol{X}$, and $j^{-1}(\boldsymbol{Y}) = (\boldsymbol{U} \cdot \boldsymbol{Y})^{(\boldsymbol{U})}$ for every $\boldsymbol{V}$-cycle $\boldsymbol{Y}$ intersecting $\boldsymbol{U}$ properly on $\boldsymbol{V}$. Assume further that every point of $\boldsymbol{U}$ is simple both on $\boldsymbol{U}$ and on $\boldsymbol{V}$; let $\boldsymbol{X}$ be a $\boldsymbol{U}$-cycle, and* *let Y be a V-cycle intersecting both U and X properly on V. Then we have* $j(X) = X$, $j^{-1}(Y) = U \cdot Y$, *and* $\{X \cdot Y\}_V = \{X \cdot j^{-1}(Y)\}_U = \mathrm{pr}_U\{\Delta_U \cdot (X \times Y)\}_{U \times V}$.

The first assertion follows easily from th. 3 (ii) of §3 and from coroll. 2 and 3 of th. 8, §3, applied to the restrictions of U and X to the set of simple points of V; the second one follows similarly from th. 3 (ii) and coroll. 1 and 3 of th. 8, §3, applied to the restrictions of U and Y to the complement on V of the set of multiple points of U. As to the second part of our theorem, the assumption implies that all the chains whose supports are contained in U are U-cycles and V-cycles; then, by the first part, we have $j(X) = X$ for every such cycle, and $j^{-1}(Y) = U \cdot Y$ for every V-cycle Y intersecting U properly on V. By restricting all cycles to the set of simple points of V, we see that we may assume V to be without multiple points. Then our assertions are special cases of the results in th. 9, provided we observe that X and Y intersect properly on V if and only if Δ_U and $X \times Y$ do so on $U \times V$; this can be seen at once by taking a common field of rationality k for U, V, X and Y, and a generic point over $\bar{k}$ of a component of $\Delta_U \cap (X \times Y)$.

By our usual method of restricting cycles to suitable open sets (in the present case, to the complements on U and on V of the set of those points of U which are multiple either on U or on V), one can at once derive from the second part of th. 10 a seemingly more general statement, involving the operations $X \to X^{(U)}$, $X \to X^{(V)}$, for the case when no assumption is made about multiple points on U and V. One may observe that th. 10 could also have been obtained as a consequence of th. 9 of Chap. VI, §3.

THEOREM 11. *Let X, Y be two properly intersecting cycles on a variety V without multiple point. Let f be a mapping of a variety U into V, such that the three cycles Γ_f, $U \times X$ and $U \times Y$ intersect properly on $U \times V$. Then the support of the cycle $f^{-1}(X \cdot Y) - f^{-1}(X) \cdot f^{-1}(Y)$ is contained in the set of the points of U where f is not defined.*

Call U' the complement of the latter set on U; by replacing all U-cycles by their restrictions to U', and all $(U \times V)$-cycles by their restrictions to $U' \times V$, one sees at once that it is enough to consider the case when f is a morphism; then we have to prove that $f^{-1}(X) \cdot f^{-1}(Y)$ is the same as $f^{-1}(X \cdot Y)$. Put $X' = f^{-1}(X)$; we can calculate $X' \cdot f^{-1}(Y)$ by means of prop. 9, in which we have to replace X, Y, Z by X', Y and Γ_f, respectively. In fact, as f is a morphism, Γ_f is everywhere complete over U; also, since V has no multiple point, the last condition in prop. 9 is fulfilled. In order to apply prop. 9, we have still to verify that Γ_f intersects $X' \times Y$ properly; in fact, if W is a component of $\Gamma_f \cap |X' \times Y|$, the geometric projection W' of W on U is contained in $|X'|$, i.e. in the support of $\mathrm{pr}_U[\Gamma_f \cdot (U \times X)]$, hence in the geometric projection W_1' on U of some component W_1 of $\Gamma_f \cap |U \times X|$. As f is a morphism, the projection from $U \times V$ to U induces on Γ_f an isomorphism φ of Γ_f onto U, so that we have $W = \varphi^{-1}(W')$, $W_1 = \varphi^{-1}(W_1')$; therefore W is contained in W_1, hence in $|U \times X|$ and therefore also in some component of $\Gamma_f \cap |U \times X| \cap |U \times Y|$. As the latter intersection is assumed to be proper, one sees at once, by counting dimensions, that, if W is simple on $U \times V$, it must be proper in $\Gamma_f \cap |X' \times Y|$, which proves our assertion. Now prop. 9 shows that $X' \cdot f^{-1}(Y)$ is the same as $\mathrm{pr}_U T$, with $T = \Gamma_f \cdot (X' \times Y)$. As Γ_f intersects $X' \times Y$ properly, the three cycles Γ_f, $X' \times V$ and $U \times Y$ intersect properly, so that we get:

$$X' \cdot f^{-1}(Y) = \mathrm{pr}_U([\Gamma_f \cdot (X' \times V)] \cdot (U \times Y)).$$

On the other hand, we have, for similar reasons:

$$\begin{aligned} f^{-1}(X \cdot Y) &= \mathrm{pr}_U(\Gamma_f \cdot (U \times X \cdot Y)) = \mathrm{pr}_U(\Gamma_f \cdot [(U \times X) \cdot (U \times Y)]) \\ &= \mathrm{pr}_U([\Gamma_f \cdot (U \times X)] \cdot (U \times Y)). \end{aligned}$$

In order to complete the proof, all we need do now is to show that the cycle $Z = \Gamma_f \cdot (U \times X)$ is the same as $\Gamma_f \cdot (X' \times V)$; as we have $X' = \mathrm{pr}_U Z$ by definition, this is contained in coroll. 2 of th. 8, §3.

Now we consider the composition of operations of the type $X \rightarrow Z(X)$.

PROPOSITION 10. *Let U, V, W be three varieties, F a $(U \times V)$-cycle, and G a $(V \times W)$-cycle; assume either that F is everywhere complete over U or that G is so over W; put*

$$H = \mathrm{pr}_{U \times W}[(F \times W) \cdot (U \times G)].$$

Then we have $G(F(X)) = H(X)$ for every U-cycle X such that $X \times V \times W$, $F \times W$ and $U \times G$ intersect properly on $U \times V \times W$ and that the following conditions are satisfied: (a) *$F \cdot (X \times V)$ is everywhere complete over V*; (b) *there is no multiple subvariety of $U \times V \times W$, contained in*

$$|X \times V \times W| \cap |F \times W| \cap |U \times G|,$$

having a geometric projection either on $U \times W$, or on $V \times W$, which is simple on that variety and of dimension $\geqq \dim(H(X))$.

By definition, we have $G(F(X)) = \mathrm{pr}_W Y$, where Y is the $(V \times W)$-cycle defined by

$$\begin{aligned} Y &= G \cdot (\mathrm{pr}_V[F \cdot (X \times V)] \times W) \\ &= G \cdot \mathrm{pr}_{V \times W}[(F \times W) \cdot (X \times V \times W)]; \end{aligned}$$

here we have applied th. 3 (v), th. 5 and th. 4 (i) of §3. Now, put

$$Z = (U \times G) \cdot [(F \times W) \cdot (X \times V \times W)];$$

th. 8 of §3 shows that $Y = \mathrm{pr}_{V \times W} Z$ (which, by th. 3 (iv) of §3, implies $G(F(X)) = \mathrm{pr}_W Z$), provided the conditions listed in that theorem are satisfied. In fact, because of (a), $(F \times W) \cdot (X \times V \times W)$ is everywhere complete over $V \times W$. The assumption that $X \times V \times W$, $F \times W$ and $U \times G$ intersect properly implies that the two factors in Z intersect properly; and the final assumption of th. 8, §3, is contained in the final assumption of our proposition. Applying th. 4 (iv) of §3, i.e. the associativity of the intersection-product, we get now

$$\mathrm{pr}_{U\times W}Z = \mathrm{pr}_{U\times W}([(F \times W)\cdot(U \times G)]\cdot(X \times V \times W)).$$

Reasoning as above, we see now that, in order to complete the proof, it is enough to verify that we can apply th. 8 of §3 to the right-hand side of this formula; this can be done just as above.

We will now show, by means of prop. 10, that, if f is a mapping of U into V and g a mapping of V into W, we have, under suitable conditions, $g(f(X)) = h(X)$ and $f^{-1}(g^{-1}(X)) = h^{-1}(X)$ with $h = g \circ f$. These formulas have a meaning, according to what has been said above, only if $h = g \circ f$ is defined and if the graphs of f, g and h are simple subvarieties of $U \times V$, $V \times W$ and $U \times W$, respectively; when that is so, we shall say that the pair of mappings (f, g) is *consonant*. If k is a common field of rationality for U, V, W, f and g, and if P is a generic point of U over k, the pair (f, g) is consonant if and only if $f(P)$ is simple on V, g is defined at $f(P)$, and $g(f(P))$ is simple on W. We shall need the following preliminary result:

PROPOSITION 11. *Let U^n, V and W be three varieties; let (f, g) be a consonant pair of mappings of U into V and of V into W; put $h = g \circ f$, and:*

$$R = \mathrm{pr}_{U\times W}[(\Gamma_f \times W)\cdot(U \times \Gamma_g)] - \Gamma_h .$$

Then no component of R has the geometric projection U on U; and R is 0 unless $(\Gamma_f \times W) \cap (U \times \Gamma_g)$ has a proper component A whose geometric projection on $U \times W$ is of dimension n and whose geometric projection on V is contained in the set of the points of V where g is not defined.

Put $F = (\Gamma_f \times W) \cap (U \times \Gamma_g)$; let k be a common field of rationality for U, V, W, f and g; let $M \times N \times P$ be a generic point over $\bar{k}$ of a component A of F. Assume first that the dimension of $M \times N$ over $\bar{k}$ is $\geqq n$; as it is in Γ_f, it must be generic on Γ_f over $\bar{k}$; this implies that M is a generic point of U over k and that $N = f(M)$; as $N \times P$ is in Γ_g, we have then $P = g(N) = h(M)$; in that case, A is the graph of the mapping (f, h) of U into $V \times W$, and we have $\mathrm{pr}_{U\times W}A = \Gamma_h$; in particular, this would be so if we had taken for A a component of F containing $\Gamma_{(f,h)}$. Therefore $\Gamma_{(f,h)}$ is a component of F; counting dimensions, one sees then that it is proper. On the other hand, assume that the dimension of $M \times N$ over $\bar{k}$ is $< n$; if g is defined at N, then, as $N \times P$ is in Γ_g, we have $P = g(N)$, so that the dimension of A is $< n$, which, by coroll. 1 of th. 1, Chap. VI, §1, implies that A is multiple on $U \times V \times W$. Therefore, if A is proper, g is not defined at N; the $\bar{k}$-closure of N, which is the geometric projection of A on V, is then contained in the set of points where g is not defined. At the same time, if the dimension of the geometric projection of A on $U \times W$ were $< n$, A would not contribute any term to R. In order to complete the proof of our proposition, it is now only necessary to show that the multiplicity

μ of $\mathbf{\Gamma}_{(f,h)}$ in $(\mathbf{\Gamma}_f \times \boldsymbol{W})\cdot(\boldsymbol{U} \times \mathbf{\Gamma}_g)$ has the value 1. In fact, let $\boldsymbol{M}$ be a generic point of $\boldsymbol{U}$ over k; then, by what we have proved, if $\boldsymbol{A}$ is a component of $\boldsymbol{F}$ other than $\mathbf{\Gamma}_{(f,h)}$, $\boldsymbol{A}$ has no point in common with $\boldsymbol{M} \times \boldsymbol{V} \times \boldsymbol{W}$; therefore the intersection of $\boldsymbol{F}$ with $\boldsymbol{M} \times \boldsymbol{V} \times \boldsymbol{W}$ is reduced to the point $\boldsymbol{M} \times \boldsymbol{P} \times \boldsymbol{Q}$, with $\boldsymbol{P} = f(\boldsymbol{M})$, $\boldsymbol{Q} = h(\boldsymbol{M})$; this shows that the three cycles $\boldsymbol{M} \times \boldsymbol{P} \times \boldsymbol{Q}$, $\mathbf{\Gamma}_f \times \boldsymbol{W}$ and $\boldsymbol{U} \times \mathbf{\Gamma}_g$ intersect properly on $\boldsymbol{U} \times \boldsymbol{V} \times \boldsymbol{W}$; therefore, by th. 4 (iv) of §3, we have:

$$[(\boldsymbol{M} \times \boldsymbol{V} \times \boldsymbol{W})\cdot(\mathbf{\Gamma}_f \times \boldsymbol{W})]\cdot(\boldsymbol{U} \times \mathbf{\Gamma}_g)$$
$$= (\boldsymbol{M} \times \boldsymbol{V} \times \boldsymbol{W})\cdot[(\mathbf{\Gamma}_f \times \boldsymbol{W})\cdot(\boldsymbol{U} \times \mathbf{\Gamma}_g)]$$
$$= \mu\cdot(\boldsymbol{M} \times \boldsymbol{V} \times \boldsymbol{W})\cdot\mathbf{\Gamma}_{(f,h)},$$

where the second equality follows from what we have just proved. By th. 6 (i) of §3, this last cycle is $\mu\cdot(\boldsymbol{M} \times \boldsymbol{P} \times \boldsymbol{Q})$. On the other hand, the same theorem, in combination with th. 5 and th. 4 (i) of §3, shows that

$$(\boldsymbol{M} \times \boldsymbol{V} \times \boldsymbol{W})\cdot(\mathbf{\Gamma}_f \times \boldsymbol{W}) = [(\boldsymbol{M} \times \boldsymbol{V})\cdot\mathbf{\Gamma}_f] \times \boldsymbol{W} = \boldsymbol{M} \times \boldsymbol{P} \times \boldsymbol{W};$$

furthermore, the corollary of th. 7 of §3, combined with th. 6 (i), th. 5 and th. 4 (i) of §3, shows that

$$(\boldsymbol{M} \times \boldsymbol{P} \times \boldsymbol{W})\cdot(\boldsymbol{U} \times \mathbf{\Gamma}_g) = \boldsymbol{M} \times [(\boldsymbol{P} \times \boldsymbol{W})\cdot\mathbf{\Gamma}_g] = \boldsymbol{M} \times \boldsymbol{P} \times \boldsymbol{Q}.$$

This completes our proof. One will note that, instead of applying th. 6 (i) and the corollary of th. 7 of §3, one could have reached the same conclusion by applying coroll. 2 of th. 8, after replacing $\boldsymbol{U}$, $\boldsymbol{V}$ and $\boldsymbol{W}$ by suitable open subsets of these varieties (which would not have changed the multiplicities). One could also, of course, have proved that $\mu = 1$ by applying the criterion of multiplicity 1, i.e. th. 6 of Chap. VI, §2; this may be left as an exercise to the reader.

COROLLARY. *Notations and assumptions being the same as in prop.* 11, *the cycle* $\boldsymbol{R}$ *can be written in the form* $\boldsymbol{S} \times \boldsymbol{W}$, *where* $\boldsymbol{S}$ *is a* $\boldsymbol{U}$*-divisor, whenever* $\boldsymbol{W}$ *has the dimension* 1.

Let $\boldsymbol{A}$ be a component of $\boldsymbol{R}$, with the geometric projection $\boldsymbol{A}'$ on $\boldsymbol{U}$; $\boldsymbol{A}$ has the same dimension n as $\boldsymbol{U}$, while, by prop. 11, $\boldsymbol{A}'$ is of dimension $\leqq n - 1$; as $\boldsymbol{A}$ is contained in $\boldsymbol{A}' \times \boldsymbol{W}$ which, under our present assumptions, is of dimension $\leqq n$, we must have $\boldsymbol{A} = \boldsymbol{A}' \times \boldsymbol{W}$.

THEOREM 12. *Let* $\boldsymbol{U}$, $\boldsymbol{V}$ *be varieties without multiple points,* $\boldsymbol{W}$ *a variety, and* (f, g) *a consonant pair of mappings of* $\boldsymbol{U}$ *into* $\boldsymbol{V}$ *and of* $\boldsymbol{V}$ *into* $\boldsymbol{W}$; *put* $h = g \circ f$. *Then, if* $\boldsymbol{X}$ *is a* $\boldsymbol{U}$*-cycle, we have* $g(f(\boldsymbol{X})) = h(\boldsymbol{X})$ *in each one of the following cases*: (a) f *is a proper morphism of* $\boldsymbol{U}$ *into* $\boldsymbol{V}$ *and* g *is a morphism of* $\boldsymbol{V}$ *into* $\boldsymbol{W}$; (b) g *is a proper morphism of* $\boldsymbol{V}$ *into* $\boldsymbol{W}$, $\mathbf{\Gamma}_f$ *intersects* $\boldsymbol{X} \times \boldsymbol{V}$ *properly on* $\boldsymbol{U} \times \boldsymbol{V}$, *and* $\mathbf{\Gamma}_f\cdot(\boldsymbol{X} \times \boldsymbol{V})$ *is everywhere complete over* $\boldsymbol{V}$.

As g is a morphism, the cycle $\boldsymbol{R}$ defined in prop. 11 is 0; therefore, in order to prove our theorem, all we need do is to check the conditions for the validity of prop. 10 for $F = \Gamma_f$, $G = \Gamma_g$. As U and V have no multiple point, the final condition in prop. 10 is satisfied; $\Gamma_f \cdot (X \times V)$ is everywhere complete over V in cases (a) and (b); in case (a), Γ_f is everywhere complete over U, and in case (b) Γ_g is so over W. Now we have to verify that $X \times V \times W$, $\Gamma_f \times W$ and $U \times \Gamma_g$ intersect properly. Let A be a component of the intersection of their supports; let k be a common field of rationality for U, V, W, f, g and X, and let $M \times N \times P$ be a generic point of A over $\bar{k}$. As A is in $U \times \Gamma_g$, and as g is a morphism, we have $P = g(N)$. Similarly, in case (a), we have $N = f(M)$, so that the dimension of A is the same as that of M over $\bar{k}$; as M is in $|X|$, this shows that the dimension of A is at most that of X, so that, if A is simple on $U \times V \times W$, it is proper. In case (b), the dimension of A is the same as that of the locus A' of $M \times N$ over $\bar{k}$; as A' is contained in $\Gamma_f \cap |X \times V|$, and as Γ_f and $X \times V$ intersect properly on $U \times V$, we get the same conclusion.

THEOREM 13. *Let V, W be two varieties without multiple points, U a variety, and (f, g) a consonant pair of mappings of U into V and of V into W; put $h = g \circ f$. Then, if Z is a W-cycle, we have $f^{-1}(g^{-1}(Z)) = h^{-1}(Z)$ in each one of the following cases:* (a) *f and g are morphisms, and Γ_h intersects $U \times Z$ properly on $U \times W$;* (b) *g is a proper morphism, and the cycles $U \times V \times Z$, $\Gamma_f \times W$ and $U \times \Gamma_g$ intersect properly on $U \times V \times W$.*

The proof is quite similar to that of th. 12; we again observe that $R = 0$ and apply prop. 10 to the varieties W, V, U and to the cycles Γ'_g, Γ'_f and Z. In order to check, in case (a), that the cycles $U \times V \times Z$, $\Gamma_f \times W$ and $U \times \Gamma_g$ intersect properly, one considers a component of the intersection of their supports, a generic point of that component over a suitable field, and proceeds as in the proof for th. 12. All the other conditions can be checked immediately.

A more precise result can be given in the particularly important case when W is of dimension 1. A variety of dimension 1 is called a *curve*; it is said to be *non-singular* if it has no multiple point. Before proving the theorem we have in view, it is convenient to dispose of a side-issue:

PROPOSITION 12. *Let f be a mapping of U into V, and g a mapping of V into W, such that $h = g \circ f$ is defined and that Γ_h is everywhere complete over U; also, assume either that Γ_f is everywhere complete over U or that Γ_g is so over W. Then, if U' is any simple subvariety of U, of codimension 1 on U, both h and f are defined at U'.*

As to h, this is contained in coroll. 1 of th. 9, Chap. VII, §7; the same holds for f if Γ_f is everywhere complete over U. Now assume that Γ_g is everywhere complete over W; let k be a common field of rationality for U, V, W, f, g and U'; let M and M' be generic points of U and of U' over k; put

$$N = f(M), \qquad P = g(N) = h(M), \qquad P' = h(M');$$

then P' is the only specialization of P over $M \to M'$ with reference to k. Let N' be a specialization of N over $(M, P) \to (M', P')$ with reference to k; then (N', P') is a specialization of (N, P) over k; as $N \times P$ is on Γ_g, which is everywhere complete over W, N' must be a point of V. Call A the locus of $M' \times N'$ over $\bar{k}$; this is a subvariety of Γ_f with the geometric projection U' on U, and is therefore contained in $\Gamma_f \cap (U' \times V)$. As A has at least the dimension of U', which is $n - 1$, there can be no variety, contained in Γ_f and containing A, other than Γ_f and A; therefore A is a component of $\Gamma_f \cap (U' \times V)$. Our conclusion follows from this by th. 9 of Chap. VII, §7.

THEOREM 14. *Let U and V be two varieties, W a complete non-singular curve, and (f, g) a consonant pair of mappings of U into V and of V into W; assume either that Γ_f is everywhere complete over U or that Γ_g is so over W; and put $h = g \circ f$. Then there are a U-divisor S, and a finite number of simple subvarieties A_i of U, of codimension 1 on U, with the following properties:*

(i) *we have* $\mathrm{pr}_{U \times W} [(\Gamma_f \times W) \cdot (U \times \Gamma_g)] = \Gamma_h + S \times W$;

(ii) *f is defined at each A_i, and the geometric image B_i of A_i by f is a multiple subvariety of V;*

(iii) *if h is not a constant mapping and P is any point of W, or if h is constant and P is any point of W other than the constant value of h, every component of the U-divisor $f^{-1}(g^{-1}(P)) - h^{-1}(P) - S$ is one of the A_i such that $B_i \times P$ is contained in Γ_g.*

The fact that (i) defines a U-divisor S is contained in prop. 11 and its corollary. Call U' the open subset of U where f is defined; call F' the set of those points P' of U' for which $f(P')$ is a multiple point of V; by th. 2 of Chap. VII, §2, this is a closed subset of U'; it is not U', since (f, g) is a consonant pair; call A_i' all the components of F' which are simple subvarieties of U' of codimension 1, and call A_i their closures in U; they have the property (ii). Conversely, let A be any simple subvariety of U of codimension 1; by prop. 12, f is defined at A, so that $A' = A \cap U'$ is not empty and is a subvariety of U'; then the geometric image of A by f is multiple on V if and only if A' is contained in F', in which case it must be a component of F'; therefore A is then one of the A_i. Now let P be any point of W other than the constant value of h if h is constant, and otherwise any point of W; call F'' the union of those among the A_i for which $B_i \times P$ is contained in Γ_g, and put $U'' = U - F''$. If we restrict all U-cycles to U'', all $(U \times V)$-cycles to $U'' \times V$ and all $(U \times V \times W)$-cycles to $U'' \times V \times W$, it is easily seen that this does not affect any of the statements in our theorem. Therefore it is enough to prove that $f^{-1}(g^{-1}(P)) = h^{-1}(P) + S$ if we make the additional assumption that there is no A_i for which $B_i \times P$ is contained in Γ_g.

Let that be assumed from now on. If we put $R = S \times W$, we have:

$$R'(P) = \mathrm{pr}_U[(S \times W) \cdot (U \times P)] = \mathrm{pr}_U(S \times P) = S.$$

Therefore all we need do, just as in the proof for th. 13, is to verify that the conditions of validity of prop. 10 are satisfied for the varieties W, V, U and the cycles Γ_g', Γ_f' and P. As W is complete, Γ_g is everywhere complete over V; and, by assumption, Γ_g is everywhere complete over W or Γ_f is so over U. Now call n the dimension of $\boldsymbol{U}$; let $\boldsymbol{X}$ be a variety contained in the intersection of $\boldsymbol{U} \times \boldsymbol{V} \times \boldsymbol{P}$, of $\boldsymbol{\Gamma}_f \times \boldsymbol{W}$ and of $\boldsymbol{U} \times \boldsymbol{\Gamma}_g$; let k be a common field of rationality for $\boldsymbol{U}$, $\boldsymbol{V}$, $\boldsymbol{W}$, f, g, $\boldsymbol{P}$ and $\boldsymbol{X}$; then a generic point of $\boldsymbol{X}$ over k must be of the form $\boldsymbol{M} \times \boldsymbol{N} \times \boldsymbol{P}$, where $\boldsymbol{M} \times \boldsymbol{N}$ is in $\boldsymbol{\Gamma}_f$ and $\boldsymbol{N} \times \boldsymbol{P}$ is in $\boldsymbol{\Gamma}_g$, and the dimension of $\boldsymbol{X}$ is that of $\boldsymbol{M} \times \boldsymbol{N}$ over k. Assume that the dimension of $\boldsymbol{X}$ is $> n - 1$; then $\boldsymbol{M} \times \boldsymbol{N}$ must be generic on $\boldsymbol{\Gamma}_f$ over k; this implies that $\boldsymbol{M}$ is generic on $\boldsymbol{U}$ over k, that $\boldsymbol{N} = f(\boldsymbol{M})$, and that $\boldsymbol{P} = g(\boldsymbol{N}) = h(\boldsymbol{M})$; therefore h has the constant value $\boldsymbol{P}$, which is against our assumptions. Therefore $\boldsymbol{U} \times \boldsymbol{V} \times \boldsymbol{P}$, $\boldsymbol{\Gamma}_f \times \boldsymbol{W}$ and $\boldsymbol{U} \times \boldsymbol{\Gamma}_g$ intersect properly on $\boldsymbol{U} \times \boldsymbol{V} \times \boldsymbol{W}$. Now we have to check the final condition in prop. 10; as one sees at once, all we have to do is to assume that $\boldsymbol{N}$ is multiple on $\boldsymbol{V}$, $\boldsymbol{M}$ simple on $\boldsymbol{U}$ and at least of dimension $n - 1$ over k, and to show that this contradicts our former assumptions. In fact, if that is so, $\boldsymbol{M}$ cannot be generic on $\boldsymbol{U}$ over k, for then $\boldsymbol{N}$ would be the same as $f(\boldsymbol{M})$ which is not multiple on $\boldsymbol{V}$; therefore $\boldsymbol{M}$ must have the dimension $n - 1$ over k; call $\boldsymbol{A}$ its locus over k. By prop. 12, f is defined at $\boldsymbol{A}$, hence at $\boldsymbol{M}$, so that we have $\boldsymbol{N} = f(\boldsymbol{M})$; the geometric image $\boldsymbol{B}$ of $\boldsymbol{A}$ by f, which is the locus of $\boldsymbol{N}$ over k, is then multiple on $\boldsymbol{V}$, so that $\boldsymbol{A}$ is one of the $\boldsymbol{A}_i$. As $\boldsymbol{N} \times \boldsymbol{P}$ is in $\boldsymbol{\Gamma}_g$, the locus of $\boldsymbol{N} \times \boldsymbol{P}$ over k, which is $\boldsymbol{B} \times \boldsymbol{P}$, is contained in $\boldsymbol{\Gamma}_g$. As we assumed that there is no $\boldsymbol{A}_i$ with that property, this concludes the proof.

COROLLARY. *Assumptions being the same as in th.* 14, *let* $\boldsymbol{Z}$ *be any* $\boldsymbol{W}$*-divisor if* h *is not constant; if* h *is constant, let* $\boldsymbol{Z}$ *be any* $\boldsymbol{W}$*-divisor such that the constant value of* h *is not a component of* $\boldsymbol{Z}$. *Also, assume that* $\boldsymbol{V}$ *has no multiple point. Then we have* $f^{-1}(g^{-1}(\boldsymbol{Z})) = h^{-1}(\boldsymbol{Z})$ *in each one of the following cases:* (a) g *is a morphism*; (b) $\boldsymbol{Z}$ *is of degree* 0.

As $\boldsymbol{V}$ has no multiple point, there are no varieties $\boldsymbol{A}_i$; by linearity, this gives us, independently of the assumptions (a) and (b):

$$f^{-1}(g^{-1}(\boldsymbol{Z})) = h^{-1}(\boldsymbol{Z}) + \deg(\boldsymbol{Z})\cdot\boldsymbol{S}.$$

In case (a), $\boldsymbol{S}$ is 0, by prop. 11; therefore, in both cases, the last term in the right-hand side is 0.

We formulate as a proposition, for purposes of reference, the following obvious result, which is occasionally useful in connection with the above theorems:

PROPOSITION 13. *Let* f *be a mapping of* $\boldsymbol{U}$ *into* $\boldsymbol{V}$, *and* g *a mapping of* $\boldsymbol{V}$ *into* $\boldsymbol{W}$, *such that* $h = g \circ f$ *is defined. Then, if* $\boldsymbol{\Gamma}_f$ *is everywhere complete over* $\boldsymbol{U}$ *and* $\boldsymbol{\Gamma}_g$ *is so over* $\boldsymbol{V}$, $\boldsymbol{\Gamma}_h$ *is everywhere complete over* $\boldsymbol{U}$; *if* $\boldsymbol{\Gamma}_f$ *is everywhere complete over* $\boldsymbol{V}$ *and* $\boldsymbol{\Gamma}_g$ *is so over* $\boldsymbol{W}$, $\boldsymbol{\Gamma}_h$ *is everywhere complete over* $\boldsymbol{W}$. *In particular, if* f *and* g *are proper morphisms,* $g \circ f$ *is defined and is a proper morphism.*

PROPOSITION 14. *Let* $\boldsymbol{U}_1, \cdots, \boldsymbol{U}_n, \boldsymbol{V}_1, \cdots, \boldsymbol{V}_n$ *be* $2n$ *varieties; for each* i, *let* f_i *be a mapping of* $\boldsymbol{U}_i$ *into* $\boldsymbol{V}_i$, *such that the geometric image of* $\boldsymbol{U}_i$ *by* f_i *is simple on* $\boldsymbol{V}_i$; *let* k *be a field of rationality for all the* $\boldsymbol{U}_i$, $\boldsymbol{V}_i$ *and* f_i. *Put* $\boldsymbol{U} = \boldsymbol{U}_1 \times \cdots \times \boldsymbol{U}_n$, $\boldsymbol{V} = \boldsymbol{V}_1 \times \cdots \times \boldsymbol{V}_n$, *and let* f *be the mapping of* $\boldsymbol{U}$ *into* $\boldsymbol{V}$, *rational over k, such that*

$$f(\mathbf{M}_1, \cdots, \mathbf{M}_n) = f_1(\mathbf{M}_1) \times \cdots \times f_n(\mathbf{M}_n)$$

for $\mathbf{M}_1 \times \cdots \times \mathbf{M}_n$ *generic over k on* $\mathbf{U}$. *For each i, let* $\mathbf{Y}_i$ *be a cycle on* $\mathbf{V}_i$. *Then we have*

$$f^{-1}(\mathbf{Y}_1 \times \cdots \times \mathbf{Y}_n) = f_1^{-1}(\mathbf{Y}_1) \times \cdots \times f_n^{-1}(\mathbf{Y}_n).$$

Moreover, if, for every i, $\mathbf{X}_i$ *is a cycle on* $\mathbf{U}_i$, $\mathbf{\Gamma}_f$ *intersects the cycle*

$$(\mathbf{X}_1 \times \cdots \times \mathbf{X}_n) \times (\mathbf{Y}_1 \times \cdots \times \mathbf{Y}_n)$$

properly on $\mathbf{U} \times \mathbf{V}$ *if and only if, for every i,* $\mathbf{\Gamma}_{f_i}$ *intersects* $\mathbf{X}_i \times \mathbf{Y}_i$ *properly on* $\mathbf{U}_i \times \mathbf{V}_i$ *or, for some i, no component of* $\mathbf{\Gamma}_{f_i} \cap |\mathbf{X}_i \times \mathbf{Y}_i|$ *is simple on* $\mathbf{U}_i \times \mathbf{V}_i$.

In fact, let φ be the isomorphism of

$$\mathbf{U} \times \mathbf{V} = (\mathbf{U}_1 \times \cdots \times \mathbf{U}_n) \times (\mathbf{V}_1 \times \cdots \times \mathbf{V}_n)$$

onto $(\mathbf{U}_1 \times \mathbf{V}_1) \times \cdots \times (\mathbf{U}_n \times \mathbf{V}_n)$ obtained by the obvious permutation of the factors; this transforms $\mathbf{\Gamma}_f$ into $\mathbf{\Gamma}_{f_1} \times \cdots \times \mathbf{\Gamma}_{f_n}$; our second assertion follows from this immediately, and the first one follows from this, from th. 5 of §3, and from th. 3 (iv–v) of §3.

Corollary. *Let* $\mathbf{U}$, $\mathbf{V}$, $\mathbf{W}$ *be three varieties; let p be the projection mapping of* $\mathbf{U} \times \mathbf{V}$ *onto* $\mathbf{U}$; *let f be a mapping of* $\mathbf{U}$ *into* $\mathbf{W}$, *such that the geometric image of* $\mathbf{U}$ *by f is simple on* $\mathbf{W}$; *and put* $F = f \circ p$. *Then, if* $\mathbf{Z}$ *is any* $\mathbf{W}$*-cycle, we have* $F^{-1}(\mathbf{Z}) = f^{-1}(\mathbf{Z}) \times \mathbf{V}$; *and, if* $\mathbf{X}$ *is a* $\mathbf{U}$*-cycle and* $\mathbf{Y}$ *a* $\mathbf{V}$*-cycle other than* 0, $\mathbf{\Gamma}_F$ *intersects* $\mathbf{X} \times \mathbf{Y} \times \mathbf{Z}$ *properly on* $\mathbf{U} \times \mathbf{V} \times \mathbf{W}$ *if and only if* $\mathbf{\Gamma}_f$ *intersects* $\mathbf{X} \times \mathbf{Z}$ *properly on* $\mathbf{U} \times \mathbf{W}$.

Except for the notations, this is the special case of prop. 14 for which $n = 2$, $\mathbf{V}_2$ is reduced to a point, and $\mathbf{Y}_2 = \mathbf{V}_2$; then f_2 is the constant mapping of $\mathbf{U}_2$ into $\mathbf{V}_2$, we have $f_2^{-1}(\mathbf{Y}_2) = \mathbf{U}_2$, and the product $\mathbf{V} = \mathbf{V}_1 \times \mathbf{V}_2$ can be identified with $\mathbf{V}_1$ in an obvious manner.

Proposition 15. *Let f be a mapping of a product* $\mathbf{U} \times \mathbf{V}$ *into a variety* $\mathbf{W}$, *such that the geometric image of* $\mathbf{U} \times \mathbf{V}$ *by f is simple on* $\mathbf{W}$; *let* $\mathbf{Z}$ *be a* $\mathbf{W}$*-cycle such that* $\mathbf{U} \times \mathbf{V} \times \mathbf{Z}$ *intersects properly the graph* $\mathbf{\Gamma}_f$ *of f on* $\mathbf{U} \times \mathbf{V} \times \mathbf{W}$; *and let* $\mathbf{M}$ *be a generic point of* $\mathbf{U}$ *over a common field of rationality k for* $\mathbf{U}$, $\mathbf{V}$, $\mathbf{W}$, *f and* $\mathbf{Z}$. *Then f is defined on* $\mathbf{M} \times \mathbf{V}$, *and, if* $f_{\mathbf{M}}$ *is the mapping of* $\mathbf{M} \times \mathbf{V}$ *into* $\mathbf{W}$ *induced by f, we have* $f_{\mathbf{M}}^{-1}(\mathbf{Z}) = f^{-1}(\mathbf{Z}) \cdot (\mathbf{M} \times \mathbf{V})$.

If $\mathbf{N}$ is a generic point of $\mathbf{V}$ over $k(\mathbf{M})$, $\mathbf{M} \times \mathbf{N}$ is generic on $\mathbf{U} \times \mathbf{V}$ over k, and on $\mathbf{M} \times \mathbf{V}$ over $k(\mathbf{M})$; this makes the first assertion obvious. Call φ the isomorphism of $\mathbf{M} \times \mathbf{V}$ onto $\mathbf{V}$ induced on $\mathbf{M} \times \mathbf{V}$ by the projection from $\mathbf{U} \times \mathbf{V}$ onto $\mathbf{U}$, so that, if $\mathbf{X}$ is any point, variety or chain on $\mathbf{V}$, we have $\varphi^{-1}(\mathbf{X}) = \mathbf{M} \times \mathbf{X}$; also, call g the mapping of $\mathbf{V}$ into $\mathbf{W}$, rational over $k(\mathbf{M})$, with the value $f(\mathbf{M}, \mathbf{N})$ at $\mathbf{N}$; then we have $f_{\mathbf{M}} = g \circ \varphi$, and the graphs of $f_{\mathbf{M}}$ and of g are the loci of $\mathbf{M} \times \mathbf{N} \times f(\mathbf{M}, \mathbf{N})$ and of $\mathbf{N} \times f(\mathbf{M}, \mathbf{N})$, respectively, over $k(\boldsymbol{M})$, while the graph of f is the locus of $\boldsymbol{M} \times \boldsymbol{N} \times f(\boldsymbol{M}, \boldsymbol{N})$ over k. Therefore, by th. 6 (i) of §3, we have

$$\boldsymbol{\Gamma}_{f_{\boldsymbol{M}}} = \boldsymbol{M} \times \boldsymbol{\Gamma}_g = \boldsymbol{\Gamma}_f \cdot (\boldsymbol{M} \times V \times W).$$

By prop. 8 of §3, $\boldsymbol{M} \times V \times W$ intersects properly every cycle which is rational over k; as $\boldsymbol{\Gamma}_f$ and $U \times V \times Z$ intersect properly, this implies that the three cycles $\boldsymbol{\Gamma}_f$, $U \times V \times Z$ and $\boldsymbol{M} \times V \times W$ intersect properly on $U \times V \times W$. By associativity, i.e. by th. 4 (iv) of §3, this gives:

$$[\boldsymbol{\Gamma}_f \cdot (U \times V \times Z)] \cdot (\boldsymbol{M} \times V \times W) = (\boldsymbol{M} \times \boldsymbol{\Gamma}_g) \cdot (U \times V \times Z)$$
$$= \boldsymbol{M} \times [\boldsymbol{\Gamma}_g \cdot (V \times Z)],$$

and therefore

$$\mathrm{pr}_{U \times V}([\boldsymbol{\Gamma}_f \cdot (U \times V \times Z)] \cdot (\boldsymbol{M} \times V \times W))$$
$$= \boldsymbol{M} \times \mathrm{pr}_V[\boldsymbol{\Gamma}_g \cdot (V \times Z)] = \boldsymbol{M} \times g^{-1}(Z).$$

By the corollary of th. 6, §3, the left-hand side is $f^{-1}(Z) \cdot (\boldsymbol{M} \times V)$; as to the right-hand side, it is the image of $g^{-1}(Z)$ by the isomorphism φ^{-1}, and is therefore equal to $f_{\boldsymbol{M}}^{-1}(Z)$. This completes the proof.

CHAPTER IX

DIVISORS AND LINEAR SYSTEMS

1. Mappings into curves. Before considering mappings of varieties into the projective line, we begin with some preliminary results, valid for mappings into curves.

Let f be a mapping of a variety $\boldsymbol{U}^n$ into a curve $\boldsymbol{C}$; then the geometric image of $\boldsymbol{U}$ by f is either $\boldsymbol{C}$ or a point $\boldsymbol{P}$ of $\boldsymbol{C}$; it is a point $\boldsymbol{P}$ if and only if f is constant with the constant value $\boldsymbol{P}$, i.e. if and only if the graph $\boldsymbol{\Gamma}_f$ of f is $\boldsymbol{U} \times \boldsymbol{P}$. When that is so, then, if $\boldsymbol{P}'$ is any point of $\boldsymbol{C}$, the intersection of $\boldsymbol{\Gamma}_f$ and of $\boldsymbol{U} \times \boldsymbol{P}'$ is empty or is $\boldsymbol{U} \times \boldsymbol{P}$ according as $\boldsymbol{P}' \neq \boldsymbol{P}$ or $\boldsymbol{P}' = \boldsymbol{P}$. On the other hand, if f is not constant, and if $\boldsymbol{P}$ is any point of $\boldsymbol{C}$, then, by prop. 11 of Chap. VII, §5, every component of $\boldsymbol{\Gamma}_f \cap (\boldsymbol{U} \times \boldsymbol{P})$ has at least the dimension $n - 1$ and therefore has exactly that dimension, since otherwise it would coincide with $\boldsymbol{U} \times \boldsymbol{P}$; as every subvariety of $\boldsymbol{U} \times \boldsymbol{P}$ must be of the form $\boldsymbol{W} \times \boldsymbol{P}$, this shows that, if f is not constant, every component of $\boldsymbol{\Gamma}_f \cap (\boldsymbol{U} \times \boldsymbol{P})$ is of the form $\boldsymbol{W} \times \boldsymbol{P}$, where $\boldsymbol{W}$ is a subvariety of $\boldsymbol{U}$ of codimension 1. In particular, if at the same time $\boldsymbol{P}$ is simple on $\boldsymbol{C}$, $\boldsymbol{\Gamma}_f$ and $\boldsymbol{U} \times \boldsymbol{P}$ are properly intersecting divisors on $\boldsymbol{U} \times \boldsymbol{C}$, as could also have been deduced from prop. 5 of Chap. VIII, §3.

As we have already observed in Chap. VIII, §4, the graph $\boldsymbol{\Gamma}_f$ of a mapping f of a variety $\boldsymbol{U}$ into a curve $\boldsymbol{C}$ is a divisor on $\boldsymbol{U} \times \boldsymbol{C}$ unless the geometric image of $\boldsymbol{U}$ by f is a multiple point of $\boldsymbol{C}$. If $\boldsymbol{\Gamma}_f$ is a divisor on $\boldsymbol{U} \times \boldsymbol{C}$, and if $\boldsymbol{P}$ is any simple point of $\boldsymbol{C}$, then we have by definition

$$\boldsymbol{\Gamma}_f \cdot (\boldsymbol{U} \times \boldsymbol{P}) = f^{-1}(\boldsymbol{P}) \times \boldsymbol{P}.$$

If f is a constant, $f^{-1}(\boldsymbol{P})$ is always 0, since we have seen that the intersection of $\boldsymbol{\Gamma}_f$ and $\boldsymbol{U} \times \boldsymbol{P}$ can never have a proper component in that case.

PROPOSITION 1. *Let $\boldsymbol{U}$ be a variety without multiple subvarieties of codimension 1; let f be a mapping of $\boldsymbol{U}$ into a curve $\boldsymbol{C}$; let $\boldsymbol{P}$ be a simple point of $\boldsymbol{C}$; assume that the geometric image of $\boldsymbol{U}$ by f is neither $\boldsymbol{P}$ nor a multiple point of $\boldsymbol{C}$. Then the support $|f^{-1}(\boldsymbol{P})|$ of $f^{-1}(\boldsymbol{P})$ is the set of all points $\boldsymbol{M}$ of $\boldsymbol{U}$ such that $\boldsymbol{M} \times \boldsymbol{P}$ is in the graph $\boldsymbol{\Gamma}_f$ of f.*

The definition of $f^{-1}(\boldsymbol{P})$ shows that a point $\boldsymbol{M}$ is in the support of that cycle if and only if $\boldsymbol{M} \times \boldsymbol{P}$ is in a proper component of $\boldsymbol{\Gamma}_f \cap (\boldsymbol{U} \times \boldsymbol{P})$; but, as we have seen, every component of that intersection is of the form $\boldsymbol{W} \times \boldsymbol{P}$, where $\boldsymbol{W}$ is of codimension 1 on $\boldsymbol{U}$; our assumptions imply that every such component is proper.

COROLLARY 1. *Assumptions and notations being as in prop. 1, $f^{-1}(\boldsymbol{P}) = 0$ if and only if $\boldsymbol{\Gamma}_f \cap (\boldsymbol{U} \times \boldsymbol{P}) = \emptyset$; in particular, if at the same time $\boldsymbol{U}$ is a complete variety, then $f^{-1}(\boldsymbol{P}) = 0$ if and only if f is a constant mapping.*

The first assertion follows at once from prop. 1. If f is not constant, the geometric projection of $\mathbf{\Gamma}_f$ on $\boldsymbol{C}$ is $\boldsymbol{C}$; if $\boldsymbol{U}$ is complete, $\mathbf{\Gamma}_f$ is everywhere complete over $\boldsymbol{C}$, so that $\mathbf{\Gamma}_f \cap (\boldsymbol{U} \times \boldsymbol{P})$ is not empty; therefore, when that is so, $f^{-1}(\boldsymbol{P})$ is not 0. If f is constant, $f^{-1}(\boldsymbol{P})$ is 0, as we have seen above.

It is sometimes useful to observe that the second part of our corollary holds even if one merely assumes that $\boldsymbol{U}$ is the complement, on some complete variety $\bar{\boldsymbol{U}}$ without multiple subvarieties of codimension 1, of the union of finitely many subvarieties of $\bar{\boldsymbol{U}}$ of codimension $\geqq 2$ on $\bar{\boldsymbol{U}}$; in fact, when that is so, the closure of $\mathbf{\Gamma}_f$ on $\bar{\boldsymbol{U}} \times \boldsymbol{C}$ is the graph of a non-constant mapping $\bar{f}$ of $\bar{\boldsymbol{U}}$ into $\boldsymbol{C}$, and $f^{-1}(\boldsymbol{P})$ is the restriction of $\bar{f}^{-1}(\boldsymbol{P})$ to $\boldsymbol{U}$; as our corollary shows that, if f is not constant, $\bar{f}^{-1}(\boldsymbol{P})$ is not 0, the same must then be true of $f^{-1}(\boldsymbol{P})$.

COROLLARY 2. *Assumptions and notations being as in prop.* 1, *a simple point* $\boldsymbol{M}$ *of* $\boldsymbol{U}$ *is in* $|f^{-1}(\boldsymbol{P})|$ *if and only if either* f *is defined at* $\boldsymbol{M}$ *and* $f(\boldsymbol{M}) = \boldsymbol{P}$, *or* $\boldsymbol{M} \times \boldsymbol{C}$ *is contained in* $\mathbf{\Gamma}_f$; *and* $|f^{-1}(\boldsymbol{P})|$ *is the closure of the set of the simple points of* $\boldsymbol{U}$ *where* f *is defined and has the value* $\boldsymbol{P}$.

By prop. 1, $\boldsymbol{M}$ is in $|f^{-1}(\boldsymbol{P})|$ if and only if $\boldsymbol{M} \times \boldsymbol{P}$ is in $\mathbf{\Gamma}_f$, i.e. if and only if it is in $\mathbf{\Gamma}_f \cap (\boldsymbol{M} \times \boldsymbol{C})$; if that is so, and if $\boldsymbol{M} \times \boldsymbol{C}$ is not contained in $\mathbf{\Gamma}_f$, $\boldsymbol{M} \times \boldsymbol{P}$ must then be a component of $\mathbf{\Gamma}_f \cap (\boldsymbol{M} \times \boldsymbol{C})$; by th. 9 of Chap. VII, §7, this implies that f is defined at $\boldsymbol{M}$, so that it must have the value $\boldsymbol{P}$ at that point. Therefore, if $\boldsymbol{X}$ is the closure of the set of the simple points of $\boldsymbol{U}$ where f is defined and has the value $\boldsymbol{P}$, $\boldsymbol{X}$ is contained in $|f^{-1}(\boldsymbol{P})|$. Now let $\boldsymbol{N}$ be any point of $|f^{-1}(\boldsymbol{P})|$; let $\boldsymbol{W}$ be a component of $f^{-1}(\boldsymbol{P})$, containing $\boldsymbol{N}$; let k be a field of definition for $\boldsymbol{U}$, $\boldsymbol{C}$, f, $\boldsymbol{W}$ and all the components of $\boldsymbol{X}$, so that $\boldsymbol{X}$ is k-closed. Let $\boldsymbol{M} \times \boldsymbol{Q}$ be a generic point of $\boldsymbol{W} \times \boldsymbol{C}$ over k; if $\boldsymbol{M} \times \boldsymbol{Q}$ were in $\mathbf{\Gamma}_f$, its locus $\boldsymbol{W} \times \boldsymbol{C}$ over k would be contained in $\mathbf{\Gamma}_f$, which is impossible, since it has the same dimension as $\mathbf{\Gamma}_f$ and is not $\mathbf{\Gamma}_f$; therefore $\boldsymbol{M} \times \boldsymbol{C}$ is not contained in $\mathbf{\Gamma}_f$. As $\boldsymbol{M}$ is in $|f^{-1}(\boldsymbol{P})|$, the first part of our corollary shows now that f is defined at $\boldsymbol{M}$ and has the value $\boldsymbol{P}$ there; as $\boldsymbol{N}$ is in the k-closure of $\boldsymbol{M}$, which is $\boldsymbol{W}$, this implies that $\boldsymbol{N}$ is in $\boldsymbol{X}$.

COROLLARY 3. *Assumptions and notations being as in prop.* 1, *a simple subvariety* $\boldsymbol{V}$ *of* $\boldsymbol{U}$ *is contained in* $|f^{-1}(\boldsymbol{P})|$ *if and only if either* f *is defined at* $\boldsymbol{V}$ *and induces on* $\boldsymbol{V}$ *a constant mapping with the constant value* $\boldsymbol{P}$, *or* $\boldsymbol{V} \times \boldsymbol{C}$ *is contained in* $\mathbf{\Gamma}_f$.

Let k be a common field of definition for $\boldsymbol{U}$, $\boldsymbol{C}$, f, $\boldsymbol{P}$ and $\boldsymbol{V}$; let $\boldsymbol{M}$ be a generic point of $\boldsymbol{V}$ over k. As $|f^{-1}(\boldsymbol{P})|$ is k-closed, it contains $\boldsymbol{V}$ if and only if it contains $\boldsymbol{M}$; applying coroll. 2 to $\boldsymbol{M}$, we get coroll. 3.

COROLLARY 4. *Assumptions and notations being as in prop.* 1, *let* $\boldsymbol{Q}$ *be a simple point of* $\boldsymbol{C}$, *other than* $\boldsymbol{P}$; *then the divisors* $f^{-1}(\boldsymbol{P})$ *and* $f^{-1}(\boldsymbol{Q})$ *intersect properly on* $\boldsymbol{U}$, *and the support of the cycle* $f^{-1}(\boldsymbol{P}) \cdot f^{-1}(\boldsymbol{Q})$ *is the closure of the set of the simple points* $\boldsymbol{M}$ *of* $\boldsymbol{U}$ *such that* $\boldsymbol{M} \times \boldsymbol{C}$ *is contained in* $\mathbf{\Gamma}_f$.

Let $\boldsymbol{U}'$ be the set of simple points on $\boldsymbol{U}$; by restricting $\boldsymbol{U}$-cycles to $\boldsymbol{U}'$ and

$(U \times C)$-cycles to $U' \times C$, we see that it is enough to consider the case when U has no multiple point. Then, by coroll. 3, a subvariety V of U is contained both in $|f^{-1}(P)|$ and in $|f^{-1}(Q)|$ if and only if $V \times C$ is contained in Γ_f; this implies that V has at least the codimension 2 on U, since otherwise $V \times C$ would have the same dimension as Γ_f and would coincide with it, which is impossible. In particular, this shows that $f^{-1}(P)$ and $f^{-1}(Q)$ cannot have a common component; therefore they intersect properly, by prop. 5 of Chap. VIII, §3. That being so, the support of $f^{-1}(P) \cdot f^{-1}(Q)$ is the intersection of $|f^{-1}(P)|$ and $|f^{-1}(Q)|$ and consists of the points M such that $M \times C \subset \Gamma_f$.

PROPOSITION 2. *Let f be a mapping of a variety U into a complete non-singular curve C, and let V be a simple subvariety of U. Then f is defined at V if and only if $V \times C$ is not contained in the graph Γ_f of f; moreover, when that is so, the cycle $\Gamma_f \cdot (V \times C)$ can be written as $\Gamma_g + X \times C$, where Γ_g is the graph of the mapping g of V into C induced on V by f, and X is a U-cycle such that $|X| \subset V$.*

As C is complete, th. 7 of Chap. VII, §5, shows that Γ_f is everywhere complete over V, so that, by prop. 13 of Chap. VII, §5, $\Gamma_f \cap (V \times C)$ has a component X with the projection V on U. If $V \times C$ is not contained in Γ_f, X must then have the same dimension as V, so that, by th. 9 of Chap. VII, §7, f is defined at V. Conversely, if f is defined at V and induces on V the mapping g of V into C, Γ_g is the only component of $\Gamma_f \cap (V \times C)$ with the projection V on U; in particular, when that is so, $V \times C$ is not contained in Γ_f, which completes the proof of the first assertion. Now let U' be the open subset of U consisting of the simple points of U where f is defined; restricting all U-cycles to U' and all $(U \times C)$-cycles to $U' \times C$, we see, by coroll. 2 of th. 8, Chap. VIII, §3, that Γ_g has the coefficient 1 in $\Gamma_f \cdot (V \times C)$. Now consider any component W of $\Gamma_f \cdot (V \times C)$, other than Γ_g; its dimension is equal to that of V; on the other hand, its geometric projection W' on U is contained in V and cannot be V, so that its codimension in V is $\geqq 1$. Then W is contained in $W' \times C$ and has at least the same dimension as $W' \times C$, so that it must be the same as $W' \times C$.

One can make use of the first part of prop. 2 in order to reformulate some of the corollaries of prop. 1 in the case when the curve C is complete and non-singular; for instance, the support of $f^{-1}(P) \cdot f^{-1}(Q)$ is then the closure of the set of the simple points of U where f is not defined.

2. Divisors of functions. In Chap. VII, §3, we defined the projective line D as an abstract variety with two representatives D_1, D_2, both equal to S^1; it is a complete curve and is obviously non-singular, so that we may apply to it all the results of §1.

If x is the coordinate of a point P of D, then, as explained in Chap. VII, we also write (x) for P; P has a representative P_1 in D_1 if and only if $x \neq \infty$, and then we have $P_1 = x$. By abuse of notation, one frequently writes x, instead of (x), for the point of D with the coordinate x.

Let f be a mapping of a variety U into D; let k be a field of rationality for f, and $\boldsymbol{M}$ a generic point of $\boldsymbol{U}$ over k; $f(\boldsymbol{M})$ has a representative $f_1(\boldsymbol{M})$ in D_1 if and only if it is not the point (∞), i.e. if and only if f is not the constant (∞) on $\boldsymbol{U}$; when that is so, we say that f is a *numerical function* or more briefly a *function on* $\boldsymbol{U}$. Then f_1 is a mapping of $\boldsymbol{U}$ into $D_1 = S^1$, rational over k; f_1 is defined at a point $\boldsymbol{P}$ of $\boldsymbol{U}$ if and only if f is defined at $\boldsymbol{P}$ and $f(\boldsymbol{P}) \neq (\infty)$. By abuse of notation, if f is a function on a variety $\boldsymbol{U}$, one frequently makes no distinction between the value $f(\boldsymbol{P})$ of f at a point $\boldsymbol{P}$ where it is defined, and the coordinate of that value, so that the symbol $f(\boldsymbol{P})$ is also used to denote that coordinate. Sometimes, by abuse of notation, one also makes no distinction between the mapping f of $\boldsymbol{U}$ into $\boldsymbol{D}$ and the mapping f_1 of $\boldsymbol{U}$ into $D_1 = S^1$ determined by f, the latter being also called the function f; the same abuse of language has long been current in the classical theory of meromorphic functions on Riemann surfaces (or more generally on complex-analytic manifolds) and ordinarily causes no confusion.

Let f be a numerical function on $\boldsymbol{U}$, k a field of rationality for f, and $\boldsymbol{M}$ a generic point of $\boldsymbol{U}$ over k; let f_1 be the mapping of $\boldsymbol{U}$ into D_1 determined by f, and put $z = f_1(\boldsymbol{M})$, so that z is the coordinate of $f(\boldsymbol{M})$. Let $\boldsymbol{P}$ be a point of $\boldsymbol{U}$; we shall say that f is *finite at* $\boldsymbol{P}$ if $\boldsymbol{P} \times (\infty)$ is not in the graph $\boldsymbol{\Gamma}_f$ of f; this will be so if and only if z is finite over $\boldsymbol{M} \to \boldsymbol{P}$, with reference to k. If f is defined at $\boldsymbol{P}$, it is finite there if and only if $f(\boldsymbol{P}) \neq (\infty)$; on the other hand, by prop. 2 of §1 (or by th. 5 of Chap. V, §3), if $\boldsymbol{P}$ is simple on $\boldsymbol{U}$ and f is finite at $\boldsymbol{P}$, it is defined at $\boldsymbol{P}$. If $\boldsymbol{V}$ is any subvariety of $\boldsymbol{U}$, we say that f is *finite at* $\boldsymbol{V}$ or *along* $\boldsymbol{V}$ if $\boldsymbol{V} \times (\infty)$ is not contained in $\boldsymbol{\Gamma}_f$; this will be so if and only if f is finite at a generic point of $\boldsymbol{V}$ over a common field of rationality for $\boldsymbol{V}$ and f.

If f is a function on a variety $\boldsymbol{U}$, and (a) is a point of $\boldsymbol{D}$, we shall write $f^{-1}(a)$ instead of $f^{-1}((a))$; this is therefore the $\boldsymbol{U}$-divisor defined by the formula

$$\boldsymbol{\Gamma}_f \cdot (\boldsymbol{U} \times (a)) = f^{-1}(a) \times (a).$$

Once for all, we denote by $\boldsymbol{\Theta}$ the divisor $(0) - (\infty)$ on $\boldsymbol{D}$; it is rational over the prime field; if f is a function on a variety $\boldsymbol{U}$, we have

$$\boldsymbol{\Gamma}_f \cdot (\boldsymbol{U} \times \boldsymbol{\Theta}) = f^{-1}(0) \times (0) - f^{-1}(\infty) \times (\infty).$$

Whenever f is a numerical function, *other than the constant* 0, on a variety $\boldsymbol{U}$, we shall call the divisor $f^{-1}(\boldsymbol{\Theta})$ *the divisor of* f on $\boldsymbol{U}$, and we shall denote it by $\operatorname{div}(f)$; sometimes it is denoted more briefly by (f). In other words, we write:

$$\operatorname{div}(f) = f^{-1}(\boldsymbol{\Theta}) = f^{-1}(0) - f^{-1}(\infty) = \operatorname{pr}_{\boldsymbol{U}}[\boldsymbol{\Gamma}_f \cdot (\boldsymbol{U} \times \boldsymbol{\Theta})].$$

Also, under the same assumptions, we shall write

$$v_{\boldsymbol{A}}(f) = \gamma_{\boldsymbol{A}}(\operatorname{div}(f))$$

for the coefficient of $\boldsymbol{A}$ in $\operatorname{div}(f)$, where $\boldsymbol{A}$ is any simple subvariety of $\boldsymbol{U}$ of codimension 1.

If f is constant, we have $f^{-1}(0) = 0$, $f^{-1}(\infty) = 0$. Therefore, if f is any constant function other than 0, we have $\operatorname{div}(f) = 0$, and $v_{\boldsymbol{A}}(f) = 0$ for every $\boldsymbol{A}$.

We now list, for convenient reference, the following results, which are special cases of those in §1.

THEOREM 1. *Let f be a numerical function on a variety* $\mathbf{U}$ *without multiple subvarieties of codimension* 1. *Then* $|f^{-1}(0)|$ *and* $|f^{-1}(\infty)|$ *have no common component;* $|f^{-1}(\infty)|$ *is the set of the points of* $\mathbf{U}$ *where f is not finite. If* $\mathbf{V}$ *is a simple subvariety of* $\mathbf{U}$, $\mathbf{V}$ *is contained in* $|f^{-1}(\infty)|$ *(resp. in* $|f^{-1}(0)|$*) if and only if either f is not defined at* $\mathbf{V}$, *or f is defined at* $\mathbf{V}$ *and induces on* $\mathbf{V}$ *the constant* ∞ *(resp. the constant* 0*).*

COROLLARY 1. *Assumptions and notations being as in th.* 1, *let* $\mathbf{V}$ *be a simple subvariety of* $\mathbf{U}$; *let k be a field of rationality for* $\mathbf{U}$, $\mathbf{V}$ *and f, and let* $\mathbf{M}$ *be a generic point of* $\mathbf{U}$ *over k. Then* $\mathbf{V}$ *is contained in* $|f^{-1}(\infty)|$ *if and only if* $f(\mathbf{M})$ *is not in the specialization-ring of* $\mathbf{V}$ *in* $k(\mathbf{M})$.

COROLLARY 2. *Assumptions and notations being as in th.* 1, *let* $\mathbf{A}$ *be a simple subvariety of* $\mathbf{U}$ *of codimension* 1. *Then f is defined at* $\mathbf{A}$; *if f is not the constant* 0, *we have* $v_{\mathbf{A}}(f) > 0$ *if and only if f induces on* $\mathbf{A}$ *the constant* 0; *we have* $v_{\mathbf{A}}(f) \geqq 0$ *if and only if f is finite at* $\mathbf{A}$, *i.e. if and only if it does not induce on* $\mathbf{A}$ *the constant* ∞. *If k is a field of rationality for* $\mathbf{U}$, $\mathbf{A}$ *and f, and* $\mathbf{M}$ *a generic point of* $\mathbf{U}$ *over k, we have* $v_{\mathbf{A}}(f) \geqq 0$ *if and only if* $f(\mathbf{M})$ *is in the specialization-ring of* $\mathbf{A}$ *in* $k(\mathbf{M})$.

COROLLARY 3. *Assumptions and notations being as in th.* 1, *we have* $f^{-1}(\infty) = 0$ *if and only if f is everywhere finite on* $\mathbf{U}$; *if at the same time* $\mathbf{U}$ *is complete, then we have* $f^{-1}(\infty) = 0$ *if and only if f is constant. If f is other than the constant* 0, *and if* $\mathbf{U}$ *is complete, then* $\mathrm{div}(f) \succ 0$ *implies that f is constant and that* $\mathrm{div}(f) = 0$.

The following result is essentially a special case of th. 14, Chap. VIII, §4:

PROPOSITION 3. *Let* φ *be a mapping of a variety* $\mathbf{U}$ *into a variety* $\mathbf{V}$, *and f a numerical function on* $\mathbf{V}$. *Then we have*

$$\varphi^{-1}(\mathrm{div}(f)) = \mathrm{div}(f \circ \varphi)$$

provided the following conditions are satisfied: (i) *the geometric image of* $\mathbf{U}$ *by* φ *is neither contained in the set of multiple points of* $\mathbf{V}$ *nor in the set of points where f is not defined;* (ii) $f \circ \varphi$ *is neither the constant* 0 *nor the constant* ∞; (iii) *either the graph* $\mathbf{\Gamma}_\varphi$ *of* φ *is everywhere complete over* $\mathbf{U}$, *or* $\mathbf{\Gamma}_f$ *is so over* $\mathbf{D}$; (iv) *there is no simple subvariety* $\mathbf{A}$ *of* $\mathbf{U}$ *of codimension* 1 *whose geometric image* $\mathbf{B}$ *by* φ *is multiple on* $\mathbf{V}$ *and such that* $\mathbf{B} \times (0)$ *or* $\mathbf{B} \times (\infty)$ *is contained in* $\mathbf{\Gamma}_f$.

In fact, (i) says that (φ, f) is a consonant pair of mappings, in the sense of Chap. VIII, §4. Then we get the result stated above by applying th. 14 of Chap. VIII, §4, successively to φ, f and $\mathbf{P} = (0)$ and to φ, f and $\mathbf{P} = (\infty)$.

Now let x, y be two independent variables over the prime field k_0; then $(x) \times (y)$ is a generic point of $\mathbf{D} \times \mathbf{D}$ over k_0, and there are two functions s, p on $\mathbf{D} \times \mathbf{D}$, both rational over k_0, such that

$$s(x, y) = (x + y), \qquad p(x, y) = (xy).$$

It is easily seen that s is everywhere defined on $\boldsymbol{D} \times \boldsymbol{D}$ except at the point $(\infty) \times (\infty)$, and p everywhere except at $(0) \times (\infty)$ and at $(\infty) \times (0)$; if x', y' are any quantities (not ∞), we have

$$s(x', y') = (x' + y'), \qquad p(x', y') = (x'y').$$

Let f, g be two functions on a variety $\boldsymbol{U}$; let k be a field of rationality for $\boldsymbol{U}$, f and g, and let $\boldsymbol{M}$ be a generic point of $\boldsymbol{U}$ over k. Then (f, g) is a mapping of $\boldsymbol{U}$ into $\boldsymbol{D} \times \boldsymbol{D}$; as neither $f(\boldsymbol{M})$ nor $g(\boldsymbol{M})$ is ∞, the mappings $s \circ (f, g)$ and $p \circ (f, g)$ are defined; they are the functions on $\boldsymbol{U}$, rational over k, whose values at $\boldsymbol{M}$ are respectively $f(\boldsymbol{M}) + g(\boldsymbol{M})$ and $f(\boldsymbol{M})g(\boldsymbol{M})$; we will denote these functions by $f + g$ and fg, respectively. If $\boldsymbol{P}$ is a point of $\boldsymbol{U}$ where f and g are both defined and finite, then $f + g$ and fg are also defined at $\boldsymbol{P}$ and have at $\boldsymbol{P}$ the values $f(\boldsymbol{P}) + g(\boldsymbol{P})$, $f(\boldsymbol{P})g(\boldsymbol{P})$. Similarly, if f is not the constant 0, we write $1/f$ for the function, rational over k, whose value at $\boldsymbol{M}$ is $1/f(\boldsymbol{M})$. It is clear that, for these operations, the functions on $\boldsymbol{U}$ constitute an "abstract field", *the function-field of* $\boldsymbol{U}$; the functions on $\boldsymbol{U}$, rational over k, constitute a subfield of that field, which is mapped isomorphically onto $k(\boldsymbol{M})$ by the mapping $f \to f(\boldsymbol{M})$. The constant functions on $\boldsymbol{U}$ make up a subfield of the function-field of $\boldsymbol{U}$, isomorphic to the universal domain, with which (by abuse of language) it is frequently identified, each constant function being identified with its constant value.

Notations being as above, f and g are defined and finite at a point $\boldsymbol{P}$ of $\boldsymbol{U}$ if and only if $f(\boldsymbol{M})$ and $g(\boldsymbol{M})$ are in the specialization-ring of $\boldsymbol{P}$ in $k(\boldsymbol{M})$, and then $f + g$ and fg have the same property. Therefore the functions on $\boldsymbol{U}$ which are defined and finite at $\boldsymbol{P}$ make up a ring, which will be called *the specialization-ring of* $\boldsymbol{P}$ *on* $\boldsymbol{U}$; similarly, if $\boldsymbol{V}$ is any subvariety of $\boldsymbol{U}$, the functions on $\boldsymbol{U}$ which are defined and finite at $\boldsymbol{V}$ make up a ring, *the specialization-ring of* $\boldsymbol{V}$ *on* $\boldsymbol{U}$.

THEOREM 2. *Let f and g be two functions on a variety $\boldsymbol{U}$, neither of which is the constant* 0. *Then* $\operatorname{div}(fg) = \operatorname{div}(f) + \operatorname{div}(g)$.

We apply prop. 3, in which we replace f by p, $\boldsymbol{V}$ by $\boldsymbol{D} \times \boldsymbol{D}$ and φ by (f, g). As the conditions (i)–(iv) are obviously satisfied, we get $\operatorname{div}(fg) = \varphi^{-1}(\operatorname{div}(p))$. Th. 1 shows at once that the components of $p^{-1}(0)$ are $(0) \times \boldsymbol{D}$ and $\boldsymbol{D} \times (0)$ and that those of $p^{-1}(\infty)$ are $(\infty) \times \boldsymbol{D}$ and $\boldsymbol{D} \times (\infty)$, and the criterion of multiplicity 1, i.e. th. 6 of Chap. VI, §2, shows that their coefficients in those cycles are 1, so that we have

$$\operatorname{div}(p) = \boldsymbol{\Theta} \times \boldsymbol{D} + \boldsymbol{D} \times \boldsymbol{\Theta}.$$

Our theorem will be proved if we show that $\varphi^{-1}(\boldsymbol{\Theta} \times \boldsymbol{D})$ is the same as $\operatorname{div}(f)$; for then, by exchanging the two factors in $\boldsymbol{D} \times \boldsymbol{D}$, one sees in the same manner that $\varphi^{-1}(\boldsymbol{D} \times \boldsymbol{\Theta})$ is the same as $\operatorname{div}(g)$. But that is an immediate consequence of the formula

$$\operatorname{pr}_{\boldsymbol{U}\times\boldsymbol{D}}[\boldsymbol{\Gamma}_\varphi \cdot (\boldsymbol{U} \times \boldsymbol{\Theta} \times \boldsymbol{D})] = \boldsymbol{\Gamma}_f \cdot (\boldsymbol{U} \times \boldsymbol{\Theta}),$$

which one gets by a straightforward application of th. 8, Chap. VIII, §3.

COROLLARY 1. *If f is a function on U, other than the constant* 0, *we have*

$$\operatorname{div}(1/f) = -\operatorname{div}(f).$$

This follows from th. 2 by taking $g = 1/f$.

COROLLARY 2. *Let f and g be two functions on a variety U, neither of which is the constant* 0; *let A be a simple subvariety of U of codimension* 1. *Then we have*

$$v_A(fg) = v_A(f) + v_A(g), \qquad v_A(1/f) = -v_A(f).$$

If also $f + g$ is not the constant 0, *then*

$$v_A(f + g) \geqq \min\,[v_A(f), v_A(g)].$$

The first part follows from th. 2 and coroll. 1. As to the second part, put $a = v_A(f)$, $b = v_A(g)$, and assume for instance that $a \leqq b$. The first part, applied to f and $h = g/f$, shows that $v_A(h) = b - a \geqq 0$; by coroll. 2 of th. 1, this amounts to saying that h is in the specialization-ring of A; therefore $1 + h$ is also in that ring, so that $v_A(1 + h) \geqq 0$. As we have $f + g = f\cdot(1 + h)$, we get $v_A(f + g) \geqq a$.

Corollary 2 is frequently expressed by saying that, for a given A, $v_A(f)$ is a "valuation" of the function-field of U. In order to include formally the constants 0 and ∞ in the statements made about $v_A(f)$, one writes sometimes $v_A(0) = +\infty$, $v_A(\infty) = -\infty$.

COROLLARY 3. *Let $f_1, \cdots, f_m$ be any functions, $c_1, \cdots, c_m$ constant functions, and X a divisor on a variety U; put $f = \sum_i c_i f_i$, and assume that none of the functions $f_1, \cdots, f_m, f$ is the constant* 0. *Then, if $\operatorname{div}(f_i) \succ X$ for every i, we have $\operatorname{div}(f) \succ X$.*

In fact, to say that $\operatorname{div}(f) \succ X$ is the same as to say that $v_A(f) \geqq \gamma_A(X)$ for every simple subvariety A of U of codimension 1. Our assertion now follows immediately from coroll. 2, by induction on m.

For formal reasons, we will, from now on, write $\operatorname{div}(0) \succ X$ if X is any divisor on U and 0 denotes the constant function on U with the value 0; with this convention, coroll. 3 of th. 2 remains valid even if some (or all) of the functions f_i, f are 0, and can be expressed by saying that, if X is given, the functions f on U which satisfy the condition $\operatorname{div}(f) \succ X$ make up a vector-space over the field of the constant functions on U, or, more briefly, over the field of constants (which we have agreed to identify with the universal domain). *This vector-space will be denoted by $\mathfrak{L}(-X)$.* Coroll. 3 of th. 1 can be expressed by saying that, if U is a complete variety without multiple subvarieties of codimension 1, $\mathfrak{L}(0)$ is the field of constants, and $\mathfrak{L}(-X)$ is reduced to $\{0\}$ for $X \succ 0$, $X \neq 0$. If k is a common field of rationality for U and X, we will denote by $\mathfrak{L}_k(-X)$ the set of the functions in $\mathfrak{L}(-X)$ which are rational over k; coroll. 3 of th. 2 shows that this is a vector-space over k.

THEOREM 3. *Let f be a function on a variety U, other than the constant* 0; *let V be a simple subvariety of U. Then f is defined at V and induces on V a function*

g other than the constant 0 *if and only if* $\mathrm{div}(f)$ *and* V *intersect properly on* U. *When that is so, we have*

$$\mathrm{div}(f)\cdot V = \mathrm{pr}_U[\Gamma_g\cdot(U \times \Theta)].$$

Moreover, if A *is a subvariety of* V *of codimension* 1 *on* V, *simple on* U *and on* V, *then* $v_A(g) = \gamma_A(\mathrm{div}(f)\cdot V)$.

By prop. 5 of Chap. VIII, §3, $\mathrm{div}(f)$ and V intersect properly if and only if V is not contained in the support of $\mathrm{div}(f)$; in view of this, the first assertion in our theorem is only another statement for the latter part of th. 1. Assume, from now on, that f induces on V a function g, other than the constant 0. As V intersects $f^{-1}(0)$ properly on U, $V \times D$ intersects $f^{-1}(0) \times (0)$ properly on $U \times D$; similarly, it intersects $f^{-1}(\infty) \times (\infty)$ properly; therefore, it intersects $\Gamma_f\cdot(U \times \Theta)$ properly. As Γ_f and $U \times \Theta$ intersect properly, this implies that the three cycles Γ_f, $U \times \Theta$ and $V \times D$ do so. Therefore we have, by associativity, i.e. by th. 4(iv) of Chap. VIII, §3:

$$[\Gamma_f\cdot(U \times \Theta)]\cdot(V \times D) = [\Gamma_f\cdot(V \times D)]\cdot(U \times \Theta).$$

Now we can apply th. 8 of Chap. VIII, §3, to the left-hand side; this gives

$$\mathrm{pr}_U([\Gamma_f\cdot(U \times \Theta)]\cdot(V \times D)) = \mathrm{div}(f)\cdot V.$$

On the other hand, by prop. 2 of §1, $\Gamma_f\cdot(V \times D)$ is of the form $\Gamma_g + X \times D$, so that we have

$$\mathrm{pr}_U([\Gamma_f\cdot(V \times D)]\cdot(U \times \Theta)) = \mathrm{pr}_U[\Gamma_g\cdot(U \times \Theta)] + \mathrm{pr}_U(X \times \Theta);$$

and the last term in the right-hand side is 0 by th. 3 (iii) of Chap. VIII, §3. This proves the first formula in our theorem. As to the second one, it is enough to prove it under the additional assumption that there is no subvariety of V, of codimension 1 on V, which is multiple either on V or on U; for otherwise, calling X the union of the sets of multiple points on U and on V, we can restrict all U-cycles to $U' = U - X$, all V-cycles to $V' = V - (V \cap X)$, $(U \times D)$-cycles to $U' \times D$ and $(V \times D)$-cycles to $V' \times D$; then, calling f', g' the restrictions of f to U' and of g to V', respectively, and putting $A' = A \cap U'$, one sees at once that all our assumptions are fulfilled for U', V', f', g', A', and that the coefficients of A' in $\mathrm{div}(g')$ and in $\mathrm{div}(f')\cdot V'$ are the same as those of A in $\mathrm{div}(g)$ and in $\mathrm{div}(f)\cdot V$, respectively. Assume now that all subvarieties of V of codimension 1 are simple on U and on V; call j the injection mapping of V into U. Our assumptions imply now that $f \circ j$ is defined and coincides with g, and that prop. 3 can be applied to j and f; this gives $\mathrm{div}(g) = j^{-1}(\mathrm{div}(f))$. By th. 10 of Chap. VIII, §4, the right-hand side is the same as $\mathrm{div}(f)\cdot V$; this completes our proof. Alternatively, one could also apply th. 10 of Chap. VIII, §4, to the $(U \times D)$-cycle $\Gamma_g\cdot(U \times \Theta)$ and to the injection mapping of $V \times D$ into $U \times D$; this would show that $\Gamma_g\cdot(U \times \Theta)$, taken on $U \times D$, is the same as $\Gamma_g\cdot(V \times \Theta)$, taken on $V \times D$, whenever every point of V is simple on U and on V.

COROLLARY. *Assumptions and notations being as in th. 3, we have*

$$\mathrm{div}(g) = \mathrm{div}(f)\cdot \boldsymbol{V}$$

provided every subvariety of $\boldsymbol{V}$ *of codimension* 1 *on* $\boldsymbol{V}$ *is simple both on* $\boldsymbol{V}$ *and on* $\boldsymbol{U}$.

This was proved above, and is also an immediate consequence of the final formula in th. 3.

THEOREM 4. *Let* f *be a function, other than the constant* 0, *on the product* $\boldsymbol{U}\times \boldsymbol{V}$ *of two varieties* $\boldsymbol{U}^n$, $\boldsymbol{V}$. *Let* $\boldsymbol{Z}^n$ *be a cycle on* $\boldsymbol{U}\times\boldsymbol{V}$, *everywhere complete over* $\boldsymbol{U}$ *and intersecting* $\mathrm{div}(f)$ *properly on* $\boldsymbol{U}\times\boldsymbol{V}$. *Let* k *be a common field of rationality for* $\boldsymbol{U}$, $\boldsymbol{V}$, f *and* $\boldsymbol{Z}$; *let* $\boldsymbol{P}$ *be a generic point of* $\boldsymbol{U}$ *over* k; *put* $\boldsymbol{Z}(\boldsymbol{P}) = \sum_\nu a_\nu \boldsymbol{Q}_\nu$, *where the* $\boldsymbol{Q}_\nu$ *are the components of* $\boldsymbol{Z}(\boldsymbol{P})$. *Then there is a function* F *on* $\boldsymbol{U}$, *rational over* k, *such that* $F(\boldsymbol{P}) = \prod_\nu f(\boldsymbol{P}, \boldsymbol{Q}_\nu)^{a_\nu}$; *and we have*

$$\mathrm{div}(F) = \mathrm{pr}_{\boldsymbol{U}}(\mathrm{div}(f)\cdot\boldsymbol{Z})$$

provided the following condition is satisfied: $|\boldsymbol{Z}|$ *contains no multiple subvariety* $\boldsymbol{W}$ *of* $\boldsymbol{U}\times\boldsymbol{V}$ *such that* $\boldsymbol{W}\times(0)$ *or* $\boldsymbol{W}\times(\infty)$ *is contained in* $\boldsymbol{\Gamma}_f$ *and whose geometric projection on* $\boldsymbol{U}$ *is simple and of codimension* 1 *on* $\boldsymbol{U}$.

By th. 3, f induces on each component of $\boldsymbol{Z}$ a function other than the constant 0; as everyone of the points $\boldsymbol{P}\times\boldsymbol{Q}_\nu$ is a generic point over $\bar{k}$ of one of these components, it follows that, for every ν, $f(\boldsymbol{P}, \boldsymbol{Q}_\nu)$ is defined and is neither 0 nor ∞, so that the product $p = \prod_\nu f(\boldsymbol{P}, \boldsymbol{Q}_\nu)^{a_\nu}$ is defined and is not 0. Now write $\boldsymbol{Z} = \boldsymbol{Z}' - \boldsymbol{Z}''$, where $\boldsymbol{Z}'$, $\boldsymbol{Z}''$ are positive cycles with no component in common; then $\boldsymbol{Z}'$, $\boldsymbol{Z}''$ are rational over k and intersect $\mathrm{div}(f)$ properly. If we call p', p'' the products, built up from $\boldsymbol{Z}'$ and $\boldsymbol{Z}''$ just as p was built up from $\boldsymbol{Z}$, we have $p = p'/p''$, and one sees at once that, if our theorem is true for $\boldsymbol{Z}'$ and for $\boldsymbol{Z}''$, it is true for $\boldsymbol{Z}$. It is therefore enough to consider the case $\boldsymbol{Z} > 0$. Call d the degree of $\boldsymbol{Z}(\boldsymbol{P})$; we can write $\boldsymbol{Z}(\boldsymbol{P}) = \sum_{i=1}^d \boldsymbol{Q}_i$, and this is a rational 0-cycle over $k(\boldsymbol{P})$ on $\boldsymbol{V}$. Now, if we consider d independent generic points $\boldsymbol{N}_1, \cdots, \boldsymbol{N}_d$ of $\boldsymbol{V}$ over $k(\boldsymbol{P})$, we define a function g, rational over $k(\boldsymbol{P})$, on the product $\boldsymbol{V}\times\cdots\times\boldsymbol{V}$ of d factors equal to $\boldsymbol{V}$, by putting

$$g(\boldsymbol{N}_1, \cdots, \boldsymbol{N}_d) = \prod_{i=1}^d f(\boldsymbol{P}, \boldsymbol{N}_i),$$

and this is a symmetric mapping of $\boldsymbol{V}\times\cdots\times\boldsymbol{V}$ into $\boldsymbol{D}$. Therefore, by th. 2 of Chap. VIII, §2, $g(\boldsymbol{Q}_1, \cdots, \boldsymbol{Q}_d)$ is rational over $k(\boldsymbol{P})$. This implies that we define a function F on $\boldsymbol{U}$, rational over k, by putting

$$F(\boldsymbol{P}) = g(\boldsymbol{Q}_1, \cdots, \boldsymbol{Q}_d) = \prod_{i=1}^d f(\boldsymbol{P}, \boldsymbol{Q}_i),$$

which proves the first assertion in our theorem.

Now, except for the rationality of F over k, which we have just proved, nothing is changed in the statement of our theorem if we replace k by $\bar{k}$, so that it is enough to proceed with the proof under the additional assumption that k

is algebraically closed, or more generally that it is a common field of rationality for all the components of Z. Just as above, we see that, if $Z = Z' + Z''$ with Z' and Z'' positive, the theorem will be true for Z if it is so for Z' and Z''; therefore it will be enough if we complete the proof for the case when Z is a variety, which may be assumed to have the geometric projection U on U, since otherwise, by th. 6(ii) of Chap. VIII, §3, $Z(P)$ would be 0.

We first treat the case when $V = D$ and f is the projection from $U \times D$ to D; then, if z_i is the coordinate of Q_i, we have $Z(P) = \sum_i (z_i)$ and $F(P) = z_1 z_2 \cdots z_d$. Let π be the function, on the product $D^{(d)}$ of d factors equal to D, which is such that $\pi(x_1, \cdots, x_d) = x_1 x_2 \cdots x_d$ when none of the x_i is ∞. Using the corollary of prop. 14 of Chap. VIII, §4, and th. 2 above, and proceeding by induction on d, one sees at once that $\operatorname{div}(\pi)$ is the sum of the d distinct divisors obtained from $\Theta \times D^{(d-1)}$ by the permutations of the factors of $D^{(d)}$. On the other hand, consider on $D^{(d)}$ the 0-cycle of degree $d!$

$$Y(P) = \sum (z_{i_1}) \times \cdots \times (z_{i_d}),$$

where the sum is extended to the $d!$ permutations $(i_1, \cdots, i_d)$ of $(1, \cdots, d)$; by prop. 4 of Chap. VIII, §3, this is a rational cycle over $k(P)$, so that, by th. 6(iii) of Chap. VIII, §3, there is a rational cycle Y over k on $U \times D^{(d)}$, whose components all have the geometric projection U on U, such that

$$Y \cdot (P \times D^{(d)}) = P \times Y(P).$$

Moreover, by that same theorem, every component of Y has over $\bar{k}$ a generic point of the form $P \times (z_{i_1}) \times \cdots \times (z_{i_d})$; as none of the z_i is 0 or ∞, no component of Y is contained in any component of $U \times \operatorname{div}(\pi)$, so that, by prop. 5 of Chap. VIII, §3, Y and $U \times \operatorname{div}(\pi)$ intersect properly on $U \times D^{(d)}$. Now, e.g. by th. 7 of Chap. VIII, §3 (or by coroll. 2 of th. 8 of the same Chapter), we have

$$\mathrm{pr}_D[(Y(P) \times D) \cdot \Gamma_\pi] = d!(F(P))$$

where pr_D denotes the algebraic projection on the last factor of the product $D^{(d)} \times D$. From this, we get at once

$$\mathrm{pr}_{U \times D}[(P \times Y(P) \times D) \cdot (U \times \Gamma_\pi)] = d!(P \times F(P))$$

where $\mathrm{pr}_{U \times D}$ is the algebraic projection on the product of the first and last factors in $U \times D^{(d)} \times D$. By the definition of Y, this can also be written as

$$\mathrm{pr}_{U \times D}([(P \times D^{(d)} \times D) \cdot (Y \times D)] \cdot (U \times \Gamma_\pi)) = d!(P \times F(P)).$$

By prop. 5 of Chap. VIII, §3, $Y \times D$ and $U \times \Gamma_\pi$ intersect properly, and, by prop. 8 of Chap. VIII, §3, $P \times D^{(d)} \times D$ and $(Y \times D) \cdot (U \times \Gamma_\pi)$ also intersect properly on $U \times D^{(d)} \times D$; therefore the three cycles $P \times D^{(d)} \times D$, $Y \times D$ and $U \times \Gamma_\pi$ do so too. By associativity, then, i.e. by th. 4(iv) of Chap. VIII, §3, the last formula can be rewritten as

$$\mathrm{pr}_{U \times D}([(Y \times D) \cdot (U \times \Gamma_\pi)] \cdot (P \times D^{(d)} \times D)) = d!(P \times F(P)).$$

We can apply to the left-hand side the corollary of th. 6, Chap. VIII, §3; also, e.g. by th. 6 of Chap. VIII, §3 (or by coroll. 2 of th. 8 in the same Chapter), $\boldsymbol{P} \times F(\boldsymbol{P})$ is the same as $\boldsymbol{\Gamma}_F \cdot (\boldsymbol{P} \times \boldsymbol{D})$. This gives:

$$(\mathrm{pr}_{\boldsymbol{U}\times\boldsymbol{D}}[(\boldsymbol{Y} \times \boldsymbol{D}) \cdot (\boldsymbol{U} \times \boldsymbol{\Gamma}_\pi)]) \cdot (\boldsymbol{P} \times \boldsymbol{D}) = d!\boldsymbol{\Gamma}_F \cdot (\boldsymbol{P} \times \boldsymbol{D}).$$

If we put

$$\boldsymbol{S} = \mathrm{pr}_{\boldsymbol{U}\times\boldsymbol{D}}[(\boldsymbol{Y} \times \boldsymbol{D}) \cdot (\boldsymbol{U} \times \boldsymbol{\Gamma}_\pi)] - d!\boldsymbol{\Gamma}_F,$$

the last formula shows, in view of th. 6(ii) of Chap. VIII, §3, that every component $\boldsymbol{W}$ of $\boldsymbol{S}$ has on $\boldsymbol{U}$ a projection $\boldsymbol{W}'$ other than $\boldsymbol{U}$; as $\boldsymbol{W}$ has then at least the dimension of $\boldsymbol{W}' \times \boldsymbol{D}$ in which it is contained, this implies that $\boldsymbol{W} = \boldsymbol{W}' \times \boldsymbol{D}$; as this is true for every component of $\boldsymbol{S}$, we can write $\boldsymbol{S} = \boldsymbol{T} \times \boldsymbol{D}$, where $\boldsymbol{T}$ is a $\boldsymbol{U}$-divisor.

We are now in a position to apply prop. 10 of Chap. VIII, §4, to the three varieties $\boldsymbol{D}$, $\boldsymbol{D}^{(d)}$ and $\boldsymbol{U}$ and to the cycles $\boldsymbol{\Theta}$ on $\boldsymbol{D}$, $\boldsymbol{\Gamma}'_\pi$ on $\boldsymbol{D} \times \boldsymbol{D}^{(d)}$ and $\boldsymbol{Y}'$ on $\boldsymbol{D}^{(d)} \times \boldsymbol{U}$, where $\boldsymbol{Y}'$, according to the notations explained in Chap. VIII, §4, denotes the transform of $\boldsymbol{Y}$ when the two factors of $\boldsymbol{U} \times \boldsymbol{D}^{(d)}$ are interchanged, and $\boldsymbol{\Gamma}'_\pi$ is similarly defined. In fact, since $\boldsymbol{Y}$ intersects $\boldsymbol{U} \times \mathrm{div}(\pi)$ properly, it intersects properly both $\boldsymbol{U} \times \pi^{-1}(0)$ and $\boldsymbol{U} \times \pi^{-1}(\infty)$, so that $\boldsymbol{Y} \times \boldsymbol{D}$ intersects properly $\boldsymbol{U} \times \pi^{-1}(0) \times (0)$ and $\boldsymbol{U} \times \pi^{-1}(\infty) \times (\infty)$, and therefore also the cycle $(\boldsymbol{U} \times \boldsymbol{\Gamma}_\pi) \cdot (\boldsymbol{U} \times \boldsymbol{D}^{(d)} \times \boldsymbol{\Theta})$; as $\boldsymbol{U} \times \boldsymbol{\Gamma}_\pi$ and $\boldsymbol{U} \times \boldsymbol{D}^{(d)} \times \boldsymbol{\Theta}$ intersect properly, this implies that the three cycles $\boldsymbol{Y} \times \boldsymbol{D}$, $\boldsymbol{U} \times \boldsymbol{\Gamma}_\pi$ and $\boldsymbol{U} \times \boldsymbol{D}^{(d)} \times \boldsymbol{\Theta}$ intersect properly on $\boldsymbol{U} \times \boldsymbol{D}^{(d)} \times \boldsymbol{D}$; that was one of the conditions which had to be verified in order to apply prop. 10 of Chap. VIII, §4, as we have said; the other conditions are trivially satisfied in the present case. Using the fact that $\boldsymbol{S}$ can be written as $\boldsymbol{T} \times \boldsymbol{D}$, one gets now, by a trivial calculation:

$$\mathrm{pr}_{\boldsymbol{U}}[\boldsymbol{Y} \cdot (\boldsymbol{U} \times \mathrm{div}(\pi))] = d!\,\mathrm{div}(F).$$

The left-hand side is the sum of

$$\mathrm{pr}_{\boldsymbol{U}}[\boldsymbol{Y} \cdot (\boldsymbol{U} \times \boldsymbol{\Theta} \times \boldsymbol{D}^{(d-1)})]$$

and of the terms derived from that by substituting for $\boldsymbol{U} \times \boldsymbol{\Theta} \times \boldsymbol{D}^{(d-1)}$ its distinct transforms by the permutations of the last d factors in the product $\boldsymbol{U} \times \boldsymbol{D}^{(d)}$; as these permutations leave $\boldsymbol{Y}$ invariant, those d terms are equal, and we get

$$\mathrm{pr}_{\boldsymbol{U}}[\boldsymbol{Y} \cdot (\boldsymbol{U} \times \boldsymbol{\Theta} \times \boldsymbol{D}^{(d-1)})] = (d-1)!\,\mathrm{div}(F).$$

Using th. 8 of Chap. VIII, §3, we can rewrite the left-hand side as

$$\mathrm{pr}_{\boldsymbol{U}}[\boldsymbol{Y}_1 \cdot (\boldsymbol{U} \times \boldsymbol{\Theta})],$$

with $\boldsymbol{Y}_1 = \mathrm{pr}_{\boldsymbol{U}\times\boldsymbol{D}}\boldsymbol{Y}$, where $\mathrm{pr}_{\boldsymbol{U}\times\boldsymbol{D}}$ is the algebraic projection on the product of the first two factors in $\boldsymbol{U} \times \boldsymbol{D} \times \boldsymbol{D}^{(d-1)}$. Applying again the corollary of th. 6,

Chap. VIII, §3, we have

$$\begin{aligned} \boldsymbol{Y}_1\cdot(\boldsymbol{P}\times\boldsymbol{D}) &= \mathrm{pr}_{\boldsymbol{U}\times\boldsymbol{D}}[\boldsymbol{Y}\cdot(\boldsymbol{P}\times\boldsymbol{D}^{(d)})] = \mathrm{pr}_{\boldsymbol{U}\times\boldsymbol{D}}(\boldsymbol{P}\times\boldsymbol{Y}(\boldsymbol{P})) \\ &= \boldsymbol{P}\times\mathrm{pr}_{\boldsymbol{D}}\boldsymbol{Y}(\boldsymbol{P}) = (d-1)!(\boldsymbol{P}\times\sum_{i=1}^{d}(z_i)) \\ &= (d-1)!\boldsymbol{Z}\cdot(\boldsymbol{P}\times\boldsymbol{D}). \end{aligned}$$

Applying again th. 6(ii), Chap. VIII, §3, in the same manner as above, we see that $\boldsymbol{Y}_1-(d-1)!\,\boldsymbol{Z}$ must be of the form $\boldsymbol{R}\times\boldsymbol{D}$, where $\boldsymbol{R}$ is a $\boldsymbol{U}$-divisor. This gives finally

$$\mathrm{pr}_{\boldsymbol{U}}[\boldsymbol{Z}\cdot(\boldsymbol{U}\times\boldsymbol{\Theta})] = \mathrm{div}(F),$$

which completes the proof in the special case which we have been considering. In view of what was said above, this shows that, if $\boldsymbol{V}=\boldsymbol{D}$ and if f is the projection from $\boldsymbol{U}\times\boldsymbol{D}$ to $\boldsymbol{D}$, our theorem is true for all $(\boldsymbol{U}\times\boldsymbol{D})$-divisors $\boldsymbol{Z}$ intersecting $\mathrm{div}(f)=\boldsymbol{U}\times\boldsymbol{\Theta}$ properly on $\boldsymbol{U}\times\boldsymbol{D}$.

Now we return to the general case, assuming, as explained above, that $\boldsymbol{Z}^n$ is a simple subvariety of $\boldsymbol{U}\times\boldsymbol{V}$, with the geometric projection $\boldsymbol{U}$ on $\boldsymbol{U}$, and complete over every point of $\boldsymbol{U}$. Put

$$\boldsymbol{X} = \mathrm{pr}_{\boldsymbol{U}\times\boldsymbol{D}}[\boldsymbol{\Gamma}_f\cdot(\boldsymbol{Z}\times\boldsymbol{D})];$$

then we have, by the corollary of th. 6, Chap. VIII, §3:

$$\boldsymbol{X}\cdot(\boldsymbol{P}\times\boldsymbol{D}) = \mathrm{pr}_{\boldsymbol{U}\times\boldsymbol{D}}([\boldsymbol{\Gamma}_f\cdot(\boldsymbol{Z}\times\boldsymbol{D})]\cdot(\boldsymbol{P}\times\boldsymbol{V}\times\boldsymbol{D})).$$

Acording to our usual notation, we write $\boldsymbol{P}\times\boldsymbol{X}(\boldsymbol{P})$ for the left-hand side; on the other hand, we see, just as above, that $\boldsymbol{\Gamma}_f$, $\boldsymbol{Z}\times\boldsymbol{D}$ and $\boldsymbol{P}\times\boldsymbol{V}\times\boldsymbol{D}$ intersect properly on $\boldsymbol{U}\times\boldsymbol{V}\times\boldsymbol{D}$, so that we get, by associativity:

$$\begin{aligned} \boldsymbol{P}\times\boldsymbol{X}(\boldsymbol{P}) &= \mathrm{pr}_{\boldsymbol{U}\times\boldsymbol{D}}[\boldsymbol{\Gamma}_f\cdot(\boldsymbol{P}\times\boldsymbol{Z}(\boldsymbol{P})\times\boldsymbol{D})] \\ &= \sum_{i=1}^{d}\mathrm{pr}_{\boldsymbol{U}\times\boldsymbol{D}}[\boldsymbol{\Gamma}_f\cdot(\boldsymbol{P}\times\boldsymbol{Q}_i\times\boldsymbol{D})], \end{aligned}$$

and therefore, by th. 7 of Chap. VIII, §3, since f is defined at $\boldsymbol{P}\times\boldsymbol{Q}_i$:

$$\boldsymbol{X}(\boldsymbol{P}) = \sum_{i=1}^{d}(f(\boldsymbol{P},\boldsymbol{Q}_i)).$$

Now, since $\boldsymbol{Z}$ intersects $\mathrm{div}(f)$ properly, it intersects $f^{-1}(0)$ and $f^{-1}(\infty)$ properly, so that $\boldsymbol{Z}\times\boldsymbol{D}$ intersects $f^{-1}(0)\times(0)$ and $f^{-1}(\infty)\times(\infty)$, hence also $\boldsymbol{\Gamma}_f\cdot(\boldsymbol{U}\times\boldsymbol{V}\times\boldsymbol{\Theta})$ properly. From this, one concludes at once that the three cycles $\boldsymbol{Z}\times\boldsymbol{D}$, $\boldsymbol{\Gamma}_f$ and $\boldsymbol{U}\times\boldsymbol{V}\times\boldsymbol{\Theta}$, as well as the two cycles $\boldsymbol{\Gamma}_f\cdot(\boldsymbol{Z}\times\boldsymbol{D})$ and $\boldsymbol{U}\times\boldsymbol{V}\times\boldsymbol{\Theta}$, intersect properly on $\boldsymbol{U}\times\boldsymbol{V}\times\boldsymbol{D}$. In view of the assumptions in our theorem, we can now apply th. 8 of Chap. VIII, §3, to $\boldsymbol{X}\cdot(\boldsymbol{U}\times\boldsymbol{\Theta})$; this gives:

$$\boldsymbol{X}\cdot(\boldsymbol{U}\times\boldsymbol{\Theta}) = \mathrm{pr}_{\boldsymbol{U}\times\boldsymbol{D}}([\boldsymbol{\Gamma}_f\cdot(\boldsymbol{Z}\times\boldsymbol{D})]\cdot(\boldsymbol{U}\times\boldsymbol{V}\times\boldsymbol{\Theta})).$$

Applying th. 4(iv) of Chap. VIII, §3 (the associativity formula) to the cycles $\mathbf{\Gamma}_f$, $\mathbf{Z} \times \mathbf{D}$ and $\mathbf{U} \times \mathbf{V} \times \mathbf{\Theta}$, and applying to $\mathbf{X}$ and the projection from $\mathbf{U} \times \mathbf{D}$ to $\mathbf{D}$ the special case of our theorem which has been treated above, we get:

$$\begin{aligned}\operatorname{div}(F) &= \mathrm{pr}_{\mathbf{U}}([\mathbf{\Gamma}_f \cdot (\mathbf{U} \times \mathbf{V} \times \mathbf{\Theta})] \cdot (\mathbf{Z} \times \mathbf{D}))\\ &= \mathrm{pr}_{\mathbf{U}}([f^{-1}(0) \times (0)] \cdot (\mathbf{Z} \times \mathbf{D})) - \mathrm{pr}_{\mathbf{U}}([f^{-1}(\infty) \times (\infty)] \cdot (\mathbf{Z} \times \mathbf{D}))\\ &= \mathrm{pr}_{\mathbf{U}}[\operatorname{div}(f) \cdot \mathbf{Z}],\end{aligned}$$

which completes the proof.

3. Some auxiliary results. We group together here some results (most of which could have been given immediately after Chap. V) which will be needed in §§4–5.

PROPOSITION 4. *Let V be a variety in an affine space, P a simple point of V, and L the tangent linear variety to V at P; let L' be any linear subvariety of L, containing P; let k be a field of definition for V, P and L'. Then there is a subvariety V' of V, defined over k, having P as a simple point, and whose tangent linear variety at P is L'.*

Let the $F_i(X) = 0$ be a minimal set of linear equations for L, with coefficients in k; then there is a minimal set of linear equations for L' with coefficients in k, consisting of the $F_i(X) = 0$ and of some further equations $G_j(X) = 0$; and, if M is the linear variety defined by the equations $G_j(X) = 0$ alone, M is transversal to L, and we have $L' = L \cap M$. By the criterion of multiplicity 1 (or by prop. 21 of Chap. V, §3), there is one and only one component V' of $V \cap M$ which contains P; as every conjugate of V' over k must then have the same property, this implies that V' has no conjugate over k, other than itself. Moreover, by the same result, V' is proper and of multiplicity 1 in $V \cap M$, and it has a simple point at P; as the cycle $V \cdot M$ is rational over k, this implies that V' has the coefficient 1 in the prime rational cycle over k which has V' as one of its components; therefore, by prop. 1 of Chap. VIII, §1, V' is defined over k. Finally, by prop. 23 of Chap. IV, §6, the tangent linear variety to V' at P must be contained in L and in M, hence in L'; as V' is proper in $V \cap M$, it has the same dimension as L'; therefore its tangent linear variety at P is L'.

PROPOSITION 5. *Let V^r be a variety defined over a field k in S^N. Put*

$$L_i(X) = \sum_{j=1}^{N} u_{ij} X_j \qquad (1 \leqq i \leqq n)$$

where $n > r$ and where the u_{ij} are nN independent variables over k. Let (x) be a generic point of V over $K = k(u)$, and let (x') be a point of S^N whose dimension over k is $\leqq n - r - 1$; put $y_i = L_i(x)$ and $y'_i = L_i(x')$ for $1 \leqq i \leqq n$. Then no specialization of (x, y) over K can be of the form (x'', y') with $(x'') \neq (x')$; moreover, one can choose, from among the $L_i(X)$, $r + 1$ forms whose $(r + 1)N$ coefficients are independent variables over $k(x')$.

Assume that (x'', y') is a specialization of (x, y) over K and that $x''_h \neq x'_h$ for some value of h. By prop. 24 of Chap. II, §5, (x'') must be finite; that being so, the relations $y_i = L_i(x)$ imply $y'_i = L_i(x'')$, which can also be written $L_i(x'' - x') = 0$, or again, since $x''_h \neq x'_h$:

$$u_{ih} = -\sum_{j \neq h} u_{ij}(x''_j - x'_j)/(x''_h - x'_h).$$

Here (x'') has at most the dimension r over k, since it is a specialization of (x) over K, hence also over k; and (x') has at most the dimension $n - r - 1$ over k; therefore these relations imply that $(u_{1h}, \cdots, u_{nh})$ has at most the dimension $n - 1$ over the field generated over k by the u_{ij} for $j \neq h$. This contradicts the assumption that the u_{ij} are independent variables over k. Now assume that one can find, among the $L_i(X)$, s forms, say $L_1(X), \cdots, L_s(X)$, whose coefficients are independent variables over $k(x')$, but not $s + 1$ forms with that property; let K' be the field generated over $k(x')$ by the u_{ij} for $1 \leqq i \leqq s$; this has the dimension sN over $k(x')$, hence at most the dimension $sN + n - r - 1$ over k. Then, for $s + 1 \leqq i \leqq n$, $(u_{i1}, \cdots, u_{iN})$ has at most the dimension $N - 1$ over K'; therefore $K(x')$ has at most the dimension

$$sN + n - r - 1 + (n - s)(N - 1) = nN + s - r - 1$$

over k; as this must be at least nN, we have $s \geqq r + 1$.

Let now $L_1(X), \cdots, L_n(X)$ be n linearly independent forms in $X_1, \cdots, X_N$, with coefficients in a field k; call λ the linear mapping of S^N into S^n, rational over k, which maps every point (x) of S^N onto the point (y) given by $y_i = L_i(x)$ for $1 \leqq i \leqq n$. Take $N - n$ linear forms $M_1(X), \cdots, M_{N-n}(X)$ in $k[X]$, such that the N forms $L_i(X)$, $M_\nu(X)$ are linearly independent; call α the linear isomorphism of S^N onto $S^n \times S^{N-n}$, rational over k, which maps every point (x) of S^N onto the point (y, z) given by $y_i = L_i(x)$, $z_\nu = M_\nu(x)$; if p is the projection from $S^n \times S^{N-n}$ to S^n, we have $\lambda = p \circ \alpha$. Let L be the linear variety defined in S^N by the equations $L_i(X) = 0$ $(1 \leqq i \leqq n)$; this is the image of $(0) \times S^{N-n}$ by α^{-1}; and, if (x) is any point of S^N, the image of $\lambda(x) \times S^{N-n}$ by α^{-1} is the linear variety, parallel to L, going through (x). Assume now that (x) is a generic point over k of a variety V defined over k in S^N; put $W = \alpha(V)$, and let W' be the geometric projection of W on S^n, which is the same as the geometric image of V by λ; also, let Z be the image of $W' \times S^{N-n}$ by α^{-1}. If (u) is a generic point of L over $k(x)$, its image $\alpha(u) = (0, v)$ by α is a generic point of $(0) \times S^{N-n}$ over $k(x)$; also, if we put $\alpha(x) = (y, z)$, hence $\lambda(x) = (y)$, $(y, z + v)$ is generic over $k(x)$ on $(y) \times S^{N-n}$ and over k on $W' \times S^{N-n}$; therefore the locus of $(x + u)$ over $k(x)$ is the linear variety parallel to L through (x), and its locus over k is Z; in particular, if (x') is any point of V and (u') any point of L, $(x' + u')$, being a specialization of $(x + u)$ over k, is in Z. This shows that Z contains the union of the linear varieties, parallel to L, which go through the points of V. More precisely, it is the closure of that union; in fact, if Z_1 is that closure, and if K is a common field of definition, containing k, for all the components of Z_1, then, taking for (x) a generic point of V over K, and for (u) a generic point of L over $K(x)$, we see that Z_1 must contain $(x + u)$, hence its locus Z over K; as Z_1 is clearly contained in Z, this gives $Z = Z_1$. In particular, this shows that Z depends only upon V and L; Z will be called *the projecting cylinder of V in the direction of L* (or of any linear variety parallel to L), or also *in the direction determined by the equations $L_i(X) = 0$.* If $\mathfrak{P}$ is the ideal in $k[X]$ defining V over k, and if σ is the isomorphism of $k[Y, Z]$ onto $k[X]$ over k which maps Y_i onto $L_i(X)$ and Z_ν onto $M_\nu(X)$ for all i, ν, then the ideal $\mathfrak{Q}$ in $k[Y, Z]$ which defines $W = \alpha(V)$ over k is the transform of $\mathfrak{P}$ by σ^{-1}, and the ideal defining W' over k is $\mathfrak{Q}' = \mathfrak{Q} \cap k[Y]$. If the $F_\rho(Y)$ are a basis for $\mathfrak{Q}'$, i.e. if W' is defined over k in S^n by the equations $F_\rho(Y) = 0$, then this same set of equations defines $W' \times S^{N-n}$ in $S^n \times S^{N-n}$, so that Z is defined in S^N by the transform of that set by σ, i.e. by the equations

$$F_\rho(L_1(X), \cdots, L_n(X)) = 0.$$

PROPOSITION 6. *Let V be a variety defined over k in $S^n \times S^m$, with the projection V' on S^n. Let (x, y) be a generic point of V over k; let $(\bar{x}, \bar{y})$ be a simple point of V such that (y) has no other specialization than $(\bar{y})$ over $(x) \to (\bar{x})$ with reference to k. Then the projection from V to V' is regular at $(\bar{x})$ if and only if one can choose, from among the forms $X_1, \cdots, X_n$, a uniformizing set of linear forms for V at $(\bar{x}, \bar{y})$.*

Th. 14 of Chap. IV, §6, shows that our condition is necessary. In order to prove the converse, we may assume, after reordering the coordinates if necessary, that $X_1, \cdots, X_r$ is a uniformizing set of linear forms for V at $(\bar{x}, \bar{y})$, r being the dimension of V. Call L^{n-r} the linear variety defined in S^n by the equations $X_i - \bar{x}_i = 0$ $(1 \leq i \leq r)$; we will first show that $(\bar{x})$ is a proper point of intersection of V' and L. As (y) is finite over $(x) \to (\bar{x})$ with reference to k, prop. 22 of Chap. II, §5, shows that V and V' have the same dimension. Let now W' be a component of $V' \cap L$, containing $(\bar{x})$; let K be a field of definition for L, containing k; let (x') be a generic point of W' over $\bar{K}$. As (x') is in V', it is a specialization of (x) over k, so that there is a specialization (y') of (y) over $(x) \to (x')$ with reference to k. As $(\bar{x})$ is in W', it is a specialization of (x') over $\bar{K}$, so that there is a specialization $(\bar{y}')$ of (y') over $(x') \to (\bar{x})$ with reference to $\bar{K}$. Then $(\bar{y}')$ is a specialization of (y) over $(x) \to (\bar{x})$ with reference to k; by our assumptions, this implies that $(\bar{y}') = (\bar{y})$; therefore (y') must be finite, so that (x', y') is a point of V, whose locus W over $\bar{K}$ is then contained in V. As the projection W' of W on S^n is contained in L, W is contained in $L \times S^m$. The definition of L implies that this is transversal to V at $(\bar{x}, \bar{y})$; therefore, by the criterion of multiplicity 1 (or by prop. 7 of Chap. V, §1), $(\bar{x}, \bar{y})$ is a proper component of $V \cap (L \times S^m)$; as $(\bar{x}, \bar{y})$ is in W, this shows that W is reduced to $(\bar{x}, \bar{y})$, hence W' to $(\bar{x})$, as we had asserted. We can now apply prop. 11 of Chap. V, §1, to V, V', L and $(\bar{x})$; in the final formula of that proposition, the right-hand side has here the value 1 (by the criterion of multiplicity 1, or again by prop. 7 of Chap. V, §1); the left-hand side is equal to $[V : V'] \cdot \mu$, with

$\mu = j(V' \cdot L, (\bar{x}))$. This gives $[V:V'] = 1$, i.e. $k(x, y) = k(x)$, and also $\mu = 1$, which, by the criterion of multiplicity 1 (or by prop. 20 of Chap. V, §3) implies that $(\bar{x})$ is simple on V'. As (y) is finite over $(x) \to (\bar{x})$ with reference to k, our conclusion follows now from th. 5 of Chap. V, §3.

Corollary 1. *Let V be a variety defined over k in S^N; let M be a generic point of V over k, and P a simple point of V. Let $L_1(X), \cdots, L_n(X)$ be n linearly independent linear forms in $k[X]$; let λ be the linear mapping of S^N onto S^n given by $\lambda(x) = (L_1(x), \cdots, L_n(x))$ for every point (x) of S^N. Put $M' = \lambda(M)$, $P' = \lambda(P)$, and assume that M has no other specialization than P over $M' \to P'$ with reference to k. Then the following three assertions are equivalent:* (a) *λ induces on V a birational mapping of V into its geometric image by λ, and this mapping is biregular at P;* (b) *there is, among the $L_i(X)$, a uniformizing set of linear forms for V at P;* (c) *call L the linear variety through P, parallel to the linear variety defined by the equations $L_i(X) = 0$ $(1 \leqq i \leqq n)$; then, to every curve C on V, having a simple point at P, there is a linear variety containing L, of codimension 1 in S^N, which is transversal to C at P.*

After performing a suitable linear change of coordinates with coefficients in k, we may assume that the $L_i(X)$ are $X_1, \cdots, X_n$; then λ is the projection from $S^N = S^n \times S^{N-n}$ to S^n, and the assertion that (a) and (b) are equivalent is nothing else than prop. 6. Let T be the tangent linear variety to V at P; one sees at once that (b) is equivalent to: (b′) $L \cap T = P$. Also, in view of prop. 4, (c) is equivalent to the following: (c′) if D is any linear variety of dimension 1, contained in T and containing P, there is a linear variety E of codimension 1 in S^N, containing L and transversal to D. For a given D, the latter assertion holds if and only if D is not contained in L; this shows at once that (c′) is equivalent to (b′).

Corollary 2. *Let V^r be a variety defined over k in S^N. Put*

$$L_i(X) = \sum_{j=1}^{N} u_{ij} X_j \qquad (1 \leqq i \leqq n)$$

where $r < n \leqq N$ and where the u_{ij} are nN independent variables over k. Let λ be the linear mapping of S^N onto S^n given by $\lambda(x) = (L_1(x), \cdots, L_n(x))$ for every point (x) of S^N. Then λ induces on V a birational mapping of V into its geometric image by λ; and this mapping is biregular at every simple subvariety of V which is defined over k and at most of dimension $n - r - 1$.

Assume that W is such a variety, and let (x), (x') be generic points of V and of W, respectively, over $K = k(u)$; then prop. 5 shows that V, (x), (x'), the $L_i(X)$, and the field K satisfy the assumptions in coroll. 1, and also that they satisfy condition (b) in that corollary; therefore they also satisfy (a). Now let again (x) be generic over $K = k(u)$ on V; put $k' = k(x)$, $K' = K(x)$, and call W the variety reduced to the point (x); then V, the $L_i(X)$, W and k' satisfy all the assumptions in coroll. 2, so that, by what we have just proved, λ induces on V a birational mapping into its image. This completes the proof.

One should note that a somewhat less comprehensive result (expressed in other terms) had already been obtained in the course of the proof of th. 5, Chap. V, §3.

COROLLARY 3. *Let V^r be a variety defined over k in S^N; let the $L_i(X)$ be as in coroll.* 2, *and let $Z_{(u)}$ be the projecting cylinder of V in the direction determined by the equations $L_i(X) = 0$. Then $Z_{(u)}$ is birationally equivalent to $V \times S^{N-n}$ over $k(u)$; moreover, if P is any point of $Z_{(u)}$ of dimension d over k and of dimension d' over $k(u)$, and if $d - d' \leqq n - r - 1$, P is in V.*

By the definition of the projecting cylinder, $Z_{(u)}$ is birationally equivalent over $k(u)$ to the product of S^{N-n} and of the geometric image of V by the mapping λ defined in coroll. 2, so that our first assertion follows at once from coroll. 2. Now let P, d and d' be as in the second part of our corollary; let k' be the field generated over k by a maximal set of independent variables over $k(u)$ from among the coordinates of P; then k' has the dimension d' over k, $k'(P)$ has the dimension $d - d'$ over k', and k' and $k(u)$ are independent extensions of k. Put $K' = k'(u)$, $P = (x')$, and let $M = (x)$ be a generic point of V over K'; also, let again λ be as in coroll. 2. To say that P is in $Z_{(u)}$ is the same as to say that $\lambda(P)$ is in the geometric image of V by λ, i.e. that $\lambda(P)$ is a specialization of $\lambda(M)$ over K'; then this can be extended to a specialization (x'') of $M = (x)$ over K', which, by prop. 5, can be no other than (x'); therefore (x') is in V.

COROLLARY 4. *Let assumptions and notations be as in coroll.* 3; *then V is the intersection of the cylinders $Z_{(u)}$ when one takes for (u) all the sets of nN independent variables over k.*

In fact, by coroll. 3, if a point P is not in V, it cannot be in $Z_{(u)}$ when one takes for (u) a set of nN independent variables over $k(P)$, since in that case we have $d = d'$.

COROLLARY 5. *Let assumptions and notations be as in coroll.* 3; *then V is a linear variety if and only if $Z_{(u)}$ is a linear variety.*

The definitions show at once that the projecting cylinder of a linear variety in any direction is a linear variety. Also, if (u) and (u') are two sets of nN independent variables over k, $Z_{(u')}$ is the transform of $Z_{(u)}$ by the isomorphism of $k(u)$ onto $k(u')$ over k which maps u_{ij} onto u'_{ij} for all i, j; therefore, if $Z_{(u)}$ is a linear variety, so is $Z_{(u')}$; then coroll. 4 shows that V is an intersection of linear varieties, so that it is a linear variety.

PROPOSITION 7. *Let U^n be a variety in S^N and V a subvariety of U, both defined over k; let (x) be a generic point of V over k and (x') a simple point of U; let $L_1(X), \cdots, L_n(X)$ be a uniformizing set of linear forms for U at (x'), with coefficients in k, and let Z be the projecting cylinder of V in the direction determined by the equations $L_i(X) = 0$. Put $y_i = L_i(x)$ and $y'_i = L_i(x')$ for $1 \leqq i \leqq n$. Then:* (i) *if (x, y) has no specialization over k of the form (x'', y') with $(x'') \neq (x')$, (x') is not in any component of $U \cap Z$ other than V;* (ii) *if (x') is in V, V is a proper component of multiplicity* 1 *of $U \cap Z$.*

Put

$$M = (x), M' = (y), P = (x'), P' = (y').$$

After performing a suitable linear transformation on the coordinates in S^N, with coefficients in k, we may assume that the $L_i(X)$ are $X_1, \cdots, X_n$; if then we regard S^N as the product $S^n \times S^m$ with $m = N - n$, M' and P' are the projections of M and P on S^n; moreover, if V' is the geometric projection of V on S^n, we have $Z = V' \times S^m$. Assume that P is contained in a component X of $U \cap Z$ and that $X \neq V$; as V is contained in $U \cap Z$, X cannot be contained in V. Let N be a generic point of X over $\bar{k}$, and N' its projection on S^n; then N is not in V, while N' must be in V', which means that it is a specialization of M' over k. Let N_1 be any specialization of M over $M' \rightarrow N'$ with reference to k; as N is not in V, we have $N \neq N_1$. As P is in X, it is a specialization of N over $\bar{k}$, so that P' is a specialization of N' over $\bar{k}$. Let P_1 be any specialization of N_1 over $N' \rightarrow P'$ with reference to $\bar{k}$; P_1 is then a specialization of M over $M' \rightarrow P'$ with reference to k; if now we assume, as in (i), that there is no such specialization other than P, we must have $P_1 = P$, which implies in particular that N_1 is finite, hence that it is a point of V; moreover, as P is a specialization of N_1 over $\bar{k}$, prop. 25 of Chap. IV, §6, shows that $X_1, \cdots, X_n$ is a uniformizing set of linear forms for U at N_1, which is the same as to say that U is transversal to $N' \times S^m$ at N_1. Now let Q be a generic point of U over k, with the projection Q' on S^n; by prop. 24 of Chap. IV, §6, and th. 3 of Chap. V, §1, Q is separably algebraic over $k(Q')$, and a complete set of intersections of U and of the linear variety $Q' \times S^m$ is nothing else than a complete set of conjugates of Q over $k(Q')$. Consider a specialization of that complete set over $Q \rightarrow N$ with reference to k; this specialization contains N by definition; on the other hand, after the removal of the non-finite specializations in it, it is by definition a complete set of intersections of U and of the linear variety $N' \times S^m$; as such, by prop. 7 of Chap. V, §1, it must include N_1 once (and only once). Take now a specialization of this complete set over $N \rightarrow P$ with reference to $\bar{k}$; this includes P at least twice, firstly as the specialization of N, and secondly as the specialization of N_1, since it has been shown that N_1 has no other specialization than P over $N' \rightarrow P'$ with reference to $\bar{k}$. On the other hand, by prop. 7 of Chap. V, §1, it cannot include P more than once, since, after the removal of non-finite specializations, it must become a complete set of intersections of U and $P' \times S^m$, and these are transversal to each other at P. This proves (i). Now assume, as in (ii), that P is in V, i.e. that it is a specialization of M over k; as above, we see that U must then be transversal at M to the linear variety $M' \times S^m$, hence also to every linear variety containing $M' \times S^m$; in particular, if T' is the tangent linear variety to V' at M', U is transversal at M to $T' \times S^m$, which is the tangent linear variety to $Z = V' \times S^m$ at M. Therefore, by the criterion of multiplicity 1 (th. 6 of Chap. VI, §2), there is only one component V_1 of $U \cap Z$ which contains M, and it is proper and of multiplicity 1; as it is proper, it has the same dimension as V'. As V contains M

and is contained in $U \cap Z$, it is contained in V_1; as it has at least the same dimension as V', hence also as V_1, we have $V = V_1$, which completes the proof of (ii).

COROLLARY. *Let U^n be a variety in S^N and V^r a simple subvariety of U, both defined over k. Put $L_i(X) = \sum_{j=1}^N u_{ij}X_j$ for $1 \leqq i \leqq n$, where the u_{ij} are nN independent variables over k; let Z be the projecting cylinder of V in the direction determined by the equations $L_i(X) = 0$. Then V is a proper component of multiplicity 1 of $U \cap Z$ in S^N; every component of $U \cap Z$ is proper and is a simple subvariety of U; and no simple subvariety of U, defined over k, is contained in the support of $U \cdot Z - V$.*

If $V = U$, the definition of the projecting cylinder, together with prop. 24 of Chap. II, §5, shows that $Z = S^N$, hence $U \cdot Z = U$; our assertions are then trivially true. Now assume that $V \neq U$, i.e. $r < n$; then, by coroll. 3 of prop. 6, Z has the dimension $r + N - n$, and prop. 7(ii), applied to U, V, the $L_i(X)$, the field $K = k(u)$, and a generic point (x') of V over K, shows that V is proper and of multiplicity 1 in $U \cap Z$. Now let X be a component of $U \cap Z$, other than V; let P be a generic point of X over $\bar{K}$; P is not in V, since otherwise X would be contained in V. Let d' be the dimension of X, which is also the dimension of P over K; let d be the dimension of P over k. As P is in U, we have $d \leqq n$; as P is not in V, we have, by coroll. 3 of prop. 6,

$$d' \leqq d - n + r \leqq r,$$

which (by coroll. 1 of th. 1, Chap. VI, §1) implies that $d' = r$, i.e. that X is proper; then we must have $d = n$, so that P is generic over k on U, hence simple on U; this shows that X is simple on U. In order to prove the last assertion in our corollary, we have to show that X cannot contain a simple subvariety W of U, defined over k; this follows at once from prop. 5 applied to V, to a generic point (x') of W over $k(u)$, to the $L_i(X)$ and to the field $k' = k(x')$, and from prop. 7(i) applied to U, V, $K' = k'(u)$, to the $L_i(X)$ and to (x').

4. Qualitative theory of divisors. We need now an explicit knowledge of the divisors of functions in an affine space. If (x) is a generic point of S^n over a field k, and F a polynomial in $k[X]$, the function on S^n, rational over k, with the value $F(x)$ at (x), is everywhere defined and finite in S^n; its value at any point (x') of S^n is $F(x')$; by abuse of language, one makes no distinction between this function and the polynomial F. Similarly, let $R(X) = F(X)/G(X)$ be a rational expression in the X_i, F and G being mutually prime polynomials in $k[X]$; the function, rational over k, with the value $R(x)$ at (x) is defined and finite at every point (x') of S^n where $G(x') \neq 0$ and has the value $R(x')$ at that point; it is defined and has the value ∞ at (x') whenever $G(x') = 0$ and $F(x') \neq 0$; as above, we will make no distinction between this function and the rational expression R.

THEOREM 5. *Let k be a field; let (x) be a point of S^n, of dimension $n - 1$ over* *k, and let* $F(X) = 0$ *be the irreducible equation for* (x) *over* k. *Then* $\mathrm{div}(F)$ *is the prime rational divisor over* k *in* S^n *with the generic point* (x) *over* k.

Let A be that prime rational divisor; its support is the k-closure of (x); by th. 1, Chap. VII, §1, this is the set of zeros of F; by th. 1 of §2, this is also the support of $F^{-1}(0)$, and, by the same theorem, we have $F^{-1}(\infty) = 0$. As $\mathrm{div}(F)$ is rational over k, this shows that we must have $\mathrm{div}(F) = a \cdot A$, where a is an integer. Let V be the locus of (x) over $\bar{k}$. Let us first consider the case when V itself is rational over k, so that we have $A = V$; then $k(x)$ is separably generated over k, so that, by th. 2 of Chap. I, §5, one of the partial derivatives $\partial F/\partial x_i$ is not 0; by the criterion of multiplicity 1 (th. 6 of Chap. VI, §2), this implies that $V \times (0)$ has the multiplicity 1 in the intersection of the graph of F and of the variety $S^n \times (0)$ in $S^n \times \boldsymbol{D}$, since, by restricting these varieties to $S^n \times D_1 = S^{n+1}$, we get the varieties respectively defined in S^{n+1} by the equations $F(X_1, \cdots, X_n) - X_{n+1} = 0$ and $X_{n+1} = 0$. Therefore, in the present case, V has the coefficient 1 in $\mathrm{div}(F)$; this gives $\mathrm{div}(F) = V$, as asserted. Now consider the general case; put $q = [k(x):k]_\iota$, so that q is the coefficient of V in A; call $H(X) = 0$ the irreducible equation for (x) over $\bar{k}$, which is also the equation for V; by what we have just proved, we have $\mathrm{div}(H) = V$. By prop. 29 of Chap. I, §8, we have $F = H^q \cdot F'$, with F' in $\bar{k}[X]$ and such that $F'(x) \neq 0$; by th. 1 of §2, this implies that V is not a component of $\mathrm{div}(F')$; therefore the coefficient of V in $\mathrm{div}(F)$ is q. This proves that $a = 1$.

COROLLARY. *Let* k *be a field, and* Z *a rational divisor over* k *in* S^n. *Then there is a function* F *on* S^n, *rational over* k, *such that* $\mathrm{div}(F) = Z$; *it is uniquely determined up to a constant factor; and it is a polynomial if and only if* $Z > 0$.

Put $Z = \sum_\nu a_\nu A_\nu$, where the A_ν are prime rational divisors over k, and the a_ν are integers; by th. 5, there is, for each ν, an irreducible polynomial F_ν in $k[X]$ such that $\mathrm{div}(F_\nu) = A_\nu$; then the function $F = \prod_\nu (F_\nu)^{a_\nu}$ has the divisor $\mathrm{div}(F) = Z$; and, if all the a_ν are $\geqq 0$, F is a polynomial. In order to prove the unicity, it is enough to show that, if F is such that $\mathrm{div}(F) = 0$, it is a constant. By th. 1 of §2, if $\mathrm{div}(F) = 0$, both F and $1/F$ are everywhere defined and finite on S^n; if F is rational over k, and (x) is generic over k in S^n, coroll. 2 of th. 2, Chap. VII, §2, shows that $F(x)$ and $1/F(x)$ must then both be in $k[x]$, so that F is a polynomial in $k[X]$ and that there is a polynomial G in $k[X]$ for which $1/F(x) = G(x)$, hence $1 = F(x)G(x)$. As (x) is generic over k in S^n, this implies that $1 = F(X)G(X)$, so that F and G are constants.

THEOREM 6. *Let* $\boldsymbol{U}$ *be a variety, rational over a field* k; *let* $\boldsymbol{A}$ *be a prime rational divisor over* k *on* $\boldsymbol{U}$. *Then there is a function* f *on* $\boldsymbol{U}$, *rational over* k, *such that* $\mathrm{div}(f) = \boldsymbol{A} + \boldsymbol{B}$, *where* $\boldsymbol{B}$ *is a divisor without any common component with* $\boldsymbol{A}$.

By the principle of localization, it is enough to deal with the case when $\boldsymbol{U}$ is a variety in an affine space S^N. Let F be a function in S^N, defined by a polynomial in $k[X]$; then, if f is the function induced on $\boldsymbol{U}$ by F, we see, by th. 3 of

§2, that each component of $\boldsymbol{A}$ has the same coefficient in $\mathrm{div}(f)$ as in $\boldsymbol{U}\cdot\mathrm{div}(F)$. In view of the corollary of th. 5, our theorem will therefore be proved if we show that there is a divisor $\boldsymbol{Z}$ in S^N, rational over k, intersecting $\boldsymbol{U}$ properly in S^N, and such that $\boldsymbol{U}\cdot\boldsymbol{Z}$ is of the form $\boldsymbol{A}+\boldsymbol{B}$, where $\boldsymbol{B}$ has no common component with $\boldsymbol{A}$. In fact, let n be the dimension of $\boldsymbol{U}$, and let M be a generic point of $\boldsymbol{A}$ over k; after reordering the coordinates if necessary, we may assume that $X_1, \cdots, X_n$ are a uniformizing set of linear forms for $\boldsymbol{U}$ at M. Let V be the locus of M over $\bar{k}$, and put $q = [k(M):k]_\iota$; then we have $\boldsymbol{A} = q\cdot A_1$, where A_1 is the sum of all the distinct conjugates of V over k. Let M' be the projection of M on S^n when S^N is regarded as the product $S^n \times S^m$ with $m = N - n$; let V' be the locus of M' over $\bar{k}$, i.e. the geometric projection of V on S^n; let A' be the prime rational cycle in S^n with the generic point M' over k; this is equal to $q'\cdot A_1'$, where $q' = [k(M'):k]_\iota$, and A_1' is the sum of the distinct conjugates of V' over k. As the projecting cylinder of V, in the direction determined by the equations $X_i = 0$ for $1 \leqq i \leqq n$, is $V' \times S^m$, prop. 7(ii) of §3 shows that V is a proper component of multiplicity 1 in $\boldsymbol{U} \cap (V' \times S^m)$; a comparison of the dimensions shows then that $V' \times S^m$ is of codimension 1 in S^N and that it does not contain $\boldsymbol{U}$; then no conjugate of $V' \times S^m$ over k can contain $\boldsymbol{U}$, so that, by prop. 5 of Chap. VIII, §3, $A' \times S^m$ intersects $\boldsymbol{U}$ properly in S^N. The cycle $\boldsymbol{U}\cdot(A' \times S^m)$ is rational over k; as V has in it the coefficient q', and as $q' \leqq q$ by prop. 27 of Chap. I, §8, this implies that $q' = q$ and that $\boldsymbol{U}\cdot(A' \times S^m)$ is of the form $\boldsymbol{A}+\boldsymbol{B}$, where $\boldsymbol{B}$ is a rational cycle over k, such that V is not a component of $\boldsymbol{B}$. But then no conjugate of V over k can be a component of $\boldsymbol{B}$; this completes the proof.

THEOREM 7. *Let $\boldsymbol{U}$ be a variety, defined over a field k; let f be a function on $\boldsymbol{U}$, rational over a field K containing k, and everywhere defined and finite on $\boldsymbol{U}$. Then f can be written as $f = \sum_\lambda c_\lambda f_\lambda$, where the c_λ are elements of K, linearly independent over k, and the f_λ are functions on $\boldsymbol{U}$, rational over k; and, whenever f is so written, all the f_λ are everywhere defined and finite on $\boldsymbol{U}$.*

Let f_1 be the mapping of $\boldsymbol{U}$ into $D_1 = S^1$, determined by the mapping f of $\boldsymbol{U}$ into $\boldsymbol{D}$ in the manner explained at the beginning of §2; to say that f is everywhere defined and finite is the same as to say that f_1 is everywhere defined on $\boldsymbol{U}$, i.e. that it is a morphism of $\boldsymbol{U}$ into S^1. To simplify notations, write f instead of f_1, so that f is now assumed to be a morphism of $\boldsymbol{U}$ into S^1. Let $\boldsymbol{P}$ be a point of $\boldsymbol{U}$; we first show that there is an expression for f, of the form stated in th. 7, such that all the f_λ are defined and finite at $\boldsymbol{P}$. By the principle of localization, it is enough to do this in the case when $\boldsymbol{U}$ is an affine variety. Let then (x) be a generic point of $\boldsymbol{U}$ over K; as f is a morphism of $\boldsymbol{U}$ into S^1, coroll. 2 of th. 2, Chap. VII, §2, shows that $f(x)$ must be in $K[x]$, i.e. that there is a polynomial F in $K[X]$ such that $f(x) = F(x)$. Let the c_λ be a maximal set of linearly independent elements over k among the coefficients of F; we can write $F = \sum_\lambda c_\lambda F_\lambda$, with F_λ in $k[X]$ for every λ. Then, if f_λ is the morphism of $\boldsymbol{U}$ into S^1, rational over k, determined by $f_\lambda(x) = F_\lambda(x)$, we have $f = \sum_\lambda c_\lambda f_\lambda$, and all the f_λ are defined at $\boldsymbol{P}$, as asserted. The second part of our theorem is then an immediate consequence of prop. 8 of Chap. IV, §2. Alternatively, we may proceed as follows. Let $\boldsymbol{U}$ and f be again as in our theorem, and consider any expression $f = \sum_\lambda c_\lambda f_\lambda$, where the c_λ are in K and linearly independent over k, and the f_λ are functions on $\boldsymbol{U}$, rational over k; we will show that, if $\boldsymbol{P}$ is any point of $\boldsymbol{U}$, all the f_λ are defined and finite at $\boldsymbol{P}$. In fact, by what we have proved above, there is at least one expression $f = \sum_\mu d_\mu g_\mu$ for f, in which the d_μ are in K and the g_μ are functions on $\boldsymbol{U}$, rational over k, defined and finite at $\boldsymbol{P}$. Let the c'_ρ be a maximal subset of the set (d_μ), such that the c_λ, c'_ρ, taken together, are linearly independent over k; then every d_μ can be expressed as a linear combination $d_\mu = \sum_\lambda \xi_{\mu\lambda} c_\lambda + \sum_\rho \eta_{\mu\rho} c'_\rho$ of the c_λ, c'_ρ, with coefficients $\xi_{\mu\lambda}$, $\eta_{\mu\rho}$ in k. Let $\boldsymbol{M}$ be a generic point of $\boldsymbol{U}$ over K; we have

$$\sum_\lambda c_\lambda f_\lambda(\boldsymbol{M}) = \sum_\lambda c_\lambda\Big(\sum_\mu \xi_{\mu\lambda} g_\mu(\boldsymbol{M})\Big) + \sum_\rho c'_\rho\Big(\sum_\mu \eta_{\mu\rho} g_\mu(\boldsymbol{M})\Big).$$

By th. 1 of Chap. IV, §1, K and $k(\boldsymbol{M})$ are linearly disjoint over k; as the c_λ, c'_ρ are linearly independent over k, they must therefore be so over $k(\boldsymbol{M})$, so that, in the last formula, the coefficients of the c_λ and of the c'_ρ must be the same on both sides. This gives $f_\lambda = \sum_\mu \xi_{\mu\lambda} g_\mu$; as the g_μ are defined and finite at $\boldsymbol{P}$, the same is therefore true of the f_λ.

COROLLARY. *Let $\boldsymbol{U}$ be a variety, defined over a field k; let f be a function on $\boldsymbol{U}$, rational over a field K containing k. Then f can be written as $f = \sum_\lambda c_\lambda f_\lambda$, where the c_λ are in K and the f_λ are functions on $\boldsymbol{U}$, rational over k, if and only if the set of points of $\boldsymbol{U}$ where f is finite contains a non-empty k-open subset $\boldsymbol{U}'$ of $\boldsymbol{U}$.*

If f can be so written, take for $\boldsymbol{U}'$ the complement on $\boldsymbol{U}$ of the union of the set of multiple points of $\boldsymbol{U}$ and of all the sets $|f_\lambda^{-1}(\infty)|$; by th. 1 of §2 and coroll. 3 of th. 2, §2, this has the required property. Assume now that there is a set $\boldsymbol{U}'$ with that property; let $\boldsymbol{U}''$ be the k-open set of the simple points of $\boldsymbol{U}$; applying th. 7 to the restriction of f to $\boldsymbol{U}' \cap \boldsymbol{U}''$, we get for that restriction, and hence for f, an expression of the desired form.

THEOREM 8. *Let $\boldsymbol{U}$ be a variety, $\boldsymbol{X}$ a $\boldsymbol{U}$-divisor, and k a field of rationality for $\boldsymbol{U}$ and $\boldsymbol{X}$. Let K be a field containing k, and let f be a function on $\boldsymbol{U}$, rational over K, such that* $\mathrm{div}(f) \succ \boldsymbol{X}$. *Then f can be written as $f = \sum_\lambda c_\lambda f_\lambda$, where the c_λ are elements of K, linearly independent over k, and the f_λ are functions on $\boldsymbol{U}$, rational over k; moreover, whenever f is so written, we have* $\mathrm{div}(f_\lambda) \succ \boldsymbol{X}$ *for all λ.*

The first assertion follows at once from th. 7 by applying it to the set of simple points of $\boldsymbol{U} - |\boldsymbol{X}|$. Now let $\boldsymbol{V}$ be a simple subvariety of $\boldsymbol{U}$ of codimension 1, algebraic over k; let $\boldsymbol{A}$ be the prime rational divisor over k on $\boldsymbol{U}$ which has $\boldsymbol{V}$ as one of its components; we can write $\boldsymbol{X}$ as $\boldsymbol{X} = a \cdot \boldsymbol{A} + \boldsymbol{Y}$, where a is an integer (equal to 0 unless $\boldsymbol{V}$ is a component of $\boldsymbol{X}$), and $\boldsymbol{Y}$ is a divisor without any common component with $\boldsymbol{A}$. By th. 6, there is a function g on $\boldsymbol{U}$, rational over k, such that $\mathrm{div}(g) = \boldsymbol{A} + \boldsymbol{B}$, where $\boldsymbol{B}$ is a divisor without any common component with $\boldsymbol{A}$. If $f = \sum_\lambda c_\lambda f_\lambda$, where the c_λ, f_λ are as stated in our theorem, then we have $g^{-a}f = \sum_\lambda c_\lambda(g^{-a}f_\lambda)$. As $\mathrm{div}(g^{-a}f) \succ \boldsymbol{Y} - a\cdot\boldsymbol{B}$, th. 1 of §2 shows that $g^{-a}f$ is everywhere defined and finite on the k-open set of the simple points of $\boldsymbol{U} - |\boldsymbol{Y}| - |\boldsymbol{B}|$; therefore, by th. 7, the same is true of all the $g^{-a}f_\lambda$; in particular, the $g^{-a}f_\lambda$ are defined and finite at $\boldsymbol{V}$. By coroll. 2 of th. 1, §2, this gives $v_{\boldsymbol{V}}(g^{-a}f_\lambda) \geqq 0$, so that $\boldsymbol{V}$ has at least the same coefficient in $\mathrm{div}(f_\lambda)$ as in $\mathrm{div}(g^a) = a\cdot(\boldsymbol{A} + \boldsymbol{B})$, i.e. as in $\boldsymbol{X}$.

Corollary 1. *Let $\boldsymbol{U}$ be a variety, $\boldsymbol{X}$ a $\boldsymbol{U}$-divisor, and k a field of rationality for $\boldsymbol{U}$ and $\boldsymbol{X}$. Then $\mathfrak{L}(\boldsymbol{X})$ is the vector-space generated over the field of constants by $\mathfrak{L}_k(\boldsymbol{X})$.*

According to the definitions in §2, $\mathfrak{L}(\boldsymbol{X})$ consists of the functions f on $\boldsymbol{U}$ such that $\mathrm{div}(f) \succ -\boldsymbol{X}$. By th. 8, every such function is a linear combination, with constant coefficients, of functions in $\mathfrak{L}(\boldsymbol{X})$ which are rational over k, i.e. of elements of $\mathfrak{L}_k(\boldsymbol{X})$.

Corollary 2. *Let $\boldsymbol{U}$ be a complete variety without multiple subvarieties of codimension 1; let $\boldsymbol{X}$ be a $\boldsymbol{U}$-divisor, and k a field of rationality for $\boldsymbol{U}$ and $\boldsymbol{X}$. Then, if there is a function f on $\boldsymbol{U}$ such that* $\mathrm{div}(f) = \boldsymbol{X}$, *there is a function f_1, rational over k, with the same property; and $\mathfrak{L}(-\boldsymbol{X})$ consists of the functions cf_1, where c is any constant.*

A function f' is in $\mathfrak{L}(-\boldsymbol{X})$ if and only if $\mathrm{div}(f') \succ \boldsymbol{X}$; if $\boldsymbol{X} = \mathrm{div}(f)$, this is the same as to say that $\mathrm{div}(f'/f) \succ 0$; by coroll. 3 of th. 1, §2, this is so if and only if f'/f is a constant. In other words, $\mathfrak{L}(-\boldsymbol{X})$ is then a vector-space of dimension 1 over the field of constants; by coroll. 1, we can choose for it a generator f_1 in $\mathfrak{L}_k(-\boldsymbol{X})$; then f itself is of the form cf_1, where c is a constant, so that $\mathrm{div}(f_1) = \mathrm{div}(f) = \boldsymbol{X}$.

Corollary 3. *Let $\boldsymbol{U}$, $\boldsymbol{V}$ be two varieties and f a function on $\boldsymbol{U} \times \boldsymbol{V}$; let k be a field of rationality for $\boldsymbol{U}$, $\boldsymbol{V}$ and f; let $\boldsymbol{P} \times \boldsymbol{Q}$ be a generic point of $\boldsymbol{U} \times \boldsymbol{V}$ over k, and let g be the function on $\boldsymbol{V}$, rational over $k(\boldsymbol{P})$, such that $g(\boldsymbol{Q}) = f(\boldsymbol{P}, \boldsymbol{Q})$. Then the following assertions are equivalent:* (a) *there is a non-empty k-open subset of $\boldsymbol{V}$ on which g is everywhere defined and finite*; (b) *there is a $\boldsymbol{V}$-divisor $\boldsymbol{X}$, rational over k, such that* $\mathrm{div}(g) \succ \boldsymbol{X}$; (c) *there are functions f_λ on $\boldsymbol{U}$ and g_λ on $\boldsymbol{V}$, all rational over k, such that the f_λ are linearly independent over k and that*

$$f(\boldsymbol{P}, \boldsymbol{Q}) = \sum_\lambda f_\lambda(\boldsymbol{P})g_\lambda(\boldsymbol{Q}).$$

Moreover, when the f_λ, g_λ are as stated in (c), *we have $v_{\boldsymbol{A}}(g) = \inf_\lambda v_{\boldsymbol{A}}(g_\lambda)$ for every simple subvariety $\boldsymbol{A}$ of $\boldsymbol{V}$ of codimension 1, algebraic over k, and*

$$\overset{-1}{g}(\infty) = \sup_\lambda \overset{-1}{g_\lambda}(\infty).$$

By th. 1 of §2, (b) implies (a), which implies (c) by the corollary of th. 7. Now assume (c). As the f_λ are linearly independent over k, the same is true for the elements $f_\lambda(\boldsymbol{P})$ of $k(\boldsymbol{P})$; by th. 1 of Chap. IV, §1, $k(\boldsymbol{P})$ and $\bar{k}(\boldsymbol{Q})$ are linearly disjoint over k, so that the $f_\lambda(\boldsymbol{P})$ are linearly independent over $\bar{k}(\boldsymbol{Q})$;

therefore, if f is the constant 0, all the g_λ are 0; in this case our statements are trivially true, since we write $\operatorname{div}(0) \succ X$ for every X, and $v_A(0) = +\infty$. We may therefore assume that f is not the constant 0; similarly, we may omit, from the expression for $f(P, Q)$ in (c), the terms for which $g_\lambda = 0$. If we put $X = \inf_\lambda[\operatorname{div}(g_\lambda)]$, we have $\operatorname{div}(g) \succ X$ by coroll. 3 of th. 2, §2, so that (b) is satisfied. Put $X' = \sum_A v_A(g) \cdot A$, where the sum is extended to all the simple subvarieties of V of codimension 1, algebraic over k, or, what amounts to the same, to all those components of $\operatorname{div}(g)$ which are algebraic over k. Let B be any simple subvariety of V of codimension 1; if B is algebraic over k, we have, since $\operatorname{div}(g) \succ X$, and by the definition of X':

$$v_B(g) = \gamma_B(X') \geqq \gamma_B(X);$$

on the other hand, if B is not algebraic over k, it is neither a component of X nor one of X', and therefore we have

$$v_B(g) \geqq \gamma_B(X) = \gamma_B(X') = 0.$$

This shows that we have $\operatorname{div}(g) \succ X' \succ X$. Now, applying th. 8 to X', to the fields $\bar{k}$ and $\bar{k}(P)$, and to $g = \sum_\lambda f_\lambda(P) g_\lambda$, we see that $\operatorname{div}(g_\lambda) \succ X'$ for every λ; in view of the definition of X, this gives $X \succ X'$, hence $X = X'$, which is the same as to say that $v_A(g) = \inf_\lambda v_A(g_\lambda)$ for every A which is algebraic over k. As we have also shown that $v_B(g) \geqq 0$ for every B which is not algebraic over k, every component of $g^{-1}(\infty)$ must be algebraic over k; since we have $v_A(g) = \inf_\lambda v_A(g_\lambda)$ for every such variety A, $g^{-1}(\infty)$ must therefore be the same as $\sup_\lambda g_\lambda^{-1}(\infty)$.

COROLLARY 4. *Let U be a variety, V a complete variety without multiple subvarieties of codimension 1, and Z a divisor on $U \times V$; let k be a field of rationality for U, V and Z, and let $P \times Q$ be a generic point of $U \times V$ over k. Assume that there is a divisor Y on V, rational over k, and a function g on V such that*

$$\operatorname{div}(g) = Z(P) - Y.$$

Then there is a divisor X on U and a function f on $U \times V$, both rational over k, such that

$$\operatorname{div}(f) = Z - X \times V - U \times Y;$$

and there is a function h on U, rational over $k(Q)$, such that

$$\operatorname{div}(h) = Z'(Q) - X.$$

Here, according to the notations explained in Chap. VIII, §4, $Z(P)$ and $Z'(Q)$ are the divisors respectively determined on V and on U by the relations

$$Z \cdot (P \times V) = P \times Z(P), \qquad Z \cdot (U \times Q) = Z'(Q) \times Q.$$

By coroll. 2, we may assume that g has been taken rational over $k(P)$; then there is a function f on $U \times V$, rational over k, such that $f(P, Q) = g(Q)$. Put

$T = \text{div}(f) + U \times Y$; by prop. 15 of Chap. VIII, §4, we have

$$T(P) = \text{div}(g) + Y = Z(P);$$

by th. 6(ii) of Chap. VIII, §3, this implies that every component W of $Z - T$ has on U a geometric projection W' other than U; as W has the codimension 1 on $U \times V$, it has therefore at least the same dimension as $W' \times V$, in which it is contained, so that it is the same as $W' \times V$. This shows that $Z - T$ is of the form $X \times V$, where X is a divisor on U, rational over k. If h is now the function on U, rational over $k(Q)$, such that $h(P) = f(P, Q)$, then, using again prop. 15 of Chap. VIII, §4, one sees at once that $\text{div}(h)$ is as stated in our corollary.

THEOREM 9. *Let U be a variety in the affine space S^N, X a positive U-divisor, and k a field of rationality for U and X; let P be a simple point of U. Then there is a polynomial $F(X_1, \cdots, X_N)$, with coefficients in k, which induces on U a function f, other than the constant* 0, *such that* $\text{div}(f) \succ X$ *and that P is not in the support of* $\text{div}(f) - X$.

We will first prove that there is a polynomial F with the latter properties and with coefficients in some suitable extension of k. Assume first that X is a variety V. As in the first part of the proof of th. 6, we see that it is enough to show that there is a positive divisor Z in S^N, intersecting U properly in S^N, such that $U \cdot Z \succ V$ and that P is not in the support of $U \cdot Z - V$. In fact, let n be the dimension of U; let k' be a field of rationality for U, V and P; take for Z the projecting cylinder of V in the direction defined by the equations

$$\sum_j u_{ij} X_j = 0 \qquad (1 \leqq i \leqq n),$$

where the u_{ij} are nN independent variables over k'; then, by the corollary of prop. 7, §3, V is a proper component of multiplicity 1 of $U \cap Z$, and P is not in the support of $U \cdot Z - V$. As V is proper in $U \cap Z$, a comparison of the dimensions shows that Z is of codimension 1 in S^N and does not contain U; by prop. 5 of Chap. VIII, §3, this implies that Z intersects U properly in S^N, which completes the proof of our assertion in the case $X = V$. Now let X be arbitrary; call V_ν its components, and write $X = \sum_\nu a_\nu V_\nu$; by what we have proved, there is, for each ν, a polynomial H_ν, with coefficients in some extension of k, inducing on U a function h_ν other than the constant 0, such that $\text{div}(h_\nu) \succ V_\nu$ and that P is not in the support of $\text{div}(h_\nu) - V_\nu$. Then the polynomial $F = \prod_\nu (H_\nu)^{a_\nu}$ has all the properties stated in our theorem, except that its coefficients, instead of being in k, are in some extension K of k. Now let (c_λ) be a maximal set of linearly independent elements over k among the coefficients of F, and write $F = \sum_\lambda c_\lambda F_\lambda$, where the F_λ are polynomials with coefficients in k; for each λ, let f_λ be the function induced on U by F_λ. As we have $\text{div}(f) \succ X$, where f is the function induced on U by F, and $f = \sum_\lambda c_\lambda f_\lambda$, th. 8 shows that we have $\text{div}(f_\lambda) \succ X$ for every λ. Put $g_\lambda = f_\lambda / f$, $X' = \text{div}(f) - X$, and, for every λ for which f_λ is not the constant 0, $X'_\lambda = \text{div}(f_\lambda) - X$, so that

$$\text{div}(g_\lambda) = X'_\lambda - X'.$$

As the point P is not in $|X'|$, the latter relation, together with th. 1 of §2, shows that g_λ is defined and finite at P for every λ for which f_λ is not the constant 0; this is obviously also true if $f_\lambda = 0$. As we have $1 = \sum_\lambda c_\lambda g_\lambda$, not all the g_λ can have the value 0 at P; then, if λ is such that $g_\lambda(P) \neq 0$, th. 1 of §2 shows that P cannot be in $|X'_\lambda|$, so that the polynomial F_λ satisfies all the requirements in our theorem.

COROLLARY 1. *Let $\boldsymbol{U}$ be a variety, $\boldsymbol{X}$ a $\boldsymbol{U}$-divisor, k a field of rationality for $\boldsymbol{U}$ and $\boldsymbol{X}$, and $\boldsymbol{P}$ a simple point of $\boldsymbol{U}$. Then there is a function f on $\boldsymbol{U}$, rational over k, other than the constant* 0, *such that $\boldsymbol{P}$ is not in the support of the divisor* $\text{div}(f) - \boldsymbol{X}$.

If $\boldsymbol{X}$ is positive, this is an immediate consequence of the principle of localization and of th. 9. If $\boldsymbol{X} = \boldsymbol{X}' - \boldsymbol{X}''$, where $\boldsymbol{X}'$ and $\boldsymbol{X}''$ are positive divisors, take f', f'' such that $\boldsymbol{P}$ is not in the support of either one of the divisors

$$\text{div}(f') - \boldsymbol{X}', \qquad \text{div}(f'') - \boldsymbol{X}'';$$

then $f = f'/f''$ satisfies our requirements. Of course the statement in our corollary is trivially true unless $\boldsymbol{P}$ is in $|\boldsymbol{X}|$.

COROLLARY 2. *Let U be an affine variety, Z a positive U-divisor and k a field of rationality for U and Z. Let $\mathfrak{A}$ be the ideal of the polynomials F in $k[X]$ which induce on U a function f such that* $\text{div}(f) \succ Z$; *let the F_μ be a basis for $\mathfrak{A}$, and, for each μ, let f_μ be the function induced on U by F_μ. Then* $Z = \inf_\mu(\text{div}(f_\mu))$.

The fact that $\mathfrak{A}$ is an ideal is an immediate consequence of th. 2 of §2 and its corollaries, and of the corollary of th. 5. Now our assertion means that, if V is any simple subvariety of codimension 1 of U, there is μ such that V is not a component of $\text{div}(f_\mu) - Z$. In fact, apply th. 9 to U, Z, and to any point of V, simple on U; it shows that there is F in $\mathfrak{A}$, inducing on U a function f such that V is not a component of $\text{div}(f) - Z$. Write now $F = \sum_\mu F_\mu G_\mu$, where the G_μ are in $k[X]$. Then, if the G_μ induce the functions g_μ on U, we have $f = \sum_\mu f_\mu g_\mu$ and $\text{div}(g_\mu) \succ 0$; if V were a component of $\text{div}(f_\mu) - Z$ for all μ, we would have $\text{div}(f_\mu g_\mu) \succ Z + V$ for every μ, hence $\text{div}(f) \succ Z + V$ by coroll. 3 of th. 2, §2, which contradicts the definition of F.

COROLLARY 3. *Let U be an affine variety, defined over a field k; let Z be a positive U-divisor, rational over a field K containing k; let $\mathfrak{A}$ be the ideal of the polynomials in $K[X]$ which induce on U a function f such that $div(f) \succ Z$. Then a field k' between k and K is a field of rationality for Z if and only if $\mathfrak{A}$ has a basis in $k'[X]$; and, if k_0 is the smallest field with that property, any field k'' containing k is a field of rationality for Z if and only if it contains k_0. Moreover, an isomorphism of k_0 onto a field k'_0 over k leaves Z invariant if and only if it is the identity.*

Let k' be a field between k and K; if $\mathfrak{A}$ has a basis in $k'[X]$, coroll. 2 shows that we can write Z as $Z = \inf(Z_\mu)$, where the Z_μ are rational divisors over k'; as one sees at once, this implies that Z itself is rational over k'. Conversely, assume that Z is rational over k'; let F be a polynomial in $\mathfrak{A}$; let (c_λ) be a maximal set of linearly independent elements over k' among the coefficients of F, and write F as $F = \sum_\lambda c_\lambda F_\lambda$, where the F_λ are in $k'[X]$; then th. 8, together with our definitions, shows at once that all the F_λ are in $\mathfrak{A}$. Therefore any basis for the ideal $k'[X] \cap \mathfrak{A}$ is also one for $\mathfrak{A}$. By lemma 2 of Chap. I, §7, there is a smallest field k_0 between k and K such that $\mathfrak{A}$ has a basis in $k_0[X]$, and an isomorphism σ of k_0 onto a field k_0' leaves $\mathfrak{A}$ invariant if and only if it is the identity. But, if σ leaves Z invariant, it must obviously leave $\mathfrak{A}$ invariant; and the converse is an immediate consequence of coroll. 2; this proves the last assertion in our corollary. Finally, let k'' be any field containing k, and let K' be a field containing K and k''; let $\mathfrak{A}'$ be the ideal in $K'[X]$ defined just as $\mathfrak{A}$ was defined in $K[X]$. By what we have already proved, $\mathfrak{A}'$ has a basis in $K[X]$ and is therefore no other than the ideal in $K'[X]$ generated by the polynomials in $\mathfrak{A}$; therefore k_0 is also the smallest field between k and K' such that $\mathfrak{A}'$ has a basis in $k_0[X]$; and k'' is a field of rationality for Z if and only if it contains k_0.

Corollary 4. *Let* $\boldsymbol{U}$ *be a variety, defined over a field* k; *let* $\boldsymbol{Z}$ *be any divisor on* $\boldsymbol{U}$. *Then there is a smallest field of rationality* k_0 *for* $\boldsymbol{Z}$, *containing* k; *and an isomorphism of* k_0 *onto a field* k_0' *over* k *leaves* $\boldsymbol{Z}$ *invariant if and only if it is the identity.*

Let the U_α be the representatives of $\boldsymbol{U}$; for each one, there is, by prop. 16 of Chap. VII, §6, a k-isomorphism φ_α of U_α onto a k-open subset of $\boldsymbol{U}$, and the sets $\varphi_\alpha(U_\alpha)$ are a k-open covering of $\boldsymbol{U}$. As we have seen in Chap. VIII, §1, $\boldsymbol{Z}$ is rational over a field K containing k if and only if its restrictions to all the k-open sets $\varphi_\alpha(U_\alpha)$ are so; from this, one concludes immediately that our assertion will be proved for $\boldsymbol{U}$ if we prove it for each one of the $\varphi_\alpha(U_\alpha)$, or, what amounts to the same, for each U_α. In other words, it is enough to consider the case when $\boldsymbol{U}$ is an affine variety. Write then $\boldsymbol{Z} = \boldsymbol{Z}' - \boldsymbol{Z}''$, where $\boldsymbol{Z}'$, $\boldsymbol{Z}''$ are positive divisors without a common component; $\boldsymbol{Z}$ is rational over a field if and only if $\boldsymbol{Z}'$ and $\boldsymbol{Z}''$ are so; our conclusion now follows at once by applying coroll. 3 to $\boldsymbol{Z}'$ and $\boldsymbol{Z}''$.

As could be shown by examples, the conclusion of coroll. 4 does not necessarily hold if $\boldsymbol{Z}$ is merely assumed to be a $\boldsymbol{U}$-chain of codimension 1.

5. Linear systems and projective spaces. The field of all functions on a variety $\boldsymbol{V}$ being considered as a vector-space over the field of constants, we shall be concerned with its finite-dimensional subspaces. Let $\mathfrak{L}$ be such a space, not reduced to $\{0\}$; let $\lambda_0, \cdots, \lambda_n$ be a set of generators (for instance, a basis) for $\mathfrak{L}$ over the field of constants; put $\boldsymbol{X}_0 = -\inf_i \operatorname{div}(\lambda_i)$. Then we have $\operatorname{div}(\lambda_i) \succ -\boldsymbol{X}_0$ for every i, hence, by coroll. 3 of th. 2, §2, $\operatorname{div}(\lambda) \succ -\boldsymbol{X}_0$ for every $\lambda \in \mathfrak{L}$. With the notations of §2, this shows that $\mathfrak{L} \subset \mathfrak{L}(\boldsymbol{X}_0)$, and also that the set of the divisors $\operatorname{div}(\lambda)$, when we take for λ all the functions in $\mathfrak{L}$ other than the constant 0, has the lower bound $-X_0$. In view of our agreement to write $\text{div}(0) \succ X$ for every divisor X, we will write $\inf_{\lambda \in \mathfrak{L}} \text{div}(\lambda)$, or more briefly, when no confusion is possible, $\inf_{\mathfrak{L}} \text{div}(\lambda)$, for the divisor $-X_0$, when $\mathfrak{L}$ and X_0 are as we have stated.

A set Λ of positive divisors on a variety V will be called a *linear system* of divisors on V if there is a vector-space $\mathfrak{L}$ of functions on V, of finite dimension over the field of constants, and a divisor X_0, such that Λ consists of the divisors $\text{div}(\lambda) + X_0$ when one takes for λ all the functions in $\mathfrak{L}$, other than the constant 0. One must then have $X_0 \succ -\inf_{\mathfrak{L}} \text{div}(\lambda)$. The linear system Λ is called *reduced* (or "without fixed component") if $\inf_\Lambda X = 0$, or, what amounts to the same thing, if no subvariety of V is a component of all the divisors in Λ; if Λ is defined by means of $\mathfrak{L}$ and X_0 in the manner we have just described, it is reduced if and only if $X_0 = -\inf_{\mathfrak{L}} \text{div}(\lambda)$; when that is so, Λ is called *the reduced linear system determined by the vector-space* $\mathfrak{L}$. When Λ is not reduced, the divisors $X - \inf_\Lambda X$, for $X \in \Lambda$, make up a reduced linear system.

On a complete variety without multiple subvarieties of codimension 1, reduced linear systems can be characterized as follows:

PROPOSITION 8. *Let V be a complete variety without multiple subvarieties of codimension* 1. *A set Λ of positive divisors on V is a reduced linear system if and only if it has the following properties*: (i) $\inf_\Lambda X = 0$; (ii) *there is a divisor X_0 in Λ, such that every divisor $X - X_0$ with $X \in \Lambda$ is the divisor of a function on V, and that the set $\mathfrak{L}$ consisting of the constant* 0 *and of all the functions λ on V satisfying the condition* $\text{div}(\lambda) + X_0 \in \Lambda$ *is a finite-dimensional vector-space over the field of constants. Then Λ is the reduced linear system determined by $\mathfrak{L}$; and every divisor X_0 in Λ has the property* (ii).

If Λ has the properties (i), (ii), it is clearly the reduced linear system determined by the vector-space $\mathfrak{L}$. Conversely, let Λ be the reduced linear system determined by a vector-space $\mathfrak{M}$; by definition, it has the property (i); we will show that, if X_0 is any divisor in Λ, (ii) is satisfied. In fact, put

$$Y = -\inf_{\mathfrak{M}} \text{div}(\mu);$$

by definition, Λ consists of the divisors $\text{div}(\mu) + Y$ for μ in $\mathfrak{M}$ and not 0; therefore, if X_0 is in Λ, we can write $X_0 = \text{div}(\mu_0) + Y$, with μ_0 in $\mathfrak{M}$. Then, if X is in Λ, we have $X = \text{div}(\mu) + Y$, with μ in $\mathfrak{M}$, and therefore

$$X - X_0 = \text{div}(\mu/\mu_0).$$

Moreover, the set $\mathfrak{L}$ defined as in (ii) consists of 0 and of the functions λ such that $\text{div}(\lambda) + X_0$ is in Λ, i.e. such that it can be written in the form $\text{div}(\mu) + Y$ with μ in $\mathfrak{M}$; but this is the same as to say that $\text{div}(\lambda\mu_0/\mu) = 0$; by our assumptions on V, and by coroll. 3 of th. 1, §2, this is so if and only if $\lambda\mu_0/\mu$ is a constant. This shows that $\mathfrak{L}$ consists of 0 and of the functions λ, other than 0, such that $\lambda\mu_0$ is in $\mathfrak{M}$; in other words, we have $\mathfrak{L} = (1/\mu_0)\cdot\mathfrak{M}$, which shows that $\mathfrak{L}$ is a vector-space with the same dimension as $\mathfrak{M}$.

It will be shown in th. 3 of Appendix I that, if V is a complete variety without multiple subvarieties of codimension 1, and if X_0 is any divisor on V, the space $\mathfrak{L}(X_0)$ has a finite dimension over the field of constants; therefore, on such a variety, a vector-space of functions, over the field of constants, has a finite dimension if and only if it is contained in a space of the form $\mathfrak{L}(X_0)$. On such a variety V, let X_0 be a divisor such that $\mathfrak{L}(X_0) \neq \{0\}$; then the linear system consisting of the divisors $\mathrm{div}(\lambda) + X_0$, when one takes for λ all the functions in $\mathfrak{L}(X_0)$ other than the constant 0, is known as *the complete linear system determined by* X_0 *on* V. This linear system is not necessarily reduced; it can also be defined as consisting of the positive divisors X such that $X - X_0$ is the divisor of a function on V; those divisors are said to be *linearly equivalent to* X_0. On a complete variety without multiple subvarieties of codimension 1, every positive divisor belongs to one and only one complete linear system.

Two vector-spaces $\mathfrak{L}$, $\mathfrak{L}'$ of functions on V, over the field of constants, will be called *equivalent* if there is a function φ on V, other than the constant 0, such that $\mathfrak{L}' = \varphi\mathfrak{L}$; then they have the same dimension over the field of constants. With this definition, we have the following result:

PROPOSITION 9. *Let* $\mathfrak{L}$, $\mathfrak{L}'$ *be two vector-spaces of functions on a variety* V, *both of finite dimension over the field of constants and not reduced to* $\{0\}$. *Then they determine the same reduced linear system on* V *if and only if they are equivalent.*

Assume that $\mathfrak{L}' = \varphi\mathfrak{L}$, where φ is a function on V, other than 0; put $X = \mathrm{div}(\varphi)$. Then, for λ in $\mathfrak{L}$ and not 0, we have $\mathrm{div}(\varphi\lambda) = \mathrm{div}(\lambda) + X$, and hence

$$\inf_{\mathfrak{L}'} \mathrm{div}(\lambda') = \inf_{\mathfrak{L}} \mathrm{div}(\lambda) + X.$$

In view of our definitions, this shows at once that $\mathfrak{L}$ and $\mathfrak{L}'$ determine the same reduced linear system. If V is complete and without multiple subvarieties of codimension 1, the converse follows at once from what has been shown above in the proof of prop. 8; in fact, if both $\mathfrak{L}$ and $\mathfrak{L}'$ determine the linear system Λ, and if X_0 is a divisor in Λ, it has been shown there that the constant 0 and the functions φ such that $\mathrm{div}(\varphi) + X_0$ is in Λ make up a vector-space which is equivalent both to $\mathfrak{L}$ and to $\mathfrak{L}'$. In order to deal with the general case, we shall apply coroll. 3 of th. 2 in Appendix I; this is permissible, since that Appendix depends only upon results already obtained in this book (logically speaking, it could have been inserted between §4 and §5 of the present Chapter). Assume that $\mathfrak{L}$ and $\mathfrak{L}'$ determine the same reduced linear system Λ; put

$$X_0 = -\inf_{\mathfrak{L}} \mathrm{div}(\lambda), \qquad X_0' = -\inf_{\mathfrak{L}'} \mathrm{div}(\lambda');$$

then Λ consists of the divisors $\mathrm{div}(\lambda) + X_0$ for λ in $\mathfrak{L}$ and not 0, and also of the divisors $\mathrm{div}(\lambda') + X_0'$ for λ' in $\mathfrak{L}'$ and not 0; therefore, if λ_0 is in $\mathfrak{L}$ and not 0, there is λ_0' in $\mathfrak{L}'$, also not 0, such that

$$\mathrm{div}(\lambda_0) + X_0 = \mathrm{div}(\lambda_0') + X_0'.$$

Then the vector-space $\mathfrak{L}'' = (\lambda_0/\lambda_0')\mathfrak{L}'$ is equivalent to $\mathfrak{L}'$ and therefore also determines the reduced linear system Λ, and we have

$$\inf_{\mathfrak{L}''} \operatorname{div}(\lambda'') = -X_0 ;$$

that being so, Λ consists of the divisors $\operatorname{div}(\lambda'') + X_0$, with λ'' in $\mathfrak{L}''$ and not 0. Now let $\lambda_1, \cdots, \lambda_n$ be a basis for $\mathfrak{L}$, and $\lambda_1'', \cdots, \lambda_m''$ a basis for $\mathfrak{L}''$. Let P be a simple point of V; as in coroll. 3 of th. 2, App. I, call $G(V, P)$ the group of the functions f on V such that $\operatorname{div}(f) = 0$ and $f(P) = 1$; by that corollary, this group is finitely generated; let $f_1, \cdots, f_r$ be a set of generators for it; and let k be a field of rationality for V, for P, and for all the functions λ_i, λ_j'' and f_ρ. Then, if f is any function on V such that $\operatorname{div}(f) = 0$, $f(P)$ is finite and not 0 by th. 1 of §2 applied to the open set of the simple points on V, and $f/f(P)$ is in $G(V, P)$ and can therefore be written in the form $\prod_\rho f_\rho^{m_\rho}$, which implies that it is rational over k; this shows that every such function f can be written as cf', where c is a constant and f' is rational over k. Now let $u_1, \cdots, u_n$ be n independent variables over k; put $\lambda = \sum_{i=1}^n u_i\lambda_i$; then there must be a function λ'' in $\mathfrak{L}''$, other than 0, such that $\operatorname{div}(\lambda'') = \operatorname{div}(\lambda)$; by what we have just proved, this implies that λ''/λ can be written as cf, where c is a constant and f is rational over k; replacing λ'' by $(1/c)\cdot\lambda''$, which is also in $\mathfrak{L}''$, we get $\lambda'' = f\lambda$, with f rational over k. As this is in $\mathfrak{L}''$, we can write it in terms of the basis $\lambda_1'', \cdots, \lambda_m''$ of $\mathfrak{L}''$ as

$$\sum_{i=1}^{n} u_i f\lambda_i = \sum_{j=1}^{m} v_j\lambda_j''$$

with constant coefficients v_j. Let $(\lambda_1'', \cdots, \lambda_m'', \mu_1, \cdots, \mu_s)$ be a maximal set, containing the set $(\lambda_1'', \cdots, \lambda_m'')$, of linearly independent functions over k among the functions λ_j'', $f\lambda_i$; then we can write

$$f\lambda_i = \sum_{j=1}^{m} \xi_{ij}\lambda_j'' + \sum_{h=1}^{s} \eta_{ih}\mu_h$$

with coefficients ξ_{ij}, η_{ih} in k. Substituting this in the relation obtained above, we get

$$\sum_{h=1}^{s}\left(\sum_{i=1}^{n} u_i\,\eta_{ih}\right)\mu_h = \sum_{j=1}^{m}\left(v_j - \sum_{i=1}^{n} u_i\,\xi_{ij}\right)\lambda_j''.$$

Taking the value of both sides at a generic point M of V over $k(u, v)$, and taking into account the fact that $k(M)$ and $k(u, v)$ are linearly disjoint over k, we find that all the coefficients of the μ_h in the left-hand side, and of the λ_j'' in the right-hand side, must be 0. As the u_i are independent variables over k, all the η_{ih} must then be 0. As the λ_i are linearly independent over k, the above formulas imply now that $n \leqq m$; for similar reasons, we must then have $m \leqq n$, so that $m = n$. As the n functions $\sum_j \xi_{ij}\lambda_j''$ are linearly independent over k, they can be taken as a basis for $\mathfrak{L}''$; after substituting that basis for the basis (λ_j''), we get $f\lambda_i = \lambda_i''$ for $1 \leqq i \leqq n$, so that $\mathfrak{L}'' = f\mathfrak{L}$. This completes the proof.

If the vector-space $\mathfrak{L}$ of functions on a variety V has the dimension 1 over the field of constants, one sees at once that the reduced linear system determined by $\mathfrak{L}$ is $\{0\}$. If $\mathfrak{L}$ has the dimension 2, let λ_0, λ_1 be a basis for $\mathfrak{L}$ over the field of constants, and put $f = \lambda_1/\lambda_0$; then $\mathfrak{L}$ is equivalent to the vector-space $\mathfrak{L}' = \lambda_0^{-1}\mathfrak{L}$ with the basis $1, f$. For any pair of constants a, b such that $a \neq 0$, consider the function $g = af + b$; this can be written as $g = \varphi \circ f$, where φ is the isomorphism of D onto itself for which $\varphi(x) = ax + b$ when $x \neq \infty$ and $\varphi(\infty) = \infty$. We have

$$\varphi^{-1}(\infty) = \infty, \qquad \varphi^{-1}(0) = -b/a;$$

therefore we have $g^{-1}(\infty) = f^{-1}(\infty)$ and $g^{-1}(0) = f^{-1}(-b/a)$, hence

$$f^{-1}(c) = \operatorname{div}(af + b) + f^{-1}(\infty)$$

for $c = -b/a$; the latter formula remains true for $c = \infty$, $a = 0$, $b \neq 0$; as $f^{-1}(0)$ and $f^{-1}(\infty)$, by th. 1 of §2, have no common component, this shows that the divisors $f^{-1}(c)$, when one takes for c all the points of D, make up the reduced linear system determined by $\mathfrak{L}'$, hence also by $\mathfrak{L}$.

We will now extend to vector-spaces of arbitrary dimension the mode of representation which we have just obtained, by means of the projective line, for linear systems determined by vector-spaces of dimension 2; this requires the definition of the projective spaces. It is convenient to begin with some definitions on fiberings.

Let p be a morphism of a variety U into a variety V; let k be a field of rationality for U, V and p. Let V' be a k-open subset of V; by th. 2 of Chap. VII, §2, the set-theoretic inverse image of V' under p is a k-open subset U' of U; one sees at once that the restriction to $U' \times V'$ of the graph of p is the graph of a morphism p' of U' into V', called *the restriction of* p *to* (U', V'), or, by abuse of language, to V'. For $i = 1, 2$, let p_i be a morphism of a variety U_i into a variety V_i; we say that (U_1, V_1, p_1) is isomorphic to (U_2, V_2, p_2) if there are isomorphisms f, g of U_1 onto U_2 and of V_1 onto V_2, respectively, such that

$$g \circ p_1 = p_2 \circ f.$$

If the U_i, V_i, p_i and f, g are rational over k, we say that (U_1, V_1, p_1) and (U_2, V_2, p_2) are k-isomorphic. Let p be a morphism of a variety U into a variety V; let F be a variety. We say that p determines a *trivial fibering* (resp. a *k-trivial fibering*) *of* U *over* V *with the fibre* F if (U, V, p) is isomorphic (resp. k-isomorphic) to $(V \times F, V, \pi)$, where π is the projection from $V \times F$ to V. We say that p determines a *fibering* (resp. a *k-fibering*) *of* U *over* V *with the fibre* F if there is a covering (V_α) of V by open (resp. k-open) subsets V_α, such that, for every α, the restriction p_α of p to (U_α, V_α), where U_α is the set-theoretic inverse image of V_α under p, determines a trivial (resp. k-trivial) fibering of U_α over V_α with the fibre F.

We shall say that an assertion (A) about a morphism p of U into V, a field of rationality k for U, V and p, and some subvarieties and cycles on U and V, has *local character relatively to* V whenever the following holds true: if each point of V has a k-neighborhood V' such that (A) holds for V', for the set-theoretic inverse image U' of V' under p, for the restriction p' of p to (U', V'), and for the restrictions to U' (resp. to V') of all the subvarieties of U (resp. of V) and U-cycles (resp. V-cycles) occurring in (A), then (A) is true. For instance, as one sees at once, the assertion that p determines a fibering (or a k-fibering) of U over V with the fibre F has local character in this sense. It is clear that, if an assertion of this kind has local character relatively to V and is true for every trivial (resp. k-trivial) fibering, then it is true for every fibering (resp. every k-fibering). In particular, if a morphism p of U into V determines a k-fibering of U over V with the fibre F, and if U' is the set-theoretic inverse image under p of a k-open subset V' of V, then the restriction p' of p to (U', V') determines a k-fibering of U' over V' with the fibre F; for one verifies at once that this assertion has local character, and that it is true when p determines a k-trivial fibering of U over V with the fibre F; in fact, in the latter case, the fibering of U' over V' determined by p is again k-trivial. For a similar reason, the set-theoretic inverse image of a point Q of V under p is a variety $F(Q)$ which is rational over $k(Q)$ and $k(Q)$-isomorphic to F; for this is an assertion of local character, and it is true for a product $V \times F$ and the projection from $V \times F$ to V, hence also for any k-trivial fibering. This shows in particular that, if p determines a fibering of U over V, it is set-theoretically surjective. The variety $F(Q)$ is called *the fibre above* Q in the fibering determined by p; each point P of U belongs to one and only one fibre, viz. $F(p(P))$.

PROPOSITION 10. *Let p be a morphism of a variety U into a variety V; assume that p determines a k-fibering of U over V. Then a U-cycle X can be written in the form $X = p^{-1}(Y)$, where Y is a V-cycle, if and only if its support is the set-theoretic inverse image under p of a subset of V; when that is so, X is invariant under every isomorphism φ of U onto U such that $p \circ \varphi = p$; Y is uniquely determined by X; it is rational over k if and only if X is so; it is a variety if and only if X is one; and its support $|Y|$ is the image of $|X|$ by p. Moreover, if Y, Y' are V-cycles, we have $p^{-1}(Y \cdot Y') = p^{-1}(Y) \cdot p^{-1}(Y')$; and Y, Y' intersect properly on V if and only if $p^{-1}(Y), p^{-1}(Y')$ do so on U.*

It is easily seen that all the assertions in prop. 10 have local character relatively to V; therefore it is enough to prove them for the case of a k-trivial fibering, or, what amounts to the same, for the case when $U = V \times F$ and p is the projection from $V \times F$ to V. In that case, if Y is a V-cycle, the corollary of prop. 14 of Chap. VIII, §4, shows that $p^{-1}(Y) = Y \times F$. All our assertions are then obvious, except for the formula for $p^{-1}(Y \cdot Y')$, which is contained in th. 5 of Chap. VIII, §3 (and which may also be regarded as a special case of th. 11, Chap. VIII, §4).

PROPOSITION 11. *Let p be a morphism of a variety U into a variety V; assume that p determines a k-fibering of U over V. Let f be a mapping, rational over k,* *of $\boldsymbol{U}$ into a variety $\boldsymbol{W}$; and let $\boldsymbol{P}$ be a generic point of $\boldsymbol{U}$ over k. Then there is a mapping g of $\boldsymbol{V}$ into $\boldsymbol{W}$ such that $f = g \circ \boldsymbol{p}$ if and only if $f(\boldsymbol{P})$ is rational over $k(\boldsymbol{p}(\boldsymbol{P}))$; and, when that is so, f is defined at a point $\boldsymbol{P}'$ of $\boldsymbol{U}$ if and only if g is defined at $\boldsymbol{p}(\boldsymbol{P}')$; in particular, f is a morphism if and only if g is one.*

The first assertion is obvious; as to the second one, it has local character relatively to $\boldsymbol{V}$, so that it is enough to verify it in the case when $\boldsymbol{U} = \boldsymbol{V} \times \boldsymbol{F}$ and $\boldsymbol{p}$ is the projection from $\boldsymbol{V} \times \boldsymbol{F}$ to $\boldsymbol{V}$; but then it follows from prop. 4 of Chap. VII, §2.

Now take any $n \geqq 0$; we will denote by S_*^{n+1} the open subset $S^{n+1} - \{0\}$ of the affine space S^{n+1}. If V_* is any subvariety of S_*^{n+1}, its closure V in S^{n+1} is either V_* or $V_* \cup \{0\}$, and is a variety; V_* is then the restriction of V to S_*^{n+1}. This determines a one-to-one correspondence between the subvarieties of S^{n+1}, other than the point 0, and the subvarieties of S_*^{n+1}, which can be extended by linearity to an isomorphism between the groups of r-cycles in S^{n+1}, not having the point 0 as a component, and of r-cycles in S_*^{n+1}; the cycle X in S^{n+1} which corresponds in this way to a cycle X_* in S_*^{n+1} will be called *the extension of* X_* to S^{n+1}, while X_* is the restriction of X to S_*^{n+1}. Similarly, if f_* is any function in S_*^{n+1}, it may be considered, in one and only one way, as the restriction to S_*^{n+1} of a function f on S^{n+1}, which we call *the extension of* f_* *to* S^{n+1}; if $n > 0$, $\mathrm{div}(f)$ is then the extension of $\mathrm{div}(f_*)$ to S^{n+1}; by abuse of language, one frequently makes no distinction between a function on S_*^{n+1} and its extension to S^{n+1}. By a *ray* in S_*^{n+1}, we understand the restriction to S_*^{n+1} of a linear subspace of dimension 1 of S^{n+1}, i.e. of a linear variety of dimension 1 in S^{n+1}, containing the point 0. If $a = (a_0, \cdots, a_n)$ is any point of S_*^{n+1}, there is one and only one ray $R(a)$ containing a; this consists of the points τa, where τ is any quantity other than 0; if k is any field, and t is a variable quantity over $k(a)$, $R(a)$ is the locus of ta over $k(a)$ in S_*^{n+1}.

We will denote by $X_0, \cdots, X_n$ the indeterminates for S^{n+1}. For $0 \leqq \alpha \leqq n$, call P_α the linear variety in S^{n+1} determined by the equation $X_\alpha = 1$; it coincides with its restriction to S_*^{n+1}. Call p_α the mapping of S_*^{n+1} into P_α, rational over the prime field k_0, which is such that $p_\alpha(x) = x_\alpha^{-1}x$ when $x = (x_0, \cdots, x_n)$ is a generic point of S_*^{n+1} over k_0. It is easily seen that the open subset of S_*^{n+1} where p_α is defined is the complement S_α of the linear variety defined in S^{n+1} by $X_\alpha = 0$; the sets S_α, for $0 \leqq \alpha \leqq n$, make up a covering of S_*^{n+1}; if a is in S_α, we have $p_\alpha(a) = a_\alpha^{-1}a$, so that $p_\alpha(a)$ is on the ray $R(a)$ containing a; more precisely, it is the point of intersection of $R(a)$ and P_α.

Let again x be a generic point of S_*^{n+1} over k_0; put $x^{(\alpha)} = p_\alpha(x)$ for $0 \leqq \alpha \leqq n$; as we have $k_0(x^{(\alpha)}) = k_0(x^{(\beta)})$ for all α, β, we can write $x^{(\beta)} = f_{\beta\alpha}(x^{(\alpha)})$, where $f_{\beta\alpha}$ is a mapping of P_α into P_β, rational over k_0; the $f_{\beta\alpha}$ are a consistent set of mappings between the P_α; one sees at once that $f_{\beta\alpha}$ is nothing else than the mapping of P_α into P_β induced by p_β on P_α, and that the open subset of P_α where $f_{\beta\alpha}$ is defined is $P_\alpha \cap S_\beta$. If we put $x^{(\alpha)} = (x_0^{(\alpha)}, \cdots, x_n^{(\alpha)})$ for every α, we have $x_\alpha^{(\alpha)} = 1$ and $x_\beta^{(\alpha)} = x_\beta/x_\alpha$, hence $x_\beta^{(\alpha)}x_\alpha^{(\beta)} = 1$; therefore, if (a, b) is any finite specialization of $(x^{(\alpha)}, x^{(\beta)})$ over k_0, we have $a_\beta b_\alpha = 1$, hence $a_\beta \neq 0$ and $b_\alpha \neq 0$, so that $f_{\beta\alpha}$ is defined at a and $f_{\alpha\beta}$ at b; this shows that $f_{\beta\alpha}$ is a coherent mapping of P_α into P_β. Therefore we define an abstract variety $\boldsymbol{P}^n$ by putting

$$\boldsymbol{P}^n = [P_\alpha, f_{\beta\alpha}]_{0 \leq \alpha, \beta \leq n};$$

$\boldsymbol{P}^n$ is called *the projective space of dimension* n; it is rational over the prime field k_0, and it is without multiple points, since the P_α are so.

Take any specialization $(a^{(\alpha)})$ of the set of quantities

$$(x^{(\alpha)})_{0 \leq \alpha \leq n} = (x_\beta^{(\alpha)})_{0 \leq \alpha \leq n;\, 0 \leq \beta \leq n}$$

over k_0; apply prop. 10 of Chap. II, §3, to this specialization and to the set of quantities $x = (x_0, \cdots, x_n)$; it shows that, for some β, the set $z = x_\beta^{-1}x$ has a finite specialization b over $(x^{(\alpha)}) \rightarrow (a^{(\alpha)})$ with reference to k_0; but then we have $z = x^{(\beta)}$, hence $b = a^{(\beta)}$. This shows that, in the given specialization $(a^{(\alpha)})$ of $(x^{(\alpha)})$, at least one of the $a^{(\alpha)}$ must be finite. In other words, this proves that $\boldsymbol{P}^n$ is a complete variety.

For $n = 0$, the "projective space" $\boldsymbol{P}^0$ is clearly reduced to a point. In the case $n = 1$, put $t = x_1/x_0$; then t is variable over k_0, and we have $x^{(0)} = (1, t)$ and $x^{(1)} = (1/t, 1)$; one sees at once that the mapping of $\boldsymbol{P}^1$ into $\boldsymbol{D}$, rational over k_0, which maps the point $\boldsymbol{x}$ of $\boldsymbol{P}^1$ with the representatives $x^{(0)}$ on P_0 and $x^{(1)}$ on P_1 onto the point of $\boldsymbol{D}$ with the coordinate $t = x_1/x_0$ is an isomorphism of $\boldsymbol{P}^1$ onto $\boldsymbol{D}$; one frequently identifies $\boldsymbol{D}$ with $\boldsymbol{P}^1$ by means of this isomorphism.

Notations being as above, call $\boldsymbol{x}$ the generic point of $\boldsymbol{P}^n$ over k_0 with the representative $x^{(\alpha)}$ in P_α for every α; we can then define a mapping $\boldsymbol{p}$ of S_*^{n+1} into $\boldsymbol{P}^n$, rational over k_0, by putting $\boldsymbol{p}(x) = \boldsymbol{x}$. As p_α is everywhere defined on S_α, $\boldsymbol{p}$ is everywhere defined on the union of the open sets S_α, i.e. on S_*^{n+1}. The mapping $\boldsymbol{p}$ will be called *the canonical morphism of* S_*^{n+1} *into* $\boldsymbol{P}^n$.

Let $\boldsymbol{a}$ be a point of $\boldsymbol{P}^n$ with a representative $a^{(\alpha)}$ in P_α; $\boldsymbol{a}$ is the image of a point a of S_*^{n+1} by $\boldsymbol{p}$ if and only if p_α is defined and has the value $a^{(\alpha)}$ at a; in view of what has been proved above, this will be the case if and only if a and $a^{(\alpha)}$ determine the same ray in S_*^{n+1}. Therefore the set-theoretic inverse image of any point $\boldsymbol{a}$ of $\boldsymbol{P}^n$ by $\boldsymbol{p}$ is a ray in S_*^{n+1}, and this determines a one-to-one correspondence between the points of $\boldsymbol{P}^n$ and the rays in S_*^{n+1}. If a is in the ray corresponding to the point $\boldsymbol{a}$ in $\boldsymbol{P}^n$, i.e. if $\boldsymbol{a} = \boldsymbol{p}(a)$, one says that

$$a = (a_0, \cdots, a_n)$$

is "a set of homogeneous coordinates" for $\boldsymbol{a}$. If we denote by $\boldsymbol{P}_\alpha$ the open subset of $\boldsymbol{P}^n$ consisting of the points which have a representative in P_α, we see that a point $\boldsymbol{a} = \boldsymbol{p}(a)$ of $\boldsymbol{P}^n$ is in $\boldsymbol{P}_\alpha$ if and only if $R(a)$ has a point of intersection $a^{(\alpha)}$ with P_α, i.e. if and only if $a_\alpha \neq 0$; in other words, the set-theoretic inverse image of $\boldsymbol{P}_\alpha$ under $\boldsymbol{p}$ is S_α.

For each α, consider the mapping F_α of $P_\alpha \times S_*^1$ into S^{n+1}, rational over k_0, such that $F_\alpha(x^{(\alpha)}, t) = tx^{(\alpha)}$, where t is a variable quantity over $k_0(x)$, or, what amounts to the same, a generic point of S_*^1 over $k_0(x)$; one sees at once that this is an isomorphism of $P_\alpha \times S_*^1$ onto S_α, that $F_\alpha^{-1}(x) = (p_\alpha(x), x_\alpha)$, and that $p_\alpha \circ F_\alpha$ is the projection from $P_\alpha \times S_*^1$ to P_α. In view of the definitions given above, this shows that the canonical morphism $\boldsymbol{p}$ of S_*^{n+1} into $\boldsymbol{P}^n$ determines a k_0-fibering of S_*^{n+1} over $\boldsymbol{P}^n$ with the fibre S_*^1. Applying prop. 10 to this fibering, we get the following result:

PROPOSITION 12. *Let $\boldsymbol{p}$ be the canonical morphism of $S_*^{n+1} = S^{n+1} - \{0\}$ onto the projective space $\boldsymbol{P}^n$. Then a cycle $\boldsymbol{X}$ in S_*^{n+1} can be written as $\boldsymbol{X} = \boldsymbol{p}^{-1}(\boldsymbol{Y})$, where $\boldsymbol{Y}$ is a $\boldsymbol{P}^n$-cycle, if and only if its support $|\boldsymbol{X}|$ is the union of rays in S_*^{n+1}; when that is so, $\boldsymbol{X}$ is invariant under every automorphism $x \to \tau x$ of S_*^{n+1}, where τ is any quantity other than 0. The cycle $\boldsymbol{Y}$ is uniquely determined by $\boldsymbol{X}$; it is rational over a field k if and only if $\boldsymbol{X}$ is so; it is a variety if and only if $\boldsymbol{X}$ is one. Moreover, if $\boldsymbol{Y}$, $\boldsymbol{Y}'$ are two $\boldsymbol{P}^n$-cycles, we have $\boldsymbol{p}^{-1}(\boldsymbol{Y}\cdot\boldsymbol{Y}') = \boldsymbol{p}^{-1}(\boldsymbol{Y})\cdot\boldsymbol{p}^{-1}(\boldsymbol{Y}')$; and $\boldsymbol{Y}$, $\boldsymbol{Y}'$ intersect properly in $\boldsymbol{P}^n$ if and only if $\boldsymbol{p}^{-1}(\boldsymbol{Y})$, $\boldsymbol{p}^{-1}(\boldsymbol{Y}')$ do so in S_*^{n+1}.*

A subvariety of S_*^{n+1} is called a *cone* if it is a union of rays, i.e., by prop. 12, if it is of the form $\boldsymbol{p}^{-1}(\boldsymbol{Y})$, where $\boldsymbol{Y}$ is a subvariety of $\boldsymbol{P}^n$; as the closure of a ray R in S^{n+1} is obviously $R \cup \{0\}$, the extension to S^{n+1} of any cone C_* in S_*^{n+1} is $C = C_* \cup \{0\}$; this is called a *cone* in S^{n+1}. A cycle in S_*^{n+1}, or in S^{n+1}, is called *conical* if all its components are cones. With this definition, we have the following corollary to prop. 12:

COROLLARY 1. *A cycle $\boldsymbol{X}$ in S_*^{n+1} can be written as $\boldsymbol{X} = \boldsymbol{p}^{-1}(\boldsymbol{Y})$, where $\boldsymbol{Y}$ is a $\boldsymbol{P}^n$-cycle, if and only if it is conical. If k is a field of rationality for $\boldsymbol{X}$, $\boldsymbol{X}$ is conical if and only if it is invariant under the automorphism $x \to tx$ of S_*^{n+1}, where t is a variable quantity over k.*

In view of prop. 12, only the last point has to be verified. Let $\boldsymbol{X}$ be a cycle in S_*^{n+1}, rational over k, and invariant under $x \to tx$, where t is variable over k. Let V be a component of $\boldsymbol{X}$, v a generic point of V over $\bar{k}(t)$, and V' the locus of tv over $\bar{k}$. As $\boldsymbol{X}$ is invariant under $x \to tx$, tv is in $|\boldsymbol{X}|$; as $|\boldsymbol{X}|$ is k-closed, hence also $\bar{k}$-closed, the $\bar{k}$-closure V' of tv is contained in $|\boldsymbol{X}|$. As t and v are independent over $\bar{k}$, $(1, v)$ is a specialization of (t, v) over $\bar{k}$, so that v is a specialization of tv over $\bar{k}$; this implies that the locus V of v over $\bar{k}$ is contained in V'; as V is a component of $\boldsymbol{X}$, and as V' is contained in $|\boldsymbol{X}|$, this implies that $V = V'$. Now let v' be any point of V; the ray $R(v')$ through v' consists of the points $t'v'$, where t' is any quantity other than 0; as (t', v') is then a specialization of (t, v) over $\bar{k}$, $t'v'$ is a specialization of tv over $\bar{k}$; as tv is in V, $t'v'$ is therefore in V. This shows that V is a cone; therefore $\boldsymbol{X}$ is a conical cycle.

COROLLARY 2. *A variety V in S^{n+1} is a cone, rational over a field k, if and only if it has a set of equations $F_\mu(X) = 0$, where every F_μ is a homogeneous polynomial in $X_0, \cdots, X_n$, with coefficients in k. If V is of codimension 1, then it can be defined over k by a single homogeneous equation $F(X) = 0$.*

If V is defined by a set of homogeneous equations, one sees at once that it is a cone. Conversely, let V be a cone in S^{n+1}, rational over k; let P be any polynomial in the ideal $\mathfrak{P}$ which defines V over k; write it as $P = \sum_{i=0}^{d} P_i$, where P_i is, for every i, a homogeneous polynomial of degree i. Let v be a generic point of V over k; let t be variable over $k(v)$; as tv is in V, we have

$$P(tv) = \sum_{i=0}^{d} t^i P_i(v) = 0.$$

As $k(t)$ and $k(v)$ are linearly disjoint over k, and as the t^i, for $0 \leqq i \leqq d$, are linearly independent over k, this implies that $P_i(v) = 0$ for every i, so that each P_i is in the ideal $\mathfrak{P}$. Applying this to all the polynomials in a basis for $\mathfrak{P}$, we see that we get for $\mathfrak{P}$ another basis consisting of homogeneous polynomials. If V is of dimension n, then, by prop. 2 of Chap. IV, §1, $\mathfrak{P}$ has a basis consisting of a single polynomial P; if the homogeneous polynomials P_i are defined as above, we see that each P_i must be a multiple of P in $k[X]$; if P is of degree d, this implies that $P_i = 0$ for $i < d$, so that $P = P_d$.

By prop. 12, we determine a one-to-one correspondence between the varieties $\boldsymbol{W}$ of dimension r in $\boldsymbol{P}^n$, the cones C_* of dimension $r + 1$ in S_*^{n+1}, and the cones C of dimension $r + 1$ in S^{n+1}, by putting $C_* = p^{-1}(\boldsymbol{W})$, $C = C_* \cup \{0\}$; any set of homogeneous equations for the cone C will be called *a set of homogeneous equations for* $\boldsymbol{W}$ *in* $\boldsymbol{P}^n$. Obviously any linear subspace of S^{n+1}, i.e. any linear subvariety of S^{n+1} containing 0, is a cone; a subvariety of $\boldsymbol{P}^n$ is called *linear* if it corresponds to a linear subspace of S^{n+1}, i.e. if it can be defined by a set of homogeneous linear equations. A point in $\boldsymbol{P}^n$ corresponds to a ray in S_*^{n+1} and is therefore a linear variety of dimension 0. A linear variety of codimension 1 in $\boldsymbol{P}^n$ is called a *hyperplane*; a subvariety of $\boldsymbol{P}^n$ is linear if and only if it can be written as the intersection of a set of hyperplanes. Let $\boldsymbol{W}$ be any subvariety of $\boldsymbol{P}^n$; the intersection of all the hyperplanes containing $\boldsymbol{W}$ is a linear variety $L(\boldsymbol{W})$; more precisely, it is the smallest linear variety containing $\boldsymbol{W}$. If $\boldsymbol{W}$ is rational over a field k, so is $L(\boldsymbol{W})$; in fact, if $\mathfrak{P}$ is the ideal in $k[X_0, \cdots, X_n]$ defining the cone in S^{n+1} which corresponds to $\boldsymbol{W}$, and if the linear forms $L_\mu(X)$ are a basis for the set of linear forms contained in $\mathfrak{P}$, one sees at once that $L(\boldsymbol{W})$ is defined by the equations $L_\mu(X) = 0$.

A subvariety $\boldsymbol{W}$ of $\boldsymbol{P}^n$ is called a *hypersurface* if it has the codimension 1 in $\boldsymbol{P}^n$; by coroll. 2 of prop. 12, this is so if and only if $\boldsymbol{W}$ can be defined by a single homogeneous equation $F(X) = 0$, which is then uniquely determined up to a constant factor; the degree of the homogeneous polynomial F will be called *the degree of* $\boldsymbol{W}$, and also of the cones in S_*^{n+1} and in S^{n+1} which correspond to $\boldsymbol{W}$; it will be denoted by $\deg(\boldsymbol{W})$. A hypersurface is a hyperplane if and only if its degree is 1. If $\boldsymbol{X}$ is a divisor in $\boldsymbol{P}^n$, with the components $\boldsymbol{W}_\mu$, and if

$$\boldsymbol{X} = \sum_\mu a_\mu \boldsymbol{W}_\mu,$$

the integer $\sum_\mu a_\mu \cdot \deg(\boldsymbol{W}_\mu)$ is called *the degree of* $\boldsymbol{X}$ (or also of the corresponding conical divisors in S_*^{n+1} and S^{n+1}) and is denoted by $\deg(\boldsymbol{X})$. For $n = 1$, divisors in $\boldsymbol{P}^1$ are the same as 0-cycles in $\boldsymbol{P}^1$; as every point is a linear variety, the definition of the degree of a divisor in $\boldsymbol{P}^1$, as given here, coincides in this case with the definition for the degree of a 0-cycle, as given in Chap. VIII, §2.

PROPOSITION 13. *A divisor in S^{n+1} is a conical divisor of degree d if and only if it is the divisor of a homogeneous rational function of degree d in $X_0, \cdots, X_n$.*

Let $\boldsymbol{X}$ be a conical divisor of degree d with the components V_μ; put

$$\boldsymbol{X} = \sum_\mu a_\mu V_\mu .$$

Each V_μ is defined by a homogeneous equation $F_\mu(X) = 0$, of degree d_μ equal to the degree of V_μ; by th. 5 of §4, we have $V_\mu = \text{div}(F_\mu)$, so that $\boldsymbol{X} = \text{div}(F)$ with $F = \prod_\mu F_\mu^{a_\mu}$; and F is homogeneous of degree $\sum_\mu a_\mu d_\mu$, equal to the degree d of $\boldsymbol{X}$. Conversely, if F is homogeneous of degree d, with coefficients in k, and if t is variable over k, we have $F(tX) = t^d F(X)$, so that $\text{div}(F)$ is invariant under the automorphism $x \to tx$ of S^{n+1}; by coroll. 1 of prop. 12, this implies that the restriction of $\text{div}(F)$ to S_*^{n+1}, hence also $\text{div}(F)$ itself, are conical divisors; in view of what we have already proved, and of the unicity statement in the corollary of th. 5, §4, $\text{div}(F)$ must then be of degree d.

COROLLARY 1. *A divisor in $\boldsymbol{P}^n$ is the divisor of a function in $\boldsymbol{P}^n$ if and only if it is of degree 0.*

Let $\boldsymbol{Y}$ be a divisor of degree d in $\boldsymbol{P}^n$; let $\boldsymbol{X}$ be the extension of $\boldsymbol{p}^{-1}(\boldsymbol{Y})$ to S^{n+1}; this is a conical divisor of degree d, hence, by prop. 13, the divisor of a homogeneous rational function F of degree d in $X_0, \cdots, X_n$. If $\boldsymbol{Y} = \text{div}(\varphi)$, where φ is a function in $\boldsymbol{P}^n$, prop. 3 of §2 shows that $\text{div}(\varphi \circ \boldsymbol{p}) = \boldsymbol{p}^{-1}(\boldsymbol{Y})$, so that $\boldsymbol{X}$ is the divisor of the extension of $\varphi \circ \boldsymbol{p}$ to S^{n+1}, which must therefore, by the corollary of th. 5, §4, coincide with F up to a constant factor. Let k be a field of rationality for F and φ; let x be generic over k in S^{n+1}; let t be variable over $k(x)$; then we have just shown that $\varphi(\boldsymbol{p}(x)) = cF(x)$, where c is a constant; we have $\boldsymbol{p}(tx) = \boldsymbol{p}(x)$, and on the other hand $F(tx) = t^d F(x)$ since F is of degree d; this gives $d = 0$. Conversely, assume that F is homogeneous of degree 0; then we have $F(x) = F(p_\alpha(x))$ for every α; this shows that $F(x)$ is in $k(\boldsymbol{p}(x))$ and can therefore be written as $\varphi(\boldsymbol{p}(x))$, where φ is a function in $\boldsymbol{P}^n$, rational over k, so that the restriction of F to S_*^{n+1} coincides with $\varphi \circ \boldsymbol{p}$. This gives $\boldsymbol{p}^{-1}(\boldsymbol{Y}) = \text{div}(\varphi \circ \boldsymbol{p})$; $\text{div}(\varphi \circ \boldsymbol{p})$ is the same as $\boldsymbol{p}^{-1}(\text{div}(\varphi))$; in view of prop. 12, this implies $\boldsymbol{Y} = \text{div}(\varphi)$.

COROLLARY 2. *Let $\boldsymbol{Y}$ be a divisor of degree d in $\boldsymbol{P}^n$; let $\boldsymbol{X}$ be the extension of $\boldsymbol{p}^{-1}(\boldsymbol{Y})$ to S^{n+1}; let F be a homogeneous rational function of degree d in $X_0, \cdots, X_n$ such that $\boldsymbol{X} = \text{div}(F)$. Then, to every function φ on $\boldsymbol{P}^n$ such that $\text{div}(\varphi) \succ -\boldsymbol{Y}$, there is a homogeneous polynomial P of degree d such that $\varphi \circ \boldsymbol{p} = P(X)/F(X)$; and this determines a one-to-one linear correspondence between the space $\mathfrak{L}(\boldsymbol{Y})$ of such functions φ and the space of homogeneous polynomials of degree d in $X_0, \cdots, X_n$.*

Let φ be any function in $\mathfrak{L}(\boldsymbol{Y})$, other than the constant 0; then, if we put $\operatorname{div}(\varphi) = \boldsymbol{Z} - \boldsymbol{Y}$, $\boldsymbol{Z}$ is a positive divisor, and, by coroll. 1, it is of degree d. By prop. 13, the extension to S^{n+1} of $\boldsymbol{p}^{-1}(\boldsymbol{Z})$ is the divisor of a homogeneous rational function P of degree d; by the corollary of th. 5, §4, P is a polynomial. Then $\operatorname{div}(P/F)$ coincides with the extension to S^{n+1} of $\operatorname{div}(\varphi \circ \boldsymbol{p}) = \boldsymbol{p}^{-1}(\operatorname{div}(\varphi))$, so that, by the same corollary, we must have $\varphi \circ \boldsymbol{p} = cP/F$, where c is a constant; replacing P by cP, we get the first assertion in our corollary. Conversely, let P be any homogeneous polynomial of degree d; by prop. 13, $\operatorname{div}(P)$ is a positive conical divisor of degree d, whose restriction to S_*^{n+1} can therefore be written as $\boldsymbol{p}^{-1}(\boldsymbol{Z})$, where $\boldsymbol{Z}$ is a positive divisor of degree d in $\boldsymbol{P}^n$. By coroll. 1, $\boldsymbol{Z} - \boldsymbol{Y}$ is the divisor of a function φ in $\boldsymbol{P}^n$, and we see as above that P/F must coincide with $\varphi \circ \boldsymbol{p}$ up to a constant factor, so that, after replacing φ by $c\varphi$, where c is a suitable constant, we have $P/F = \varphi \circ \boldsymbol{p}$.

Corollary 3. *Let $\boldsymbol{H}$ be a hyperplane in $\boldsymbol{P}^n$, defined by the homogeneous equation $L(X) = 0$; let $\boldsymbol{L}$ be the linear variety defined in S^{n+1} by the equation $L(X) = 1$. Then the vector-space $\mathfrak{L}(\boldsymbol{H})$ has a basis over the field of constants, consisting of the functions φ_α determined by $\varphi_\alpha \circ \boldsymbol{p} = X_\alpha/L(X)$ for $0 \leqq \alpha \leqq n$; and $\boldsymbol{p}$ induces on $\boldsymbol{L}$ an isomorphism of $\boldsymbol{L}$ onto $\boldsymbol{P}^n - \boldsymbol{H}$, whose inverse is the mapping induced on $\boldsymbol{P}^n - \boldsymbol{H}$ by the mapping $\Phi = (\varphi_0, \cdots, \varphi_n)$ of $\boldsymbol{P}^n$ into S^{n+1}.*

The first assertion is nothing but a special case of coroll. 2. Now let x be any point of S_*^{n+1} such that $L(x) \neq 0$, or, what amounts to the same, that the point $\boldsymbol{x} = \boldsymbol{p}(x)$ is not in $\boldsymbol{H}$; then we have $\varphi_\alpha(\boldsymbol{x}) = x_\alpha/L(x)$, hence $\Phi(\boldsymbol{x}) = L(x)^{-1}x$, which shows that $\Phi(\boldsymbol{x})$ is the point of intersection of the ray $R(x)$ and of $\boldsymbol{L}$. In particular, if $x \in \boldsymbol{L}$, we have $\Phi(\boldsymbol{x}) = x$, which shows that $\Phi \circ \boldsymbol{p}$ induces on $\boldsymbol{L}$ the identity mapping. Taking for x a generic point of S^{n+1} over a field k containing the coefficients of $L(X)$, we see that the geometric image of $\boldsymbol{P}^n$ by Φ is contained in $\boldsymbol{L}$, so that Φ may be regarded as a mapping of $\boldsymbol{P}^n$ into $\boldsymbol{L}$. On the other hand, the φ_α are everywhere defined on $\boldsymbol{P}^n - \boldsymbol{H}$ (e.g. by th. 1 of §2), so that the same is true of Φ. As $\Phi(\boldsymbol{x})$ is in $R(x)$, $\boldsymbol{p} \circ \Phi$ is the identity mapping of $\boldsymbol{P}^n$. As $\boldsymbol{p}$ maps every point of $\boldsymbol{L}$ onto a point of $\boldsymbol{P}^n - \boldsymbol{H}$, and Φ maps every point of $\boldsymbol{P}^n - \boldsymbol{H}$ onto a point of $\boldsymbol{L}$, this completes the proof.

Proposition 14. *Let $\boldsymbol{p}$ be the canonical mapping of S_*^{n+1} onto $\boldsymbol{P}^n$. Let f be a mapping, rational over a field k, of S_*^{n+1} into a variety $\boldsymbol{W}$; let x be a generic point of S_*^{n+1} over k, and let t be a variable quantity over $k(x)$. Then there is a mapping g of $\boldsymbol{P}^n$ into $\boldsymbol{W}$, such that $f = g \circ \boldsymbol{p}$, if and only if $f(tx) = f(x)$. When that is so, g is uniquely determined and is rational over k; f is defined at a point a of S_*^{n+1} if and only if g is defined at $\boldsymbol{a} = \boldsymbol{p}(a)$; and f is a morphism if and only if g is one.*

Assume that $f(tx) = f(x)$, and put $x^{(\alpha)} = x_\alpha^{-1}x$; one sees at once that $(x_\alpha, tx^{(\alpha)})$ is a generic specialization of (t, x) over k; therefore we have $f(x_\alpha tx^{(\alpha)}) = f(tx^{(\alpha)})$; as $x_\alpha tx^{(\alpha)} = tx$, this gives

$$f(x) = f(tx) = f(tx^{(\alpha)}),$$

so that, if we put $K = k(x^{(\alpha)})$, $f(x)$ is rational over $K(t)$; it is also rational over $k(x) = K(x_\alpha)$. This means that every coordinate of any representative of the point $f(x)$ is in $K(t)$ and in $K(x_\alpha)$, hence in the intersection of these fields. As x_α and t are independent variables over K, $K(x_\alpha)$ and $K(t)$ are linearly disjoint over K, and their intersection is K. We have thus shown that $f(x)$ is rational over $K = k(\boldsymbol{p}(x))$, so that it can be written as $g(\boldsymbol{p}(x))$, where g is a mapping of $\boldsymbol{P}^n$ into $\boldsymbol{W}$, rational over k. Conversely, assume that $f = g' \circ \boldsymbol{p}$, where g' is a mapping of $\boldsymbol{P}^n$ into $\boldsymbol{W}$; let k' be a field of rationality for g', containing k; let x' be a generic point of S_*^{n+1} over k', and t' a variable over $k'(x')$. As $\boldsymbol{p}(t'x') = \boldsymbol{p}(x')$, and $f(x') = g'(\boldsymbol{p}(x'))$, we have $f(t'x') = f(x')$; as (t, x) is a generic specialization of (t', x') over k, this gives $f(tx) = f(x)$; therefore, as we have seen, there is a mapping g of $\boldsymbol{P}^n$ into $\boldsymbol{W}$, rational over k, such that $f = g \circ \boldsymbol{p}$; we have then $g'(\boldsymbol{p}(x')) = g(\boldsymbol{p}(x'))$, which implies that $g = g'$. The other assertions in prop. 14 are special cases of prop. 11.

COROLLARY. *Let A be a morphism of S_*^{n+1} into S_*^{m+1}, determined by a linear homogeneous mapping of S^{n+1} into S^{m+1}; let $\boldsymbol{p}$, $\boldsymbol{q}$ be the canonical morphisms of S_*^{n+1} onto $\boldsymbol{P}^n$ and of S_*^{m+1} onto $\boldsymbol{P}^m$, respectively. Then there is a morphism α of $\boldsymbol{P}^n$ into $\boldsymbol{P}^m$ such that $\boldsymbol{q} \circ A = \alpha \circ \boldsymbol{p}$; and α determines an isomorphism of every linear subvariety of $\boldsymbol{P}^n$ onto a linear subvariety of $\boldsymbol{P}^m$. In particular, if $n = m$, α is an automorphism of $\boldsymbol{P}^n$.*

The assumption on A means that there is a matrix M such that $A(x) = Mx$ for every point x of S_*^{n+1}; as A is a morphism of S_*^{n+1} into S_*^{m+1}, we must have $Mx \neq 0$ for $x \neq 0$, so that M must be of rank $n + 1$, which implies that $m \geqq n$. We have, for $t \neq 0$:

$$\boldsymbol{q}(A(tx)) = \boldsymbol{q}(tA(x)) = \boldsymbol{q}(A(x));$$

by prop. 14, this implies our first assertion. Let k be a field containing all the coefficients in M; let $\boldsymbol{L}$ be a linear subvariety of $\boldsymbol{P}^n$, rational over a field K containing k; the cone corresponding to $\boldsymbol{L}$ in S^{n+1} is a linear subspace L of S^{n+1}, rational over K; and, if x is a generic point of L over K, $\boldsymbol{L}$ is the locus of $\boldsymbol{p}(x)$ over K. We have $\alpha(\boldsymbol{p}(x)) = \boldsymbol{q}(A(x))$; as the locus of $A(x) = Mx$ over K in S^{m+1} is a linear subspace of S^{m+1}, the locus of $\boldsymbol{q}(A(x))$, which is the geometric image of $\boldsymbol{L}$ by α, is a linear subvariety of $\boldsymbol{P}^m$. Now, in order to prove the last assertion in our corollary, it is enough to show that α determines an isomorphism of $\boldsymbol{P}^n$ onto the linear subvariety of $\boldsymbol{P}^m$ which is the geometric image of $\boldsymbol{P}^n$ by α. In fact, we can find a matrix N with coefficients in k, such that $N \cdot M = 1_{n+1}$; this determines a mapping B (not a morphism, unless $n = m$) of S_*^{m+1} into S_*^{n+1}, such that $B(y) = Ny$ for every point y of S_*^{m+1} for which $Ny \neq 0$; and, as above, there is a mapping β of $\boldsymbol{P}^m$ into $\boldsymbol{P}^n$ such that $\boldsymbol{p} \circ B = \beta \circ \boldsymbol{q}$. Let L^{n+1} be the image of S^{n+1} in S^{m+1} under the mapping $x \rightarrow Mx$; then the geometric image of $\boldsymbol{P}^n$ by α is the linear subvariety $\boldsymbol{L}^n$ of $\boldsymbol{P}^m$ corresponding to the linear subspace L^{n+1} of S^{m+1}. As $N \cdot M = 1_{n+1}$, we have $Ny \neq 0$ for every point y in L^{n+1}, other than 0; this shows that the mapping B of S_*^{m+1} into S_*^{n+1} is defined at every point of the restriction of L^{n+1} to S_*^{m+1}, so that, by prop. 14, β is everywhere defined on L^n; moreover, $B \circ A$ is the identity mapping of S_*^{n+1}, so that we have

$$p = p \circ B \circ A = \beta \circ q \circ A = \beta \circ \alpha \circ p,$$

which shows that $\beta \circ \alpha$ is the identity mapping of P^n. Therefore, if x is generic over k in P^n, and if we put $y = \alpha(x)$, we have $x = \beta(y)$, hence $k(x) = k(y)$; this shows that α is a birational mapping of P^n into L^n, whose inverse is the mapping of L^n into P^n induced on L^n by β. As α is everywhere defined on P^n and β on L^n, this completes our proof.

Whenever α is as defined in the corollary of prop. 14, we will say that it is a *linear morphism* of P^n into P^m; for $m = n$, it will be called a *linear automorphism* of P^n. As an immediate consequence of our corollary, we see that, if Q^n is any linear subvariety of P^m, rational over a field k, there always exists a linear morphism of P^n into P^m, rational over k, which determines an isomorphism of P^n onto Q^n; and such a morphism is uniquely determined up to a linear automorphism of P^n, rational over k. One frequently makes use of this fact in order to identify a linear variety in a projective space with a projective space.

We will now study mappings of arbitrary varieties into the projective space P^n; for $n = 1$, such a mapping is essentially the same as a function, as defined in §2. In order to avoid trivial complications, it will be agreed, from now on, that, *whenever we consider a mapping f of a variety into a projective space P^n, f is assumed not to be constant*; this implies that $n \geqq 1$. Correspondingly, from now on, whenever we consider a reduced linear system Λ on a variety V, it is to be understood that Λ *is neither empty nor reduced to* $\{0\}$.

PROPOSITION 15. *Let f be a mapping of a variety V into the projective space P^n. Let H, H' be two distinct hyperplanes in P^n, and let φ be a function in P^n such that* $\operatorname{div}(\varphi) = H - H'$. *Then $\varphi \circ f$ is defined and is a function on V if and only if H' does not contain the geometric image of V by f; it is not the constant 0 if and only if H does not contain that image; and then we have*

$$\operatorname{div}(\varphi \circ f) = f^{-1}(H) - f^{-1}(H').$$

The first assertions are immediate consequences of th. 1, §2; and the last formula is a special case of prop. 3, §2.

We can now generalize part of th. 1, §2, to mappings into projective spaces, as follows:

THEOREM 10. *Let f be a mapping of a variety V into the projective space P^n; let H be a hyperplane in P^n, not containing the geometric image of V by f; let W be a simple subvariety of V. Then W is contained in the support of $f^{-1}(H)$ if and only if either f is not defined along W, or f is defined along W and the geometric image of W by f is contained in H.*

Let k be a field of rationality for V, f, H and W; let M be a generic point of

$\boldsymbol{W}$ over k. As $|f^{-1}(\boldsymbol{H})|$ is k-closed, it contains $\boldsymbol{W}$ if and only if it contains $\boldsymbol{M}$. On the other hand, f is defined along $\boldsymbol{W}$ if and only if it is defined at $\boldsymbol{M}$; and, when that is so, the geometric image of $\boldsymbol{W}$ by f is the locus of $f(\boldsymbol{M})$ over k, so that it is contained in $\boldsymbol{H}$ if and only if $f(\boldsymbol{M})$ is in $\boldsymbol{H}$. It is therefore enough to prove our theorem in the case when $\boldsymbol{W}$ is reduced to a point $\boldsymbol{M}$. Let us first assume that $\boldsymbol{M}$ is in $|f^{-1}(\boldsymbol{H})|$; then it is in the geometric projection on $\boldsymbol{V}$ of some component $\boldsymbol{Z}$ of $\boldsymbol{\Gamma}_f\cdot(\boldsymbol{V}\times\boldsymbol{H})$. By th. 7 of Chap. VII, §5, $\boldsymbol{Z}$ is complete over $\boldsymbol{M}$, so that it contains a point $\boldsymbol{M}\times\boldsymbol{N}$ with the projection $\boldsymbol{M}$ on $\boldsymbol{V}$. As $\boldsymbol{M}\times\boldsymbol{N}$ is in $\boldsymbol{V}\times\boldsymbol{H}$, $\boldsymbol{N}$ is in $\boldsymbol{H}$; as $\boldsymbol{M}\times\boldsymbol{N}$ is in $\boldsymbol{\Gamma}_f$, f is either not defined at $\boldsymbol{M}$, or it is defined there and we have $\boldsymbol{N} = f(\boldsymbol{M})$; therefore, in the latter case, $f(\boldsymbol{M})$ is in $\boldsymbol{H}$. Now assume that $\boldsymbol{M}$ is not in $|f^{-1}(\boldsymbol{H})|$; we will prove that, when that is so, f is defined at $\boldsymbol{M}$, and $f(\boldsymbol{M})$ is not in $\boldsymbol{H}$; this will complete the proof of our theorem. Let $L(X) = 0$ be a homogeneous equation for $\boldsymbol{H}$; $L(X)$ is a linear form, and we may assume that its coefficients are in k. Let $\boldsymbol{p}$ be the canonical mapping of S_*^{n+1} onto $\boldsymbol{P}^n$; let the φ_α be the functions on $\boldsymbol{P}^n$ defined by $\varphi_\alpha\circ\boldsymbol{p} = X_\alpha/L(X)$. By coroll. 3 of prop. 13, $\Phi = (\varphi_0, \cdots, \varphi_n)$ determines an isomorphism of $\boldsymbol{P}^n - \boldsymbol{H}$ onto the linear variety $\boldsymbol{L}$ defined in S^{n+1} by the equation $L(X) = 1$. Put $\psi_\alpha = \varphi_\alpha\circ f$ and $\Psi = \Phi\circ f$; by prop. 15, the ψ_α are functions on $\boldsymbol{V}$, satisfying $\operatorname{div}(\psi_\alpha) \succ -f^{-1}(\boldsymbol{H})$; as $\boldsymbol{M}$ is not in $|f^{-1}(\boldsymbol{H})|$, th. 1 of §2 shows that all the ψ_α are defined and finite at $\boldsymbol{M}$; therefore Ψ is defined at $\boldsymbol{M}$. Now, again by coroll. 3 of prop. 13, $\boldsymbol{p}\circ\Phi$ is the identity mapping of $\boldsymbol{P}^n$, so that we have $\boldsymbol{p}\circ\Psi = \boldsymbol{p}\circ\Phi\circ f = f$; this shows that f is defined at $\boldsymbol{M}$. Also, as $\Psi(\boldsymbol{M})$ is in $\boldsymbol{L}$, $f(\boldsymbol{M})$, which is the same as $\boldsymbol{p}(\Psi(M))$, is in $\boldsymbol{P}^n - \boldsymbol{H}$, again by coroll. 3 of prop. 13; so it is not in $\boldsymbol{H}$.

If $\boldsymbol{M}$ is merely assumed not to be contained in any multiple subvariety of $\boldsymbol{V}$ of codimension 1, we can still conclude that all the ψ_α are finite at $\boldsymbol{M}$; if $\boldsymbol{M}$ has the property of "normality" (as defined in App. I), this again implies that the ψ_α are defined at $\boldsymbol{M}$, and the proof can proceed as above. This shows that *th.* 10 *remains valid if* $\boldsymbol{V}$ *is merely assumed to be normal along* $\boldsymbol{W}$.

Corollary 1. *Let* $\boldsymbol{V}$ *and* f *be as in th.* 10, *and let* $\boldsymbol{H}_0, \cdots, \boldsymbol{H}_n$ *be* $n + 1$ *hyperplanes in* $\boldsymbol{P}^n$ *with an empty intersection, none of which contains the geometric image of* $\boldsymbol{V}$ *by* f. *Then a simple subvariety* $\boldsymbol{W}$ *of* $\boldsymbol{V}$ *is contained in* $\bigcap_\alpha |f^{-1}(\boldsymbol{H}_\alpha)|$ *if and only if* f *is not defined along* $\boldsymbol{W}$.

This follows at once from th. 10; as observed above, it remains true if one merely assumes that $\boldsymbol{V}$ is normal along $\boldsymbol{W}$.

Corollary 2. *Let* $\boldsymbol{V}$, f *and the* $\boldsymbol{H}_\alpha$ *be as in coroll.* 1. *Then no subvariety of* $\boldsymbol{V}$ *is a component of all the divisors* $f^{-1}(\boldsymbol{H}_\alpha)$.

In fact, such a variety $\boldsymbol{W}$ would have to be simple and of codimension 1 on $\boldsymbol{V}$; but then, by coroll. 1 of th. 9, Chap. VII, §7, f is defined along $\boldsymbol{W}$.

Corollary 3. *Let* $\boldsymbol{V}$, f *and* $\boldsymbol{H}$ *be as in th.* 10. *Then we have*

$$-f^{-1}(\boldsymbol{H}) = \inf_{\varphi\in\mathfrak{L}(\boldsymbol{H})} \operatorname{div}(\varphi\circ f).$$

By coroll. 2 and 3 of prop. 13, if $L(X) = 0$ is a homogeneous equation for H, $\mathfrak{L}(H)$ consists of the functions φ on P^n for which $\varphi \circ p = L'(X)/L(X)$, where $L'(X)$ is a linear form; and, for such a function, we have

$$\mathrm{div}(\varphi) = H' - H,$$

where H' is the hyperplane with the equation $L'(X) = 0$. By prop. 15, we have $\varphi \circ f = 0$ if H' contains the geometric image of V by f, and

$$\mathrm{div}(\varphi \circ f) = f^{-1}(H') - f^{-1}(H)$$

otherwise. Our assertion is now seen to be equivalent to $\inf_{H'} f^{-1}(H') = 0$; as coroll. 2 shows that $\inf_\alpha f^{-1}(H_\alpha) = 0$, this proves our corollary.

THEOREM 11. *A set of divisors Λ on a variety V is a reduced linear system if and only if there is a mapping f of V into a projective space P^n, such that Λ consists of the divisors $f^{-1}(H)$ when one takes for H all the hyperplanes in P^n, not containing the geometric image of V by f. Moreover, if Λ is given, there is such a mapping f, for which the geometric image of V by f is not contained in any hyperplane; this mapping f is uniquely determined up to a linear automorphism of P^n.*

Let f be a mapping of V into P^n; let H_0 be a hyperplane in P^n, not containing the geometric image of V by f; let $L_0(X) = 0$ be a homogeneous equation for H_0. By coroll. 3 of prop. 13, the vector-space $\mathfrak{L}(H_0)$ consists of the functions φ on P^n, defined by $\varphi \circ p = L(X)/L_0(X)$, where $L(X)$ is a linear form; for such a function φ, other than the constant 0, we have $\mathrm{div}(\varphi) = H - H_0$, where H is the hyperplane $L(X) = 0$. By prop. 15, the mapping $\varphi \to \psi = \varphi \circ f$ maps $\mathfrak{L}(H_0)$ onto a vector-space $\mathfrak{L}$ of functions on V; the kernel of that mapping consists of the functions φ for which H contains the geometric image of V by f; and, for any φ not in that kernel, we have $\mathrm{div}(\psi) = f^{-1}(H) - f^{-1}(H_0)$. The reduced linear system determined on V by the vector-space $\mathfrak{L}$ consists of the divisors $\mathrm{div}(\psi) - \inf_{\mathfrak{L}} \mathrm{div}(\psi)$; in view of coroll. 3 of th. 10, this is the same as the set of all divisors $f^{-1}(H)$, when one takes for H all the hyperplanes which do not contain the geometric image of V by f. Conversely, consider any reduced linear system Λ, determined on V by a vector-space $\mathfrak{L}$ of functions on V, of dimension $n + 1$ over the field of constants; let $\lambda_0, \cdots, \lambda_n$ be a basis for $\mathfrak{L}$. The λ_α are linearly independent over the field of constants; in particular, none of them is 0; therefore we may consider $F = (\lambda_0, \cdots, \lambda_n)$ as a mapping of V into S_*^{n+1}; put $f = p \circ F$. If the geometric image of V by f were contained in a hyperplane H, with the equation $L(X) = 0$, the geometric image of V by F would be contained in $p^{-1}(H)$, hence in the linear variety defined in S^{n+1} by the equation $L(X) = 0$; this means that we would have $L(\lambda_0, \cdots, \lambda_n) = 0$, which is against our assumption. That being so, by what we have proved above, the divisors $f^{-1}(H)$ make up a reduced linear system Λ_1 when one takes for H all the hyperplanes in P^n; moreover, if H_0 is a hyperplane with the equation $L_0(X) = 0$, Λ_1 is the reduced linear system determined by the vector-space $\mathfrak{L}_1$ consisting of the functions $\psi = \varphi \circ f$ when one takes for φ all the functions in $\mathfrak{L}(H_0)$, i.e. all the functions on P^n such that $\varphi \circ p = L(X)/L_0(X)$, where

$L(X)$ is a linear form. But then we have

$$\psi = \varphi \circ \boldsymbol{p} \circ F = L(\lambda_0, \cdots, \lambda_n)/L_0(\lambda_0, \cdots, \lambda_n),$$

and therefore $\mathfrak{L}_1 = \mu^{-1}\mathfrak{L}$ with $\mu = L_0(\lambda_0, \cdots, \lambda_n)$; this implies that $\mathfrak{L}$ and $\mathfrak{L}_1$ determine the same reduced linear system, i.e. that $\Lambda = \Lambda_1$. Now let f' be another mapping of $\boldsymbol{V}$ into a projective space $\boldsymbol{P}^{n'}$, such that the geometric image of $\boldsymbol{V}$ by f' is not contained in any hyperplane and that Λ is the set of all divisors $f'^{-1}(\boldsymbol{H}')$ when one takes for $\boldsymbol{H}'$ all the hyperplanes in $\boldsymbol{P}^{n'}$. Take any hyperplane $\boldsymbol{H}_0'$ in $\boldsymbol{P}^{n'}$; as above, Λ is then the reduced linear system determined by the vector-space $\mathfrak{L}_1'$ of the functions $\varphi' \circ f'$ with $\varphi' \in \mathfrak{L}(\boldsymbol{H}_0')$. By prop. 9, $\mathfrak{L}_1'$ must be equivalent to $\mathfrak{L}_1$, so that we have $\mathfrak{L}_1' = \theta\,\mathfrak{L}_1$, where θ is a function other than 0; this implies that $n' = n$, so that we may take $\boldsymbol{H}_0' = \boldsymbol{H}_0$; bases for $\mathfrak{L}_1, \mathfrak{L}_1'$ consist of the functions $\varphi_\alpha \circ f$, $\varphi_\alpha \circ f'$, with $\varphi_\alpha \circ \boldsymbol{p} = X_\alpha/L_0(X)$. Then the relation $\mathfrak{L}_1' = \theta\mathfrak{L}_1$ means that there is an invertible matrix $M = \| m_{\alpha\beta} \|$ such that

$$\varphi_\alpha \circ f' = \theta \sum_\beta m_{\alpha\beta}\varphi_\beta \circ f.$$

As in coroll. 3 of prop. 13, put $\Phi = (\varphi_0, \cdots, \varphi_n)$, so that, by that corollary, $\boldsymbol{p} \circ \Phi$ is the identity mapping of $\boldsymbol{P}^n$; as in the corollary of prop. 14, call A the automorphism $x \rightarrow Mx$ of S_*^{n+1}, and call α the linear automorphism of $\boldsymbol{P}^n$ defined by $\boldsymbol{p} \circ A = \alpha \circ \boldsymbol{p}$. Then the above relations can be written

$$\Phi \circ f' = \theta \cdot A \circ \Phi \circ f,$$

which gives

$$f' = \boldsymbol{p} \circ \Phi \circ f' = \boldsymbol{p} \circ A \circ \Phi \circ f = \alpha \circ \boldsymbol{p} \circ \Phi \circ f = \alpha \circ f.$$

This completes our proof.

A mapping f of a variety $\boldsymbol{V}$ into a projective space $\boldsymbol{P}^n$ will be called *non-degenerate* if the geometric image of $\boldsymbol{V}$ by f is not contained in any hyperplane. Let f be an arbitrary mapping of $\boldsymbol{V}$ into $\boldsymbol{P}^n$; let $\boldsymbol{L}^r$ be the smallest linear subvariety of $\boldsymbol{P}^n$ containing the geometric image of $\boldsymbol{V}$ by f; by the corollary of prop. 14, there is a linear morphism α of $\boldsymbol{P}^r$ into $\boldsymbol{P}^n$ which determines an isomorphism of $\boldsymbol{P}^r$ onto $\boldsymbol{L}^r$; then we can write $f = \alpha \circ f'$, where f' is a mapping of $\boldsymbol{V}$ into $\boldsymbol{P}^r$; one sees at once that f' is non-degenerate, and also that α and f' are uniquely determined by f up to a linear automorphism of $\boldsymbol{P}^r$. If $\boldsymbol{X}$ is a cycle intersecting $\boldsymbol{L}^r$ properly in $\boldsymbol{P}^n$, th. 10 of Chap. VIII, §4, shows that $\alpha^{-1}(\boldsymbol{X})$ is the $\boldsymbol{P}^r$-cycle corresponding to $\boldsymbol{X} \cdot \boldsymbol{L}^r$ in the isomorphism between $\boldsymbol{P}^r$ and $\boldsymbol{L}^r$ determined by α; in particular, if $\boldsymbol{H}$ is a hyperplane in $\boldsymbol{P}^n$, not containing $\boldsymbol{L}^r$, $\alpha^{-1}(\boldsymbol{H})$ is the cycle in $\boldsymbol{P}^r$ corresponding to $\boldsymbol{H} \cdot \boldsymbol{L}^r$, which, by prop. 12, is the same as the linear variety $\boldsymbol{H} \cap \boldsymbol{L}^r$ of dimension $r - 1$; therefore $\alpha^{-1}(\boldsymbol{H})$ is a hyperplane in $\boldsymbol{P}^r$. Conversely, if $\boldsymbol{H}'$ is any hyperplane in $\boldsymbol{P}^r$, and if we take for $\boldsymbol{H}$ a hyperplane in $\boldsymbol{P}^n$ containing $\alpha(\boldsymbol{H}')$ and not $\boldsymbol{L}^r$, we have $\boldsymbol{H}' = \alpha^{-1}(\boldsymbol{H})$. Furthermore, th. 13(b) of Chap. VIII, §4, shows that, if $\boldsymbol{H}$ does not contain $\boldsymbol{L}^r$, then

$$f^{-1}(\boldsymbol{H}) = f'^{-1}(\alpha^{-1}(\boldsymbol{H})).$$

If f is a mapping of a variety V into a projective space $\boldsymbol{P}^n$, the linear system Λ_f consisting of the divisors $f^{-1}(\boldsymbol{H})$, when one takes for $\boldsymbol{H}$ all the hyperplanes not containing the geometric image of V by f, is said to be *determined by f*; by th. 11, a linear system is of this form if and only if it is reduced. As we have shown above, if f is such a mapping, one can write (in one and essentially one way) $f = \alpha \circ f'$, where f' is a non-degenerate mapping of V into a projective space $\boldsymbol{P}^r$, and α is a linear morphism of $\boldsymbol{P}^r$ into $\boldsymbol{P}^n$; and then the linear system determined by f' is the same as Λ_f. This shows again that every reduced linear system Λ on a variety V can be determined by a non-degenerate mapping of V into a projective space; by th. 11, this mapping is essentially unique, in the sense that it is unique up to a linear automorphism on the projective space; one says sometimes, by abuse of language, that it is the mapping determined by the linear system Λ.

Let again Λ be a reduced linear system on a variety V; let f be a non-degenerate mapping of V into a projective space $\boldsymbol{P}^n$, determining Λ on V; let V' be the geometric image of V by f; then we can write $f = j \circ g$, where j is the injection mapping of V' into $\boldsymbol{P}^n$ and g is a mapping of V into V' which we will call the mapping of V into V' *induced by f on V*. That being so, we will say that Λ is *ample* if g is a birational mapping and is everywhere biregular on V; then g determines an isomorphism of V onto the open subset of V' where g^{-1} is defined; when that is so, one also says that f induces that isomorphism. One sees at once that, if α is then a linear morphism of $\boldsymbol{P}^n$ into a projective space, the mapping $f' = \alpha \circ f$ also induces an isomorphism of V onto an open subset of the geometric image of V by f'.

On a complete variety without multiple subvarieties of codimension 1, a divisor X_0 will be called *ample* if the complete linear system determined by X_0 is reduced and ample.

We will now give a criterion for a linear system to be ample on a complete variety without multiple points; this will be an immediate consequence of the foregoing results and of the following one:

PROPOSITION 16. *Let f be a mapping of a variety V into $\boldsymbol{P}^n$, V' the geometric image of V by f, and Λ the linear system determined by f on V. Let k be a field of rationality for V and f, $\boldsymbol{M}$ a generic point of V over k, and $\boldsymbol{N}$ a simple point of V. Assume that f is defined at $\boldsymbol{N}$ and that $\boldsymbol{M}$ has no other specialization than $\boldsymbol{N}$ over $f(\boldsymbol{M}) \to f(\boldsymbol{N})$ with reference to k. Then the following assertions are equivalent*: (a) *f induces a birational mapping g of V into V', and g is biregular at $\boldsymbol{N}$*; (b) *to every curve $\boldsymbol{C}$ on V with a simple point at $\boldsymbol{N}$, there is a divisor $\boldsymbol{X}$ in Λ such that $\boldsymbol{N}$ is a component of $\boldsymbol{C} \cdot \boldsymbol{X}$ with the coefficient* 1.

It is clearly enough to deal with the case when f is non-degenerate; then Λ consists of the divisors $f^{-1}(\boldsymbol{H})$ when one takes for $\boldsymbol{H}$ all the hyperplanes in $\boldsymbol{P}^n$. Also, by the principle of localization, it is enough to consider the case when V is a variety in an affine space S^m. Put $\boldsymbol{M}' = f(\boldsymbol{M})$, $\boldsymbol{N}' = f(\boldsymbol{N})$; let $\boldsymbol{H}_0$ be a hyperplane in $\boldsymbol{P}^n$, rational over k and not containing $\boldsymbol{N}'$; let $L_0(X) = 0$

be a homogeneous equation for H_0 with coefficients in k. Then H_0 does not contain V'; let f_0 be the mapping of V into $P^n - H_0$, rational over k, such that $f_0(M) = M'$; by the principle of localization, (a) is satisfied if and only if the mapping of V into the restriction V'_0 of V' to $P^n - H_0$ which is induced by f_0 is birational and biregular at N. As in coroll. 3 of prop. 13, let the functions φ_α on P^n be defined by $\varphi_\alpha \circ p = X_\alpha/L_0(X)$; put $\Phi = (\varphi_0, \cdots, \varphi_n)$, $\psi_\alpha = \varphi_\alpha \circ f$ and $\Psi = \Phi \circ f$. By coroll. 3 of prop. 13, $p \circ \Phi$ is the identity mapping of P^n, so that $f = p \circ \Psi$; moreover, Φ determines an isomorphism of $P^n - H_0$ onto the linear variety defined in S^{n+1} by $L_0(X) = 1$; therefore it is defined at M' and at N', so that we can put

$$M'' = \Phi(M') = \Psi(M),\ N'' = \Phi(N') = \Psi(N);$$

and, if V'' is the geometric image of V by Ψ, i.e. the locus of M'' over k, we see that (a) is satisfied if and only if the mapping of V into V'' determined by Ψ is birational and biregular at N. Now let $\bar{V}$ be the graph of Ψ, which is the same as the locus of the point $\bar{M} = (M, M'')$ over k in $S^m \times S^{n+1}$; put $\bar{N} = (N, N'')$; as Ψ is defined at N, the projection from $\bar{V}$ to V is regular at N; this is the same as to say that this projection determines a mapping h of $\bar{V}$ into V which is birational and biregular at $\bar{N}$; as V'' is the geometric projection of $\bar{V}$ on S^{n+1}, and as the projection from $\bar{V}$ to V'' is nothing else than $h \circ \Psi$, we see now that (a) is equivalent to the following assertion: (a′) the projection π' from $S^m \times S^{n+1}$ to S^{n+1} induces on $\bar{V}$ a birational mapping of $\bar{V}$ into V'', biregular at $\bar{N}$. As M has no other specialization than N over $M' \rightarrow N'$ with reference to k, $\bar{M}$ has no other specialization than $\bar{N}$ over $M'' \rightarrow N''$ with reference to k; therefore we can apply coroll. 1 of prop. 6, §3, to $\bar{V}$, $\bar{N}$ and π'; this shows that (a′) is equivalent to the following: (b′) to every curve $\bar{C}$ on $\bar{V}$, having a simple point at $\bar{N}$, there is a linear variety L^n in S^{n+1}, containing N'', such that $S^m \times L$ is transversal to $\bar{C}$ at $\bar{N}$; it will now be shown that this is equivalent to (b) in prop. 16. In fact, if $\bar{C}$ is as in (b′), its geometric projection C on V is its geometric image by h; as h is biregular at $\bar{N}$, C has then a simple point at N, and this determines a one-to-one correspondence between the curves $\bar{C}$ on $\bar{V}$ with a simple point at $\bar{N}$ and the curves C on V with a simple point at N. Let now $\bar{C}$ and C be such corresponding curves, and let L^n be a linear variety in S^{n+1}, defined by the equation

$$F(X) = \sum_{\alpha=0}^{n} a_\alpha X_\alpha - b = 0;$$

then this same equation defines in $S^m \times S^{n+1}$ the variety $S^m \times L$, which is therefore, by th. 5 of §4, the divisor of the polynomial function F in $S^m \times S^{n+1}$. By th. 3 of §2, and by the criterion of multiplicity 1 (th. 6 of Chap. VI, §2), $S^m \times L$ is transversal to $\bar{C}$ at $\bar{N}$ if and only if F induces on $\bar{C}$ a function other than the constant 0 and $\bar{N}$ has the coefficient 1 in the divisor of that function. Let $\bar{F}$ be the function induced by F on $\bar{V}$; we have

$$\bar{F}(\bar{M}) = \sum_{\alpha} a_\alpha \psi_\alpha(M) - b = \sum_{\alpha} a_\alpha \psi_\alpha(M) - bL_0(\Psi(M)))$$

since Ψ maps V into the linear variety $L_0(X) = 1$; if we put

$$L(X) = \sum_\alpha a_\alpha X_\alpha - bL_0(X),$$

this can be written, for the same reason, as

$$\bar{F}(\bar{M}) = L(\Psi(M))/L_0(\Psi(M));$$

therefore, if φ is the function defined on P^n by $\varphi \circ p = L(X)/L_0(X)$, and if we put $\psi = \varphi \circ f$, we have $\bar{F}(\bar{M}) = \psi(M)$; as we have $M = h(\bar{M})$, this can be written as $\bar{F} = \psi \circ h$. As the birational mapping h of $\bar{V}$ into V is biregular at $\bar{N}$, the principle of localization shows that the function induced on $\bar{C}$ by F, or, what amounts to the same, by $\bar{F}$ is not the constant 0, and that $\bar{N}$ has the coefficient 1 in the divisor of that function, if and only if the function induced on C by ψ is not the constant 0, and N has the coefficient 1 in its divisor. Let H be the hyperplane defined in P^n by the homogeneous equation $L(X) = 0$; by prop. 15, ψ is 0 if and only if H contains V', and, if this is not so, we have $\operatorname{div}(\psi) = f^{-1}(H) - f^{-1}(H_0)$. We have thus shown that, if the assertion in (b′) holds for $\bar{C}$ and L^n, the assertion in (b) holds for C and $X = f^{-1}(H)$, and also that, if the assertion in (b) holds for C and $X = f^{-1}(H)$, then (b′) holds for $\bar{C}$ and the linear variety L^n corresponding to H in S^{n+1}; in the latter case, if $L(X) = 0$ is the homogeneous equation for H, L^n is defined in S^{n+1} by that same equation, and we have to take $F(X) = L(X)$ in the above calculation. This completes our proof.

THEOREM 12. *Let V be a complete variety without multiple points. Then a linear system Λ on V is ample if and only if it satisfies the following conditions:* (i) *to every pair of distinct points M, N on V, there is a divisor X in Λ such that $|X|$ contains M and not N;* (ii) *to every curve C on V and every simple point M of C, there is a divisor X in Λ such that C is not contained in $|X|$ and that M is a component of $C \cdot X$ with the coefficient* 1.

If (i) is satisfied, Λ is obviously reduced, so that it is determined by a non-degenerate mapping f of V into a projective space P^n. It follows at once from th. 10 that (i) is satisfied if and only if f is a morphism and is set-theoretically injective (this is still true if V is any everywhere normal variety). It is therefore enough to show that, when (i) is satisfied, Λ is ample if and only if (ii) is satisfied; this is an immediate consequence of prop. 16.

We will now apply to projective spaces the concept of projecting cylinders. Let V^r be a variety and L^s a linear variety in P^n; call W^{r+1} and M^{s+1} the corresponding varieties in S^{n+1}: then W is a cone, and M is a linear variety containing 0. Let Z be the projecting cylinder of W in the direction of M; as this is the closure of the set of the points $x + y$, where x is any point in W and y any point in M, it is a cone; the variety J in P^n, corresponding to the cone Z in S^{n+1}, will be called *the join of V and L*. In order to obtain a set of homogeneous equations for J, one may follow the procedure indicated in §3. In fact, let k be a field of definition for V and L, hence also for W and M; let the

$L_i(X) = 0$, for $0 \leqq i \leqq n - s - 1$, be a set of homogeneous linear equations for L, or, what amounts to the same, for M, with coefficients in k; let x be a generic point of W over k, and put $y_i = L_i(x)$; the locus W' of $y = (y_i)$ in S^{n-s} is a cone, so that, by coroll. 2 of prop. 12, it can be defined by a set of homogeneous equations $F_\mu(Y) = 0$ with coefficients in k. Then, as shown in §3, the equations

$$F_\mu(L_0(X), \cdots, L_{n-s-1}(X)) = 0$$

define Z in S^{n+1}, so that they are a set of homogeneous equations for the join J of V and L.

In particular, let V^r be a variety in P^n, other than P^n and rational over k. Take $L_i(X) = \sum_{\alpha=0}^{n} u_{i\alpha} X_\alpha$ for $0 \leqq i \leqq r + 1$, where the $u_{i\alpha}$ are $(r + 2)(n + 1)$ independent variables over k. Put $K = k(u)$; let x be generic over k on the cone W^{r+1} corresponding to V^r in S^{n+1}; and put $y_i = L_i(x)$ for $0 \leqq i \leqq r + 1$. By coroll. 2 of prop. 6, §3, the locus W' of y over K in S^{r+2} is birationally equivalent to W; therefore it has the codimension 1 in S^{r+2} and can be defined over K by an equation $F(Y_0, \cdots, Y_{r+1}) = 0$, where F is an irreducible polynomial in $K[Y]$, uniquely determined up to a factor in K. More precisely, by prop. 10 of Chap. I, §3, the latter factor can be uniquely determined (up to a factor in k) in such a way that F is given by

$$F(Y_0, \cdots, Y_{r+1}) = \Phi(Y_0, \cdots, Y_{r+1}; (u_{i\alpha})_{0 \leqq i \leqq r+1, 0 \leqq \alpha \leqq n})$$

where Φ is the polynomial in the Y_i and the $u_{i\alpha}$, with coefficients in k, such that $\Phi(Y; U) = 0$ is the irreducible equation for $(y; u)$ over k. This polynomial $\Phi(Y; U)$ is called *the characteristic form of V in P^n*; it is uniquely determined, up to a constant factor; in particular, up to a constant factor, it does not depend upon the choice of the field of definition k for V, nor upon the choice of the $u_{i\alpha}$. The join J of V and of the variety L defined in P^n by the homogeneous equations $L_i(X) = 0$ is then the hypersurface given in P^n by the homogeneous equation

$$\Phi(L_0(X), \cdots, L_{r+1}(X); (u_{i\alpha})) = 0;$$

its degree, which is by definition the degree of this equation in the X_α, is the same as the degree d of Φ itself in $Y_0, \cdots, Y_{r+1}$; this will be called *the degree of V*. If V is a hypersurface, then, with the same notations as above, M is reduced to the point 0, and L is empty, so that we have $Z = W$ and $J = V$; therefore, in this case, our definition of the degree coincides with the previous one for hypersurfaces. Also, by coroll. 5 of prop. 6, §3, V is a linear variety if and only if J is so, i.e. if and only if it has the degree 1; in particular, a point in P^n is of degree 1. If V is of degree d, the coefficient of Y_0^d in the characteristic form Φ of V is a polynomial in the $U_{i\alpha}$, known as *the associated form* (or Chow form) *of V*; it is easily seen that this contains only the $U_{i\alpha}$ for $1 \leqq i \leqq r + 1$; one can also show that it determines Φ uniquely.

If now X^r is any positive cycle in P^n, write $X = \sum_\nu a_\nu V_\nu$, where the V_ν are the components of X; for each ν, call d_ν the degree of V_ν and Φ_ν its characteristic form; then the integer $d = \sum_\nu a_\nu d_\nu$ will be called *the degree of* X and will be denoted by $\deg(X)$, and the polynomial $\Phi = \prod_\nu (\Phi_\nu)^{a_\nu}$, of degree d in $Y_0, \cdots, Y_{r+1}$, will be called its *characteristic form.*

PROPOSITION 17. *Let X be a cycle in P^n, of dimension $r < n$, rational over a field k. Then its characteristic form is (up to a constant factor) a polynomial with coefficients in k.*

Put $L_i(X) = \sum_{\alpha=0}^n u_{i\alpha} X_\alpha$ for $0 \leqq i \leqq n$, where the $u_{i\alpha}$ are $(n+1)^2$ independent variables over k; let A be the linear automorphism of S^{n+1}, rational over $K = k(u)$, which maps every point $(x_0, \cdots, x_n)$ onto the point

$$(L_0(x), \cdots, L_n(x)).$$

Let the V_ν be the components of X, and call W_ν, for each ν, the cone in S^{n+1} corresponding to V_ν; these are all defined over $\bar{k}$. By definition, the characteristic form Φ_ν of V_ν is the irreducible polynomial in the Y_i for $0 \leqq i \leqq r+1$, and in the $U_{i\alpha}$ for $0 \leqq i \leqq r+1$, $0 \leqq \alpha \leqq n$, with coefficients in $\bar{k}$, such that the equation $\Phi_\nu(Y; (u_{i\alpha})) = 0$ defines the locus W'_ν of the point

$$(L_0(x), \cdots, L_{r+1}(x))$$

over $\bar{K}$ when one takes for x a generic point of W_ν over $\bar{K}$; this variety W'_ν is clearly the same as the geometric projection on S^{r+2} of the transform $A(W_\nu)$ of W_ν by A, when the ambient space S^{n+1} of this transform is regarded as the product $S^{r+2} \times S^{n-r-1}$. By coroll. 2 of prop. 6, §3, the projection from $A(W_\nu)$ to W'_ν is a birational mapping of $A(W_\nu)$ into W'_ν; therefore W'_ν is also the algebraic projection of $A(W_\nu)$ on S^{r+2}. Now write $X = \sum_\nu a_\nu V_\nu$, and put

$$Z = \sum_\nu a_\nu W_\nu, \qquad Z' = \sum_\nu a_\nu W'_\nu;$$

by what we have just proved, we have $Z' = \mathrm{pr}_{S^{r+2}} A(Z)$. By prop. 12, Z is a rational cycle over k; therefore $A(Z)$ is so over K; the same must then be true of Z'. But, by th. 5 of §4, W'_ν is, for each ν, the divisor of $\Phi_\nu(Y; (u_{i\alpha}))$ in S^{r+2}; therefore, if $\Phi = \prod_\nu (\Phi_\nu)^{a_\nu}$ is the characteristic form of X, Z' is the divisor of the function $\Phi(Y; (u_{i\alpha}))$ in S^{r+2}. As Z' is rational over K, th. 5 of §4 shows now that there is a polynomial $\Psi(Y)$ with coefficients in K which differs from $\Phi(Y; (u_{i\alpha}))$ at most by a factor in $\bar{k}(u)$. After multiplying Ψ by a suitable element in K, we may assume that it is of the form $\Phi'(Y; (u_{i\alpha}))$, where $\Phi'(Y; (U_{i\alpha}))$ is a polynomial in the Y_i and the $U_{i\alpha}$ with coefficients in k. This implies an identity of the form

$$F(U)\Phi(Y; U) = F'(U)\Phi'(Y; U),$$

where F, F' are in $\bar{k}[U]$, mutually prime, and not 0. By definition, each Φ_ν is irreducible and is of degree >0 in the Y_j; therefore F' is prime to the left-hand side, hence a constant, which we may take to be 1; we see now that Φ' is a multiple of $F(U)$, hence also of the polynomial of smallest degree $G(U)$ in $k[U]$ which is a multiple of $F(U)$. That being so, we have $\Phi' = G\Phi''$, hence

$\Phi = (G/F)\cdot\Phi''$, with Φ'' in $k[Y; U]$; as we have already shown that Φ cannot be a multiple of a polynomial in $\bar{k}[U]$ unless that polynomial is a constant, we see now that G/F must be a constant; this completes our proof.

One should note that the converse of prop. 17 is not true. For instance, if $\boldsymbol{M}$ is a point of $\boldsymbol{P}^n$ with the homogeneous coordinates $(t_0, \cdots, t_n)$, its characteristic form is $\sum_\alpha t_\alpha(Y_0U_{1\alpha} - Y_1U_{0\alpha})$; therefore, if k is of characteristic $p > 1$, the characteristic form of the 0-cycle $p\cdot\boldsymbol{M}$ has coefficients in k whenever all the t_α^p are in k; as already observed in Chap. VIII, §1, this does not imply that $p\cdot\boldsymbol{M}$ is rational over k. By making use of the results in §§3–4, one could show, however, that the converse of prop. 17 is true if one adds the condition that $\boldsymbol{X}$ is a divisor on a variety defined over k.

PROPOSITION 18. *Let Λ be a linear system on a variety $\boldsymbol{V}$, determined by a mapping f of $\boldsymbol{V}$ into a projective space $\boldsymbol{P}^n$; let $\boldsymbol{V}'$ be the geometric image of $\boldsymbol{V}$ by f, and let $\boldsymbol{A}$ be a positive divisor on $\boldsymbol{V}$. For any $d \geqq 1$, let $\Lambda_{d,\boldsymbol{A}}$ be the set of all divisors of the form $f^{-1}(\boldsymbol{Y}) - \boldsymbol{A}$ when one takes for $\boldsymbol{Y}$ all the positive divisors of degree d in $\boldsymbol{P}^n$ such that $|\boldsymbol{Y}|$ does not contain $\boldsymbol{V}'$ and that $f^{-1}(\boldsymbol{Y}) \succ \boldsymbol{A}$. Then $\Lambda_{d,\boldsymbol{A}}$ is either empty or a linear system.*

Let $\boldsymbol{H}_0$ be a hyperplane in $\boldsymbol{P}^n$, not containing $\boldsymbol{V}'$, with the homogeneous equation $L_0(X) = 0$. By coroll. 2 of prop. 13, the functions φ on $\boldsymbol{P}^n$ such that $\mathrm{div}(\varphi) \succ -d\boldsymbol{H}_0$ are those for which $\varphi \circ \boldsymbol{p} = F(X)/L_0(X)^d$, where F is a homogeneous polynomial of degree d in the X_α; they make up a vector-space $\mathfrak{L}$ of finite dimension over the field of constants; moreover, if φ and F are such, and if F is not 0, we have $\mathrm{div}(\varphi) = \boldsymbol{Y} - d\boldsymbol{H}_0$, where $\boldsymbol{Y}$ is the divisor of degree d in $\boldsymbol{P}^n$ corresponding to the conical divisor $\mathrm{div}(F)$ in S^{n+1}. Let $\mathfrak{L}'$ be the vector-space consisting of the functions $\psi = \varphi \circ f$ on $\boldsymbol{V}$, with φ in $\mathfrak{L}$; it has a finite dimension, at most equal to that of $\mathfrak{L}$; by th. 1 of §2, ψ is the constant 0 if and only if $|\boldsymbol{Y}|$ contains $\boldsymbol{V}'$; and, when that is not so, prop. 3 of §2 shows that

$$\mathrm{div}(\psi) = f^{-1}(\boldsymbol{Y}) - d\cdot f^{-1}(\boldsymbol{H}_0).$$

Put $\boldsymbol{A}_1 = d\cdot f^{-1}(\boldsymbol{H}_0) - \boldsymbol{A}$ and $\mathfrak{L}'' = \mathfrak{L}' \cap \mathfrak{L}(\boldsymbol{A}_1)$; $\mathfrak{L}''$ is the vector-space consisting of the functions ψ in $\mathfrak{L}'$ such that $\mathrm{div}(\psi) \succ -\boldsymbol{A}_1$; its definition shows that it has a finite dimension. Then $\Lambda_{d,\boldsymbol{A}}$ consists by definition of the divisors $\mathrm{div}(\psi) + \boldsymbol{A}_1$ for ψ in $\mathfrak{L}''$ and not 0; this is empty if $\mathfrak{L}'' = \{0\}$; otherwise it is a linear system.

THEOREM 13. *Let $\boldsymbol{V}$ be a variety without multiple points in a projective space $\boldsymbol{P}^n$; let $\boldsymbol{A}$ be a positive divisor on $\boldsymbol{V}$, and let d_0 be the degree of the $\boldsymbol{P}^n$-cycle $\boldsymbol{A}$. For any $d \geqq 1$, let $\Lambda_{d,\boldsymbol{A}}$ be the set of all $\boldsymbol{V}$-divisors of the form $\boldsymbol{V}\cdot\boldsymbol{Y} - \boldsymbol{A}$ when one takes for $\boldsymbol{Y}$ all the positive divisors of degree d in $\boldsymbol{P}^n$ such that $|\boldsymbol{Y}|$ does not contain $\boldsymbol{V}$ and that $\boldsymbol{V}\cdot\boldsymbol{Y} \succ \boldsymbol{A}$. Then $\Lambda_{d,\boldsymbol{A}}$ is an ample linear system for every $d > d_0$.*

Let j be the injection mapping of $\boldsymbol{V}$ into $\boldsymbol{P}^n$; by th. 10 of Chap. VIII, §4, we have $j(\boldsymbol{X}) = \boldsymbol{X}$ for every $\boldsymbol{V}$-cycle $\boldsymbol{X}$, and $j^{-1}(\boldsymbol{Y}) = \boldsymbol{V}\cdot\boldsymbol{Y}$ for every $\boldsymbol{P}^n$-cycle $\boldsymbol{Y}$ intersecting $\boldsymbol{V}$ properly in $\boldsymbol{P}^n$; prop. 18, applied to $\boldsymbol{V}$, j and $\boldsymbol{A}$, shows now that

$\Lambda_{d,A}$ is either empty or a linear system for every $d \geqq 1$. Write $A = \sum_\nu A_\nu$, where the A_ν are subvarieties of V; let M be a point of V, and let k be a field of rationality for V, M and the A_ν. Let r be the dimension of V; put

$$L_i(X) = \sum_\alpha u_{i\alpha} X_\alpha \qquad (0 \leqq i \leqq r + 1)$$

where the $u_{i\alpha}$ are $(r + 2)(n + 1)$ independent variables over k. For each ν, let J_ν be the join of A_ν and of the linear variety defined by the homogeneous equations $L_i(X) = 0$; put $J = \sum_\nu J_\nu$. From the definition of the characteristic form, it follows immediately that J is a divisor of degree d_0 in P^n. Also, the corollary of prop. 7, §3, combined with prop. 12, shows at once that, for every ν, $V \cdot J_\nu \succ A_\nu$ and that M is not in the support of $V \cdot J_\nu - A_\nu$; therefore we have $V \cdot J \succ A$, and M is not in the support of $V \cdot J - A$. Now take $d = d_0 + \delta$ with $\delta \geqq 1$; if H is any hyperplane, not containing M, the V-divisor $V \cdot (J + \delta H) - A$ is in $\Lambda_{d,A}$, and its support does not contain M. If N is another point of V, and if we take for H a hyperplane containing N and not M, this construction yields a divisor in $\Lambda_{d,A}$ whose support contains N and not M. This shows that $\Lambda_{d,A}$ is not empty and satisfies condition (i) in th. 12. Now let C be a curve on V with a simple point at M; then th. 12, applied to the linear system determined on V by j, shows that there is a hyperplane H', not containing V, such that $V \cdot H'$ satisfies condition (ii) of th. 12 (actually, one sees easily that this amounts to saying that H' is transversal to C at M in P^n). Then the V-divisor

$$V \cdot (J + (\delta - 1)H + H') - A$$

is in $\Lambda_{d,A}$ and satisfies condition (ii) of th. 12. We can now apply th. 12, which completes our proof.

Corollary. *Let V be a complete variety without multiple points; let X_0 be an ample divisor and B any divisor on V. Then there is an integer d_0 such that the divisor $dX_0 + B$ is ample on V for every $d \geqq d_0$.*

To say that X_0 is ample is to say that the complete linear system Λ determined by X_0 is so; Λ is therefore determined by a non-degenerate mapping f of V into a projective space P^n which induces on V an isomorphism of V onto its geometric image; we can then identify V with that image, so that f becomes the injection of V into P^n and that Λ consists of the V-divisors $V \cdot H$ when one takes for H all the hyperplanes in P^n. If $X_1 = V \cdot H_1$ is such a divisor, it is linearly equivalent to X_0, so that $dX_1 + B$ is linearly equivalent to $dX_0 + B$; the latter is ample if the former is so. Put $B = B' - B''$, where B', B'' are positive divisors without a common component; call d', d'' the degrees of the P^n-cycles B', B''. With the notations of th. 13, $\Lambda_{d'+1,B'}$ is ample and therefore not empty, so that there is a P^n-divisor Y' of degree $d' + 1$ such that $|Y'|$ does not contain V and that $V \cdot Y' \succ B'$. Put $A' = V \cdot Y' - B'$;

we have

$$dX_1 + B = d(V\cdot H_1) + V\cdot Y' - A' - B'' = V\cdot(dH_1 + Y') - A' - B''.$$

Let Y be a positive divisor of degree $d + d' + 1$ in P^n, whose support does not contain V; by coroll. 1 of prop. 13, there is a function φ in P^n whose divisor is $Y - dH_1 - Y'$; by the corollary of th. 3, §2, the divisor of the function induced by φ on V is then $V\cdot(Y - dH_1 - Y')$; this shows that $V\cdot Y - A' - B''$ is linearly equivalent to $dX_1 + B$. Therefore, with the notations of th. 13, $\Lambda_{d+d'+1, A'+B''}$ consists of divisors linearly equivalent to $dX_1 + B$; moreover, by th. 13, it is ample provided $d + d' \geqq \deg(A' + B'')$. Therefore, when d is so chosen, the complete linear system determined by $dX_1 + B$ contains an ample linear system; it is then an immediate consequence of th. 12 that it must itself be ample; this completes the proof. One should note that, by applying Bézout's theorem (cf. Chap. X, §9) to V and Y', one sees at once that A' has the degree $\delta(d' + 1) - d'$, where δ is the degree of V in P^n; therefore we can take

$$d_0 = d'(\delta - 2) + \delta + d''$$

in our corollary.

6. The generic divisors of a linear system. It will now be shown that the divisors of a linear system can be "parametrized" by the points of a projective space. To begin with, this will be done for the hyperplanes in a projective space.

Call p_2 the mapping of $S_*^{n+1} \times S_*^{n+1}$ onto $P^n \times P^n$ which maps each point (x, y) onto $(p(x), p(y))$; one sees at once that this determines a fibering of $S_*^{n+1} \times S_*^{n+1}$ over $P^n \times P^n$ with the fibre $S_*^1 \times S_*^1$. Let E be the subvariety of $S^{n+1} \times S^{n+1}$ defined by the equation $\sum_{\alpha=0}^{n} X_\alpha Y_\alpha = 0$, where $X_0, \cdots, X_n$ and $Y_0, \cdots, Y_n$ are the indeterminates for the two factors of the product $S^{n+1} \times S^{n+1}$. Let E_* be the restriction of E to the open subset $S_*^{n+1} \times S_*^{n+1}$ of that product. By prop. 10 of §5, we have $E_* = p_2^{-1}(\boldsymbol{E})$, where $\boldsymbol{E}$ is a subvariety of codimension 1 of $P^n \times P^n$. Let $\boldsymbol{a}$ be a point of P^n; let $a = (a_0, \cdots, a_n)$ be a set of homogeneous coordinates for $\boldsymbol{a}$, so that we have $\boldsymbol{a} = p(a)$; then, by prop. 12 of §5, $p^{-1}(\boldsymbol{a})$ is the ray $R(a)$ determined by a in S_*^{n+1}. By prop. 10 of §5, and by prop. 14 of Chap. VIII, §4, we have

$$p_2^{-1}[(\boldsymbol{a} \times P^n)\cdot \boldsymbol{E}] = p_2^{-1}(\boldsymbol{a} \times P^n)\cdot p_2^{-1}(\boldsymbol{E}) = (R(a) \times S_*^{n+1})\cdot E_*.$$

One sees at once that the intersection of $R(a) \times S_*^{n+1}$ and of E_* is $R(a) \times L_*(a)$, where $L_*(a)$ is the restriction to S_*^{n+1} of the linear variety $L(a)$ defined in S^{n+1} by the equation $\sum_\alpha a_\alpha X_\alpha = 0$. If we call $\bar{R}(a)$ the extension of $R(a)$ to S^{n+1}, $\bar{R}(a) \times S^{n+1}$ is a linear subvariety of $S^{n+1} \times S^{n+1}$, which is easily seen to be transversal to E at every point of $R(a) \times L_*(a)$. This shows that the right-hand side of the relation written above is equal to $R(a) \times L_*(a)$. On the other hand, with the notations of Chap. VIII, §§3–4, the cycle $(\boldsymbol{a} \times P^n)\cdot\boldsymbol{E}$ may be written as $\boldsymbol{a} \times \boldsymbol{E}(\boldsymbol{a})$; then, by prop. 14 of Chap. VIII, §4, the left-hand side of the above relations is $R(a) \times p^{-1}(\boldsymbol{E}(\boldsymbol{a}))$. This shows that $p^{-1}(\boldsymbol{E}(\boldsymbol{a}))$ is equal to $L_*(a)$; therefore, by prop. 12 of §5, $\boldsymbol{E}(\boldsymbol{a})$ is the linear variety corresponding to $L_*(a)$ in $\boldsymbol{P}^n$, i.e. the hyperplane with the homogeneous equation $\sum_\alpha a_\alpha X_\alpha = 0$. At the same time, we have also proved that

$$(\boldsymbol{a} \times \boldsymbol{P}^n) \cap \boldsymbol{E} = \boldsymbol{a} \times \boldsymbol{E}(\boldsymbol{a}),$$

hence also

$$(\boldsymbol{P}^n \times \boldsymbol{a}) \cap \boldsymbol{E} = \boldsymbol{E}(\boldsymbol{a}) \times \boldsymbol{a}.$$

THEOREM 14. *Let f be a non-degenerate mapping of a variety $\boldsymbol{V}$ into a projective space $\boldsymbol{P}^n$. Let k be a field of rationality for $\boldsymbol{V}$ and f; let $\boldsymbol{M}$ be a generic point of $\boldsymbol{V}$ over k, and let $\boldsymbol{u}$ be a generic point over $k(\boldsymbol{M})$ of the hyperplane $\boldsymbol{E}(f(\boldsymbol{M}))$ in $\boldsymbol{P}^n$. Then the point $\boldsymbol{u} \times \boldsymbol{M}$ has a locus $\boldsymbol{S}$ over k in $\boldsymbol{P}^n \times \boldsymbol{V}$; for every point $\boldsymbol{a}$ of $\boldsymbol{P}^n$, we have $f^{-1}(\boldsymbol{E}(\boldsymbol{a})) = \boldsymbol{S}(\boldsymbol{a})$; and the linear system Λ determined by f on $\boldsymbol{V}$ consists of the divisors $\boldsymbol{S}(\boldsymbol{a})$ when one takes for $\boldsymbol{a}$ all the points in $\boldsymbol{P}^n$.*

As f is non-degenerate, we can find for $f(\boldsymbol{M})$ a set of homogeneous coordinates of the form $(1, z_1, \cdots, z_n)$; then the z_i are in $k(\boldsymbol{M})$. Let $u_1, \cdots, u_{n-1}$ be independent variables over $k(\boldsymbol{M})$; put $u_n = 1$ and $u_0 = -\sum_{i=1}^n z_i u_i$; let $\boldsymbol{u}$ be the point in $\boldsymbol{P}^n$ with the homogeneous coordinates $(u_0, \cdots, u_n)$; one sees immediately that $\boldsymbol{u}$ is a generic point of $\boldsymbol{E}(f(\boldsymbol{M}))$ over $k(\boldsymbol{M})$; by th. 6 of Chap. I, §7, $\boldsymbol{u} \times f(\boldsymbol{M}) \times \boldsymbol{M}$ has a locus $\boldsymbol{T}$ over k in $\boldsymbol{P}^n \times \boldsymbol{P}^n \times \boldsymbol{V}$, $\boldsymbol{u} \times \boldsymbol{M}$ has a locus $\boldsymbol{S}$ over k in $\boldsymbol{P}^n \times \boldsymbol{V}$, and we have $\boldsymbol{S} = \mathrm{pr}_{13}\, \boldsymbol{T}$, where pr_{13} denotes the algebraic projection on the product of the first and third factors of $\boldsymbol{P}^n \times \boldsymbol{P}^n \times \boldsymbol{V}$. On the other hand, the linear system Λ consists of the divisors $f^{-1}(\boldsymbol{E}(\boldsymbol{a}))$, when one takes for $\boldsymbol{a}$ all the points in $\boldsymbol{P}^n$. As in Chap. VIII, §4, call $\boldsymbol{\Gamma}'_f$ the locus of $f(\boldsymbol{M}) \times \boldsymbol{M}$ over k; it is easily seen that one can apply prop. 10 of Chap. VIII, §4, to the varieties $\boldsymbol{P}^n$, $\boldsymbol{P}^n$, $\boldsymbol{V}$, to the cycles $\boldsymbol{E}$ on $\boldsymbol{P}^n \times \boldsymbol{P}^n$ and $\boldsymbol{\Gamma}'_f$ on $\boldsymbol{P}^n \times \boldsymbol{V}$, and to the 0-cycle $\boldsymbol{a}$ on $\boldsymbol{P}^n$; this gives $f^{-1}(\boldsymbol{E}(\boldsymbol{a})) = \boldsymbol{X}(\boldsymbol{a})$ with $\boldsymbol{X} = \mathrm{pr}_{13}\, \boldsymbol{Y}$, $\boldsymbol{Y} = (\boldsymbol{E} \times \boldsymbol{V}) \cdot (\boldsymbol{P}^n \times \boldsymbol{\Gamma}'_f)$. Now prop. 5 of Chap. VIII, §3, shows that the varieties $\boldsymbol{E} \times \boldsymbol{V}$ and $\boldsymbol{P}^n \times \boldsymbol{\Gamma}'_f$ intersect properly in $\boldsymbol{P}^n \times \boldsymbol{P}^n \times \boldsymbol{V}$; $\boldsymbol{T}$ is obviously contained in both; it will now be shown that $\boldsymbol{T}$ is the only proper component of their intersection. In fact, let $\boldsymbol{Z}$ be such a component; let $\boldsymbol{v} \times \boldsymbol{w} \times \boldsymbol{N}$ be a generic point of $\boldsymbol{Z}$ over $\bar{k}$. Call r the dimension of $\boldsymbol{V}$; as $\boldsymbol{v} \times \boldsymbol{w}$ is in $\boldsymbol{E}$, $\boldsymbol{v}$ is in $\boldsymbol{E}(\boldsymbol{w})$ and has at most the dimension $n - 1$ over $k(\boldsymbol{w}, \boldsymbol{N})$; as $\boldsymbol{w} \times \boldsymbol{N}$ is in $\boldsymbol{\Gamma}'_f$, it has at most the dimension r over k; as $\boldsymbol{Z}$ has the dimension $n + r - 1$, this shows that $\boldsymbol{w} \times \boldsymbol{N}$ is generic over k on $\boldsymbol{\Gamma}'_f$, so that $\boldsymbol{w} = f(\boldsymbol{N})$, and that $\boldsymbol{v}$ is generic over $k(\boldsymbol{w}, \boldsymbol{N})$ on $\boldsymbol{E}(\boldsymbol{w})$. Therefore $\boldsymbol{v} \times \boldsymbol{w} \times \boldsymbol{N}$ is a generic specialization of $\boldsymbol{u} \times f(\boldsymbol{M}) \times \boldsymbol{M}$ over k, so that $\boldsymbol{Z} = \boldsymbol{T}$. This proves that $\boldsymbol{Y} = a \cdot \boldsymbol{T}$, where a is an integer. Now we have, by th. 4(iv) and th. 6(i) of Chap. VIII, §3:

$$\boldsymbol{Y} \cdot (\boldsymbol{P}^n \times \boldsymbol{P}^n \times \boldsymbol{M}) = (\boldsymbol{E} \times \boldsymbol{V}) \cdot (\boldsymbol{P}^n \times f(\boldsymbol{M}) \times \boldsymbol{M})$$

$$= \boldsymbol{E}(f(\boldsymbol{M})) \times f(\boldsymbol{M}) \times \boldsymbol{M},$$

and this is a variety. Therefore we have $a = 1$, hence $\boldsymbol{X} = \boldsymbol{S}$, which completes the proof.

COROLLARY. *Let assumptions and notations be as in th.* 14. *Then* $\boldsymbol{u}$ *is a generic point of* $\boldsymbol{P}^n$ *over* k, *and the divisor* $f^{-1}(\boldsymbol{E}(\boldsymbol{u})) = \boldsymbol{S}(\boldsymbol{u})$ *is the prime rational cycle over* $k(\boldsymbol{u})$ *in* $\boldsymbol{V}$ *with the generic point* $\boldsymbol{M}$ *over* $k(\boldsymbol{u})$.

The first assertion amounts to saying that $\boldsymbol{S}$ has the geometric projection $\boldsymbol{P}^n$ on $\boldsymbol{P}^n$; in fact, if this were not so, we would have $\boldsymbol{S}(\boldsymbol{a}) = 0$ for all $\boldsymbol{a}$, by the corollary of prop. 7, Chap. VIII, §3, so that, by th. 14, Λ would be reduced to the divisor 0. The second assertion is now a special case of th. 6(i) of Chap. VIII, §3.

Assumptions and notations being as in th. 14, $\boldsymbol{S}$ will be called a *parametrizing variety for* Λ. One sees at once that $\boldsymbol{S}$ is independent of the choice of k, $\boldsymbol{u}$ and $\boldsymbol{M}$, once $\boldsymbol{V}$ and f are given. Moreover, by th. 11, when the reduced linear system Λ is given on $\boldsymbol{V}$, f is uniquely determined up to a linear automorphism of $\boldsymbol{P}^n$. Let now α be a linear automorphism of $\boldsymbol{P}^n$, determined by an automorphism $x \to Mx$ of S_*^{n+1}, where M is an invertible matrix; let α' be the automorphism of $\boldsymbol{P}^n$ determined by $x \to {}^tM^{-1}x$, where ${}^tM$ is the transpose of M; one sees at once that, for $\boldsymbol{a}$ in $\boldsymbol{P}^n$, the hyperplane $\boldsymbol{E}(\alpha\boldsymbol{a})$ is the transform of $\boldsymbol{E}(\boldsymbol{a})$ by α'; therefore, if α is rational over k, and if notations are still those in th. 14, $\alpha'\boldsymbol{u}$ is a generic point of $\boldsymbol{E}(\alpha f(\boldsymbol{M}))$ over $k(\boldsymbol{M})$. This shows that, if we replace f by $f' = \alpha \circ f$, the variety $\boldsymbol{S}$ is replaced by its transform $\boldsymbol{S}'$ under the automorphism $\boldsymbol{u} \times \boldsymbol{M} \to \alpha'\boldsymbol{u} \times \boldsymbol{M}$ of $\boldsymbol{P}^n \times \boldsymbol{V}$. In this sense, the parametrizing variety $\boldsymbol{S}$ is uniquely determined by Λ, up to a linear automorphism of $\boldsymbol{P}^n$.

Assumptions and notations still being as in th. 14 and its corollary, the divisor $f^{-1}(\boldsymbol{E}(\boldsymbol{u})) = \boldsymbol{S}(\boldsymbol{u})$ will be called a *generic divisor* in Λ. Let now $\boldsymbol{S}'$ be another parametrizing variety for Λ; then, as we have just seen, there is a linear automorphism β of $\boldsymbol{P}^n$ such that $\boldsymbol{S}'$ is the transform of $\boldsymbol{S}$ by the automorphism $\boldsymbol{v} \times \boldsymbol{M} \to \beta\boldsymbol{v} \times \boldsymbol{M}$ of $\boldsymbol{P}^n \times \boldsymbol{V}$; and, if we apply the latter automorphism to both sides of the formula $\boldsymbol{v} \times \boldsymbol{S}(\boldsymbol{v}) = \boldsymbol{S}\cdot(\boldsymbol{v} \times \boldsymbol{V})$ which defines $\boldsymbol{S}(\boldsymbol{v})$ for any $\boldsymbol{v}$ in $\boldsymbol{P}^n$, we get

$$\beta\boldsymbol{v} \times \boldsymbol{S}(\boldsymbol{v}) = \boldsymbol{S}'\cdot(\beta\boldsymbol{v} \times \boldsymbol{V}),$$

which shows that we have $\boldsymbol{S}'(\beta\boldsymbol{v}) = \boldsymbol{S}(\boldsymbol{v})$ for every $\boldsymbol{v}$. Now let k' be a field of rationality for $\boldsymbol{S}'$, and $\boldsymbol{u}'$ a generic point of $\boldsymbol{P}^n$ over k'; let K be a field of rationality for β, containing both k and k', and take for $\boldsymbol{v}$ a generic point of $\boldsymbol{P}^n$ over K. Then $\beta\boldsymbol{v}$ is also generic over K in $\boldsymbol{P}^n$. As $\boldsymbol{u}$ and $\boldsymbol{v}$ are both generic over k in $\boldsymbol{P}^n$, there is an isomorphism of $k(\boldsymbol{v})$ onto $k(\boldsymbol{u})$ over k, mapping $\boldsymbol{v}$ onto $\boldsymbol{u}$; this can be extended to an isomorphism σ of $K(\boldsymbol{v})$ onto some field L containing $k(\boldsymbol{u})$; and we have $S(\boldsymbol{u}) = S(\boldsymbol{v})^\sigma$. Similarly, there is an isomorphism of $k'(\beta\boldsymbol{v})$ onto $k'(\boldsymbol{u}')$ over k', mapping $\beta\boldsymbol{v}$ onto $\boldsymbol{u}'$, which can be extended to an isomorphism τ of $K(\beta\boldsymbol{v}) = K(\boldsymbol{v})$ onto some field L' containing $k'(\boldsymbol{u}')$, and we have $\boldsymbol{S}'(\boldsymbol{u}') = \boldsymbol{S}'(\beta\boldsymbol{v})^\tau$. As we have $\boldsymbol{S}(\boldsymbol{v}) = \boldsymbol{S}'(\beta\boldsymbol{v})$, we get $\boldsymbol{S}'(\boldsymbol{u}') = \boldsymbol{S}(\boldsymbol{u})^{\sigma^{-1}\tau}$; thus we have shown that any two generic divisors of a reduced linear system are the transforms of each other by a suitable isomorphism.

By the corollary of th. 14, a generic divisor of a reduced linear system Λ is a prime rational cycle over a suitable field; as such, it must be of the form

$$p^s(X_1 + \cdots + X_r),$$

where the X_i are its distinct components and p is the characteristic; by what we have just proved, p^s and r depend only upon Λ, and not upon the choice of a generic divisor in it. The linear system Λ will be called *separable* if $p^s = 1$, and *irreducible* if $p^s = 1$ and $r = 1$, i.e. if every generic divisor in it is a variety. Let assumptions and notations be again as in th. 14 and its corollary; then, by that corollary and the results of Chap. VIII, §1, Λ is separable if and only if $k(\boldsymbol{M}, \boldsymbol{u})$ is separably generated over $k(\boldsymbol{u})$; it is irreducible if and only if $k(\boldsymbol{M}, \boldsymbol{u})$ is regular over $k(\boldsymbol{u})$, i.e. if and only if it is separably generated over $k(\boldsymbol{u})$ and $k(\boldsymbol{u})$ is algebraically closed in $k(\boldsymbol{M}, \boldsymbol{u})$. These conditions will now be transformed into equivalent ones in terms of the mapping f of $\boldsymbol{V}$ into $\boldsymbol{P}^n$.

LEMMA 1. *Let $k(x_1, \cdots, x_m)$ be a separably generated extension of a field k of characteristic $p > 1$; let $z_1, \cdots, z_n$ be elements of $k(x)$, not all in $\bar{k}$; let $u_1, \cdots, u_{n-1}$ be independent variables over $k(x)$, and put $v = \sum_{\nu=1}^{n-1} z_\nu u_\nu + z_n$. Then v is variable over $k(u)$; and $k(u, x)$ is separably generated over $k(u, v)$ if and only if $k(z)$ is not contained in $k(x_1^p, \cdots, x_m^p)$.*

Take u'_n variable over $k(u, x)$, and put $u'_i = u_i u'_n$ for $1 \leqq i \leqq n - 1$; then $u'_1, \cdots, u'_n$ are independent variables over $k(x)$, hence over $k(z)$. As $k(z)$ is assumed to be of dimension at least 1 over k, it follows immediately from prop. 24 of Chap. II, §5, that the quantity $u'_n v = \sum_{\nu=1}^{n} u'_\nu z_\nu$ is variable over $k(u')$; therefore v itself is variable over $k(u')$, hence also over $k(u)$. Now let r be the dimension of $k(x)$ over k, and let $t_1, \cdots, t_r$ be r independent variables over k in $k(x)$, such that $k(x)$ is separably algebraic over $k(t)$; then, by prop. 15 of Chap. I, §5, the derivations $\partial/\partial t_i$ of $k(u, t)$ over $k(u)$ can be extended to derivations D_i of $k(u, x)$ over $k(u)$; and, by prop. 16 of Chap. I, §5, the D_i are a basis over $k(u, x)$ for the vector-space of the derivations in $k(u, x)$ over $k(u)$. On the other hand, as v is variable over $k(u)$, the dimension of $k(u, x)$ over $k(u, v)$ is $r - 1$. Assume now that the z_ν are not all in $k(x_1^p, \cdots, x_m^p)$; then, by lemma 3 of Chap. VIII, §2, there is a derivation D of $k(x)$ over k such that the Dz_ν are not all 0; this can be extended to a derivation of $k(u, x)$ over $k(u)$, which we also denote by D, and we have

$$Dv = \sum_{\nu=1}^{n-1} u_\nu Dz_\nu + Dz_n \neq 0.$$

As D is a linear combination of the D_i, this implies that the $D_i v$ are not all 0; after reordering the t_i if necessary, we may then assume that $D_1 v \neq 0$. Then $k(u, x)$ can have no non-trivial derivation over $k(u, v, t_2, \cdots, t_r)$; for such a derivation would be one of $k(u, x)$ over $k(u)$, hence of the form $D' = \sum_i w_i D_i$; as we must have $D't_i = 0$ for $2 \leqq i \leqq r$, we have $w_2 = \cdots = w_r = 0$, so that $D' = w_1 D_1$, and then $D'v = 0$ gives $w_1 = 0$. By th. 1 of Chap. I, §5, this proves that $k(u, x)$ is separably algebraic over $k(u, v, t_2, \cdots, t_r)$; as it has the dimension $r - 1$ over $k(u, v)$, it is therefore separably generated over $k(u, v)$. Assume now, on the other hand, that all the z_ν are in $k(x_1^p, \cdots, x_m^p)$; then we have $D_i z_\nu = 0$ for all i, ν, hence $D_i v = 0$ for all i; then the D_i are r linearly independent derivations in $k(u, x)$ over $k(u, v)$; by prop. 16 of Chap. I, §5, this implies that $k(u, x)$ is not separably generated over $k(u, v)$.

In order to apply this lemma to linear systems, we need the concept of the Frobenius morphism. If k is a field of characteristic $p > 1$, the mapping $\xi \rightarrow \xi^p$ of k onto k^p is called *the Frobenius isomorphism of* k *onto* k^p; it is called *the Frobenius automorphism of* k if $k = k^p$, i.e. if k is "perfect". If V is any variety, defined over a field k, and if π is the Frobenius automorphism of the universal domain, V^π is a variety, defined over k^p (hence also over k), and $V^{\pi^{-1}}$ is a variety, defined over $k^{1/p}$; if M is a generic point of V over k, M^π is then a generic point of V^π over k^p, and we have $k^p(M^\pi) = k(M)^p$, hence $k(M^\pi) \subset k(M)$, so that we may write $M^\pi = \varphi(M)$, where φ is a mapping of V into V^π, rational over k; by considering first the case of an affine variety, and then using the principle of localization, one sees at once that φ is a proper morphism, and that, if P is any point of V, we have $\varphi(P) = P^\pi$; this also shows that φ is set-theoretically bijective. The mapping φ is called *the Frobenius morphism of* V *onto* V^π. If f is a mapping of a variety V into a variety W, and φ_V, φ_W are the Frobenius morphisms of V onto V^π and of W onto W^π, respectively, then f^π is a mapping of V^π into W^π, and we have $\varphi_W \circ f = f^\pi \circ \varphi_V$, as one sees at once by comparing the values of these mappings at a generic point M of V over a field of rationality k for V, W and f.

PROPOSITION 19. *Let* V^n *be a variety, defined over a field of characteristic* $p > 1$; *let* π *be the Frobenius automorphism of the universal domain, and* φ *the Frobenius morphism of* V *onto* V^π. *Then, if* W *is a subvariety of* V, W^π *is the geometric and the set-theoretic image of* W *by* φ; *and, if* W *is of dimension* r *and simple on* V, *we have* $\varphi(W) = p^r \cdot W^\pi$ *and* $\varphi^{-1}(W^\pi) = p^{n-r} \cdot W$.

The first statement is an immediate consequence of the above definitions. Now let k be an algebraically closed field of definition for V and W; let P be a generic point of W over k; let Γ_φ be the graph of φ, and Z the locus of $P \times P^\pi$ over k, which is the graph of the Frobenius morphism of W into W^π. If W is simple on V, we have, by coroll. 1 of th. 8, Chap. VIII, §3, $Z = \Gamma_\varphi \cdot (W \times V^\pi)$, hence $\varphi(W) = \mathrm{pr}_{V^\pi}(Z) = a \cdot W^\pi$, with $a = [Z : W^\pi] = [k(P) : k(P^\pi)]$. Now let $x_1, \cdots, x_r$ be r independent variables over k in $k(P)$, such that $k(P)$ is separably algebraic over $k(x)$; as $k(P)$ is purely inseparable over $k(P^\pi)$, it is then both separably algebraic and purely inseparable over $k(x, P^\pi)$, so that we have $k(P) = k(x, P^\pi)$, and therefore $a = [k(x, P^\pi) : k(P^\pi)]$. As $k(P)$ is separably algebraic over $k(x)$, and as $k = k^p$, $k(P^\pi)$ is separably algebraic over $k(x^\pi)$; also, we have $k(x^\pi) = k(x)^p$, hence $k(x) = k(x^\pi)^{1/p}$; therefore, by prop. 19 of Chap. I, §7, $k(x)$ and $k(P^\pi)$ are linearly disjoint over $k(x^\pi)$. If now we apply prop. 6 of Chap. I, §2, to the extension $k(x)$ of $k(x^\pi)$ and to the field $K = k(\mathbf{P}^\pi)$, we see that a, which is the degree of $K(x)$ over $K = K(x^\pi)$, is equal to $[k(x):k(x^\pi)]$; by induction on r, one sees at once that the latter degree is equal to p^r. This completes the proof of the relation $\varphi(\mathbf{W}) = p^r \cdot \mathbf{W}^\pi$. In order to prove the last formula in our proposition, we may restrict all cycles, and the mapping φ, to the open sets of simple points on $\mathbf{V}$ and $\mathbf{V}^\pi$, and therefore assume $\mathbf{V}$, hence also $\mathbf{V}^\pi$, to have no multiple points. One sees at once that $\mathbf{\Gamma}_\varphi$ and $\mathbf{V} \times \mathbf{W}^\pi$ have the intersection $\mathbf{Z}$, so that we have

$$\mathbf{\Gamma}_\varphi \cdot (\mathbf{V} \times \mathbf{W}^\pi) = b \cdot \mathbf{Z},$$

where b is an integer, and therefore $\varphi^{-1}(\mathbf{W}^\pi) = b \cdot \mathbf{W}$. Now apply th. 9 of Chap. VIII, §4, to the morphism φ of $\mathbf{V}$ into $\mathbf{V}^\pi$, to the $\mathbf{V}$-cycle $\mathbf{X} = \mathbf{V}$ and to the $\mathbf{V}^\pi$-cycle $\mathbf{Y} = \mathbf{W}^\pi$. This gives $\varphi(\mathbf{V}) \cdot \mathbf{W}^\pi = b \cdot \varphi(\mathbf{W})$; as we have just shown that $\varphi(\mathbf{W}) = p^r \cdot \mathbf{W}^\pi$, hence in particular $\varphi(\mathbf{V}) = p^n \cdot \mathbf{V}^\pi$, we get $b = p^{n-r}$; this completes the proof.

THEOREM 15. *Let $\mathbf{V}$ be a variety, defined over a field of characteristic $p > 1$; let f be a mapping of $\mathbf{V}$ into $\mathbf{P}^n$, and Λ the linear system determined on $\mathbf{V}$ by f; let φ be the Frobenius morphism of $\mathbf{P}^n$ onto itself. Then Λ is not separable if and only if f can be written as $f = \varphi \circ g$, where g is a mapping of $\mathbf{V}$ into $\mathbf{P}^n$; and, when that is so, Λ consists of the divisors $p \cdot \mathbf{Y}$, when one takes for $\mathbf{Y}$ all the divisors in the linear system determined on $\mathbf{V}$ by g.*

Let π be the Frobenius automorphism of the universal domain. Assume first that $f = \varphi \circ g$; let k be a field of rationality for $\mathbf{V}$ and g; let $\mathbf{M}$ be a generic point of $\mathbf{V}$ over k. We have $f(\mathbf{M}) = g(\mathbf{M})^\pi$; therefore, if $\mathbf{V}'$ is the geometric image of $\mathbf{V}$ by g, its geometric image by f is $\mathbf{V}'^\pi$. The mapping $\mathbf{H} \to \mathbf{H}^\pi$ is clearly a bijection of the set of the hyperplanes in $\mathbf{P}^n$ onto itself; moreover, if $\mathbf{H}$ is such a hyperplane, $\mathbf{V}'$ is contained in $\mathbf{H}$ if and only if $\mathbf{V}'^\pi$ is contained in $\mathbf{H}^\pi$. One sees now at once that the conditions for applying th. 13(b) of Chap. VIII, §4, to $\mathbf{V}$, $\mathbf{P}^n$, $\mathbf{P}^n$, the mappings g and φ, and the cycle $\mathbf{H}^\pi$, are satisfied if $\mathbf{V}'$ is not contained in $\mathbf{H}$; as we have $\varphi^{-1}(\mathbf{H}^\pi) = p \cdot \mathbf{H}$ by prop. 19, this gives:

$$f^{-1}(\mathbf{H}^\pi) = g^{-1}(\varphi^{-1}(\mathbf{H}^\pi)) = g^{-1}(p \cdot \mathbf{H}) = p \cdot g^{-1}(\mathbf{H}).$$

This shows that Λ consists of the divisors $p \cdot g^{-1}(\mathbf{H})$, as we had asserted; in particular, Λ is not separable. Conversely, assume that Λ is not separable; take first the case when f is non-degenerate. Let k be a field of rationality for $\mathbf{V}$ and f, and $\mathbf{M}$ a generic point of $\mathbf{V}$ over k; let $\mathbf{u}$ be a generic point of the hyperplane $\mathbf{E}(f(\mathbf{M}))$ over $k(\mathbf{M})$; then, as we have seen above, $k(\mathbf{M}, \mathbf{u})$ is not separably generated over $k(\mathbf{u})$. As in the proof of th. 14, we see that $f(\mathbf{M})$ has a set of homogeneous coordinates $(1, z_1, \cdots, z_n)$, where the z_i are in $k(\mathbf{M})$; then $\mathbf{u}$ has a set of homogeneous coordinates $(u_0, \cdots, u_{n-1}, 1)$, where $u_1, \cdots, u_{n-1}$ are independent variables over $k(\mathbf{M})$, and $u_0 = -\sum_{i=1}^{n-1} u_i z_i - z_n$. By lemma 1, our assumptions imply now that $k(z) \subset k(\mathbf{M}^\pi)$; this can also be written

$$k^{1/p}(z^{\pi^{-1}}) \subset k^{1/p}(\mathbf{M});$$

therefore we can write $f(M)^{\pi^{-1}} = g(M)$, where g is a mapping of V into P^n, rational over $k^{1/p}$; then we have $f = \varphi \circ g$, as was to be proved. Now, if f is degenerate, we can write it as $f = \alpha \circ f'$, where α is a linear morphism of a projective space P^r into P^n, and f' is a non-degenerate mapping of V into P^r which also determines Λ; by what we have proved, we can write $f' = \varphi' \circ g'$, where g' is a morphism of V into P^r and φ' is the Frobenius morphism for P^r. This gives $f = \alpha \circ \varphi' \circ g' = \varphi \circ \alpha^{\pi^{-1}} \circ g'$, which completes our proof.

COROLLARY. *Let assumptions and notations be as in th.* 15; *put* $\varphi_1 = \varphi$ *and* $\varphi_s = \varphi \circ \varphi_{s-1}$ *for* $s > 1$. *Then a generic divisor in* Λ *is of the form* $p^s \cdot Z$ *if and only if* f *can be written as* $f = \varphi_s \circ g$, *where* g *is a mapping of* V *into* P^n; *and, when that is so,* Λ *consists of the divisors* $p^s \cdot Z'$ *when one takes for* Z' *all the divisors in the linear system determined on* V *by* g.

This follows at once from th. 15, if one uses induction on s.

The determination of the separable linear systems which are irreducible depends upon the following lemma.

LEMMA 2. *Let* $k(x)$ *be an extension of a field* k, *such that the algebraic closure of* k *in* $k(x)$ *is purely inseparable over* k. *Let* y, z *be two independent variables over* k *in* $k(x)$; *let* u *be a variable quantity over* $k(x)$, *and put* $t = y + uz$. *Then the algebraic closure of* $k(t, u)$ *in* $k(x, u)$ *is purely inseparable over* $k(t, u)$.

Let X be the locus of (x) over $\bar{k}$; by th. 1 of Chap. IV, §1, this is also the locus of (x) over $\bar{k}(u)$. By our assumption and by prop. 23 of Chap. I, §7, the smallest field of definition k' for X, containing k, is purely inseparable over k; by the same proposition, $k'(u)$ must then contain the algebraic closure of $k(u)$ in $k(x, u)$; therefore the algebraic closure of k in $k(x, u)$ is contained in $k'(u)$, hence in k' since k' is algebraically closed in $k'(u)$, e.g. by prop. 21 and th. 5 of Chap. I, §7. In particular, if w is in $k(x, u)$ and separably algebraic over $k(t, u)$, the algebraic closure of k in $k(t, u, w)$ is contained in k'. As the field $k(y, z, u) = k(t, u, z)$ has the dimension 3 over k, t, u, z are independent variables over k; therefore, if w is as we have said, $k(t, u, w)$ is separably generated over k; by prop. 23 of Chap. I, §7, the smallest field of definition, containing k, for the locus of (t, u, w) over $\bar{k}$ must then be separable over k; as it is at the same time, by the same proposition, purely inseparable over k', hence over k, it is k; in other words, $k(t, u, w)$ is then a regular extension of k. Now put $K = k(y, z)$ and $L = K(u) = k(y, z, u)$. Let Z be the locus of (x) over $\bar{K}$, which is also its locus over $\bar{K}(u)$. Let K_0 be the smallest field of definition for Z, containing K; this is a finite algebraic extension of K, and, by prop. 23 of Chap. I, §7, it is a purely inseparable extension of the algebraic closure K_1 of K in $K(x) = k(x)$, hence also of the maximal separably algebraic extension K_2 of K contained in $k(x)$. Therefore, if p is the characteristic, there is an integer $q = p^\nu$ such that $K_0^q \subset K_2$. Again by prop. 23 of Chap. I, §7, the smallest field of definition for Z, containing L, must contain the algebraic closure L_1 of L in $L(x) = k(x, u)$; as $K_0(u)$ contains L and is a field of definition for Z, this shows that $K_0(u) \supset L_1$. Let again w be an element of $L(x)$, separably algebraic over $k(t, u)$. As the latter field is contained in $L = K(u)$, hence also in $K_2(u)$, w is separably algebraic over $K_2(u)$. At the same time, as w is in L_1, it is in $K_0(u)$, so that w^q is in $K_2(u)$. As this shows that w is at the same time separably algebraic and purely inseparable over $K_2(u)$, it is in $K_2(u)$; therefore, if we put $L' = L(w)$ and $L_2 = K_2(u)$, we have $L \subset L' \subset L_2$. Now, as u is variable over K, and as K_2 is a separably algebraic extension of K, Galois theory shows that there is a one-to-one correspondence between the fields K' such that $K \subset K' \subset K_2$ and the fields L' such that $L \subset L' \subset L_2$, this correspondence being given by $L' = K'(u)$; therefore there is a separably algebraic extension K' of K, such that $L(w) = K'(u)$. Put $d = [K':K]$; by prop. 6 of Chap. I, §2, this is also the degree of $K'(u) = L(w)$ over $L = K(u)$. But we have $L = k(t, u, z)$, and w is algebraic over $k(t, u)$; as t, u, z are independent variables over k, prop. 6 of Chap. I, §2, shows that $L(w)$ has the same degree over L as $k(t, u, w)$ over $k(t, u)$, so that d is also the degree of w over $k(t, u)$. Let u' be a variable quantity over $k(x, u)$; the isomorphism of $K'(u)$ onto $K'(u')$ over K' which maps u onto u' maps t onto $t' = y + u'z$; then the image w' of w under that isomorphism is algebraic of degree d over $k(t', u')$, and the relation $K'(u) = k(t, u, z, w)$ implies that we have $K'(u') = k(t', u', z, w')$. Now we have

$$K'(u, u') = L(w, u') = k(y, z, u, u', w) = k(t, t', u, u', w),$$

and therefore also, since w' is in $K'(u')$,

$$K'(u, u') = k(t, t', u, u', w, w').$$

Again by prop. 6 of Chap. I, §2, the degree of $K'(u, u')$ over the field

$$K(u, u') = k(t, t', u, u')$$

is d; for the same reason, and since t, t', u, u' are independent variables over k, the degree of $k(t, t', u, u', w)$ over $k(t, t', u, u')$ is d. Also, as $k(t, u, w)$ is regular over k, th. 5 of Chap. I, §7, shows that $k(t, t', u, u', w)$ is regular over $k(t', u')$, hence linearly disjoint from $k(t', u', w')$ over $k(t', u')$. Therefore, by prop. 6 of Chap. I, §2, the degree of $k(t, t', u, u', w, w')$ over $k(t, t', u, u', w)$ is the same as that of $k(t', u', w')$ over $k(t', u')$, which is d. This proves that $k(t, t', u, u', w, w')$ has the degree d^2 over $k(t, t', u, u')$; as we have shown that this degree must be equal to d, we see that $d = 1$, so that w is in $k(t, u)$. Now let v be any element of the algebraic closure of $k(t, u)$ in $k(x, u)$; then there is n such that the quantity $w = v^{p^n}$ is separably algebraic over $k(t, u)$; by what we have proved, this must then be in $k(t, u)$, so that v itself is purely inseparable over $k(t, u)$.

THEOREM 16. *Let Λ be a separable linear system on a variety V, determined by a non-degenerate mapping f of V into a projective space $\boldsymbol{P}^n$, such that the geometric image of V by f has a dimension ≥ 2. Then Λ is irreducible.*

Let k be a field of rationality for V and f; let $\boldsymbol{M}$ be a generic point of V over k; let $(1, z_1, \cdots, z_n)$ be a set of homogeneous coordinates for $f(\boldsymbol{M})$. Our assumption amounts to saying that $k(z)$ has a dimension $\geqq 2$ over k. Let $u_1', \cdots, u_n', u_1'', \cdots, u_n'', v$ be $2n + 1$ independent variables over $k(\boldsymbol{M})$; by prop. 24 of Chap. II, §5, the quantities $y' = \sum_{\nu=1}^{n} u_\nu' z_\nu$, $y'' = \sum_{\nu=1}^{n} u_\nu'' z_\nu$ are independent variables over $k(u', u'', v)$; therefore, by lemma 2, if we put $t = y' + vy''$, the algebraic closure of $k(u', u'', t, v)$ in $k(u', u'', \boldsymbol{M}, v)$ is purely inseparable over $k(u', u'', t, v)$. Now put $u_0 = -t$, and $u_\nu = u_\nu' + vu_\nu''$ for $1 \leqq \nu \leqq n$; call $\boldsymbol{u}$ the point of $\boldsymbol{P}^n$ with the homogeneous coordinates

$$(u_0, u_1, \cdots, u_n);$$

and put $K = k(u'', t, v)$. One verifies at once that we have

$$K(\boldsymbol{u}) = k(\boldsymbol{u}, u'', t, v) = k(u', u'', t, v),$$

hence

$$K(\boldsymbol{M}, \boldsymbol{u}) = k(\boldsymbol{M}, u', u'', v);$$

therefore the algebraic closure of $K(\boldsymbol{u})$ in $K(\boldsymbol{M}, \boldsymbol{u})$ is purely inseparable over $K(\boldsymbol{u})$. On the other hand, $k(\boldsymbol{M}, u', u'', v)$ has the dimension $2n + 1$ over $k(\boldsymbol{M})$, so that this is the dimension of $K(\boldsymbol{M}, \boldsymbol{u})$ over $k(\boldsymbol{M})$. But we have $u_0 + \sum_{\nu=1}^{n} u_\nu z_\nu = 0$, which means that $\boldsymbol{u}$ is in the hyperplane $\boldsymbol{E}(f(\boldsymbol{M}))$; this implies, in particular, that $K(\boldsymbol{M}, \boldsymbol{u})$ has at most the dimension $n - 1$ over $K(\boldsymbol{M})$, and that it has that dimension if and only if $\boldsymbol{u}$ is generic over $K(\boldsymbol{M})$ in $\boldsymbol{E}(f(\boldsymbol{M}))$. Also, the field $K(\boldsymbol{M}) = k(\boldsymbol{M}, u'', t, v)$ has at most the dimension $n + 2$ over $k(\boldsymbol{M})$, and it has that dimension if and only if $u_1'', \cdots, u_n'', t, v$ are independent variables over $k(\boldsymbol{M})$. As $K(\boldsymbol{M}, \boldsymbol{u})$ has the dimension $2n + 1$ over $k(\boldsymbol{M})$, this shows that $\boldsymbol{u}$ is generic over $K(\boldsymbol{M})$ in $\boldsymbol{E}(f(\boldsymbol{M}))$, and that $\boldsymbol{M}$ is generic over K on $\boldsymbol{V}$. Therefore, by the corollary of th. 14, the prime rational cycle over $K(\boldsymbol{u})$ on $\boldsymbol{V}$ with the generic point $\boldsymbol{M}$ over $K(\boldsymbol{u})$ is a generic divisor in Λ. As we have assumed Λ to be separable, this divisor is not of the form $p \cdot \boldsymbol{X}$; this amounts to saying that $K(\boldsymbol{M}, \boldsymbol{u})$ is separably generated over $K(\boldsymbol{u})$, which implies (e.g. by prop. 23 of Chap. I, §7) that the algebraic closure of $K(\boldsymbol{u})$ in $K(\boldsymbol{M}, \boldsymbol{u})$ is separably algebraic over $K(\boldsymbol{u})$; since we have shown that it is at the same time purely inseparable over $K(\boldsymbol{u})$, this proves that $K(\boldsymbol{u})$ is algebraically closed in $K(\boldsymbol{M}, \boldsymbol{u})$. Thus, by th. 5 of Chap. I, §7, $K(\boldsymbol{M}, \boldsymbol{u})$ is a regular extension of $K(\boldsymbol{u})$, so that $\boldsymbol{M}$ has a locus over $K(\boldsymbol{u})$; this locus is then, as we have seen, a generic divisor in Λ. This proves our theorem.

PROPOSITION 20. *Let g be a non-constant mapping of a variety $\boldsymbol{V}$ into a complete non-singular curve $\boldsymbol{C}$; let φ be a non-degenerate mapping of $\boldsymbol{C}$ into a projective space $\boldsymbol{P}^n$; put $f = \varphi \circ g$. Then, if $\boldsymbol{H}$ is any hyperplane in $\boldsymbol{P}^n$, we have*

$$f^{-1}(\boldsymbol{H}) = g^{-1}(\varphi^{-1}(\boldsymbol{H})).$$

This is a special case of th. 13(b) of Chap. VIII, §4; we merely have to verify that the conditions in that theorem are satisfied here. By coroll. 1 of th. 9, Chap. VII, §7, φ is a morphism; as $\boldsymbol{C}$ is complete, it is a proper one. As φ is non-degenerate, $\boldsymbol{\Gamma}_\varphi$ and $\boldsymbol{C} \times \boldsymbol{H}$ intersect properly on $\boldsymbol{C} \times \boldsymbol{P}^n$; therefore $\boldsymbol{V} \times \boldsymbol{\Gamma}_\varphi$

and $V \times C \times H$ do so on $V \times C \times P^n$, and every component of their intersection is of the form $V \times M \times a$, where M is a point of C and a a point of P^n. Such a variety intersects $\Gamma_g \times P^n$ properly on $V \times C \times P^n$, for $V \times M$ is of codimension 1 on $V \times C$ and does not contain Γ_g since g is not constant.

Prop. 20 may be expressed by saying that the linear system determined on V by f consists of the divisors $g^{-1}(X)$ when one takes for X all the divisors in the linear system determined on C by φ.

COROLLARY. *Assumptions and notations being as in prop.* 20, *assume also either that* $n \geqq 2$, *or that* $n = 1$ *and that* φ *is not an isomorphism of* C *onto* P^1. *Then the linear system* Λ *determined on* V *by* f *is not irreducible.*

Let k be a field of rationality for V, C, g and φ. Take first the case $n \geqq 2$. Let M, M' be two independent generic points of V over k; put $N = g(M)$, $z = \varphi(N)$, $N' = g(M')$, $z' = \varphi(N')$; as g is not constant, N and N' are independent generic points of C over k; as φ is non-degenerate, the geometric image of C by φ is a curve, and z and z' are independent generic points of that curve over k. This implies that the hyperplanes $E(z)$, $E(z')$ are distinct, so that their intersection is a linear variety of codimension 2 in P^n; let u be a generic point of that intersection over $k(M, M')$. Then u has the dimension $n - 2$ over $k(M, M')$, hence at least that dimension over $k(N, N')$, so that $k(N, N', u)$ has at least the dimension n over k. As u is in $E(z)$ and $E(z')$, the points $z = \varphi(N)$, $z' = \varphi(N')$ are in $E(u)$; this implies at once that N, N' are components of the divisor $X = \varphi^{-1}(E(u))$ on C; in particular, they are algebraic over $k(u)$, so that $k(N, N', u)$ has the same dimension as $k(u)$ over k. As this dimension is at least n, this shows that u is generic in P^n over k; therefore X is a generic divisor in the linear system determined by φ on C; and, in view of prop. 20, $g^{-1}(X)$ is a generic divisor in Λ. Now, by what we have just proved, we have $X \succ N + N'$, and therefore $g^{-1}(X) \succ g^{-1}(N) + g^{-1}(N')$. It follows at once from the definitions, and from th. 6(i) of Chap. VIII, §3, that $g^{-1}(N)$ is the prime rational cycle with the generic point M over $k(N)$ on V; it is therefore a positive cycle and not 0; the same is true of $g^{-1}(N')$. This shows that $g^{-1}(X)$ cannot be a variety.

Take now $n = 1$; let M be generic over k on V; put $N = g(M)$ and $z = \varphi(N)$. As above, we see that N, z are generic points of C and of P^1 over k. By coroll. 1 of th. 9, Chap. VII, §7, φ is a morphism; for the same reason, if φ is a birational mapping of C into P^1, φ^{-1} is a morphism, so that φ is then an isomorphism of C onto P^1; therefore, if we assume that this is not so, we have $k(z) \neq k(N)$; $k(N)$ is then an algebraic extension of $k(z)$ of degree $d > 1$. As above, we see that $\varphi^{-1}(z)$ is the prime rational cycle with the generic point N over $k(z)$ on C, so that it can be written as $\sum_{i=1}^{d} N_i$, where $(N_1, \cdots, N_d)$ is a complete set of conjugates of N over $k(z)$. Then, as above, $f^{-1}(z)$ is a generic divisor in Λ, and it can be written as $\sum_i g^{-1}(N_i)$; as above, we see that each term in this sum is a positive divisor and not 0; as $d \geqq 2$, $f^{-1}(z)$ cannot be a variety.

THEOREM 17. *Let f be a non-degenerate mapping of a variety V into a projective space P^n. Then the linear system determined by f on V is irreducible if and only if one of the following two conditions is satisfied*: (a) *the geometric image of V by f has a dimension $\geqq 2$, and f cannot be written as $f = \varphi \circ g$, where g is a mapping of V into P^n and φ is the Frobenius morphism of P^n onto itself*; (b) $n = 1$, *and f cannot be written in the form $f = \varphi \circ g$, where g is a mapping of V into a complete non-singular curve C, and φ is a morphism of C into P^1 and is not an isomorphism of C onto P^1.*

If (a) is satisfied, then th. 15 shows that Λ is separable, and th. 16 shows that it is irreducible. Assume that (b) is satisfied; let k be an algebraically closed field of rationality for V and f, and M a generic point of V over k; put $u = f(M)$; then u is generic on P^1 over k, so that $f^{-1}(u)$ is a generic divisor in Λ. By th. 15, Λ is separable, so that, as we have seen, the field $k(M, u) = k(M)$ is separably generated over $k(u)$, and Λ is irreducible if and only $k(u)$ is algebraically closed in $k(M)$. Let K be the algebraic closure of $k(u)$ in $k(M)$; by prop. 23 of Chap. I, §7, this is finitely generated over k and can therefore be written as $k(v)$; let X be the locus of (v) over k. By coroll. 2 of th. 2, Appendix I (which it is permissible to use here, for the reasons explained in the proof of prop. 9, §5), there is a complete non-singular curve C, rational over k, which is birationally equivalent to X over k; let ψ be a birational mapping of X into C, rational over k, and put $N = \psi(v)$; then we have $k(N) = K$, hence

$$k(u) \subset k(N) \subset k(M),$$

and we may write $N = g(M)$ and $u = \varphi(N)$, where g is a mapping of V into C and φ a mapping of C into P^1, both rational over k; this gives $f = \varphi \circ g$. By coroll. 1 of th. 9, Chap. VII, §7, φ must then be a morphism; as we have assumed that (b) is satisfied, it must be an isomorphism; therefore we have $K = k(u)$, which shows that $k(u)$ is algebraically closed in $k(M)$, as we had to prove. In order to prove the converse, assume now that Λ is irreducible. Then, if the dimension of the geometric image of V by f is $\geqq 2$, th. 15 shows that (a) is satisfied. If that image is a curve C', coroll. 2 of th. 2, Appendix I, says that there is a complete non-singular curve C, birationally equivalent to C'; let φ be a birational mapping of C into C', and put $g = \varphi^{-1} \circ f$; then we have $f = \varphi \circ g$; as f is non-degenerate, g is not constant, and φ is non-degenerate. Then, by the corollary of prop. 20, we must have $n = 1$; that being so, the same corollary shows that (b) must be satisfied.

CHAPTER X

COMMENTS AND DISCUSSIONS

1. Qualitative and quantitative algebraic geometry. The ultimate purpose of this book has been to obtain quantitative relations of a global nature on algebraic varieties; theorems 7 and 8 of Chapter VIII are typical relations of that kind. Their validity invariably depends upon suitable assumptions about the completeness and non-singular character of the varieties under study.

On the other hand, many problems in algebraic geometry are of a predominantly qualitative nature; this includes, for instance, a large number of questions concerning algebraic groups and homogeneous spaces, multiple points, and a considerable portion of the theory of divisors (even though, in our treatment of the latter topic in Chapter IX, we have chosen to emphasize the use of quantitative methods). The systematic attempts, made in recent years, to isolate such problems and deal with them under more general assumptions have already begun to bear fruit; they have led to the investigation of concepts, extending those introduced in this book, which make it possible to study geometric objects defined over rings rather than over fields, without excluding the possible occurrence of zero-divisors and nilpotent elements in those rings.

Even within the framework of classical geometry, the need for such generalizations had made itself felt for a long time. If, for instance, a variety V is the parameter variety for a family F of geometric objects (say, of curves), and if k denotes a suitable groundfield and M is a generic point of V over k, then a "generic object" in the family F will be an object $C(M)$, defined over the groundfield $k(M)$; this, in fact, in the early days of "abstract" algebraic geometry, has been one of the strongest motives for studying geometric objects over more general fields than the field of complex numbers. Now, if P is a point of the parameter variety V, the local properties of V in the neighborhood of P may be regarded, algebraically speaking, as properties of the specialization-ring $\mathfrak{r}$ of P in $k(M)$; this is a "local ring" (a word originating just from that situation), which means that its non-units make up an ideal $\mathfrak{m}$, the maximal ideal of $\mathfrak{r}$; in the same sense, the local properties of V, in the neighborhood of P, up to an order of approximation n, are the properties of the ring $\mathfrak{r}/\mathfrak{m}^n$. Thus, in order to study the local properties of the family in the neighborhood of P, one may wish to consider $C(M)$ as being, in a suitable sense, defined over the groundring $\mathfrak{r}$; similarly, when studying these same properties up to a given order of approximation n, one must be able to carry out a reduction process modulo $\mathfrak{m}^n$, which will make out of $C(M)$ an object defined over the ring $\mathfrak{r}/\mathfrak{m}^n$. Moreover, just as the global study of V does not differ from the study of the collection of the local rings in $k(M)$ attached to all the points of V, the global study of the family F is nothing else than the study of a collection of objects respectively defined over all those local rings.

Also, in attempting to close up the gap between algebraic geometry and number-theory, one has come to realize more and more clearly that, from the arithmetical point of view, geometric objects have to be studied over the ring of integers, and their local properties have to be studied over the ring of p-adic integers (or, in the n-th approximation, over the ring of integers modulo p^n), rather than over the rational number-field.

A very general framework for concepts of this kind has lately been set up and developed by Grothendieck in his theory of "schemata" and has already aroused wide attention; alternative definitions, not altogether equivalent to Grothendieck's (and presumably not so well adapted to the needs of a comprehensive theory) have been independently propounded by Kähler. For the number-theorist, all these have the fundamental defect that they take no account of the archimedean valuation (the "infinite prime") of the rational number-field, so that no property of completeness can be expected from objects defined over the integers by any of those methods; thus, at present, they do not appear as useful as the methods based on the adèle concept, even though those two lines of investigation may be expected soon to supplement each other and perhaps eventually to get somehow fused together. As to the algebraic geometer, he finds that the systematic consideration of groundrings, particularly such with zero-divisors, deprives him of the very convenient tool of the "universal domain," making a change of groundring, at this high level of generality, a far more serious and delicate operation than a change in the field of definition for a variety has ever been for us in this book. Of no less moment is the fact that the new concepts seem too general to lend themselves well to the needs of quantitative geometry. This is so because the main theorems on intersection-multiplicities, seen from the point of view of local algebra, are properties of rings of a rather special nature, viz., the rings of formal power-series (in any number of indeterminates) over a field, or at most over a ring with a discrete valuation, and all attempts to extend them to regular local rings of a more general type seem to have failed so far.

It is clear, however, that algebraic geometry has much to gain from a further study of the new concepts; this is being carried out, largely (but, so far, somewhat one-sidedly) by the sheaf-theoretic and cohomological methods which have already added so much to our understanding of the related problems of complex-analytic geometry. It is to be hoped that these investigations will soon have passed the preliminary stage of foundational research and will turn more and more (as they have already so promisingly begun to do) towards specific problems, which alone can demonstrate the scope of the new theory as well as its limitations. This can well go on side by side with a continued study of quantitative geometry in the sense of this book, which is still far from being finished; for instance, the problems concerning the cycles of codimension $\geqq 2$ on the ambient variety have hardly been touched at all.

2. The universal domain. The use of a universal domain depends upon the fact that all fields of finite degree of transcendency (or even of infinite but bounded degree of transcendency) over a given one, as well as all finitely generated integral domains over such fields, can be isomorphically embedded within one and the same field. In order to handle fields of different characteristics simultaneously, more than one universal domain is needed, but this hardly detracts from the usefulness of the method. No such device can be applied to rings with zero-divisors. However, the problems of algebraic geometry where divisors of zero do not occur have been in the past, and are perhaps even now, important enough to deserve systematic treatment by the methods best adapted to their study; from this point of view, there seems to be abundant justification for introducing a universal domain, as has been done in this book, or several, where fields of different characteristics do appear.

The question now arises whether our results depend in any way upon the initial selection of the universal domain in the opening paragraph of Chapter I. The reader may have noticed that it has always remained in the background and has hardly ever been mentioned explicitly again, so that it is now proper to ask how and where it has been used.

The situation may be loosely described as follows. Every statement in this book, if one goes back to the definitions, concerns fields, points and varieties in finite number. What is required of the universal domain is merely that there should be room enough in it for all our fields and all our constructions. From the fact that every variety has fields of definition which are finitely generated over the prime field, and that every one of our constructions, except that of the algebraic closure of a field, involves no more than a finite number of quantities, it follows that we could have assumed all fields to be of finite degree of transcendency over the prime field; as to algebraic closures, they could have been avoided altogether, and replaced on every occasion by finite algebraic extensions; but such a procedure, which would conform to Kroneckerian orthodoxy, would be so inconvenient as hardly to deserve consideration. It is thus apparent that, in order to be able to consider varieties of arbitrarily high dimension, one must work within a universal domain which is algebraically closed and contains an enumerably infinite set of algebraically independent elements over the prime field; but to enlarge it beyond that point does no more, from the algebraist's point of view, than to introduce inflationary money, without any corresponding increase in the amount of goods available at any time.

Therefore, for a given value of the characteristic p, every result, involving only a finite number of points and of varieties, which has been proved for some choice of the universal domain remains valid without restriction; there is but one algebraic geometry of characteristic p for each value of p, not one algebraic geometry for each choice of the universal domain. For instance, as has been rightly stressed by Lefschetz on various occasions, one may, in proving a result of that kind for characteristic 0, take as the universal domain the field of complex numbers, and apply topological or function-theoretic methods; one may equally well, if this happens to be more convenient, work over the algebraic closure of the field of p-adic numbers.

To justify by a formal proof the above statements would require a formal "metamathematical" characterization of the type of proposition to which they apply, a type which would then be found to include all the results formulated in this book; this would have to depend upon the "metamathematical", i.e. logical analysis of all our definitions, one by one. Instead of doing this, we shall try to make the matter clear by discussing a typical example and sketching a proof for the following theorem:

Let U^n be a complete variety without multiple points, defined over a field of characteristic 0; *let r be such that* $0 \leqq r \leqq n$. *Then there are finitely many U-cycles X_i of dimension r with the following property: for every U-cycle X^r, there are integers a_i such that*

$$\deg(X \cdot Y) = \sum_i a_i \cdot \deg(X_i \cdot Y)$$

whenever Y^{n-r} is a U-cycle intersecting X and all the X_i properly on U.

Assume first that we take, as universal domain, the field C of complex numbers; then, as shown in Appendix III, U is canonically provided with a complex-analytic structure; for that structure, it is a compact manifold; and every subvariety of U in the sense of algebraic geometry is also a subvariety of U (possibly with singular points, of course) in the complex-analytic sense. As shown by Borel and Haefliger[1], one can then define, for every r, a homomorphism h of the group of r-cycles on U into $H_{2r}(U, Z)$, the $2r$th homology group of U over the integers, in such a way that, whenever two cycles X, Y intersect properly on U, we have $h(X \cdot Y) = h(X) \cdot h(Y)$ in the sense of the homology ring on U. For $r = 0$, $H_0(U, Z)$ is generated by the class e_0 of a cycle consisting of a point, and we have $h(X) = \deg(X) \cdot e_0$ for every 0-cycle X. Now, for any r, let X^r be a U-cycle such that $h(X)$ is an element of finite order ν in $H_{2r}(U, Z)$, so that we have $h(\nu X) = 0$ with $\nu \neq 0$; and let Y^{n-r} be a U-cycle, intersecting X properly on U; then we have $h(\nu X \cdot Y) = \nu \deg(X \cdot Y) \cdot e_0$; this is also equal to $h(\nu X) \cdot h(Y) = 0$, so that we have $\deg(X \cdot Y) = 0$. Let H'_{2r} be the quotient-group of the group $H_{2r}(U, Z)$ by the subgroup of its elements of finite order, or in other words the canonical image of $H_{2r}(U, Z)$ in $H_{2r}(U, Q)$; for each cycle X^r, let $h'(X)$ be the image of $h(X)$ in H'_{2r}. As $H_{2r}(U, Z)$ is finitely generated, H'_{2r} is a finitely generated free abelian group; the same is therefore true of the image by h' of the group of the r-cycles on U, and we can choose a finite number of such cycles $X_1, \cdots, X_m$ such that the $h'(X_i)$ generate that image. It is now obvious that the X_i have the property stated in our theorem.

From this, we shall now deduce that the same theorem holds for any universal domain K of characteristic 0. Let U^n be a complete K-variety without multiple points; then there is a field of rationality k for U which is finitely generated over the prime field; there is an isomorphism σ of k into C; and U^σ is a complete C-variety without multiple points, to which we can apply the theorem proved

[1] A. Borel and A. Haefliger, Bull. Soc. Math. France vol. 89 (1961) p. 461–513.

above. Let $X'_1, \cdots, X'_m$ be r-cycles on U^σ with the property stated in that theorem; there is a field of rationality K' for all the X'_i, containing k^σ and finitely generated over k^σ; the isomorphism σ^{-1} of k^σ onto k can then be extended to an isomorphism τ of K' onto a finitely generated extension K of k; put $X_i = X_i'^\tau$ for $1 \leqq i \leqq m$; these are r-cycles on U, rational over K. Let now X be any r-cycle on U; let L be a field of rationality for X, finitely generated over K; extend τ^{-1} to an isomorphism ω of L onto some extension L' of K', and put $X' = X^\omega$. Then there are integers a_i such that the cycle $(X' - \sum_i a_i X'_i) \cdot Y'$ is of degree 0 whenever Y' is an $(n - r)$-cycle on U^σ, intersecting X' and all the X'_i properly on U. Applying the same argument once more shows then that $(X - \sum_i a_i X_i) \cdot Y$ is of degree 0 whenever Y is an $(n - r)$-cycle on U, intersecting X and all the X_i properly on U.

3. The concept of affine variety. All existing systems of algebraic geometry start from the consideration of "affine objects" of a certain type, and then give prescriptions for gluing such objects together so as to obtain more general ones (projective varieties, abstract varieties, $\mathfrak{p}$-varieties, schemata, thaumata, etc.); the global problems are those which concern the latter, while local problems can be studied on affine objects. For instance, in the theory of schemata, an affine schema is just a commutative ring (or, what amounts to the same, a certain object canonically associated with such a ring).

From that point of view, our affine varieties can be described as follows. Let k be a field; let R be a ring, finitely generated over k; let $(x_1, \cdots, x_n)$ be a finite set of elements of R, generating R over k; assume that R satisfies the condition:

($\mathfrak{R}$) *If K is any field containing k, the tensor-product $K \otimes_k R$ is a ring without zero-divisors.*

By the results of Chapter I, ($\mathfrak{R}$) is equivalent to the following:

($\mathfrak{R}'$) *R has no zero-divisors, and its field of fractions is a regular extension of k.*

Also, if $\mathfrak{P}$ is the ideal determined by the set (x) in $k[X_1, \cdots, X_n]$, R is isomorphic to $k[X]/\mathfrak{P}$. It is usual to say that an ideal $\mathfrak{P}$ in $k[X]$ is *absolutely prime* if it is prime and remains so under every extension of the groundfield, i.e. if it generates a prime ideal in $K[X]$ whenever K is a field containing k. Now, if $\mathfrak{A}$ is any ideal in $k[X]$, and $\mathfrak{A}'$ is the ideal generated by $\mathfrak{A}$ in $K[X]$, where K is a field containing k, the tensor-product $K \otimes_k (k[X]/\mathfrak{A})$ is isomorphic to $K(X)/\mathfrak{A}'$. Therefore ($\mathfrak{R}$) is also equivalent to the following:

($\mathfrak{R}''$) *The ideal $\mathfrak{P}$ determined by (x) over k is absolutely prime.*

According to our definitions, the point (x) has a locus V over k if and only if any one of the three equivalent conditions ($\mathfrak{R}$), ($\mathfrak{R}'$), ($\mathfrak{R}''$) is satisfied. If k, R' and (x') satisfy the same conditions as k, R, (x), then, by coroll. 2 of th. 2, Chap. VII, §2, the locus V' of (x') over k is k-isomorphic to V if and only if there is an isomorphism of R onto R' over k; it coincides with V if and only if there is such an isomorphism which maps (x) onto (x'). If k', R', (x') satisfy the same conditions as k, R, (x), and if K is a field containing both k and k', the locus V' of (x') over k' is the same as V if and only if there is an isomorphism of $K \otimes_k R$ onto $K \otimes_{k'} R'$, mapping $\xi \otimes 1$ onto $\xi \otimes 1$ for every $\xi \in K$ and mapping $1 \otimes x_i$

onto $1 \otimes x'_i$ for every i; this defines an equivalence relation between the triples $(k, R, (x))$, where k is a "field" in the sense of our Chapter I (in a universal domain, fixed once for all), and R, (x) are as above and satisfy $(\mathfrak{R})$. An affine variety, in the sense of this book, is a class of equivalence with respect to this relation. From this point of view, if the triples $(k, R, (x))$, $(k, S, (y))$ define the varieties V, W, then the product $V \times W$ is defined by the triple $(k, R \otimes_k S, (z))$, where (z) is the set of generators of $R \otimes_k S$ which consists of the elements $x_i \otimes 1$, $1 \otimes y_j$; here again, it is because R and S have been assumed to satisfy $(\mathfrak{R})$ that $R \otimes_k S$ turns out to be without zero-divisors (and to satisfy $(\mathfrak{R})$).

As our varieties arise from identifications between objects defined over different fields, they do not drag their groundfields along with them, making it possible to give priority, whenever convenient, to those results which are independent of the groundfield, and deal later with the more delicate questions where it is of primary importance. In a sense, this amounts to operating first over the universal domain taken as a temporary groundfield, and then re-adjusting the groundfield according to the needs of each specific problem. Condition $(\mathfrak{R})$ originated from the wish to preserve this ability of changing the groundfield with the utmost ease, while at the same time warding off the zero-divisors until they could be handled safely and harnessed to the geometer's working team. It is the equivalence between $(\mathfrak{R})$ and $(\mathfrak{R}')$ which motivates the emphasis put on regular extensions in this book, both explicitly and through our concept of variety.

4. Derivations and differential forms. In this book, derivations have been introduced only as an auxiliary tool; they yield the simplest proof for the corollary of th. 1, and for th. 2, in Chap. I, §5, which play an essential role in the theory of simple points; and they are occasionally useful in dealing with inseparability. From a more general point of view, the primary concept would not be that of derivations, but that of the differential ring of a given ring, which can best be defined as follows. Let R be a commutative ring (with unit-element, as always); on the tensor product $R_2 = R \otimes R$ of the underlying additive group of R with itself (over the integers), we put a structure of R-module by writing $x \cdot (y \otimes z) = (xy) \otimes z$ for all x, y, z in R. Let R' be the submodule of R_2 generated by the elements $1 \otimes xy - x \otimes y - y \otimes x$; the quotient-module $D(R) = R_2/R'$ is called *the differential module of* R; for any x in R, the image of $1 \otimes x$ in $D(R)$ is denoted by $d_R x$ and is called *the* R*-differential of* x. Then, if M is any R-module, the derivations of R in M are the mappings $\varphi \circ d_R$ of R into M, where φ is any homomorphism of $D(R)$ into M as R-modules. If R_0 is any subring of R, the quotient $D(R/R_0)$ of $D(R)$ by the submodule of $D(R)$ generated by $d_R(R_0)$ is called *the relative differential module of* R *over* R_0; the image $d_{R/R_0} x$ of $d_R x$ in that module is called *the* (R/R_0)*-differential of* x. One can then extend in a well-known manner the mapping d_R of R into $D(R)$ to a differential operator, also denoted by d_R, on the exterior algebra $\bigwedge D(R)$ defined over R by the R-module $D(R)$; this makes it into a differential algebra $A(R)$, known as *the differential algebra of R*. The *relative differential algebra* $A(R/R_0)$ *of R over* R_0 is defined similarly. The homogeneous elements of $A(R)$ resp. $A(R/R_0)$ are known as *the differential forms of R* resp. *of R over* R_0. The work of Fitting and of Kähler indicates that a general theory of the so-called "different" and of the discriminant can be developed from this point of view, which seems well adapted to the needs of algebraic geometry, particularly over algebraic number-fields. One can also consider in a similar manner the tensor algebras built up over R from the modules $D(R)$, $D(R/R_0)$, and also from their duals, since other kinds of tensors than the alternating covariant tensors (which are substantially the same as the differential forms) are occasionally of interest in algebraic geometry; but it is only for the latter that the operator d_R can be defined.

For instance, if k is a field, and K a separably generated extension of k of dimension n, the differential module $D(K/k)$ is a vector-space of dimension n over K; a basis for that space consists of the differentials $d_{K/k}x_1, \cdots, d_{K/k}x_n$ (usually written $dx_1, \cdots, dx_n$) of any n elements $x_1, \cdots, x_n$ of K such that K is separably algebraic over $k(x)$. Let V be a variety, rational over k, with a generic point $\boldsymbol{M}$ over k; take $K = k(\boldsymbol{M})$, and call R the specialization-ring in K of a point $\boldsymbol{P}$ of V; then there is an obvious homomorphism of $D(R/k)$ into $D(K/k)$, hence also one of $A(R/k)$ into $A(K/k)$; it does not seem to be known whether these are always injective, but they can be shown to be so if $\boldsymbol{P}$ is a simple point of V, so that, in the latter case, $A(R/k)$ can be identified with its image in $A(K/k)$; that being so, a differential form, i.e. a homogeneous element of $A(K/k)$, is said to be *finite* at a simple point $\boldsymbol{P}$ of V if it is in $A(R/k)$ when one takes for R the specialization-ring of $\boldsymbol{P}$ in $k(\boldsymbol{M})$; on a complete variety without multiple points, a differential form is said to be "of the first kind" if it is everywhere finite. There is an extensive theory (based on the geometric theory of hermitian metrics of Kähler type on complex-analytic manifolds) which deals with the differential forms of the first kind on projective varieties without multiple points over the field of complex numbers; by Lefschetz's principle (cf. §2), the results of that theory which can be formulated in a purely algebraic manner remain valid over any field of characteristic 0. The main results about differentials of the first kind on curves over fields of characteristic 0 remain true over fields of arbitrary characteristic; on varieties of higher dimension, however, those differentials develop pathological traits (for instance, Mumford has found that non-closed differential forms of the first kind may occur; Igusa has found that the number of linearly independent differentials of degree 1, of the first kind, may be strictly greater than the dimension of the Albanese variety), so that they cannot be expected to be as useful in general as they are in the case of characteristic 0. Perhaps the new methods, based on the theory of schemata, which sometimes make it possible to go back from characteristic p to characteristic 0 by a kind of "variation of structure", might help to bring some order here.

5. Specializations. As already pointed out at the end of Chapter II, a specialization of a finite set of quantities can always be extended to any given set, finite or infinite; for instance, a specialization (x') of a set (x) over a field k can be extended to a specialization of all the elements of $k(x)$, or of any field containing $k(x)$. A specialization over a field k of all the quantities in a field K containing k is called a *place* of K over k. Let π be such a place, mapping every $x \in K$ onto a generalized quantity $x(\pi)$; the set R of the elements x of K such that $x(\pi) \neq \infty$ is called the *valuation-ring* belonging to π; it determines π uniquely up to an isomorphism. If U is the group of units, i.e. of invertible elements, of R, and if K^* is the multiplicative group of the non-zero elements of K, then one can put on K^*/U, in an obvious manner, a structure of ordered group, and the canonical mapping of K^* onto this ordered group K^*/U is known as the *valuation* belonging to R, or to π. There are questions in algebraic geometry (for instance, in the theory of multiple points) where valuations play an essential role; in many others (including all the topics treated in this book, with the exception of Chapter III, §3), one need not specialize more than a finite number of quantities at a time. It seems somewhat better to keep those two types of questions apart by refraining, as we have done, from introducing places and valuations when specializations of finitely many quantities can do the trick; however, this is hardly more than a matter of taste or of convenience. What is of far greater moment is that, by considering specializations over fields, we have imposed upon ourselves, in this book, a limitation which seemed wise at the time when the first edition was written, but which the later progress of algebraic geometry has shown to be both unnecessary and troublesome.

This can best be expressed in terms of the homomorphism corresponding to a specialization; for obviously it is the same thing to consider a finite specialization (x') of a set of quantities (x) over a field k, or the homomorphism of $k[x]$ onto $k[x']$ over k which maps (x) onto (x'). Since, by definition, this homomorphism induces the identity on k, it maps the integral domain $k[x]$ onto one of equal characteristic. But of course a homomorphism of one integral domain onto another may well change the characteristic; if it does so, it must change it from 0 to some $p > 1$. This is the case of "unequal characteristic", which is of decisive importance in all arithmetical applications of algebraic geometry.

The extension of the concept of a specialization which is needed here is as follows. Let R be a ring, I an ideal in R, (x) a set of elements of some ring containing R. For every $a \in R$, denote by $\bar{a}$ its image in the ring $\bar{R} = R/I$ by the canonical homomorphism h of R onto R/I; for every polynomial $F \in R[X]$, denote by $\bar{F}$ the polynomial in $\bar{R}[X]$ derived from F by applying h to all the coefficients of F. A set $(\bar{x})$ of elements of a ring containing $\bar{R}$ is then said to be a *specialization of* (x) *over* h if it satisfies $\bar{F}(\bar{x}) = 0$ for every F in $R[X]$ such that $F(x) = 0$; if R is a local ring (i.e. one in which the set M of the non-invertible elements is an ideal) and I is the maximal ideal M of R, this is also called a specialization of (x) *at the center of* R or more briefly *over* R; this includes the case when R is a field, the maximal ideal of R being then $M = (0)$. As the methods used in this book depend upon the systematic avoidance of zero-divisors, we also require that R, $R[x]$, $\bar{R}$, $\bar{R}[\bar{x}]$ should be integral domains; this implies that I must be a prime ideal. One can then define, just as in this book, generalized quantities and non-finite specializations. In the case of unequal characteristic, R must be of characteristic 0 and I must contain a natural prime p, so that $\bar{R}$ is of characteristic p; one needs two universal domains in order to fit this case into our usual scheme. On the other hand, if R and $\bar{R}$ have the same characteristic, one may, without substantially restricting the scope of our definitions, assume that all the integral domains under consideration have been isomorphically embedded into one and the same universal domain.

If $(\bar{x})$ is a finite specialization of a set of quantities (x) over a field k, and R is the specialization-ring of $(\bar{x})$ in $k(x)$, then R is a local ring, and a specialization of a set (y) over R, as defined above, is nothing else than a specialization of (y) over $(x) \rightarrow (\bar{x})$ with reference to k, as defined in Chapter II. More generally, if I is a prime ideal in a ring R, and h is the canonical homomorphism of R onto R/I, the corresponding specialization-ring is the local ring R_I, consisting of the elements a/b of the field of fractions of R with $a \in R$, $b \in R - I$; its maximal ideal M_I consists of the elements a/b with $a \in I$, $b \in R - I$; then a specialization over h is nothing else than a specialization at the center of R_I. Thus, in the theory of specializations, it is no restriction to consider only specializations over local rings.

It is now an elementary and almost trivial matter to extend all the main results of Chapter II to the more general concept of specialization which has just been explained. The same has been done by Northcott and by Shimura[2] for the results of Chapter III. It turns out that theorem 1 of Chapter III remains valid if the ring $\mathfrak{o}$ in it, instead of being of the form $k\{x\}$, is any Noetherian complete local ring without zero-divisors; theorem 3 remains valid if the specialization-ring of (0) in $k(x)$ is replaced by any Noetherian local ring whose completion has no zero-divisors; if that ring is "regular," then the conclusion of prop. 7 of Chapter III is also true, and from this one derives easily the corresponding extension of theorem 4. This is the foundation of Shimura's theory of the specialization of cycles and of reduction modulo $\mathfrak{p}$ (cf. infra §7).

One can also reach the same conclusions very simply by applying a famous result of Zariski's, frequently quoted in the literature as "Zariski's main theorem" (and which, conversely, as Northcott has shown, can be proved by considerations similar to those of our Chapter III, once it is known that "normality" implies "analytic irreducibility"). A general formulation of this result, as given recently by Grothendieck,[3] is the following: *let R be a Noetherian local ring without zero-divisors, integrally closed in its field of fractions K; then, if a set* $(y) = (y_1, \cdots, y_m)$

[2] D. G. Northcott, Proc. London Math. Soc. (III) vol. 1 (1951) pp. 129–137; G. Shimura, Amer. J. Math. vol. 77 (1955) pp. 134–176.

[3] Cf. Grothendieck-Dieudonné, *El. Gé. Al.* Chap. III. The theorem was originally formulated and proved by Zariski for the case when K is an extension $k(x)$ of a field k, and R is the specialization-ring in $k(x)$ of a finite specialization $(\bar{x})$ of (x) over k. It would be of interest to give a local proof for Grothendieck's generalization.

of elements of K has a proper specialization $(\bar{y})$ at the center of R, all the y_j must be in R. Naturally, the assumption that $(\bar{y})$ is proper means that the $\bar{y}_j$ are contained in an algebraic extension of the residue-field $\mathfrak{k} = R/M$, and that there is no set (y') of elements of any extension of $\mathfrak{k}$, not all algebraic over $\mathfrak{k}$, such that (y') is a specialization of (y) at the center of R and $(\bar{y})$ one of (y') over $\mathfrak{k}$. Applied to the specialization-ring of a point on a variety, this theorem amounts to saying that th. 9 of Chap. VII, §7, remains valid if the assumption of simplicity (for $\boldsymbol{A}$ on $\boldsymbol{V}$) in its statement is replaced by the assumption of normality, or even of k-normality when k is any field of rationality for $\boldsymbol{V}$, $\boldsymbol{W}$ and f.

With the help of Zariski's theorem, one can now deal as follows with the existence of multiplicities, i.e. with the qualitative part of theorem 4 of Chapter III. Take for R an integrally closed local ring without zero-divisors; call K its field of fractions, M its maximal ideal, and $\mathfrak{k} = R/M$ its residue field. Let $(y) = (y_1, \cdots, y_m)$ be a set of elements of an algebraic closure $\bar{K}$ of K, and call $(y^{(1)}, \cdots, y^{(n)})$ a complete set of conjugates of (y) over K in $\bar{K}$. We distinguish three cases:

(a) Let (y) consist of only one quantity y, integral over R. Let $F(Y)$ be the monic polynomial in $K[Y]$ such that $F(y) = 0$; we have $F(Y) = \prod_{\nu=1}^{n}(Y - y^{(\nu)})$, so that all the coefficients of F are integral over R; as R is integrally closed, F is in $R[Y]$. Call $\bar{F}$ the polynomial in $\mathfrak{k}[Y]$ derived from F by applying to all the coefficients in F the canonical homomorphism of R onto $\mathfrak{k} = R/M$; then, if $(\bar{y}^{(1)}, \cdots, \bar{y}^{(n)})$ is any specialization of $(y^{(1)}, \cdots, y^{(n)})$ at the center of R, in a field containing $\mathfrak{k}$, we have $\bar{F}(Y) = \prod_{\nu}(Y - \bar{y}^{(\nu)})$; this shows that the $\bar{y}^{(\nu)}$ are algebraic over $\mathfrak{k}$ and are uniquely determined up to a permutation.

(b) Take $(y) = (y_1, \cdots, y_m)$, and assume that (y) is finite at the center of R, which amounts to saying that all the y_j are integral over R. Let $(u_1, \cdots, u_m)$ be a set of m independent variables over K in some extension K' of $\bar{K}$; let $(\bar{u}_1, \cdots, \bar{u}_m)$ be a set of m independent variables over $\mathfrak{k}$ in some extension $\mathfrak{k}'$ of the algebraic closure $\bar{\mathfrak{k}}$ of $\mathfrak{k}$; then $(\bar{u})$ is a specialization of (u) over R; the corresponding specialization-ring S consists of the elements v/w of $K(u)$ with $v \in R[u]$, $w \in R[u] - M[u]$; if N is its maximal ideal, we can identify S/N with $\mathfrak{k}(\bar{u})$ by identifying the image of R in S/N with $\mathfrak{k}$ in an obvious manner, and the image of u_j in S/N with $\bar{u}_j$ for every j. Moreover, it is easily verified (for instance, by induction on m) that S is integrally closed. Now put $z = \sum_j u_j y_j$, and $z_\nu = \sum_j u_j y_j^{(\nu)}$ for $1 \leqq \nu \leqq n$. By prop. 13 of Chap. I, §4, and coroll. 1 of th. 3, Chap. I, §6, $(y^{(1)}, \cdots, y^{(n)})$ is a complete set of conjugates of (y) over $K(u)$, so that, by prop. 11 of Chap. I, §4, $(z_1, \cdots, z_n)$ consists of a complete set of conjugates of z over $K(u)$ repeated a number of times equal to $[K(u, y):K(u, z)]$. By a trivial modification of the corollary of th. 5, Chap. II, §1, one sees at once that any specialization $(\bar{y}^{(1)}, \cdots, \bar{y}^{(n)})$ of $(y^{(1)}, \cdots, y^{(n)})$ over R is also one over S; therefore, if we put $\bar{z}_\nu = \sum_j \bar{u}_j \bar{y}_j^{(\nu)}$, $(\bar{z}_1, \cdots, \bar{z}_n)$ is a specialization of $(z_1, \cdots, z_n)$ over S; by the case (a) of our theorem, this is uniquely determined up to a permutation. Therefore, if the $(\bar{y}'^{(\nu)})$ make up another specialization of $(y^{(1)}, \cdots, y^{(n)})$ over R, and if we put $\bar{z}'_\nu = \sum_j \bar{u}_j \bar{y}_j'^{(\nu)}$, we can reorder the $(\bar{y}'^{(\nu)})$ so that $\bar{z}_\nu = \bar{z}'_\nu$ for all ν. As the $\bar{y}_j^{(\nu)}, \bar{y}_j'^{(\nu)}$ are all in $\bar{\mathfrak{k}}$ by (a), and as the $\bar{u}_j$ are independent variables over $\mathfrak{k}$, this implies that $(\bar{y}^{(\nu)}) = (\bar{y}'^{(\nu)})$ for all ν. Therefore, in the present case (sometimes known as the "elementary case" of our theorem), any two specializations of $(y^{(1)}, \cdots, y^{(n)})$ over R, in one and the same extension of $\mathfrak{k}$, can differ at most by a permutation. Thus every specialization of (y) at the center of R is proper and has a multiplicity.

(c) Now we make no assumption about (y), but we assume that R is Noetherian. Let K' be the field consisting of the elements of $K(y)$ which are separably algebraic over K. Then, by a classical argument (reproduced in the proof of prop. 4, Appendix I), one sees that the integral closure S of R in K' is a finitely generated R-module, hence also a finitely generated ring over R, and that its field of fractions is K'; therefore we can write $S = R[z]$, where (z) is a set of elements of K', finite over R; and (y) is purely inseparable over $K' = K(z)$. Put $d = [K(z):K]$ and $q = [K(y):K(z)]$, so that $n = dq$; by prop. 11 of Chap. I, §4, (z, y) has a complete set of conjugates over K of the form $(z^{(1)}, y^{(1)}; \cdots; z^{(n)}, y^{(n)})$, where $(z^{(1)}, \cdots, z^{(n)})$ consists of a complete set of conjugates of (z) over K repeated q times. Let $(\bar{y})$ be a proper specialization of (y) over R. Let $(\bar{y}^{(1)}, \cdots, \bar{y}^{(n)})$ be any specialization of $(y^{(1)}, \cdots, y^{(n)})$ over R; this can be extended to a specialization $(\bar{z}^{(1)}, \cdots, \bar{z}^{(n)})$ of $(z^{(1)}, \cdots, z^{(n)})$. Let $\mathfrak{N}$ be the set of those values of ν for which $(\bar{z}^{(\nu)}, \bar{y})$ is a specialization of (z, y) over R. If, for any ν, we have $(\bar{y}^{(\nu)}) = (\bar{y})$, then $(\bar{z}^{(\nu)}, \bar{y})$ is a specialization of $(z^{(\nu)}, y^{(\nu)})$, hence also of (z, y), over R, so that ν is in $\mathfrak{N}$. Conversely, take any ν in $\mathfrak{N}$; call S_ν the specialization-ring in $K(z)$ of the specialization $(\bar{z}^{(\nu)})$ of (z) over R; this is the ring consisting of all the elements $F(z)/G(z)$ of $K(z)$, where F and G are polynomials in $R[Z]$ and $\bar{G}(\bar{z}^{(\nu)}) \neq 0$, $\bar{G}$ being the polynomial derived from G by applying to all the coefficients of G the canonical homomorphism of R onto $\mathfrak{k} = R/M$; S_ν can also be described as the ring of fractions derived from the ring $R[z]$ and the prime ideal in $R[z]$ consisting of all the elements $F(z)$ of $R[z]$ for which F is in $R[Z]$ and such that $\bar{F}(\bar{z}^{(\nu)}) = 0$; as such, it is a local ring; as $R[z]$ is Noetherian and integrally closed, one sees at once that the same is true of S_ν. To say that $(\bar{z}^{(\nu)}, \bar{y})$ is a specialization of (z, y) over R is the same as to say that $(\bar{y})$ is a specialization of (y) over S_ν; since $(\bar{y})$ is a proper specialization of (y) over R, it must also be such over S_ν; this implies that $(\bar{y}_1^q, \cdots, \bar{y}_m^q)$ is a proper specialization of $(y_1^q, \cdots, y_m^q)$ over S_ν. As each y_j is purely inseparable over $K(z)$ and has a degree over $K(z)$ which divides q, the y_j^q are in $K(z)$. That being so, Zariski's theorem shows that everyone of the y_j^q must be in S_ν and has therefore a uniquely determined specialization over S_ν, which can then be no other than $\bar{y}_j^q$; this implies that (y) has no other specialization than $(\bar{y})$ over S_ν. But $(\bar{z}^{(\nu)}, \bar{y}^{(\nu)})$ is a specialization of $(z^{(\nu)}, y^{(\nu)})$, hence also of (z, y), over R; this is the same as to say that $(\bar{y}^{(\nu)})$ is a specialization of (y) over S_ν; we have thus shown that, for every ν in $\mathfrak{N}$, we must have $(\bar{y}^{(\nu)}) = (\bar{y})$, and conversely; in other words, the multiplicity of $(\bar{y})$ in the given specialization of $(y^{(1)}, \cdots, y^{(n)})$ is equal to the number of elements in $\mathfrak{N}$. As $\mathfrak{N}$ depends only upon the set $(\bar{z}^{(1)}, \cdots, \bar{z}^{(n)})$, and as this, by (b), is uniquely determined up to a permutation, we have thus proved the existence of a multiplicity for every proper specialization $(\bar{y})$ of (y) over R. It will be observed that, if the assumptions are those of theorem 4 of Chapter III, R is the specialization-ring of a finite specialization $(\bar{x})$ of a set (x) of independent variables over a field k; in that case, nothing more is required than Zariski's theorem in its original formulation.

Once the existence of the multiplicities is established, the arguments used in Chapter III to obtain the quantitative part of theorem 4 can be greatly simplified. In the first place, just as in that Chapter, it is enough to deal with the case considered in prop. 7 of §3, in which $(\bar{x})$ is rational over k; this can at once be reduced to the case $(\bar{x}) = 0$. The reduction to the one-dimensional case, carried out in the proof of th. 2 of §3, may now be replaced by a purely algebraic reduction. In fact, take for (y), as in prop. 7, a set of algebraic quantities over $k(x)$, where (x) is a set of independent variables over k; let $(\bar{y})$ be a proper specialization of (y) over $(x) \rightarrow (0)$ with reference to k. Take a variable quantity t over $k(x)$; put $x_i = tu_i$ for all i, and $K = k(u)$; the u_i and t are independent variables over k, and we have $k(x, t) = K(t)$. If $(y^{(1)}, \cdots, y^{(n)})$ is a complete set of conjugates of (y) over $k(x)$, it is also such over $k(x, t)$, i.e. over $K(t)$; a specialization of that set over $t \rightarrow 0$ with reference to K is the same as a specialization of the same set over $(t, u) \rightarrow (0, u)$ with reference to k and is therefore also a specialization over $(x) \rightarrow (0)$ with reference to k; as such, it must contain $(\bar{y})$ a number of times equal to its multiplicity μ. This shows in particular that $(\bar{y})$ is a specialization of (y) over $t \rightarrow 0$ with reference to K; as such, one sees at once that it must be proper (since otherwise it would not be proper as a specialization over $(x) \rightarrow (0)$ with reference to k). If now we assume prop. 7 to be valid in the case of one variable x, we can apply it to K, t, (y) and $(\bar{y})$, and conclude that μ is a multiple of $[K(\bar{y}):K]_i$; by prop. 13 of Chap. I, §4, this is the same as $[k(\bar{y}):k]_i$. Thus we see that it is enough to deal with the quantitative part of prop. 7 in the case when the set (x) consists of one variable only. In that case, we consider $k(x)$ as a subfield of the field of fractions Ω of the power-series ring $\mathfrak{o} = k\{x\}$; we may assume Ω to have been embedded in the universal domain (provided the latter has been taken with a sufficiently large degree of transcendency). The mapping $\varphi(x) \rightarrow \varphi(0)$ of $\mathfrak{o}$ onto k, defined at the beginning of Chap. III, §3, is a specialization of all the elements of $\mathfrak{o}$ (called "the center of $\mathfrak{o}$" in Chapter III), which can be uniquely extended to a place π of Ω by mapping all the elements of $\Omega - \mathfrak{o}$ onto ∞; by a well-known elementary theorem (substantially equivalent to Hensel's lemma) on complete fields with a discrete valuation, this place can be uniquely extended, up to an isomorphism, to the algebraic closure of Ω. By prop. 12 of Chap. I, §4, $(y^{(1)}, \cdots, y^{(n)})$, which is a complete set of conjugates of (y) over $k(x)$, consists of complete sets of conjugates over Ω of conjugates of (y) over $k(x)$, each one being repeated a certain number of times; thus all we have to do is to show that, in a complete set of conjugates over Ω, the number of those which are mapped by π onto a given set $(\bar{y})$

is a multiple of $[k(\bar{y}):k]_i$. Just as in the proof of th. 2, §3, this can be at once reduced to showing that, if (y) is algebraic over Ω and π maps (y) onto $(\bar{y})$, $[\Omega(y):\Omega]$ is a multiple of $[k(\bar{y}):k]$. This is part of prop. 4 of §3, but it is also a well-known result in the theory of complete rings with a discrete valuation, and one can readily give for it a self-contained proof. As shown by Shimura (loc. cit.), these arguments can also be adapted to the case of unequal characteristic.

6. The theory of intersections. There is necessarily much that is arbitrary in the procedure which has been followed, in our Chapters V and VI, in order to define intersection-multiplicities; this does not mean that, by adopting a different arrangement, one would construct another intersection-theory. In fact, the contents of Chapters V and VI, and of §7 of Chapter VII, may be regarded as supplying the proof for the following statement: "For the algebraic geometry with a given universal domain (or rather, in view of what has been said in §2, for the algebraic geometry of given characteristic p), it is possible to define a symbol $i(A \cdot B, C; U)$ having the properties stated in theorems 3–12 of Chapter VI and theorem 10 of Chapter VII". That this is then possible in only one way is shown in Appendix II. From this point of view, the symbol $i(A \cdot B, C; U)$ is defined, and uniquely determined, by its properties, and its "definition" in Chapter VI becomes merely a step in the proof of its existence. This is actually how the present book was originally written; its starting point was a list of those general properties of intersection-multiplicities which had been used, explicitly or implicitly, by classical geometers, or which seemed to be required for a complete treatment of certain problems by their methods; and a brief analysis, from this point of view, of the main results of Chapter VI and of Chapter VII, §7, may not be out of place here.

Theorem 3 of Chapter VI is substantially no more than the requirement that intersection-multiplicities should be defined in a purely algebraic and finite manner, so as to be invariant, not only under all automorphisms of the universal domain, but even under all isomorphisms of the finitely generated field which is the smallest common field of definition for the varieties U, A, B and C occurring in the i-symbol. Theorem 5 of Chapter VI is the local statement corresponding to the associativity property of the intersection-product of cycles; the latter result, an essential one for all applications of intersection-theory, had already been proved by van der Waerden under certain restrictions. Theorem 6 of Chapter VI, especially that part of it which gives a sufficient condition for the multiplicity 1, expresses a property constantly used by classical algebraic geometers. Theorem 10 of Chapter VI (which includes theorem 8 as a special case) expresses the invariance of intersection-multiplicities under biregular birational mappings; in other words, it expresses the fact that the value of the i-symbol is a local property of the varieties occurring in it.

Theorem 7 of Chapter VI and theorem 10 of Chapter VII have been implicitly used in classical enumerative geometry for a long time. The latter expresses the fact that, in counting the number of solutions for a given problem, one may at will introduce auxiliary points, depending algebraically upon the data and unknowns of the problem, thereby merely multiplying the number of solutions by an obvious factor. The former expresses the fact that, when one solves simultaneously two independent problems, the numbers of solutions are simply to be multiplied by each other. The second part of theorem 12, Chapter VI, is a local formulation of the famous principle of the conservation of number, which played an essential role in the history of algebraic geometry in the last century.

It remains for us to say something of the results where the order of inseparability plays a part, viz. theorems 4 and 11 of Chapter VI and their consequences. In the classical case, when the characteristic p is 0, the former result is trivial, while the latter becomes an easy consequence of the criterion of multiplicity 1. In the case $p \neq 0$, it is the latter result which makes it necessary to introduce the order of inseparability; the purpose of this is not merely to supply the piece of information contained in theorem 4 of Chapter VI, according to which the i-symbol is in certain cases a multiple of a certain power of p, but chiefly to ensure the truth of theorem 6(i) of Chapter VIII when rational cycles over a field are defined as we have done in that Chapter; theorem 4(iii) of Chapter VIII is then a consequence of theorem 4 of Chapter VI, but it would have been equally true if no mention had been made of the order of inseparability in defining the rationality of a cycle over a field (i.e. if condition (c) has been omitted from the definition of a rational k-chain over k in Chapter VIII, §1), while theorem 6 of Chapter VIII would thereby have lost its validity. The one-to-one correspondence, described in that theorem, between certain cycles $\boldsymbol{X}$, rational over a field k on a product $\boldsymbol{U} \times \boldsymbol{V}$ (the so-called "non-degenerate correspondences" on $\boldsymbol{U} \times \boldsymbol{V}$) and the cycles $\boldsymbol{X}(\boldsymbol{P})$, rational over $k(\boldsymbol{P})$ on the factor $\boldsymbol{V}$ of that product, is an essential tool in all applications of intersection-theory; it is because of this that the concept of a rational cycle over a field is of fundamental importance for algebraic geometry in its properly geometric aspects, and not merely (as one might have thought) for the study of the arithmetical properties of algebraic varieties.

One naturally wishes to extend the range of validity of these theorems, and of the corresponding global results, beyond the situations considered in this book. In one direction, this has already been done by Shimura (loc. cit.), whose approach is partly local and partly global and will be examined in §7. But indications are not lacking that this could also be fruitfully attempted in an altogether different direction, by extending the concept of variety so as to cover at least certain types of quotient-structures which the existing theories are all unable to handle.

The problem of quotient-structures is as follows. Let $\boldsymbol{V}$ be a variety; let $\boldsymbol{R}$ be a closed subset of $\boldsymbol{V} \times \boldsymbol{V}$. Assume that $\boldsymbol{R}$ is, in the set-theoretic sense, an equivalence relation; this means that it contains the diagonal of $\boldsymbol{V} \times \boldsymbol{V}$, that it is invariant under the automorphism of $\boldsymbol{V} \times \boldsymbol{V}$ which exchanges the two factors, and that the relations $\boldsymbol{M} \times \boldsymbol{N} \in \boldsymbol{R}$, $\boldsymbol{N} \times \boldsymbol{P} \in \boldsymbol{R}$, imply $\boldsymbol{M} \times \boldsymbol{P} \in \boldsymbol{R}$. If then k is a field of definition for $\boldsymbol{V}$ such that $\boldsymbol{R}$ is k-closed on $\boldsymbol{V} \times \boldsymbol{V}$, and if $\boldsymbol{M}$ is any point of $\boldsymbol{V}$, the equivalence class of $\boldsymbol{M}$ for $\boldsymbol{R}$ is the $k(\boldsymbol{M})$-closed subset $\boldsymbol{R}(\boldsymbol{M})$ of

V defined by $R \cap (M \times V) = M \times R(M)$. The set V/R of the equivalence classes of points of V for R is not only set-theoretically well defined, but has a k-topology and a Zariski topology, derived from the corresponding topologies on V by the usual processes of general topology. Now we ask whether one can construct a variety W, and a morphism f of V onto W, with the following properties: (a) f is constant on every equivalence class of V for R and determines a homeomorphism of V/R onto W when W is also provided with its Zariski topology; (b) if W' is any open subset of W, V' its set-theoretic inverse image in V under f, and φ a morphism of V' into a variety X, constant on equivalence classes for R, then φ can be written as $\varphi = \psi \circ f'$, where f' is the morphism of V' onto W' induced on V' by f, and ψ is a morphism of W' into X. When that is so, the variety W, together with the morphism f, is usually called the quotient-variety of V by R; by using (b), one sees at once that, if it exists, it is uniquely determined up to an isomorphism. If R is the equivalence relation determined by a group G operating on V, i.e. if it is the set of the points $M \times s(M)$ where M is any point of V and s any element of G, then the quotient-variety of V by R, if it exists, is also known as the quotient-variety of V by G.

It is easily seen that, if V and R are as above, a quotient-variety of V by R cannot exist unless some additional conditions are satisfied. For instance, the equivalence class of a generic point on V must be the union of varieties, all simple on V and of the same dimension. The problem of the existence of a quotient-variety has been solved in various special cases; these include the construction of factor-groups and homogeneous spaces in the theory of algebraic groups, and the construction of the Jacobian variety of a curve. Some outstanding problems in algebraic geometry, particularly those concerning the so-called moduli of curves and more generally of varieties, can be formulated in terms of quotient-varieties.

Progress along those lines, however, seems to be blocked by the fact that the present concept of a variety is too narrow for such purposes. To take a simple example, consider a variety V without multiple points, and a finite group $\mathfrak{g}$ operating on V "freely" or "without fixed points", i.e. in such a way that no element of $\mathfrak{g}$, other than the identity, has any fixed point on V; the equivalence classes of V under $\mathfrak{g}$ are the orbits of $\mathfrak{g}$ on V. If V is affine or projective, or more generally if every orbit on V is contained in some open subset of V isomorphic to an affine variety, it is an easy matter to construct the quotient-variety $V/\mathfrak{g}$; otherwise the problem is unsolved. One is thus reminded of the situation in algebraic geometry before the concept of an abstract variety was available; at that time, certain constructions (for instance, that of the Jacobian variety of a curve) could have been carried out only with great difficulty within the framework of the theory of projective varieties, even though, once the objects that were sought for had been produced within the context of a broader definition, it was eventually not hard to show that they could be realized as projective varieties. Similarly, rather than looking in vain for a construction of the quotient of a variety by a finite group without fixed points in the most general case, it is perhaps more promising to try to broaden the concept of variety so as to make the construction a matter of course; one should then at the same time extend correspondingly the other concepts occurring in the main theorems of intersection-theory in such a way as to preserve the validity of these theorems.

In the specific case we have just been discussing, this would not be hard to do; all that is needed is to call a V-cycle, invariant under the freely operating finite group $\mathfrak{g}$, a $(V, \mathfrak{g})$-cycle, and to say that such a cycle is rational over k, if k is any field of rationality for V and all the operations of $\mathfrak{g}$, whenever it is rational over k as a V-cycle. Another related instance occurs in the operation of "restricting the field of definition of a variety", by which one understands the following. Let V be a variety, rational over a separably algebraic extension k' of a field k; put $d = [k':k]$, and call $\sigma_1, \cdots, \sigma_d$ all the distinct isomorphisms of k' into $\bar{k}$; one asks for a variety W, rational over k, and for a morphism p of W into V, rational over k', such that the mapping $(p^{\sigma_1}, \cdots, p^{\sigma_d})$ of W into $V^{\sigma_1} \times \cdots \times V^{\sigma_d}$ is an isomorphism; then W, together with p, is said to be derived from V by the restriction of the field of definition from k' to k. Here again, while it is not difficult to construct a variety W with this property when V is affine or projective, it is not known whether this can be done in the most general case; however, the difficulty disappears, so far as the theorems of intersection-theory are concerned, if one defines W as being set-theoretically the same as $V^{\sigma_1} \times \cdots \times V^{\sigma_d}$, W-cycles being the same as the cycles on that product, provided one re-defines in a suitable (and obvious) manner the rationality of points, subvarieties and cycles over fields K containing k.

One may even hope to deal in a similar manner with problems where, with classical techniques, multiple points cannot be avoided. For instance, take again a finite group $\mathfrak{g}$ operating on a variety V without multiple points, but do not assume that $\mathfrak{g}$ operates freely; a typical case is that of the symmetric group operating as the group of all permutations of the n factors in a product $U^{(n)} = U \times \cdots \times U$, where U is a variety without multiple points, the quotient being then known, if it exists, as the symmetric product of U by itself n times. As above, a quotient-variety $V/\mathfrak{g}$ can be constructed if V is affine or projective, while the general case is unsolved; but, even if it exists, it must in general have multiple points, arising from the fixed points of the operations of $\mathfrak{g}$, and the theorems of intersection-theory cannot be applied at those points. It is quite possible, however, that this difficulty is an artificial one, which could be removed by some such device as has been suggested above for the case of groups operating freely. The very promising concept of the so-called V-varieties, developed by Satake[4] for topological or complex-analytic manifolds, would certainly deserve further investigation from this point of view; according to that idea, a variety is still obtained by gluing together pieces having the requisite local properties, but each piece, instead of being a non-singular affine variety, is a pair consisting of such a variety and of a finite group operating on it (the number of elements in the group being allowed to vary from one piece to another). It is even con-

[4] I. Satake, Proc. Nat. Acad. Sci. U.S.A. vol. 42 (1956) pp. 359–363.

ceivable that, in the application of this idea, the finite groups might be replaced by equivalence relations of a much more general nature.

7. Abstract varieties and their generalizations. We now come to discuss the extensions of the concept of variety which are due to Shimura, Chevalley, Nagata, Grothendieck, and which point in an altogether different direction from the one discussed above. As to Grothendieck's "schemata", we will merely consider the typical case of the "schemata of finite type over a Noetherian ring"; this includes Shimura's $\mathfrak{p}$-varieties and the Chevalley-Nagata schemata as special cases. If one takes as a starting point the concepts developed in this book, these "schemata" can be described as follows.

Let R be a Noetherian ring; let A be a finite set; for each $\alpha \in A$, let $X_\alpha = (X_{\alpha 1}, \cdots, X_{\alpha n_\alpha})$ be a set of indeterminates; for each subset B of A, let X_B be the set $(X_\alpha)_{\alpha \in B}$ of all the indeterminates $X_{\alpha i}$ for $\alpha \in B$, $1 \leqq i \leqq n_\alpha$, and put $R_B = R[X_B]$. For each $B \subset A$, let $\mathfrak{A}_B$ be an ideal in R_B. Also, write R_α, $\mathfrak{A}_\alpha$, $R_{\alpha\beta}$, $\mathfrak{A}_{\alpha\beta}$ instead of $R_{\{\alpha\}}$, $\mathfrak{A}_{\{\alpha\}}$, $R_{\{\alpha,\beta\}}$, $\mathfrak{A}_{\{\alpha,\beta\}}$. The affine objects to be pieced together will be those defined by the rings $R_\alpha/\mathfrak{A}_\alpha$; the ideals $\mathfrak{A}_{\alpha\beta}$ will express how these have to be pieced together; the ideals $\mathfrak{A}_B$ are useful in expressing the conditions which the $\mathfrak{A}_\alpha$ and the $\mathfrak{A}_{\alpha\beta}$ have to satisfy. One may also say that, to each $\alpha \in A$, there corresponds an open subset $\boldsymbol{U}_\alpha$ of the "variety" or "schema" $\boldsymbol{U}$ which is to be defined; to each $B \subset A$, there corresponds the open subset $\boldsymbol{U}_B = \bigcap_{\alpha \in B} \boldsymbol{U}_\alpha$ of $\boldsymbol{U}$; each $\boldsymbol{U}_B$ is an affine object, determined by the ring $R_B/\mathfrak{A}_B$ just as $\boldsymbol{U}_\alpha$ is determined by $R_\alpha/\mathfrak{A}_\alpha$. We consider several cases of increasing generality:

(i) Take for R a field. Take for $\mathfrak{A}_A$ an absolutely prime ideal in R_A, i.e. one which remains prime under every extension of the groundfield; or, what amounts to the same, take for $\mathfrak{A}_A$ a prime ideal in R_A such that the field of fractions of $R_A/\mathfrak{A}_A$ is a regular extension of R. For every $B \subset A$, take $\mathfrak{A}_B = R_B \cap \mathfrak{A}_A$. As $\mathfrak{A}_A$ is absolutely prime, it defines a variety V_A over R in the affine space $S_A = \prod_{\alpha \in A} S^{n_\alpha}$, whose projection V_B onto the partial product $S_B = \prod_{\alpha \in B} S^{n_\alpha}$ is the variety defined over R by the ideal $\mathfrak{A}_B$. Let x_A be a generic point of V_A over R; let x_B be its projection on S_B; in particular, for every α, x_α will be the projection of x_A on $S_\alpha = S^{n_\alpha}$ and a generic point of V_α over R. In order for these data to determine an abstract variety, it is necessary and sufficient that $V_{\alpha\beta}$ should be, for every pair (α, β), the graph of a coherent birational mapping $f_{\beta\alpha}$ of V_α into V_β; for then we have $x_\beta = f_{\beta\alpha}(x_\alpha)$, so that the $f_{\beta\alpha}$ are consistent. By prop. 7 of Chap. VII, §2, this will be so if and only if, for every pair (α, β), the following condition is satisfied:

(I) *Let $\mathfrak{D}_{\alpha\beta}$ be the ideal of the polynomials $D(X_\alpha)$ in R_α such that*

$$D(X_\alpha)X_{\beta j} \in R_\alpha + \mathfrak{A}_{\alpha\beta} \qquad (1 \leqq j \leqq n_\beta);$$

then we have $R_{\alpha\beta} = \mathfrak{A}_{\alpha\beta} + R_{\alpha\beta}\cdot\mathfrak{D}_{\alpha\beta}$.

One should note that a polynomial $D(X_\alpha)$ is in $\mathfrak{D}_{\alpha\beta}$ if and only if there is, for each j, a polynomial $F_j(X_\alpha)$ in R_α satisfying the condition

$$D(X_\alpha)X_{\beta j} \equiv F_j(X_\alpha) \text{ mod. } \mathfrak{A}_{\alpha\beta},$$

or, what amounts to the same in the present case, the condition

$$D(x_\alpha)x_{\beta j} = F_j(x_\alpha).$$

In view of this, and of the proof of prop. 7, Chap. VII, §2, we see that (I) can be equivalently rephrased as follows:

(I′) *If* $\mathfrak{P}$ *is any prime ideal in* $R_{\alpha\beta}$, *containing* $\mathfrak{A}_{\alpha\beta}$, *there are polynomials* $D(X_\alpha)$, $F_j(X_\alpha)$ *in* R_α *such that* $D(X_\alpha)$ *is not in* $\mathfrak{P}$ *and that*

$$D(X_\alpha)X_{\beta j} \equiv F_j(X_\alpha) \text{ mod. } \mathfrak{A}_{\alpha\beta} \qquad (1 \leqq j \leqq n_\beta).$$

When (I), or (I′), is satisfied, our data define an abstract variety

$$U = [V_\alpha, f_{\beta\alpha}]_{\alpha,\beta\in A};$$

this has a covering by open sets U_α, respectively isomorphic to the affine varieties V_α; and one sees at once that, for every $B \subset A$, the set $U_B = \bigcap_{\alpha\in B} U_\alpha$ is isomorphic to V_B. Conversely, it is clear that the data defining any abstract variety can be described in this manner.

(ii) Take now for R a ring $k[y]$, where k is a field and $(y) = (y_1, \cdots, y_m)$ is a generic point of an affine variety W over k. Take for $\mathfrak{A}_A$ a prime ideal in R_A such that the field of fractions of $R_A/\mathfrak{A}_A$ is a regular extension of k; and take $\mathfrak{A}_B = R_B \cap \mathfrak{A}_A$ for every $B \subset A$. Let $\mathfrak{P}$ be the ideal in $k[Y]$ defining W over k; we may identify R with $k[Y]/\mathfrak{P}$; the canonical homomorphism of $k[Y]$ onto R determines then, for every B, a homomorphism of $k[Y, X_B]$ onto R_B; if $\mathfrak{A}'_B$ is the inverse image of $\mathfrak{A}_B$ under this homomorphism, $k[Y, X_B]/\mathfrak{A}'_B$ is isomorphic to $R_B/\mathfrak{A}_B$; in particular, $\mathfrak{A}'_A$ is then an absolutely prime ideal in $k[Y, X_A]$, defining a variety V_A over k in the space $S_A = S^m \times \prod_{\alpha\in A} S^{n_\alpha}$; for every $B \subset A$, the ideal $\mathfrak{A}'_B = k[Y, X_B] \cap \mathfrak{A}'_A$ determines then the projection V_B of V_A on the space $S_B = S^m \times \prod_{\alpha\in B} S^{n_\alpha}$. That being so, we see, just as in case (i), that these data determine an abstract variety U if and only if, for every pair (α, β), $V_{\alpha\beta}$ is the graph of a coherent birational mapping $f_{\beta\alpha}$ of V_α into V_β, and that this is so if and only if (I) is satisfied. Moreover, when that is so, the projection from V_α on S^m is a morphism φ_α of V_α into W; this can be interpreted as a morphism into W of the open subset U_α of U which corresponds to V_α; as the definition of these morphisms shows that φ_α and φ_β coincide in $U_{\alpha\beta}$, they define a morphism φ of U into W.

Conversely, it is easily seen that the data defining any pair (U, φ) consisting of an abstract variety U and of a morphism φ of U into W can be described in the above manner.

(iii) Next, take for R any Noetherian ring; take for $\mathfrak{A}_A$ a prime ideal in R_A; take $\mathfrak{A}_B = R_B \cap \mathfrak{A}_A$ for every $B \subset A$. If (I) is satisfied, these data determine what Grothendieck calls an "integral irreducible R-schema of finite type." The underlying space U of this schema is the union of subsets U_α, each of which is in a one-to-one correspondence with the set of the prime ideals in the ring $R_\alpha/\mathfrak{A}_\alpha$, or, what amounts to the same, with the set of the prime ideals in R_α which contain $\mathfrak{A}_\alpha$. If p_α is the point of U_α which corresponds to the prime ideal $\mathfrak{P}_\alpha$ in R_α, and p_β the point of U_β which corresponds to the prime ideal $\mathfrak{P}_\beta$ in R_β, we have $p_\alpha = p_\beta$ if and only if there is a prime ideal $\mathfrak{P}_{\alpha\beta}$ in $R_{\alpha\beta}$, containing $\mathfrak{A}_{\alpha\beta}$ and inducing $\mathfrak{P}_\alpha$ on R_α and $\mathfrak{P}_\beta$ on R_β; condition (I) ensures that this is an equivalence relation between the elements of the sets U_α. Put now $R'_\alpha = R_\alpha/\mathfrak{A}_\alpha$; notations being as we have just said, call $\mathfrak{P}'_\alpha$ the image of $\mathfrak{P}_\alpha$ in R'_α; and define R'_β, $\mathfrak{P}'_\beta$, $R'_{\alpha\beta}$, $\mathfrak{P}'_{\alpha\beta}$ similarly; then condition (I) ensures that the obvious homomorphisms of the specialization-rings of $\mathfrak{P}'_\alpha$ in R'_α and of $\mathfrak{P}'_\beta$ in R'_β into the specialization-ring of $\mathfrak{P}'_{\alpha\beta}$ in $R'_{\alpha\beta}$ are isomorphisms. This corresponds to the biregularity of the mappings $f_{\beta\alpha}$ at every point of $V_{\alpha\beta}$ in case (i), and makes it possible to study local properties of U, at every point, on one of its affine models U_α, i.e. to derive them from the properties of the rings $R_\alpha/\mathfrak{A}_\alpha$.

One says that the "schema" U defined by the above data is "proper", i.e. complete over R, if the criterion of prop. 12, Chap. VII, §5, is satisfied, i.e. if, for every set $(i) = (i_\alpha)$ of integers such that $1 \leqq i_\alpha \leqq n_\alpha$ for all α, there is a monic polynomial $P((X_{\alpha,i_\alpha})_{\alpha\in A})$ in $\mathfrak{A}_A$.

In particular, take for R a discrete valuation ring without zero-divisors, with the maximal ideal $\mathfrak{p}$ and the field of fractions K; we define this as a ring R without zero-divisors containing an element π such that every non-zero element of R can be written, in one and only one way, in the form $\pi^n u$, where u is an invertible element of R and n is an integer $\geqq 0$; thus our definition includes the case $R = K$, $\mathfrak{p} = (0)$, $\pi = 0$. Then we get a $\mathfrak{p}$-variety in the sense of Shimura by taking $\mathfrak{A}_A = R_A \cap \mathfrak{P}_A$, where $\mathfrak{P}_A$ is an absolutely prime ideal in $K[X_A]$, and, as above, $\mathfrak{A}_B = R_B \cap \mathfrak{A}_A$ for every $B \subset A$, and again assuming that (I) is satisfied.

(iv) We can still proceed as in (iii) whenever (I) is satisfied and $\mathfrak{A}_B = R_B \cap \mathfrak{A}_A$ for every $B \subset A$; if $\mathfrak{A}_A$ is a primary ideal, this defines, in the sense of Grothendieck, a "primary irreducible R-schema"; then all the $\mathfrak{A}_B$ are primary, and the prime ideals associated with them, which obviously also satisfy (I), define the "reduced" schema associated with that defined by the $\mathfrak{A}_B$; if the former is "proper", i.e. complete over R, then the latter is also said to be proper.

(v) In order to obtain the most general "R-schema of finite type" in the sense of Grothendieck, we merely assume, to begin with, that $\mathfrak{A}_C \subset \mathfrak{A}_B$ whenever $C \subset B \subset A$. As above, put $R'_B = R_B/\mathfrak{A}_B$ for every $B \subset A$; call U_B the set of all prime ideals $\mathfrak{P}_B$ containing $\mathfrak{A}_B$ in the ring R_B, or, what amounts to the same, the set of all the prime ideals $\mathfrak{P}'_B$ in the ring R'_B. As we have assumed $\mathfrak{A}_C \subset \mathfrak{A}_B$ for $C \subset B \subset A$, the injection mapping of R_C into R_B determines a homomorphism p_{BC} of R'_C into R'_B; also, $\mathfrak{P}_B \rightarrow \mathfrak{P}_C = \mathfrak{P}_B \cap R_C$ is a mapping f_{CB} of U_B into U_C, and, if $\mathfrak{P}'_B$, $\mathfrak{P}'_C$ are the prime ideals in R'_B, R'_C corresponding respectively to $\mathfrak{P}_B$ and $\mathfrak{P}_C$, we have $\mathfrak{P}'_C = \overset{-1}{p}_{BC}(\mathfrak{P}'_B)$. That being so, p_{BC} determines in an obvious manner a homomorphism of the local ring $(R'_C)_{\mathfrak{P}'_C}$ into the local ring $(R'_B)_{\mathfrak{P}'_B}$; and our first requirement is that this should be an isomorphism of the former onto the latter ring, for all choices of B, C and of $\mathfrak{P}_B$ in U_B. Secondly, we require that there should exist a set U (the "underlying set of the schema"), a covering (U_α) of U by subsets U_α of U and, for each $B \subset A$, a one-to-one mapping φ_B of U_B onto $\boldsymbol{U}_B = \bigcap_{\alpha\in B} U_\alpha$, such that $\varphi_C \circ f_{CB} \circ \varphi_B^{-1}$ is the natural injection of U_B into U_C whenever $C \subset B \subset A$. One finds that, when these conditions are translated into ideal-theoretic terms, they are equivalent to the conjunction of (I) and of the following conditions:

(II) *Whenever* $C \subset B \subset A$, *there is an ideal* $\mathfrak{B}_{BC}$ *in* R_C *such that*

$$\mathfrak{A}_C = (\mathfrak{A}_B \cap R_C) \cap \mathfrak{B}_{BC}, \qquad R_B = \mathfrak{A}_B + R_B \cdot \mathfrak{B}_{BC}.$$

(III) *For* $B \subset A$ *and* $\alpha \in B$, *let* $\mathfrak{P}_\alpha$ *be in* U_α *and such that* $\mathfrak{P}_\alpha \supset \mathfrak{B}_{B\alpha}$; *then there is* $\beta \in B$ *such that* $\mathfrak{P}_\alpha$ *is not of the form* $\mathfrak{P}_{\alpha\beta} \cap R_\alpha$ *with* $\mathfrak{P}_{\alpha\beta}$ *in* $U_{\alpha\beta}$.

Here, according to the notations explained above, U_α, $U_{\alpha\beta}$, $\mathfrak{B}_{B\alpha}$ stand for $U_{\{\alpha\}}$, $U_{\{\alpha,\beta\}}$, $\mathfrak{B}_{B\{\alpha\}}$; (III) seems to depend upon the choice of the latter ideals, but actually, if the validity of (I) is assumed, it depends only upon the ideals $\mathfrak{A}_B$.

A schema may be looked upon as being obtained by piecing together ideals in Noetherian rings in such a way that their primary components fit together; this is expressed by the fact that any set of ideals $\mathfrak{A}_B$ corresponding to a schema can be obtained as follows. For each α, the prime ideals belonging to the primary components of $\mathfrak{A}_\alpha$ make up a finite subset L_α of U_α; put $\boldsymbol{L}_\alpha = \varphi_\alpha(L_\alpha)$, and $\boldsymbol{L}_B = \bigcap_{\alpha \in B} \boldsymbol{L}_\alpha$ for $B \subset A$. Then, for every $B \subset A$, the prime ideals belonging to the primary components of $\mathfrak{A}_B$ make up the subset $\varphi_B^{-1}(\boldsymbol{L}_B)$ of U_B; and one can choose those primary components $\mathfrak{Q}_{B,\lambda}$ so as to satisfy the following conditions:

(IV) (a) *For every* $B \subset A$, $\mathfrak{Q}_B = \bigcap_{\lambda \in \boldsymbol{L}_B} \mathfrak{Q}_{B,\lambda}$ *is a shortest representation of* $\mathfrak{A}_B$ *as an intersection of primary ideals* $\mathfrak{Q}_{B,\lambda}$.

(b) *For* $C \subset B \subset A$, $\lambda \in \boldsymbol{L}_B$, *we have*

$$\mathfrak{Q}_{C,\lambda} = \mathfrak{Q}_{B,\lambda} \cap R_C, \qquad \mathfrak{Q}_{B,\lambda} = \mathfrak{A}_B + R_B \cdot \mathfrak{Q}_{C,\lambda}.$$

(c) *For* $C \subset B \subset A$, $\lambda \in \boldsymbol{L}_C - \boldsymbol{L}_B$, *we have*

$$R_B = \mathfrak{A}_B + R_B \cdot \mathfrak{Q}_{C,\lambda}.$$

Conversely, let $\alpha \to \boldsymbol{L}_\alpha$ be a mapping of A into the set of subsets of some finite set $\boldsymbol{L}$; put $\boldsymbol{L}_B = \bigcap_{\alpha \in B} \boldsymbol{L}_\alpha$ for $B \subset A$; for every $B \subset A$ and every $\lambda \in \boldsymbol{L}_B$, let $\mathfrak{Q}_{B,\lambda}$ be a primary ideal in R_B; assume that, if the ideals $\mathfrak{A}_B$ are defined by means of (IVa), the conditions (I), (IV) are all satisfied. Then (II) and (III) are also satisfied, and these data define a schema, which is said to be "reduced" if all the $\mathfrak{Q}_{B,\lambda}$ are prime. If, for a given $\lambda \in \boldsymbol{L}$, we call A_λ the set of the elements α of A for which $\lambda \in \boldsymbol{L}_\alpha$, then the ideals $\mathfrak{Q}_{B,\lambda}$, for $B \subset A_\lambda$, define a primary irreducible schema; the corresponding reduced schema, defined by the prime ideals $\mathfrak{P}_{B,\lambda}$ belonging respectively to the primary ideals $\mathfrak{Q}_{B,\lambda}$, is an integral irreducible schema. If everyone of these is "proper" according to the definition given above in (iii), then the schema $\boldsymbol{U}$ itself is called proper.

Once "schemata" over rings are defined, they can of course be themselves pieced together (along the lines indicated in prop. 17 of Chap. VII, §6, for the special case of varieties), so as to make up "schemata over schemata" (or "morphisms of schemata"); these represent, at the moment, the widest known generalization of the fibered varieties which we have briefly considered in Chap. IX, §5.

If a basis is given for each one of the ideals $\mathfrak{A}_B$, one sees at once that condition (I) can be expressed by a finite number of identities involving the polynomials in those bases (more specifically, in the bases of the ideals $\mathfrak{A}_{\alpha\beta}$) and some auxiliary polynomials. It is also not hard to show that (II) and (III) can be similarly expressed. From this, one concludes immediately that, if R is a subring of a Noetherian ring S, and if the ideals $\mathfrak{A}_B$ define an R-schema $\boldsymbol{U}$, the ideals respectively generated by the $\mathfrak{A}_B$ in the rings $S[X_B]$ define an S-schema, the extension of $\boldsymbol{U}$ by S. Similarly, if I is any ideal in R, and if h is the canonical homomorphism of R onto R/I, the images of the $\mathfrak{A}_B$ by the obvious extension of h to the rings $R[X_B]$ define a schema over R/I, the reduction of $\boldsymbol{U}$ modulo I. The two operations can of course be combined into one by taking any homomorphism of R into a Noetherian ring S; if S is finitely generated as an algebra over R, it defines an affine R-schema, and the operation we have just described is nothing else than the construction of the product over R of the R-schemas $\boldsymbol{U}$ and S.

Consider in particular a $\mathfrak{p}$-variety $\boldsymbol{V}$ as defined in (iii); this is a schema obtained by taking a discrete valuation ring R, with the maximal ideal $\mathfrak{p}$ and the field of fractions K, taking an absolutely prime ideal $\mathfrak{P}_A$ in $K[X_A]$, and putting $\mathfrak{A}_B = R_B \cap \mathfrak{P}_A$ for every $B \subset A$. Then the extension of $\boldsymbol{V}$ by K is the abstract variety $\boldsymbol{V}_K$ defined over K by the ideals $\mathfrak{P}_B = K[X_B] \cap \mathfrak{P}_A$ in the sense of (i). On the other hand, the reduction $\boldsymbol{V}_0$ of $\boldsymbol{V}$ modulo $\mathfrak{p}$ is a schema over the field $\mathfrak{k} = R/\mathfrak{p}$, defined by the images $\mathfrak{A}_B^0$ of the ideals $\mathfrak{A}_B$ under the canonical homomorphism of R onto $\mathfrak{k}$. As shown by Shimura (loc. cit.), if $\boldsymbol{V}_K$ has the dimension n, all the isolated primary components of the ideals $\mathfrak{A}_B^0$ belong to prime ideals of dimension n; moreover, if $\mathfrak{A}_A^0$ has only one isolated primary component and if this is an absolutely prime ideal $\mathfrak{P}_A^0$, then, for every $B \subset A$, $\mathfrak{A}_B^0$ has only one isolated primary component, viz. the absolutely prime ideal $\mathfrak{P}_B^0 = \mathfrak{k}[X_B] \cap \mathfrak{P}_A^0$, and the other primary components of $\mathfrak{A}_B^0$, if there are any, belong to multiple subvarieties of the variety defined by $\mathfrak{P}_B^0$ over $\mathfrak{k}$. When that is so, $\boldsymbol{V}$ is called $\mathfrak{p}$-*simple*, and the abstract variety defined over $\mathfrak{k}$ by the ideals $\mathfrak{P}_B^0$ is called the reduction of $\boldsymbol{V}$ modulo $\mathfrak{p}$; it is nothing else than the reduced schema derived (by omitting primary components other than the isolated one) from the reduction modulo $\mathfrak{p}$ of the R-schema $\boldsymbol{V}$.

As we have observed above, the general concept of a schema seems better adapted to qualitative than to quantitative problems; on the other hand, it is a fundamental fact, brought to light by Shimura, that the theory of intersection-multiplicities can be extended to $\mathfrak{p}$-varieties, practically without any change. Using this, Shimura attaches, to each $\mathfrak{p}$-simple $\mathfrak{p}$-variety $\boldsymbol{V}$, defined as above, and to each cycle $\boldsymbol{X}$, rational over K, on the extension $\boldsymbol{V}_K$ of $\boldsymbol{V}$ by K, a cycle $\boldsymbol{X}_0 = \rho(\boldsymbol{X}/R)$, rational over $\mathfrak{k}$, on the reduction $\boldsymbol{V}_0$ of $\boldsymbol{V}$ modulo $\mathfrak{p}$; this is called the reduction of $\boldsymbol{X}$ modulo $\mathfrak{p}$, or also its specialization over R. Now let R' be a discrete valuation ring containing R, with the maximal prime ideal $\mathfrak{p}'$ and the field of fractions K'; assume that $\mathfrak{p} = R \cap \mathfrak{p}'$, and identify $\mathfrak{k}$ with the image of R under the canonical homomorphism of R' onto the field $\mathfrak{k}' = R'/\mathfrak{p}'$. Let $\boldsymbol{V}'$ be the extension of $\boldsymbol{V}$ by R'; then the extension of $\boldsymbol{V}'$ by K' is the same abstract variety as $\boldsymbol{V}_K$, and the reduction of $\boldsymbol{V}'$ modulo $\mathfrak{p}'$ is the same as $\boldsymbol{V}_0$; therefore, if

X' is any cycle on V_K, rational over K', it has a reduction modulo $\mathfrak{p}'$, which is a cycle $X'_0 = \rho(X'/R')$ on V_0, rational over $\mathfrak{k}'$. That being so, if X' and X'_0 are cycles, on V_K and on V_0 respectively, X'_0 will be said to be a specialization of X' over R whenever there exists a ring R' such that R', X' and X'_0 have the properties which we have just described. With this definition, which one extends in an obvious manner to any number of cycles on one or more than one $\mathfrak{p}$-variety, Shimura proves that specialization has all the compatibility properties which one may expect with the operations of the calculus of cycles. Specializations over a field k, for cycles on a variety V defined over k, are included in this as a special case: one has only to take $R = K = k$, $\mathfrak{p} = (0)$, so that $V_K = V_0 = V$. This concept can often be used to great advantage, even when cycles on product-varieties could offer a more or less satisfactory substitute for it.

8. Comments on Chapter IX. The purpose of Chapter IX is in part to provide a measure of relief from the unavoidable aridity of earlier chapters (a quality which some authors who are naturally immune from such criticism have not been slow to notice), but chiefly to give examples for the calculus of cycles. It touches upon a number of important topics which would all deserve a full treatment but could not get it within the compass of this book. Some of these would find their most fitting place in an up-to-date book on projective geometry; for, strangely enough, there has appeared no successor to the classical work of Bertini, which, in bygone days, used to lead students gently into the higher reaches of algebraic geometry. Among such topics for which no adequate treatment is available at present, one may mention the theory of the characteristic form (or, what amounts to the same, of the associated or Chow form) of cycles in projective spaces. The one basic fact which was originally proved about this by Chow[5] is the following: if the coefficients of the associated form of a positive r-cycle X of degree d in P^n are regarded as the homogeneous coordinates of a point $c(X)$ in P^{N-1}, for a suitable value of N, then the set $C(r, d, n)$ of the "Chow points" $c(X)$ of all such cycles is closed over the prime field; more precisely, if Z is the ring of the rational integers, there is a homogeneous ideal $\mathfrak{C}(r, d, n)$ in $Z[X_0, \cdots, X_{N-1}]$ whose zeros are the points of $C(r, d, n)$, whatever the characteristic may be. There are some faint indications that the components of $C(r, d, n)$ themselves, at least for characteristic 0, might be rational over the prime field, but the evidence on this point is so scanty that it would be premature to hazard any conjecture about it. On the other hand, there are a number of useful elementary facts about Chow points which are known to be true but for which it would not be easy to give a reference. This includes the easily established relations between the characteristic form and the Chow form of a cycle X, between the Chow form of X and that of $X \cdot H$ when H is a hyperplane, as well as the fact (apparently discovered by Chevalley) that the intersection of all the fields of rationality for X is the field $k_0(c(X))$

[5] W. L. Chow und B. L. van der Waerden, Math. Ann. vol. 113 (1937) pp. 692–704.

generated by the Chow point $c(X)$ over the prime field k_0. Also, if Φ is the characteristic form of a positive cycle X^r in P^n, and if we write

$$\Phi(\sum_\alpha u_{0,\alpha}X_\alpha, \cdots, \sum_\alpha u_{r+1,\alpha}X_\alpha ; (u_{i\alpha})) = \sum_\mu F_\mu(X)M_\mu(u),$$

where the $M_\mu(u)$ are monomials in the $u_{i\alpha}$ and the F_μ are polynomials in the X_α, then it follows immediately from coroll. 4 of prop. 6, Chap. IX, §3, that the set of zeros of the ideal $\mathfrak{A}$ generated by the F_μ is the support $|X|$ of X; but it appears, in addition to this, that, if X is a variety, $\mathfrak{A}$ has only one isolated primary component, which is the homogeneous prime ideal defining X, and that all other primary components of $\mathfrak{A}$, if there are any, must belong to multiple subvarieties of X; this would imply that $\mathfrak{A}$ must be prime whenever X is a non-singular variety. A comprehensive treatment of the matter ought to settle such questions once for all.

The relation between the Chow form (or the characteristic form) of a cycle X and that of $X \cdot H$, where H is a hyperplane, makes it immediately clear that $X \cdot H$ has the same degree as X whenever H intersects X properly in the ambient projective space; from this, one concludes at once that the same is true of $X \cdot L$ whenever L is a linear variety intersecting X properly; in particular, instead of defining the degree of a cycle X^r in P^n as we have done in Chapter IX, by means of its characteristic form, we could have defined it as the degree of the 0-cycle $X^r \cdot L^{n-r}$ whenever L^{n-r} is a linear variety intersecting X^r properly in P^n. This is a special case of Bézout's theorem, which will be discussed in §9 in connection with rational and numerical equivalence.

It will have been noticed that we have refrained in Chapter IX from speaking of fields of rationality for linear systems. One might be tempted to say that a reduced linear system Λ on a variety V is rational over a field k if there is a non-degenerate mapping f of V into a projective space which is rational over k and which determines Λ on V; this, however, would exclude cases such as the following. Let C be a complete non-singular curve of genus 0, rational over k, having no rational point over k; for instance, one can take for C the curve defined in P^2 by the homogeneous equation $X_0^2 + X_1^2 + X_2^2 = 0$ over the rational or the real number-field; then C is not isomorphic to $P^1 = D$ over k but becomes so over $\bar{k}$; let f be an isomorphism of C onto D, rational over $\bar{k}$. The linear system determined by f on C consists of the points of C; this is a set of divisors on C which is parametrized by C itself, and which it would be unreasonable not to consider as rational over k, since C is so; but it would not be rational over k according to the definition suggested above. In order to get a reasonable definition, one can proceed as follows.

One says that a variety W^n, rational over k, is a twisted projective space over k if it is isomorphic to P^n over some extension of k; then it is easily seen that W is isomorphic to P^n over an extension k' of k if and only if it has a rational point over k'. By a known theorem in projective geometry, all automorphisms of P^n are linear; therefore two isomorphisms of W onto P^n can differ at most by a linear automorphism of P^n, and we may define the linear subvarieties of W as the subvarieties of W whose image by any isomorphism of W onto P^n is a linear subvariety of P^n; the linear subvarieties of W of codimension 1 will be called hyperplanes. That being so, we say that a reduced linear system Λ on V is rational over k if there is a twisted projective space W and a non-degenerate mapping f of V into W, both rational over k, such that Λ consists of the divisors $f^{-1}(H)$ when one takes for H all the hyperplanes in W; we say that Λ is strongly rational over k if this can be done so that W is a projective space. If a linear system Λ is not reduced, it will be called rational (resp. strongly rational) over k if the divisor $X_0 = \inf_\Lambda X$ is rational over k and if the reduced system consisting of the divisors $X - X_0$ for $X \in \Lambda$ is rational (resp. strongly rational) over k. By induction on the dimension of V, it is easily seen that the rationality of a linear system Λ over k implies its strong rationality over k whenever V has a simple point which is rational over k.

Let now k be a field of rationality for V; let Λ be a reduced linear system on V; for each divisor X in Λ, let $k(X)$ be the smallest field of rationality for X, containing k. It is easily seen, in view of the definitions given above, that, if Λ is rational over a field K containing k, K must contain the intersection K_0 of all the fields $k(X)$, and also the intersection K_1 of the fields $k(X)$ when one takes for X all the generic divisors in Λ in the sense of Chap. IX, §6. It appears that $K_0 = K_1$ and that Λ is rational over that field, which is therefore the smallest field of rationality for Λ, containing k; presumably, too, if notations are as above, W and f are uniquely determined up to a K_0-isomorphism, when Λ is given. These, again, are elementary questions for which the existing literature seems to provide no answer except under unnecessarily restrictive assumptions, and which it would be useful to settle. As to the construction of twisted projective spaces, it is a special case of the operation known as "lowering the field of definition of a variety," which is itself an easy consequence of the "restriction of the field of definition" discussed above in §6.

Another topic which, on an elementary level, could have been pursued much further than we have done, and which would be at its place in any systematic treatment of projective geometry, is that of ample linear systems, and particularly of ample complete linear systems, in conjunction with the concepts of projective normality and projective normalization; for instance, if Λ is a linear system which "separates points" (i.e. which satisfies condition (i) of th. 12, Chap. IX, §5) on a complete normal variety, then, for sufficiently large values of n, the complete linear system determined by nX, where $X \in \Lambda$, is ample. It is also hardly necessary to warn the reader that fiberings, and in particular the fibered varieties which can be defined by means of divisors (a construction which is implicit in our proof of theorem 3 of Appendix I) have been very widely generalized, and that there is now, on these and related subjects, an extensive and ever-growing literature, in which sheaf-theoretic and cohomological methods have been playing a more and more predominant role. Finally, in an altogether different direction, it may be of interest to notice that some of the results in

Chapter IX, §4, indicate the importance of rings of the type $k(x) \otimes k(y)$, where $k(x)$, $k(y)$ are two linearly disjoint regular extensions of a field k, for the geometric theory of product-varieties. If V and W are two varieties, rational over k, and if M, N are independent generic points of V and of W over k, then $k(M) \otimes k(N)$ is such a ring, and it is isomorphic to the ring of the functions F on $V \times W$, rational over k, such that $F(M, N)$ is of the form $\sum_i f_i(M)g_i(N)$, where the f_i, g_i are functions, on V and on W respectively, rational over k; but this ring does not change if V and W are replaced by varieties V', W', birationally equivalent to V and to W over k; its consideration, in a certain sense, amounts to considering only those points $P \times Q$ on $V \times W$ whose projections P, Q on V and on W are generic points (but not necessarily independent ones) of V and of W over k. This could perhaps be expressed in the language of schemata, but it is hardly likely that this language would do much to clarify such an elementary matter. The fact that the ring in question is, in the sense we have indicated, a birational invariant of the varieties V and W makes it particularly well adapted to the study of a number of questions in the theory of algebraic groups and homogeneous spaces, and in fact it plays, more or less explicitly, an important role in much recent work in that field.

9. Equivalence theories and open questions. In an "equivalence theory," one assigns, either to all varieties, or at least to all varieties satisfying certain conditions (e.g. all complete non-singular varieties) subgroups of the groups of cycles on these varieties, in such a way as to satisfy suitable conditions of the type frequently described nowadays by the catchword "functorial." In other words, an equivalence theory $\mathfrak{E}$ attaches, to each variety U of the prescribed type, and to some or all values of the integer r, not greater than the dimension of U, a subgroup $\mathfrak{E}^r(U)$ of the group of r-cycles on U; to simplify notations, we write $X \equiv 0$ mod. $\mathfrak{E}$ to denote that the r-cycle X on U is in $\mathfrak{E}^r(U)$. The conditions which one expects these groups to satisfy can be classified into the following types:

(I) *If X is a U-cycle, and if (U', X') is a specialization of (U, X) in the sense of Shimura* (cf. §7), *then $X \equiv 0$ mod. $\mathfrak{E}$ implies $X' \equiv 0$ mod. $\mathfrak{E}$*, at least under suitable conditions (for instance, one may only require that this should be so if U and U' are both complete and non-singular).

(II) *If X, Y are U-cycles, intersecting properly on U, then*, at least under certain conditions, *$X \equiv 0$ mod. $\mathfrak{E}$ implies $X \cdot Y \equiv 0$ mod. $\mathfrak{E}$.*

(III) *If X is a cycle on U, Z a cycle intersecting $X \times V$ properly on a product $U \times V$, and if $Z(X)$ is defined as in Chapter* VIII, §4, *then*, at least under certain conditions, *$X \equiv 0$ mod. $\mathfrak{E}$ implies $Z(X) \equiv 0$ mod. $\mathfrak{E}$.*

We say that an equivalence theory $\mathfrak{E}$ is stricter than another one $\mathfrak{E}'$ if $X \equiv 0$ mod. $\mathfrak{E}$ implies $X \equiv 0$ mod. $\mathfrak{E}'$. We can now define as follows the equivalence theories which are chiefly of interest to the algebraic geometer:

(a) The linear equivalence theory of divisors $\mathfrak{E}_{\text{lin}}$; this is the strictest equivalence theory such that $\Theta \equiv 0$ mod. $\mathfrak{E}_{\text{lin}}$, where Θ, as in Chapter IX, is the divisor $(0) - (\infty)$ on D, and that (III) holds whenever $U = D$, $X = \Theta$, and Z is a divisor on $U \times V$; in other words, we must have $Z(0) \equiv Z(\infty)$ mod. $\mathfrak{E}_{\text{lin}}$ whenever Z is a divisor on $D \times V$. For every variety U^n, $\mathfrak{E}^r_{\text{lin}}(U)$ is defined only for $r = n - 1$ and consists of all the divisors of the form div(f), where f is any function on U; (I) is satisfied; (II) is here meaningless; by th. 4 of Chap. IX, §2, (III) is satisfied whenever U is complete and without multiple points and Z has the same dimension as V, the latter condition ensuring that $Z(X)$ is a V-divisor when X is a U-divisor.

(b) Similarly, the algebraic equivalence for divisors, $\mathfrak{E}_{\text{alg}}$, is the strictest equivalence theory for divisors such that, if C is any complete non-singular curve, $\mathfrak{E}^0_{\text{alg}}(C)$ consists of all divisors of degree 0 on C, and that (III) holds whenever U is such a curve, X is a divisor of degree 0 on U, and Z is a divisor on $U \times V$. For every variety V, $\mathfrak{E}_{\text{alg}}(V)$ consists of the divisors $Z(X)$ with U, X and V as we have just said.

(c) So far as divisors are concerned, the only other equivalence theory which is of interest is the equivalence theory $\mathfrak{E}'_{\text{alg}}$ given, on every variety U, by the group of the U-divisors X such that $mX \equiv 0$ mod. $\mathfrak{E}_{\text{alg}}$ for some integer $m \neq 0$. Other types of equivalence, which will be introduced presently for cycles of arbitrary dimension, are found, under rather broad conditions, to be the same as $\mathfrak{E}_{\text{lin}}$, $\mathfrak{E}_{\text{alg}}$ or $\mathfrak{E}'_{\text{alg}}$, so far as divisors are concerned. For instance, it has been shown by Matsusaka[6] that the numerical equivalence of divisors, on a non-singular projective variety, is the same as $\mathfrak{E}'_{\text{alg}}$; and the same is true of homological equivalence with rational coefficients, on non-singular projective varieties over the complex numbers, while, for such varieties, homological equivalence with integral coefficients coincides with $\mathfrak{E}_{\text{alg}}$.

The work of the last fifteen years has given us a fairly thorough understanding of the various types of equivalence for divisors, and of their mutual relationships, on complete varieties of a very general nature (whereas earlier work on surfaces, based largely on topological and function-theoretic methods, had necessarily been restricted to the consideration of non-singular surfaces). The main results here are the Severi-Néron theorem and the existence theorem for the Picard variety. The latter says that, if U is complete and has no multiple subvarieties of codimension 1, one can put, in a "natural" manner, a structure of algebraic group on the group $\mathfrak{E}_{\text{alg}}(U)/\mathfrak{E}_{\text{lin}}(U)$ and that this makes it into an abelian variety, the Picard variety of U. The Néron-Severi theorem says that, if U is such a variety and is projectively embeddable (a restriction which it would perhaps not be too hard to remove), the group of U-divisors modulo $\mathfrak{E}_{\text{alg}}(U)$ is finitely generated. The restriction about multiple subvarieties of codimension 1 is a natural one to make in such a question; moreover, the normalization process will always turn any variety which does not satisfy it into one which does, so that in practice it is hardly a restriction at all.

As to cycles of codimension $\geqq 2$, the general theory has not proceeded much beyond a series of definitions. The rational equivalence theory $\mathfrak{E}_{\text{rat}}$ for cycles is most commonly defined as the strictest one for which $\Theta \equiv 0$ mod. $\mathfrak{E}_{\text{rat}}$, and

[6] T. Matsusaka, Amer. J. Math. vol. 79 (1957) pp. 53–66.

(III) holds for $U = D$, $X = \Theta$, and any Z; for divisors, it is the same as $\mathfrak{S}_{\text{lin}}$. The algebraic equivalence theory $\mathfrak{S}_{\text{alg}}$ is the strictest one for which, on every complete non-singular curve C, $\mathfrak{S}^0_{\text{alg}}(C)$ is as defined above in (b), and (III) holds whenever U is such a curve, X a divisor of degree 0 on U, and Z any cycle on $U \times V$; on any complete non-singular variety V, $\mathfrak{S}^0_{\text{alg}}(V)$ consists of the 0-cycles of degree 0. In the regular equivalence theory $\mathfrak{S}_{\text{reg}}$, one prescribes that $\mathfrak{S}^0_{\text{reg}}(U)$ should consist of all 0-cycles of degree 0 whenever U is a complete non-singular variety which has no non-constant mapping into an abelian variety; and one requires (III) to be valid whenever U is such a variety, X a 0-cycle of degree 0 on U, and Z any cycle on $U \times V$; this is less strict than $\mathfrak{S}_{\text{rat}}$ and stricter than $\mathfrak{S}_{\text{alg}}$. In the numerical equivalence theory $\mathfrak{S}_{\text{num}}$, one defines the group $\mathfrak{S}^r_{\text{num}}(U)$, on any projective non-singular variety U, as consisting of the r-cycles X such that $\deg(X \cdot Y) = 0$ for every cycle Y, of codimension r on U, intersecting X properly on U; at present the restriction to projective varieties is necessary, because it does not seem to be known whether otherwise this defines a group. Finally, some of the work of Severi suggests that one might profitably introduce various kinds of equivalence, not only for the groups of cycles on a given variety U, but also for the groups of U-cycles whose support is contained in a given closed subset F of U.

The usefulness of these equivalence concepts for cycles of arbitrary dimension seems, at the moment, to be mainly the following. As mentioned in the Introduction, the calculus of cycles developed in this book labors under the disadvantage that some of the main properties of its operations, and particularly the associativity of the intersection-product, are not universally valid; as in combinatorial topology, one may expect that their universal validity would be restored by considering, instead of individual cycles, classes of cycles modulo a suitable concept of equivalence. More precisely, suppose that, for a given equivalence theory $\mathfrak{S}$, condition (II) is satisfied without restriction by all cycles on a given variety U, and also that, if U-cycles $X, Y_1, \cdots, Y_m$ are given, there always exists a cycle X', equivalent to X modulo $\mathfrak{S}$, which intersects all the Y_i properly on U. Then, if ξ, η are two equivalence classes of U-cycles modulo $\mathfrak{S}$, one defines their product $\xi \cdot \eta$ as the class of $X \cdot Y$ modulo $\mathfrak{S}$ when X is any cycle in ξ and Y any cycle in η intersecting X properly on U; this, together with the addition of classes, makes the set of all classes of U-cycles into a graded ring, associative and commutative, called the intersection-ring of U modulo $\mathfrak{S}$ (and also known as the "Chow ring" of U if $\mathfrak{S}$ is the rational equivalence). As shown by Samuel, and, within a more general framework, by Chow, the conditions we have just stated are satisfied by the main types of equivalence (rational, algebraic and numerical) on projective varieties.

Once the intersection-ring has been defined for a suitable type of equivalence on a variety U, it becomes possible to carry out many of the processes by which topologists define characteristic classes of fibre-bundles over U. For them, these are cohomology classes; for the algebraic geometer, they are elements of the intersection-ring for whatever equivalence theory one chooses to consider, provided it has the properties stated above. As the method we have just sketched leads naturally to invariants which are classes in the rational intersection-ring (the "Chow ring"), it would be wasteful to substitute for these the corresponding classes for algebraic or numerical equivalence, since these would be theoretically weaker invariants; nevertheless, it must be confessed that, as long as we have no knowledge at all (except in the case of divisors) of the nature and structure of the groups $\mathfrak{C}_{\text{alg}}/\mathfrak{C}_{\text{rat}}$, $\mathfrak{C}_{\text{num}}/\mathfrak{C}_{\text{rat}}$, the stronger invariants yielded by rational equivalence are more than we are now equipped to handle; indeed, it is the characteristic classes in the sense of numerical equivalence which actually play the main role in most of the recent investigations in that direction.

In these investigations, it often becomes necessary to determine explicitly the intersection-rings of various types of homogeneous spaces connected with projective geometry, or more generally with the semisimple groups. This is the modern form taken by the topic formerly known as "enumerative geometry" in the narrow sense in which this word was mostly used in the last century. From this point of view, for instance, what used to be known as Bézout's theorem is nothing else than the determination of the intersection-ring of a projective space for numerical equivalence; it turns out that, in this as in other homogeneous spaces derived from the semisimple groups, numerical equivalence coincides with rational equivalence, and the simplest proof for Bézout's theorem consists in fact in showing that, if X^r is a cycle of degree d in P^n, and L^r is a linear variety in P^n, then X is rationally equivalent to $d \cdot L$. Similarly, the classical Schubert calculus amounts to the determination of the intersection-rings on Grassmann varieties and on the so-called "flag manifolds" of projective geometry.

In all these questions, algebraic geometry has fully emancipated itself from the guiding hands of topology and function-theory and has successfully sallied forth into regions where they could not have followed; not only is it now able to deal with fields of arbitrary characteristic, but also, in the theory of the Picard variety, it treats with equal ease varieties with or without multiple points, provided they are complete and normal. On the other hand, there are outstanding problems where the "transcendental methods" depending upon the use of complex numbers suggest conjectures which are still beyond the reach of the algebraic approach. This includes the theorem discussed above in §2, which says in substance that, on a complete non-singular variety, the group of r-cycles modulo numerical equivalence is finitely generated; as we pointed out there, this is trivially true over the field of complex numbers as soon as an appropriate homology theory is available, and consequently remains true whenever the characteristic is 0, but it is an open question, and presumably no easy one, when no assumption is made about the characteristic. Similar remarks could be applied to the seemingly much more special statement which says that, if X is any cycle on an abelian variety A, the automorphism $x \to -x$ of A transforms X into a cycle numerically equivalent to X.

There are also strong indications pointing to the existence of an analogue in abstract algebraic geometry to the classical fixed point formula of Lefschetz in the theory of topological manifolds; this is suggested, partly by the known facts about zeta-functions of varieties over finite fields, and partly by the fact that such a formula can actually be proved for various types of complete homogeneous varieties and also for all the complete non-singular surfaces which are birationally equivalent to $\boldsymbol{P}^2$. Indeed, it seems not unlikely that such a formula might exist, not only for complete non-singular varieties, but even for certain types of complete varieties with multiple points, for instance symmetric products of non-singular varieties, or more generally for Satake's V-varieties. As Sampson and Washnitzer[7] have pointed out, a weak result in this direction, sufficient for some applications, could be obtained if one knew that the group of n-cycles modulo numerical equivalence, on the product $V \times V$ of a complete non-singular variety V^n by itself, is finitely generated. But, in order to obtain a formula of the Lefschetz type, one would obviously have to find a suitable definition for the cohomology groups $H^0(V), H^1(V), \cdots, H^{2n}(V)$ of every complete non-singular variety V^n. A definition of such groups has been suggested by Grothendieck (under the wholly unsuitable name of "the Weil cohomology"); it remains to see whether this has the properties which are expected of it. In the meanwhile, it is of interest to note that Serre[8] has given, for characteristic 0, a purely algebraic definition of the Betti numbers h^r (more precisely, of the Hodge numbers $h^{p,q}$). The existence of this definition implies for instance that, if V is a complete non-singular variety, algebraic over the field $\boldsymbol{Q}$ of rational numbers, then all the conjugates of V over $\boldsymbol{Q}$ have the same Betti numbers (and the same Hodge numbers); it would be interesting to know whether they are homeomorphic. Unfortunately, Serre's definition, although it remains formally meaningful for arbitrary characteristic, ceases to have the required properties when the characteristic is not 0; this is related to the fact, noted above in §4, that the differential forms on algebraic varieties have pathological properties in the case of non-zero characteristic. For instance, the available evidence leaves no doubt that, if V^n is as above, the Betti numbers $h^1(V), h^{2n-1}(V)$ entering into a formula of the Lefschetz type would have to be equal to $2q$ if q is the dimension of the Picard variety of V, while Serre's definition could lead to a number $h^1(V) > 2q$.

The relation between $h^1(V), h^{2n-1}(V)$ and the Picard variety of V (for characteristic 0 and, presumably, also for arbitrary characteristic) makes it tempting to look for similar relations for other values of the dimension; but here very little evidence is available, even in the classical case. Let V^n be a projective non-singular variety over the complex numbers; then it is known that one can attach to V, for $0 \leqq r \leqq n-1$, an abelian variety $J_r(V)$ whose topological dimension is equal to the Betti number $h^{2r+1}(V)$ of V in the dimension $2r+1$, and whose algebraic dimension is consequently $h^{2r+1}(V)/2$; for $r = n-1$, this is the Picard variety of V; for any r, $J_r(V)$ and $J_{n-r-1}(V)$ are the duals, i.e. the Picard

[7] J. H. Sampson and G. Washnitzer, Amer. J. Math. vol. 81 (1959) pp. 735–748.

[8] J.-P. Serre, Proceedings International Mathematical Congress, Amsterdam, 1954, vol. 3, pp. 515–520.

varieties, of each other, so that in particular $J_0(V)$ is the dual of the Picard variety of V, also known as the Albanese variety of V. Some heuristic arguments suggest that, for every r, there is a "natural" mapping of the group $\mathcal{E}^r_{\text{alg}}(V)$ into $J_r(V)$, which, however, can certainly not be surjective unless all the Hodge numbers $h^{p,q}$ except $h^{r+1,r}$ and $h^{r,r+1}$ are 0 for $p + q = 2r + 1$; the fact that there is such a mapping, and that it is surjective, for $r = n - 1$, is nothing else than the fundamental theorem on the Picard variety; the corresponding fact for $r = 0$ is the fundamental theorem on the Albanese variety. A careful analysis of the situation, based on the method of the "variation of structure," shows that in general one should not expect to find an algebraic interpretation for the $J_r(V)$, since they do not always depend holomorphically upon the local "moduli" of V; it is conceivable, nevertheless, that the image of $\mathcal{E}^r_{\text{alg}}(V)$ in $J_r(V)$, by the mapping whose existence has been conjectured above, might be an abelian variety whose definition could be carried over to the abstract case. On the other hand, $J_r(V)$ does depend holomorphically upon the local "moduli" whenever all Hodge numbers $h^{p,q}$ except $h^{r+1,r}$ and $h^{r,r+1}$ are 0 for $p + q = 2r + 1$; this case, which includes the cases $r = 0$ and $r = n - 1$, is therefore the most promising one at present for the algebraic geometer. Perhaps a careful study, from this point of view, of varieties of some special types (for instance, cubic hypersurfaces in P^4) ought to precede any attempt at a general theory.

APPENDIX I

NORMAL VARIETIES AND NORMALIZATION

Let V be a variety, P a point of V, and f a function on V. If k is a field of rationality for V and f, M a generic point of V over k, and if we put $z = f(M)$, f is finite at P if and only if z is finite over $M \to P$ with reference to k, or also, by prop. 22 of Chap. II, §5, if and only if z is in the integral closure in $k(M)$ of the specialization-ring of P in $k(M)$. If P has a locus W over some field containing k, f is finite at W if and only if it is finite at P; this will be so if and only if $f(M)$ is in the integral closure of the specialization-ring of W in $k(M)$.

We will say that a variety V is *normal at* a point P of V if every function on V which is finite at P is defined at P; if k is a field of rationality for V, we say that V is *k-normal at* P if every function on V which is rational over k and finite at P is defined at P. If K is a field containing k, and if V is K-normal at P, it is obviously also k-normal at P; and V is normal at P if and only if it is K-normal at P for every field K containing k. If M is a generic point of V over k, V is k-normal at P if and only if the specialization-ring of P in $k(M)$ is integrally closed; if P has a locus W over some field containing k, we say then that V is *k-normal at* W or *along* W; we say that V is *normal at* W or *along* W if it is K-normal at W for every field K containing k.

Th. 5 of Chap. V, §3, says that a variety V is normal at every simple point of V; the converse is not true, as shown by the example of the variety

$$X_1^2 - X_2X_3 = 0$$

in S^3, which is normal at $(0, 0, 0)$.

PROPOSITION 1. *Let V be a variety, defined over a field k; let P be a point of V where V is k-normal. Then V is K-normal at P if K is any separably generated extension of k; and, if any function f on V is finite at P, there is an integer $q = p^N$ such that f^q is defined at P. Moreover, if V is not normal at P, there is a function f on V, rational over $k^{1/p}$ and not defined at P, such that f^p is defined and finite at P; and P is contained in a multiple subvariety of V of codimension* 1.

By the principle of localization, it is enough to consider the case when V is an affine variety. Let f be a function on V, finite at P and not defined at P; let K be a field of rationality for f, containing k; let $M = (x)$ be a generic point of V over K, and put $P = (x')$ and $z = f(M)$. Then z is integral over the specialization-ring of (x') in $K(x)$, so that it satisfies an equation of the form

$$P_0(x)z^n + P_1(x)z^{n-1} + \cdots + P_n(x) = 0,$$

where the P_i are in $K[X]$ and $P_0(x') \neq 0$. Putting $w = P_0(x)z$, we see that w is integral over $K[x]$, hence also over the specialization-ring in $K(x)$ of every point of V; this means that the function g on V, rational over K, such that $w =$

$g(\boldsymbol{M})$, is everywhere finite on $\boldsymbol{V}$, hence also on the open subset of $\boldsymbol{V}$ consisting of the simple points of $\boldsymbol{V}$; by th. 1 of Chap. IX, §2, this implies that $\mathrm{div}(g) \succ 0$; therefore, by th. 8 of Chap. IX, §4, we can write $g = \sum_{\lambda=1}^{l} c_\lambda g_\lambda$, where the c_λ are linearly independent elements of K over k, and the g_λ are functions on $\boldsymbol{V}$, rational over k. Consider first the case when K is a separably generated extension of k; then, by prop. 19 of Chap. I, §7, and prop. 19 of Chap. II, §4, there are l isomorphisms σ_μ of $k(c_1, \cdots, c_l)$ over k, such that $\det(c_\lambda^{\sigma_\mu}) \neq 0$. As we have $g^{\sigma_\mu} = \sum_\lambda c_\lambda^{\sigma_\mu} g_\lambda$, the g_λ can then be expressed as linear combinations of the functions g^{σ_μ} with constant coefficients; as g is everywhere finite on $\boldsymbol{V}$, the same is true of the g^{σ_μ}, hence of the g_λ. As $\boldsymbol{V}$ is k-normal at (x'), this implies that the g_λ are defined there; the same must then also be true of g, hence of f, which proves our first assertion. Now, making no assumption on K, call k' the smallest perfect field containing k, i.e. k itself if the characteristic is 0, and otherwise the union of the fields $k^{p^{-N}}$ for $N = 1, 2, \cdots$. Let the d_μ be a maximal set of linearly independent elements over k', taken from among the c_λ; then we can write $c_\lambda = \sum_\mu \alpha_{\lambda\mu} d_\mu$, with coefficients $\alpha_{\lambda\mu}$ in k', and there is an integer $q = p^N$ such that the $a_{\lambda\mu} = \alpha_{\lambda\mu}^q$ are all in k. We have now $g^q = \sum_\mu d_\mu^q g'_\mu$ with $g'_\mu = \sum_\lambda a_{\lambda\mu} g_\lambda^q$. As the d_μ are linearly independent over k', and as k' is perfect, the d_μ^q also are linearly independent over k'; applying now prop. 19 of Chap. II, §4, in the same manner as before, we find that the g'_μ, hence also g^q and f^q, are defined at (x'). Now assume that $\boldsymbol{V}$ is not normal at $\boldsymbol{P}$; then we may assume that the function f which we have been considering is not defined at $\boldsymbol{P}$; let p^ν be the highest power of p such that f^{p^ν} is not defined at $\boldsymbol{P}$, and replace f by f^{p^ν}, so that f^p is now defined at $\boldsymbol{P}$. Then $z = f(\boldsymbol{M})$ will satisfy an equation $P_0(x)z^p + P_1(x) = 0$, with P_0 and P_1 in $K[X]$ and $P_0(x') \neq 0$, so that, if we define g as before, we have $g(x)^p = Q(x)$ with Q in $K[X]$, g being a function on $\boldsymbol{V}$, rational over K and not defined at $\boldsymbol{P} = (x')$. As before, we can write $g = \sum_\lambda c_\lambda g_\lambda$, and we have now $\sum_\lambda c_\lambda^p g_\lambda(x)^p = Q(x)$. Let the c'_ν be a maximal set of linearly independent elements over k among the coefficients of Q and the elements c_λ^p; then we can write $Q = \sum_\nu c'_\nu Q_\nu$, with the Q_ν in $k[X]$, and $c_\lambda^p = \sum_\nu b_{\lambda\nu} c'_\nu$ with coefficients $b_{\lambda\nu}$ in k. This gives:

$$\sum_\nu c'_\nu \left(\sum_\lambda b_{\lambda\nu} g_\lambda(x)^p - Q_\nu(x) \right) = 0$$

and therefore, since K and $k(x)$ are linearly disjoint over k:

$$\sum_\lambda b_{\lambda\nu} g_\lambda(x)^p = Q_\nu(x)$$

for every ν. Now put $h_\nu = \sum_\lambda b_{\lambda\nu}^{1/p} g_\lambda$; we have $h_\nu(x)^p = Q_\nu(x)$ and $g = \sum_\nu (c'_\nu)^{1/p} h_\nu$; as g is not defined at (x'), not all the h_ν are defined there. Thus there exists a function h_ν, rational over $k^{1/p}$ and not defined at (x'), such that $h_\nu(x)^p = Q_\nu(x)$ with Q_ν in $k[X]$; this proves the second assertion in our proposition. Assume now that we have taken for g this function h_ν, so that g is rational over $k^{1/p}$, not defined at (x'), and such that $g(x)^p = Q(x)$ with Q in $k[X]$; write, as before, $g = \sum_\lambda c_\lambda g_\lambda$, where the c_λ are linearly independent elements of $k^{1/p}$ over k and the g_λ are rational over k. Then, as before, we have $\mathrm{div}(g) \succ 0$, hence, by th. 8 of Chap. IX, §4, $\mathrm{div}(g_\lambda) \succ 0$ for all λ; and at least one of the g_λ is not defined at (x') and is therefore not finite there. This means that, for that value of λ, $(x') \times (\infty)$ is in the graph $\mathbf{\Gamma}_\lambda$ of g_λ, hence in some component of $\mathbf{\Gamma}_\lambda \cap (V \times (\infty))$; we can write this component as $W \times (\infty)$, where W is a subvariety of V, of codimension 1 by prop. 11 of Chap. VII, §5. But W cannot be a proper component of $\mathbf{\Gamma}_\lambda \cap (V \times (\infty))$, since otherwise it would be a component of $g_\lambda^{-1}(\infty)$, and $\mathrm{div}(g_\lambda)$ would not be positive; therefore it is multiple on V.

COROLLARY 1. *Let V be a variety, defined over a field k, and assume either that k is perfect or that V has no multiple subvariety of codimension* 1. *Then V is normal at every point where it is k-normal.*

COROLLARY 2. *Let f be a function on a variety V; let k be a field of rationality for V and f, and let P be a point of V where V is k-normal. Then f is defined at P if and only if $P \times D$ is not contained in the graph $\mathbf{\Gamma}_f$ of f.*

Let M be a generic point of V over k; let t be a variable quantity over $k(M, P)$, and consider the function $f' = 1/(f - t)$, which is rational over $k(t)$. We have $f = t + 1/f'$; therefore, if f' is not finite at P, t is a specialization of $f(M)$ over $M \to P$ with reference to $k(t)$, so that $P \times (t)$ is in $\mathbf{\Gamma}_f$; then the locus $P \times D$ of $P \times (t)$ over $k(P)$ is contained in $\mathbf{\Gamma}_f$. Therefore, if that is not the case, f' is finite at P. As V is $k(t)$-normal by prop. 1, this implies that f' is defined at P; the same must then also be true of f. The converse is obvious.

COROLLARY 3. *Let V be a variety, defined over a field k, and let W be a subvariety of V of codimension* 1 *at which V is k-normal. Then every function on V, rational over k, is defined at W.*

Let K be a field of definition for W, containing k, and let P be a generic point of W over K. By coroll. 2, if a function f, rational over k, is not defined at P, and if t is a variable quantity over $K(P)$, $P \times (t)$ must be in $\mathbf{\Gamma}_f$; but then the locus $W \times D$ of $P \times (t)$ over K must be contained in $\mathbf{\Gamma}_f$; this is absurd, since these varieties have the same dimension and cannot coincide.

PROPOSITION 2. *Let V be a variety, defined over a field k; let W be a subvariety of V of codimension* 1, *algebraic over k and having the order of inseparability* 1 *over k. Then V is k-normal at W if and only if W is simple on V.*

If W is simple on V, V is k-normal at W. In order to prove the converse, it is enough, by the principle of localization, to consider the case when V is an affine variety; let S^N be the ambient space for V, (x) a generic point of V over k, and (x') a generic point of W over $\bar{k}$. Let n be the dimension of V; then the assumptions about W mean that $k(x')$ is separably generated and of dimension $n - 1$ over k. Therefore, by th. 2 of Chap. I, §5, one can find, in the ideal determined by (x') over k, $N - n + 1$ polynomials P_ν such that the matrix $\| \partial P_\nu / \partial x'_i \|$ is of rank $N - n + 1$. The P_ν cannot all be 0 on V, since otherwise, by prop. 21 of Chap. IV, §6, the rank of that matrix would be at most $N - n$; therefore not all the quantities $y_\nu = P_\nu(x)$ are 0. That being so, prop. 10 of Chap. II, §3, shows that, after reordering the P_ν if necessary, the set of quantities (y_ν/y_1) has a finite specialization over $(x) \to (x')$ with reference to k. On the other hand, we have $y_\nu/y_1 = P_\nu(x)/P_1(x)$, and, by coroll. 3 of prop. 1, the rational functions P_ν/P_1 on V are defined at W, hence at (x'). Therefore these functions are defined and finite at (x'), which means that there are polynomials Q_ν, Q in $k[X]$ such that $Q(x') \neq 0$ and that

$$P_\nu(x)/P_1(x) = Q_\nu(x)/Q(x)$$

for every ν; for $\nu = 1$, we see that $Q = Q_1$. In other words, the polynomials $F_\nu = Q_1 P_\nu - Q_\nu P_1$ are in the prime ideal defining V over k. But we have, in the notation of Chap. IV, §6:

$$\Delta_{x'} F_\nu(X) = Q_1(x')\Delta_{x'} P_\nu(X) - Q_\nu(x')\Delta_{x'} P_1(X).$$

As the rank of the matrix $\|\partial P_\nu/\partial x_i'\|$ is $N-n+1$, the linear forms $\Delta_{x'} P_\nu(X)$ are linearly independent; therefore the same is true of the $N - n + 1$ linear forms $\Delta_{x'} P_1(X)$, $\Delta_{x'} F_2(X)$, $\cdots$, $\Delta_{x'} F_{N-n+1}(X)$ and hence also of the $N - n$ forms $\Delta_{x'} F_\nu(X)$ for $2 \leqq \nu \leqq N - n + 1$. As the F_ν are 0 on V, this shows that (x') is simple on V.

COROLLARY. *If a variety is everywhere normal, it has no multiple subvariety of codimension* 1.

The next two propositions are well-known results, which we prove here for the sake of completeness since we need them for the construction of normalized varieties.

PROPOSITION 3. *Let k be a field and (x) a set of quantities. Then a quantity y is finite over every finite specialization of (x) with reference to k if and only if it is integral over the ring $k[x]$.*

Let $\mathfrak{P}, \mathfrak{Q}$ be the prime ideals respectively determined by the sets (x) and (x, y) over k; write every polynomial Q in $\mathfrak{Q}$ as a polynomial in Y with coefficients in $k[X]$, i.e. in the form

$$Q(X, Y) = A_0(X)Y^n + A_1(X)Y^{n-1} + \cdots + A_n(X),$$

with $A_0, \cdots, A_n$ in $k[X]$, and consider the set $\mathfrak{A}$ of all polynomials A_0 occurring as the coefficient of the highest power of Y in an expression of this form for a polynomial Q in $\mathfrak{Q}$. One sees at once that $\mathfrak{A}$ is an ideal in $k[X]$, containing $\mathfrak{P}$; therefore every zero of $\mathfrak{A}$ is a zero of $\mathfrak{P}$, i.e. a finite specialization of (x) over k. By prop. 22 of Chap. II, §5, y is finite over a finite specialization (x') of (x) with reference to k if and only if there is A_0 in $\mathfrak{A}$ such that $A_0(x') \neq 0$; therefore y is finite over every finite specialization of (x) with reference to k if and only if $\mathfrak{A}$ has no zero. By Hilbert's theorem, this is the same as to say that 1 is in $\mathfrak{A}$ i.e. that y is integral over $k[x]$.

Corollary 1. *Let k be a field and (x), (y) two sets of quantities such that (y) is finite over every finite specialization of (x) with reference to k. Then a quantity z is integral over $k[x]$ if and only if it is so over $k[x, y]$.*

In fact, assume that z is finite over every finite specialization of (x, y) with reference to k. As every finite specialization (x') of (x) over k can be extended to a specialization (x', y') of (x, y) over k, and as this is finite by our assumption, we see that z is finite over every finite specialization of (x) with reference to k; this, by prop. 3, shows that z is integral over $k[x]$ if it is so over $k[x, y]$. The converse is obvious.

Corollary 2. *Let V be an affine variety, defined over a field k; let (x) be a generic point of V over k. Then V is everywhere k-normal if and only if the ring $k[x]$ is integrally closed in $k(x)$.*

Let y be in $k(x)$ and integral over $k[x]$, and put $y = f(x)$, where f is a function on V, rational over k. By prop. 3, f is everywhere finite on V; therefore, if V is everywhere k-normal, f is everywhere defined on V, so that, by coroll. 2 of th. 2, Chap. VII, §2, y is in $k[x]$. Conversely, let f be a function on V, rational over k and finite at a point (x') of V; put $y = f(x)$. Then y satisfies an equation

$$P_0(x)y^n + \cdots + P_n(x) = 0,$$

with the P_i in $k[X]$ and $P_0(x') \neq 0$, so that $P_0(x)y$ is integral over $k[x]$; if $k[x]$ is integrally closed, this implies $P_0(x)y = Q(x)$ with Q in $k[X]$, so that f is defined at (x').

We now consider the structure of the integral closure of a ring $k[x]$, generated over a field k by a set of quantities (x), in an extension $k(x, y)$ of $k(x)$; we need the fact that this is a finite (i.e., finitely generated) $k[x]$-module. As we have observed in Chap. III, §1, every ring $k[x]$ is Noetherian; this implies, by a well-known elementary theorem, that every submodule of a finite $k[x]$-module is a finite $k[x]$-module. We first observe that, if $k(x)$ is an extension of a field k, the algebraic closure k' of k in $k(x)$ is contained (by prop. 23 of Chap. I, §7) in the smallest field k_0' such that the ideal determined by (x) over $\bar{k}$ has a basis in k_0'; as k_0' is of finite degree over k, the same is therefore true of k'. In particular, if (x), (y) are two sets of quantities, the algebraic closure of $k(x)$ in $k(x, y)$ is an algebraic extension of $k(x)$, i.e. of finite degree over $k(x)$.

Proposition 4. *Let k be a field and (x), (y) two sets of quantities. Then the integral closure I of $k[x]$ in $k(x, y)$ is a finite $k[x]$-module, and its field of fractions is the algebraic closure of $k(x)$ in $k(x, y)$.*

Replacing $k(x, y)$ by the algebraic closure of $k(x)$ in $k(x, y)$, we see that it is enough to deal with the case when (y) is algebraic over $k(x)$. Let z be any element of $k(x, y)$; as it is algebraic over $k(x)$, it satisfies an equation

$$P_0(x)z^n + \cdots + P_n(x) = 0,$$

where the P_i are in $k[X]$ and $P_0(x) \neq 0$; then $P_0(x)z$ is integral over $k[x]$. As I contains $k[x]$, this implies in particular that the field of fractions of I is $k(x, y)$. It also shows that, after replacing each quantity y_j in the set (y) by a quantity $y'_j = Q_j(x)y_j$, with Q_j in $k[X]$ and $Q_j(x) \neq 0$, we may assume that all the y_j are integral over $k[x]$, i.e. that (y) is finite over every finite specialization of (x) with reference to k. Then, by coroll. 1 of prop. 3, the integral closure of $k[x, y]$ in $k(x, y)$ is I. Moreover, every y_j satisfies then an equation

$$y_j^{n_j} + P_{j1}(x)y_j^{n_j-1} + \cdots + P_{jn_j}(x) = 0,$$

where the P_{jh} are in $k[X]$; this implies that every element of $k[x, y]$ can be written as $Q(x, y)$, where Q is a polynomial in $k[X, Y]$ whose degree in Y_j is $< n_j$ for every j; therefore $k[x, y]$ is a finite $k[x]$-module, generated over $k[x]$ by a finite number of monomials in the y_j, so that every finite $k[x, y]$-module is also a finite $k[x]$-module. Let now (z) be any set of quantities, all integral over $k[x]$; call J the integral closure of $k[x]$ in $k(x, y, z)$, which, by coroll. 1 of prop. 3, is the same as that of $k[x, y, z]$ in $k(x, y, z)$; if we show that J is a finite $k[x, y, z]$-module, then, by what we have just proved, it will also be a finite $k[x]$-module, and the same will be true of I, which is a submodule of the $k[x]$-module J. In particular, let k' be the smallest field of definition for the locus of (x, y) over $\bar{k}$, and put $k' = k(z)$; as the quantities z_h are algebraic over k, they are integral over k, hence over $k[x]$; in view of what has just been said, we see now that our proposition will be proved if we show that the integral closure of $k'[x, y]$ in $k'(x, y)$ is a finite $k'[x, y]$-module. Replacing now k' by k and (x, y) by (x), we have thus to show that, if (x) is a generic point of an affine variety V over a field k, the integral closure I of $k[x]$ in $k(x)$ is a finite $k[x]$-module.

Let K be a field containing k, such that (x) is still a generic point of V over K; we will first show that, if the integral closure I' of $K[x]$ in $K(x)$ is a finite $K[x]$-module, then I is a finite $k[x]$-module. In fact, let $z_1, \cdots, z_m$ be a set of generators for I' as a $K[x]$-module; we can write $z_i = F_i(x)$, where the F_i are functions on V, rational over K; then the F_i are everywhere finite on V. By th. 1 of Chap. IX, §2 (applied to the open set of the simple points on V), this implies that $\mathrm{div}(F_i) \succ 0$; therefore, by th. 8 of Chap. IX, §4, we can write each F_i as a linear combination, with coefficients in K, of functions $f_{i\lambda}$ on V, all rational over k; if we call (f_λ) a maximal set of linearly independent functions over k among all the $f_{i\lambda}$, we can then write $F_i = \sum_\lambda c_{i\lambda} f_\lambda$, with coefficients $c_{i\lambda}$ in K. Put $w_\lambda = f_\lambda(x)$, so that we have $z_i = \sum_\lambda c_{i\lambda} w_\lambda$; then I' is contained in the $K[x]$-module I'' generated by the w_λ, and we have $I \subset I' \subset I''$. If now y is any element of I, it can be written as a linear combination, with coefficients $d_{\lambda\nu}$ in K, of monomials $w_\lambda M_\nu(x)$, where M_ν is a monomial in the x_i. Let (d_ρ) be a maximal set of linearly independent elements over k from among $d_0 = 1$ and the $d_{\lambda\nu}$; expressing the $d_{\lambda\nu}$ in terms of the d_ρ, we get:

$$d_0 y = \sum_\rho d_\rho \sum_\lambda w_\lambda Q_{\lambda\rho}(x),$$

where the $Q_{\lambda\rho}$ are in $k[X]$. As K and $k(x)$ are linearly disjoint, this implies that the coefficients of d_0 on both sides are equal; therefore y is in the $k[x]$-module I_1 generated by the w_λ. This proves that $I \subset I_1$, and therefore that I itself is a finite $k[x]$-module, as we had asserted.

Now put $x = (x_1, \cdots, x_N)$, and call n the dimension of (x) over k. Take nN independent variables $u_{i\nu}$ over $k(x)$; put $K = k(u)$ and $y_i = \sum_{\nu=1}^{N} u_{i\nu}x_\nu$ for $1 \leqq i \leqq n$. By what we have proved above, all we need to show is that the integral closure I' of $K[x]$ in $K(x)$ is a finite $K[x]$-module. But, by prop. 24 of Chap. II, §5, and by coroll. 1 of prop. 3, I' is also the integral closure of $K[y]$ in $K(x)$; moreover, by the same proposition and prop. 24 of Chap. IV, §6, the y_i are independent variables over K, and $K(x)$ is separably algebraic over $K(y)$. Under those circumstances, it is a classical result that I' is a finite $K[y]$-module, hence also a finite $K[x]$-module; we briefly recall the proof. Put $L = K(y)$, $L' = K(x)$, $d = [L':L]$; let $t_1, \cdots, t_d$ be a basis for L' over L. Call $\sigma_1, \cdots, \sigma_d$ all the distinct isomorphisms of L' into $\bar{L}$ over L; then (by Galois theory, or by prop. 19 of Chap. II, §4, and prop. 19 of Chap. I, §7) the matrix $T = \| t_\lambda^{\sigma_\mu} \|$ has a non-zero determinant; put $T^{-1} = \| s_{\lambda\mu} \|$, where the $s_{\lambda\mu}$ are in $\bar{L}$. Every element t of L' can be written as $t = \sum_\lambda v_\lambda t_\lambda$, where the v_λ are in L and are given by $v_\lambda = \sum_\mu s_{\mu\lambda} t^{\sigma_\mu}$. Now, as before, one sees that there is a polynomial Q in $K[Y]$ such that $Q(y) \neq 0$ and that $Q(y)s_{\lambda\mu}$ is integral over $K[y]$ for all λ, μ; therefore, after replacing the basis (t_λ) by $(Q(y)^{-1}t_\lambda)$, which replaces the matrix T^{-1} by $Q(y)T^{-1}$, we may assume that all the $s_{\lambda\mu}$ are integral over $K[y]$. That being so, the formulas given above, together with prop. 3, show that, if t is integral over $K[y]$, the v_λ are so; as they are in L, and as it follows from coroll. 2 of prop. 3 that $K[y]$ is integrally closed in L, the v_λ must then be in $K[y]$. Thus I' is contained in the $K[y]$-module generated by the t_λ. This completes our proof.

Corollary. *Notations being as in prop. 4, I is a finitely generated ring over k.*

In fact, it is generated, as a ring over k, by the x_i and any set of generators of I as a $k[x]$-module.

Proposition 5. *Let $\boldsymbol{V}$, $\boldsymbol{W}$ be two varieties, rational over k; let $\boldsymbol{P}$ be a point of $\boldsymbol{V}$, and $\boldsymbol{Q}$ a point of $\boldsymbol{W}$. Then $\boldsymbol{V} \times \boldsymbol{W}$ is k-normal at $\boldsymbol{P} \times \boldsymbol{Q}$ if and only if $\boldsymbol{V}$ is k-normal at $\boldsymbol{P}$ and $\boldsymbol{W}$ is so at $\boldsymbol{Q}$.*

Assume first that $\boldsymbol{V} \times \boldsymbol{W}$ is k-normal at $\boldsymbol{P} \times \boldsymbol{Q}$, and let $\boldsymbol{M} \times \boldsymbol{N}$ be a generic point of $\boldsymbol{V} \times \boldsymbol{W}$ over $k(\boldsymbol{P}, \boldsymbol{Q})$. Let f be a function on $\boldsymbol{V}$, rational over k and finite at $\boldsymbol{P}$; call F the function on $\boldsymbol{V} \times \boldsymbol{W}$, rational over k, such that $F(\boldsymbol{M}, \boldsymbol{N}) = f(\boldsymbol{M})$; then F is finite at $\boldsymbol{P} \times \boldsymbol{Q}$, hence defined there and therefore also at $\boldsymbol{P} \times \boldsymbol{N}$ (by th. 2 of Chap. VII, §2, or by prop. 15 of Chap. II, §4); by prop. 4 of Chap. VII, §2, this implies that f is defined at $\boldsymbol{P}$, which shows that $\boldsymbol{V}$ is k-normal there. One sees in the same way that $\boldsymbol{W}$ is k-normal at $\boldsymbol{Q}$. To prove the converse, we will first show that if V and W are everywhere k-normal affine varieties, rational over k, then $V \times W$ is everywhere k-normal. In fact, let

(x, y) be a generic point of $V \times W$ over k; by coroll. 2 of prop. 3, our assumption amounts to saying that $k[x]$ and $k[y]$ are integrally closed, and we have to show that $k[x, y]$ is so. Let z be in the integral closure of $k[x, y]$ in $k(x, y)$; then, if we put $K = k(y)$, z is in the integral closure of $K[x]$ in $K(x)$. As K is regular over k, it is separably generated over k, and prop. 1 shows that V is everywhere K-normal; therefore, by coroll. 2 of prop. 3, z is in $K[x]$, so that we can write it as $F(x)$ with F in $K[X]$, hence also as $z = \sum_{i=1}^{m} v_i F_i(x)$, where the v_i are elements of K and the F_i are in $k[X]$; for instance, we can take for the v_i the coefficients of F, and for the F_i monomials in $k[X]$. Among all expressions of this form for z, choose one with the smallest possible number m of terms; then the F_i are linearly independent over k. Interchanging V and W, we see that we can also write z as $z = \sum_j w_j G_j(y)$, with the w_j in $k(x)$ and the G_j in $k[Y]$. If $F_1(x), \cdots, F_m(x), t_1, \cdots, t_s$ is a maximal set, containing all the $F_i(x)$, of linearly independent elements over k among the $F_i(x)$, w_j, we can, in the latter expression for z, replace the w_j by their expressions as linear combinations of the $F_i(x)$, t_h with coefficients in k; this gives for z an expression of the form $z = \sum_i F_i(x) G'_i(y) + \sum_h t_h G''_h(y)$, where the G'_i, G''_h are in $k[Y]$. Comparing this with the earlier expression for z, and using the fact that $k(x)$ and $k(y)$ are linearly disjoint over k, we see that all the $G''_h(y)$ must be 0 and that $v_i = G'_i(y)$ for all i, so that z is in $k[x, y]$. This proves that $V \times W$ is everywhere k-normal. Now take the case of two affine varieties V, W, rational over k, such that V is k-normal at a point (x') and W at a point (y'). By the corollary of prop. 4, the integral closure of $k[x]$ in $k(x)$ can be written as $k[z]$, where (z) is a point in an affine space; then (z) has a locus Z over k, which, by coroll. 2 of prop. 3, is everywhere k-normal, and we have $k[x] \subset k[z]$, $k(x) = k(z)$, so that we can write $(x) = p(z)$, where p is a birational morphism of Z into V; moreover, in view of prop. 3 and of the k-normality of V at (x'), p^{-1} is biregular at (x'). As k-normality is a property of local character, we may now, in proving that $V \times W$ is k-normal at (x', y'), replace V and (x') by Z and $p^{-1}(x')$; if we do the same for W and (y'), we see that our assertion follows at once from what we have proved above. Again because of the local character of our proposition, this completes our proof.

Let now $\boldsymbol{V}$ be any variety, rational over a field k. Let $\boldsymbol{W}$ be a variety, rational over k, and let p be a morphism of $\boldsymbol{W}$ into $\boldsymbol{V}$, also rational over k. We will say that the pair $(\boldsymbol{W}, p)$, or the variety $\boldsymbol{W}$ together with the morphism p, constitutes a *k-normal cover of* $\boldsymbol{V}$ if the following conditions are satisfied: (a) *$\boldsymbol{W}$ is everywhere k-normal*; (b) *$\boldsymbol{V}$ and $\boldsymbol{W}$ have the same dimension, and the geometric image of $\boldsymbol{W}$ by p is $\boldsymbol{V}$*; (c) *the graph $\boldsymbol{\Gamma}_p$ of p is everywhere complete over $\boldsymbol{V}$*; (d) *if $\boldsymbol{V}'$ is any k-open subset of $\boldsymbol{V}$, k-isomorphic to an affine variety, then the set-theoretic inverse image of $\boldsymbol{V}'$ under p is a k-open subset $\boldsymbol{W}'$ of $\boldsymbol{W}$, k-isomorphic to an affine variety.* We will call p the *canonical projection* of the k-normal cover $\boldsymbol{W}$ of $\boldsymbol{V}$ into $\boldsymbol{V}$.

If $\boldsymbol{V}$ is a complete variety, so is every k-normal cover of $\boldsymbol{V}$, by condition (c). If $(\boldsymbol{W}, p)$ is a k-normal cover of a variety $\boldsymbol{V}$, and if $\boldsymbol{V}'$ is any non-empty k-open subset of V, then, by th. 2 of Chap. VII, §2, the set-theoretic inverse image of V' under p is a non-empty k-open subset W' of W, and our definition shows at once that W', together with the mapping p' of W' into V' induced by p (i.e. whose graph is the restriction of the graph of p to $W' \times V'$), is a k-normal cover of V'; this will be called *the restriction of W to V'*; we also say that W' is *induced over V' by W*. A variety V, with the identity mapping of V onto itself, is a k-normal cover of itself if and only if it is everywhere k-normal.

PROPOSITION 6. *Let V be a variety, rational over a field k; let (W, p) be a k-normal cover of V. Let K be a field containing k; let U be a variety, rational over K; let f be a mapping of U into W, rational over K, such that the geometric image of U by f is W. Then f is defined at every point of U at which $p \circ f$ is defined and U is K-normal. In particular, if U is everywhere K-normal and $p \circ f$ is a morphism, then f is a morphism.*

Let P be a point of U where U is K-normal and where the mapping $g = p \circ f$ is defined; let V' be a k-open subset of V, containing $g(P)$ and k-isomorphic to an affine variety; let W' be the set-theoretic inverse image of V' under p, which, by condition (d) of the definition of a k-normal cover, is k-isomorphic to an affine variety. Let f' be the mapping of U into W' whose graph is the restriction of the graph of f to $U \times W'$; f is defined at P if f' is so. It is therefore enough to prove our proposition in the case when V, W are affine varieties. Let M be a generic point of U over K; then, by our assumption on f, the point $(w) = f(M)$ is generic on W over K, so that, by condition (b) of the definition of a k-normal cover, the point $(x) = p(w)$ is generic on V over K. Condition (c) of the definition of a k-normal cover means here that (w) is finite over every finite specialization of (x) with reference to k, so that, by prop. 3, all the w_j are integral over $k[x]$. To say that $p \circ f$ is defined at a point P of U is to say that all the x_i are in the specialization-ring of P in $K(M)$; when that is so, all the w_j are integral over that ring; if U is K-normal at P, this implies that the w_j are in that ring, which means that f is defined at P.

PROPOSITION 7. *Let V, V' be two affine varieties, f a coherent birational mapping of V into V', and k a field of rationality for V, V' and f. Let (x) be a generic point of V over k; put $(x') = f(x)$. Let K be an algebraic extension of $k(x)$, regular over k; let $k[w]$, $k[w']$ be the integral closures of $k[x]$ and of $k[x']$, respectively, in K; let W, W' be the loci of (w) and of (w') over k. Then there is a coherent birational mapping g of W into W', rational over k, such that $(w') = g(w)$.*

We first observe that, by the corollary of prop. 4, the integral closures of $k[x]$, $k[x']$ in K are finitely generated rings over k, which is why we may write them as $k[w]$, $k[w']$; also, by prop. 4, we have $k(w) = k(w') = K$, and this, in view of the assumption on K, shows that (w), (w') have loci W, W' over k and that we may write $(w') = g(w)$, where g is a birational mapping of W into W'; all we have now to show is that g is coherent. As we have $k[x] \subset k[w]$, $k[x'] \subset k[w']$, we may write $(x) = p(w)$, $(x') = p'(w')$, where p, p' are morphisms of W into V and of W' into V'. We have $f \circ p = p' \circ g$, since these two mappings of W into V' are rational over k and map (w) onto (x'). Now let $(\bar{w}, \bar{w}')$ be any point in the graph of g, and put $(\bar{x}) = p(\bar{w})$, $(\bar{x}') = p'(\bar{w}')$; then $(\bar{x}, \bar{x}')$ is the uniquely determined specialization of (x, x') over $(w, w') \rightarrow (\bar{w}, \bar{w}')$ with reference to k and is therefore a point in the graph of f; as f is coherent, it is then defined at $(\bar{x})$, so that $f \circ p$ is defined at $(\bar{w})$. This is the same as to say that $p' \circ g$ is defined at $(\bar{w})$; as W is everywhere k-normal by coroll. 2 of prop. 3, this, by prop. 6, implies that g is defined at $(\bar{w})$. One shows in the same manner that g^{-1} is defined at $(\bar{w}')$. This proves our proposition.

THEOREM 1. *Let* $\boldsymbol{V}$ *be a variety, rational over a field* k; *let* $\boldsymbol{M}$ *be a generic point of* $\boldsymbol{V}$ *over* k, *and let* $k(w)$ *be an algebraic extension of* $k(\boldsymbol{M})$, *regular over* k. *Then there is a* k-*normal cover* $\boldsymbol{W}$ *of* $\boldsymbol{V}$, *with the canonical projection* p *onto* $\boldsymbol{V}$ *and a generic point* $\boldsymbol{N}$ *over* k, *such that* $\boldsymbol{M} = p(\boldsymbol{N})$ *and* $k(\boldsymbol{N}) = k(w)$; *and* $\boldsymbol{W}$, p *and* $\boldsymbol{N}$ *are uniquely determined up to a* k-*isomorphism.*

Put $\boldsymbol{V} = [V_\alpha, f_{\beta\alpha}]_{\alpha,\beta\in A}$; let (x_α) be the representative of $\boldsymbol{M}$ in V_α; let (w_α) be such that $k[w_\alpha]$ is the integral closure of $k[x_\alpha]$ in $k(w)$; let W_α be the locus of (w_α) over k, and let $g_{\beta\alpha}$ be the birational mapping of W_α into W_β, rational over k, such that $(w_\beta) = g_{\beta\alpha}(w_\alpha)$. This is obviously a consistent set of birational mappings between the W_α; prop. 7 shows that they are coherent; therefore they define a variety $\boldsymbol{W} = [W_\alpha, g_{\beta\alpha}]_{\alpha,\beta\in A}$. Also, if $\boldsymbol{N}$ is the generic point of $\boldsymbol{W}$ over k with the representative (w_α) in W_α for every α, we have $k(\boldsymbol{N}) = k(w)$, and we can write $\boldsymbol{M} = p(\boldsymbol{N})$, where p is a mapping of $\boldsymbol{W}$ into $\boldsymbol{V}$, rational over k. For every α, the mapping p_α of W_α into V_α, rational over k, given by

$$(x_\alpha) = p_\alpha(w_\alpha),$$

is a morphism; therefore p is a morphism. By coroll. 2 of prop. 3, each W_α is everywhere k-normal; the same is therefore true of $\boldsymbol{W}$, so that condition (a) in the definition of a k-normal cover is satisfied. Condition (b) is obviously so. By prop. 3, (w_α) is finite over every finite specialization of (x_α) with reference to k; this is the same as to say that the graph of p_α is complete over every point of V_α; as this is so for every α, it shows that the graph of p is everywhere complete over $\boldsymbol{V}$, so that condition (c) is satisfied. As to condition (d), let f be a k-isomorphism of an affine variety V' onto a k-open subset Ω of $\boldsymbol{V}$; then the point $(x') = f^{-1}(\boldsymbol{M})$ is generic on V' over k. Let (w') be such that $k[w']$ is the integral closure of $k[x']$ in $k(w)$; let W' be the locus of (w') over k; call g the birational mapping of W' into $\boldsymbol{W}$, rational over k, such that $\boldsymbol{N} = g(w')$; we will verify (d) by showing that g is a k-isomorphism of W' onto the set-theoretic inverse image Ω' of Ω under p. In fact, let p' be the morphism of W' into V', rational over k, such that $(x') = p'(w')$; we have $p \circ g = f \circ p'$, since these two mappings of W' into $\boldsymbol{V}$ are rational over k and map (w') onto $\boldsymbol{M}$; as f and p' are morphisms, this shows that $p \circ g$ is a morphism; therefore, by prop. 6, g is a morphism. As $f \circ p'$ maps W' into Ω, and as $p \circ g = f \circ p'$, g maps W' into Ω', so that the graph of g is contained in $W' \times \Omega'$; in order to prove our assertion on g, it will now be enough to show that g^{-1} is everywhere defined on

Ω'. In fact, the definition of Ω' shows at once that $f^{-1} \circ p$ is everywhere defined on Ω'; as we have $f^{-1} \circ p = p' \circ g^{-1}$, the same is therefore true of $p' \circ g^{-1}$, hence also of g^{-1} by prop. 6. This completes the proof of the first assertion in our theorem. Now assume that $\boldsymbol{W}^*$, p^* and $\boldsymbol{N}^*$ satisfy the same conditions as $\boldsymbol{W}$, p and $\boldsymbol{M}$ in our theorem; then there is a birational mapping φ of $\boldsymbol{W}$ into $\boldsymbol{W}^*$, rational over k, such that $\boldsymbol{N}^* = \varphi(\boldsymbol{N})$, and we have

$$p = p^* \circ \varphi, \qquad p^* = p \circ \varphi^{-1};$$

by prop. 6, this shows that φ is an isomorphism of $\boldsymbol{W}$ onto $\boldsymbol{W}^*$.

COROLLARY 1. *Assumptions and notations being as in th.* 1, *assume that* $\boldsymbol{V}$ *is an affine variety; put* $\boldsymbol{M} = (x)$, *and let* $k[y]$ *be the integral closure of* $k[x]$ *in* $k(w)$. *Then one can take for* $\boldsymbol{N}$ *the point* (y), *for* $\boldsymbol{W}$ *the locus of* (y) *over* k, *and for* p *the mapping of* $\boldsymbol{W}$ *into* $\boldsymbol{V}$, *rational over* k, *given by* $(x) = p(y)$.

In fact, by condition (d) of the definition of a k-normal cover, we can take for $\boldsymbol{W}$ an affine variety; then, if we put $\boldsymbol{N} = (y)$, condition (c) shows that (y) is finite over every finite specialization of (x) with reference to k, so that, by prop. 3, $k[y]$ is contained in the integral closure of $k[x]$ in $k(w)$. As p must be a morphism, coroll. 2 of th. 2, Chap. VII, §2, shows that $k[y]$ must contain $k[x]$. By condition (a) and coroll. 2 of prop. 3, $k[y]$ must be integrally closed in $k(y) = k(w)$. In view of coroll. 1 of prop. 3, this proves our assertion.

COROLLARY 2. *Let* $(\boldsymbol{W}, p)$ *be a* k-*normal cover of a variety* $\boldsymbol{V}$. *Then the set-theoretic inverse image of every point of* $\boldsymbol{V}$ *under* p *is a finite point-set.*

By condition (d) of the definition of a k-normal cover and the principle of localization, it is enough to prove this when $\boldsymbol{V}$ and $\boldsymbol{W}$ are affine varieties. In that case, it is an immediate consequence of coroll. 1.

COROLLARY 3. *Let* $\boldsymbol{V}$ *be a variety, rational over* k, *and let* K *be a field containing* k. *Then a* k-*normal cover of* $\boldsymbol{V}$ *is a* K-*normal cover of* $\boldsymbol{V}$ *if and only if it is everywhere* K-*normal.*

Let $\boldsymbol{W}$ be a k-normal cover of $\boldsymbol{V}$, with the projection p onto $\boldsymbol{V}$; by definition, if it is a K-normal cover, it must be everywhere K-normal. In order to prove the converse, let $\boldsymbol{N}$ be a generic point of $\boldsymbol{W}$ over K, and put $\boldsymbol{M} = p(\boldsymbol{N})$. By th. 1, there is a K-normal cover $\boldsymbol{W}^*$ of $\boldsymbol{V}$, with the projection p^* onto $\boldsymbol{V}$ and a generic point $\boldsymbol{N}^*$ over K, such that $\boldsymbol{M} = p^*(\boldsymbol{N}^*)$ and $K(\boldsymbol{N}^*) = K(\boldsymbol{N})$; then there is a birational mapping φ of $\boldsymbol{W}$ into $\boldsymbol{W}^*$, rational over K, such that $\boldsymbol{N}^* = \varphi(\boldsymbol{N})$, and we have $p = p^* \circ \varphi$, $p^* = p \circ \varphi^{-1}$. By prop. 6, φ^{-1} is a morphism; and φ is one if $\boldsymbol{W}$ is everywhere K-normal; therefore, when that is so, φ is a K-isomorphism of $\boldsymbol{W}$ onto $\boldsymbol{W}^*$.

COROLLARY 4. *Let* $\boldsymbol{V}$ *be a variety, rational over* k; *then there is a* k-*normal cover* $\boldsymbol{W}$ *of* $\boldsymbol{V}$ *whose canonical projection* p *onto* $\boldsymbol{V}$ *is a birational mapping of* $\boldsymbol{W}$ *into* $\boldsymbol{V}$; *this is uniquely determined up to a* k-*isomorphism; and the points where* $\boldsymbol{V}$ *is* k-*normal are those where* p^{-1} *is defined.*

By taking $k(w) = k(\boldsymbol{M})$ in th. 1, we get the first two assertions. As p is a morphism, p^{-1} is biregular at every point of $\boldsymbol{V}$ where it is defined; as $\boldsymbol{W}$ is everywhere k-normal, this implies that $\boldsymbol{V}$ is k-normal wherever p^{-1} is defined. Conversely, as $p \circ p^{-1}$ is the identity mapping of $\boldsymbol{V}$ onto itself, prop. 6 shows that p^{-1} is defined wherever $\boldsymbol{V}$ is k-normal.

The variety $\boldsymbol{W}$ defined in coroll. 4 is called the *k-normalization of $\boldsymbol{V}$.*

Corollary 5. *If $\boldsymbol{V}$ is a variety, rational over k, the set of the points where $\boldsymbol{V}$ is k-normal is k-open on $\boldsymbol{V}$.*

This is in fact an immediate consequence of coroll. 4.

We will say that a variety $\boldsymbol{W}$, with a morphism p into a variety $\boldsymbol{V}$, is a *normal cover of $\boldsymbol{V}$* if there is a field of rationality k for $\boldsymbol{V}$, $\boldsymbol{W}$ and p such that $\boldsymbol{W}$, with the projection p, is a K-normal cover of $\boldsymbol{V}$ for every field K containing k. By coroll. 3 of th. 1, this is so if and only if $\boldsymbol{W}$ is a k-normal cover of $\boldsymbol{V}$ and is everywhere normal; such is the case, by coroll. 1 of prop. 1, if k is perfect and $\boldsymbol{W}$ is a k-normal cover of $\boldsymbol{V}$. For instance, if $\boldsymbol{V}$ is a variety, and k is a perfect field of rationality for $\boldsymbol{V}$, the k-normalization of $\boldsymbol{V}$ is also the K-normalization of $\boldsymbol{V}$ for every field K containing k; this can be characterized, up to an isomorphism, as the normal cover of $\boldsymbol{V}$ whose canonical projection onto $\boldsymbol{V}$ is a birational mapping; it is called *the normalization of $\boldsymbol{V}$.*

As an application of the normalization process, we can now prove the following:

Theorem 2. *Let V be a k-normal affine variety, rational over k. Then V is k-isomorphic to a k-open subset of an everywhere k-normal complete variety.*

Let S^n be the ambient space for V. If the representative $D_1 = S^1$ of the projective line $\boldsymbol{D}$ is identified in the usual manner with its image $\boldsymbol{D} - \{\infty\}$ in $\boldsymbol{D}$, we obtain an identification of $S^n = S^1 \times \cdots \times S^1$ with the open subset of $\boldsymbol{D} \times \cdots \times \boldsymbol{D}$ consisting of all the points $(z_1, \cdots, z_n)$ of that product whose coordinates are all finite. We may then consider V as a subvariety of that open subset. Let M be a generic point of V over k; let $\bar{V}$ be the locus of M over k in $\boldsymbol{D} \times \cdots \times \boldsymbol{D}$; this is the closure of V in $\boldsymbol{D} \times \cdots \times \boldsymbol{D}$, and V is its restriction to S^n. Now let $\boldsymbol{W}$ be the k-normalization of $\bar{V}$, with the projection p onto $\bar{V}$; this is a complete and everywhere k-normal variety, since $\boldsymbol{D} \times \cdots \times \boldsymbol{D}$, hence also $\bar{V}$, are complete. Let Ω be the set-theoretic inverse image, under p, of the k-open subset V of $\bar{V}$; let f be the mapping of Ω into V whose graph is the restriction of the graph of p to $\Omega \times V$; as p is a morphism, f is one; as p^{-1} is everywhere defined on V, by coroll. 4 of th. 1, f^{-1} is a morphism; therefore f is an isomorphism of Ω onto V.

Corollary 1. *Let $\boldsymbol{V}$ be a variety, rational over k; then there is a birational mapping, rational over k, of $\boldsymbol{V}$ into a complete and everywhere k-normal variety.*

Let V_α be any representative of $\boldsymbol{V}$, and let W_α be the k-normalization of V_α; $\boldsymbol{V}$ is birationally equivalent, over k, to V_α, hence also to W_α, and therefore, by th. 2, to a k-open subset of an everywhere k-normal complete variety $\boldsymbol{W}$; this implies that V is birationally equivalent to W. One should observe that, if k is perfect, W is then everywhere normal and therefore has no multiple subvariety of codimension 1, by the corollary of prop. 2.

COROLLARY 2. *Every curve, rational over a perfect field k, is birationally equivalent over k to a complete non-singular curve, which is uniquely determined up to a k-isomorphism.*

The first assertion is contained in coroll. 1 and the remark we have just made. As to the unicity, prop. 2 of Chap. IX, §1, shows that every mapping of a non-singular curve into a complete non-singular curve is a morphism; therefore a birational mapping of a complete non-singular curve into another one is an isomorphism. The example of the curve $X_1^p - X_2^2 - a = 0$, over a field k of characteristic $p > 2$ such that $a^{1/p}$ is not in k, shows that the first assertion in our corollary need not be true when k is not perfect.

The result contained in the next corollary is due to Rosenlicht.

COROLLARY 3. *Let V be a variety, and P a simple point of V; let $G(V, P)$ be the set of the functions f on V such that* $\operatorname{div}(f) = 0$ *and* $f(P) = 1$. *Then $G(V, P)$ is a finitely generated multiplicative group.*

If we apply th. 1 of Chap. IX, §2, to the open set of the simple points on V, we see that a function f on V, such that $\operatorname{div}(f) = 0$, is defined, finite and not zero, at every simple point of V; in particular, $f(P)$ is then defined, $\neq \infty$ and $\neq 0$. By th. 2 of Chap. IX, §2, $G(V, P)$ is a group under multiplication. Now let V' be an open subset of V, containing P; as every function in $G(V, P)$ induces on V' a function belonging to $G(V', P)$, we can identify $G(V, P)$ with a subgroup of $G(V', P)$, so that it is enough to show that the latter group, for a suitable choice of V', is finitely generated. Thus, by taking for V' the set of the simple points of V, we see that it is enough to prove our assertion for a variety V without multiple points. Taking then for V' an open subset of V, isomorphic to an affine variety, we see that it is enough to prove our assertion for an affine variety without multiple points. Let k be a perfect field of rationality for such a variety V; by th. 2, we may identify V with an open subset of an everywhere k-normal complete variety W; then, by coroll. 1 of prop. 1 and the corollary of prop. 2, W has no multiple subvariety of codimension 1. Call G' the group consisting of the functions f on W such that $f(P) = 1$ and that the restriction of $\operatorname{div}(f)$ to V is 0; $G(V, P)$ consists of the restrictions to V of the functions belonging to G' and is therefore isomorphic to G'. Let $A_1, \cdots, A_m$ be all the distinct components of the closed subset $W - V$ on W which have the codimension 1 on W. By th. 2 of Chap. IX, §2, the mapping $f \to \operatorname{div}(f)$ is a homomorphism of G' into the (additively written) free abelian group generated by $A_1, \cdots, A_m$; by coroll. 3 of th. 1, Chap. IX, §2, the kernel of that homomorphism contains only the constant 1; therefore G' is isomorphic to a subgroup of a free abelian group with m generators; this proves that it is finitely generated.

Another important application of the normalization process is contained in the following theorem:

THEOREM 3. *Let X be a divisor on a complete variety U without multiple subvarieties of codimension* 1. *Then the space* $\mathfrak{L}(X)$ *of the functions f on U such that* $\operatorname{div}(f) \succ -X$ *has a finite dimension over the field of constants.*

We use induction on the dimension n of U, and therefore assume our assertion to be true for varieties of dimension $n - 1$. If $X = X' - X''$, where X', X'' are positive divisors, $\mathfrak{L}(X)$ is contained in $\mathfrak{L}(X')$; therefore it is enough to consider the case when X is positive. Put $X = \sum_i a_i V_i$, where the V_i are the components of X, and $a = \sum_i a_i$; we use induction on a, since for $a = 0$ our assertion is contained in coroll. 3 of th. 1, Chap. IX, §2; therefore we may assume that $\mathfrak{L}(X - V_1)$ has a finite dimension, so that it is enough to show that $\mathfrak{L}(X - V_1)$ has a finite codimension in $\mathfrak{L}(X)$. By th. 6 of Chap. IX, §4, there is a function g on U such that V_1 is not a component of $\operatorname{div}(g) - V_1$; put $X' = X - a_1 \operatorname{div}(g)$; then V_1 is not a component of X'; also, the mapping $f \to g^{a_1} f$ maps the vector-space $\mathfrak{L}(X)$, over the field of constants, isomorphically onto the vector-space $\mathfrak{L}(X')$, and maps $\mathfrak{L}(X - V_1)$ onto $\mathfrak{L}(X' - V_1)$, so that it is enough to show that $\mathfrak{L}(X' - V_1)$ has a finite codimension in $\mathfrak{L}(X')$.

Changing notations, we see that it is enough for us to prove the following: let X be any divisor on U; let V be a subvariety of U of codimension 1 which is not a component of X; then $\mathfrak{L}(X - V)$ has a finite codimension in $\mathfrak{L}(X)$. If f is in $\mathfrak{L}(X)$, then, since V is not a component of X, we have $v_V(f) \geqq 0$, so that, by coroll. 2 of th. 1, Chap. IX, §2, f induces on V a function f_V; the mapping $f \to f_V$ is a linear mapping, over the field of constants, of $\mathfrak{L}(X)$ onto a subspace $\mathfrak{L}'$ of the field of functions on V. The kernel of that mapping consists of the functions f in $\mathfrak{L}(X)$ which induce on V the constant 0, i.e., by coroll. 2 of th. 1, Chap. IX, §2, those for which $v_V(f) > 0$; therefore this kernel is $\mathfrak{L}(X - V)$, so that the codimension of $\mathfrak{L}(X - V)$ in $\mathfrak{L}(X)$ is equal to the dimension of $\mathfrak{L}'$. Now let W be the normalization of V, and let p be its canonical projection onto V; as V is complete, W is so, and, as W is everywhere normal, it has no multiple subvariety of codimension 1, by the corollary of prop. 2; therefore, by the induction assumption, our theorem is true for W. As p is a birational mapping of W into V, it determines an isomorphism $g \to g \circ p$ of the function-field on V onto the function-field on W; therefore the dimension of $\mathfrak{L}'$ is the same as that of its image $\mathfrak{L}''$ by that isomorphism, which is the set of the functions $f_V \circ p$, for f in $\mathfrak{L}(X)$. In view of the induction assumption, it is now enough for us to show that there is a divisor Y on W, such that $\mathfrak{L}''$ is contained in $\mathfrak{L}(Y)$.

Put $U = [U_\alpha, f_{\beta\alpha}]_{\alpha,\beta \in A}$, and let φ_α be the birational mapping of U_α into U defined as in prop. 16 of Chap. VII, §6, which maps U_α isomorphically onto the open set Ω_α of the points of U which have a representative in U_α. Let X'_α be the image by φ_α^{-1} of the restriction X_α of X to Ω_α. Let B be the set of the elements β of A such that V has a representative V_β in U_β, i.e. such that the restriction V_β of V to Ω_β is not empty; for $\beta \in B$, V_β is not a component of X'_β, so that there is a point P_β in V_β and not in $|X'_\beta|$; then, by th. 9 of Chap. IX, §4, there is a function F_β on U_β, induced on U_β by a polynomial in the ambient space, such that $\operatorname{div}(F_\beta) \succ X'_\beta$ and $F_\beta(P_\beta) \neq 0$. Put $G_\beta = F_\beta \circ \varphi_\beta^{-1}$; the restriction of $\operatorname{div}(G_\beta)$ to Ω_β is then $\succ X_\beta$, and G_β induces on V_β an everywhere finite function Φ_β which is not the constant 0; therefore the function $\Psi_\beta = \Phi_\beta \circ p$ is not 0 and is everywhere finite on the set-theoretic inverse image W_β of V_β under p. Let now f be any function in $\mathfrak{L}(X)$, other than the constant 0; for every $\beta \in B$, the restriction of $\operatorname{div}(f)$ to Ω_β is $\succ -X_\beta$, so that the restriction of $\operatorname{div}(G_\beta f)$ to Ω_β is $\succ 0$; then, by th. 1 of Chap. IX, §2, $G_\beta f$ is everywhere finite on Ω_β, so that $\Phi_\beta f_V$ is everywhere finite on V_β, and $\Psi_\beta \cdot (f_V \circ p)$ is so on W_β. This shows that, if h is any function in $\mathfrak{L}''$, $\Psi_\beta h$ is everywhere finite on W_β for every β; if h is not the constant 0, this implies that the restriction of $\operatorname{div}(\Psi_\beta) + \operatorname{div}(h)$ to W_β is positive. Therefore, if Y is a divisor on W such that $\operatorname{div}(\Psi_\beta) \prec Y$ for every β, the restriction of $\operatorname{div}(h) + Y$ to W_β is positive for every β. As the V_β are a covering of V, the W_β are a covering of W. We have thus shown that $\operatorname{div}(h) \succ -Y$ for every function h in $\mathfrak{L}''$. This completes our proof.

APPENDIX II

CHARACTERIZATION OF THE *i*-SYMBOL BY ITS PROPERTIES

The properties which have been proved for the symbol $i(A \cdot B, C; U)$ defined in Chap. VI are characteristic of this symbol. More precisely, we shall prove here that a symbol $i'(A \cdot B, C; U)$, defined whenever $i(A \cdot B, C; U)$ is defined, and having some of the properties of the latter symbol which will now be stated in detail, must coincide with it.

We assume therefore that (in the algebraic geometry with a given universal domain $\boldsymbol{K}$) we have attached, to every set of four varieties U, A, B, C such that C is a proper component of $A \cap B$ on U, a positive integer $i'(A \cdot B, C; U)$ having the following properties:

(a) Th. 5 of Chap. VI, §2, holds true if i is replaced therein by i'.

(b) Th. 8 of Chap. VI, §3, holds true if i is replaced therein by i'.

(c) If two subvarieties A and B of a variety U are transversal to each other on U at a simple point P of U, and if C is the component of $A \cap B$ which contains P, then we have $i'(A \cdot B, C; U) = 1$.

(d) Notations and assumptions being the same as in th. 12 of Chap. VI, §3, there exists a specialization $(Q'^{(1)}, \cdots, Q'^{(d)})$ of $(Q^{(1)}, \cdots, Q^{(d)})$ over $P \to P'$ with reference to k, in which Q' appears among the $Q'^{(\lambda)}$ a number of times equal to $i'[W \cdot (P' \times V), P' \times Q'; U \times V]$.

Then we shall prove that $i'(A \cdot B, C; U)$ is equal to $i(A \cdot B, C; U)$ whenever these symbols are defined.

In the first place, it follows from (c), and from th. 6 of Chap. VI, §2, that, whenever $i(A \cdot B, C; U)$ is defined and has the value 1, $i'(A \cdot B, C; U)$ is defined and has that same value.

Furthermore, th. 9 and 10 of Chap. VI, §3, hold true if i is replaced therein by i'; for, if their proofs are followed step by step, one sees that these proofs depend only upon results which are independent of the i-symbol, upon the application of th. 5 and 8 of Chap. VI which, by (a) and (b), hold also for the i'-symbol, and upon the fact that certain i-symbols have the value 1, which implies, as we have seen, that the corresponding i'-symbols have that same value.

We shall now prove that, in the special case of the theory of intersections which has been treated in Chap. V, §1, our i'-symbol must coincide with the j-symbol; in other words, we shall prove that our assumptions (a), (b), (c) and (d) imply the following property:

(e) If P is a proper point of intersection of a variety V^r and of a linear variety L^{n-r} in S^n, we have $i'(V \cdot L, P; S^n) = j(V \cdot L, P)$.

In fact, put $\mu = j(V \cdot L, P)$, and $\mu' = i'(V \cdot L, P; S^n)$. Let k be a common field of definition for V and for L; let L be defined over k by a minimal set of linear equations $F_i(X) - v_i = 0$ $(1 \leqq i \leqq r)$, where the $F_i(X)$ are linear forms with coefficients in k; and let $F_{r+1}(X), \cdots, F_n(X)$ be $n - r$ linear forms with coefficients in k, such that the n forms $F_1(X), \cdots, F_n(X)$ are linearly independent. If then (x) is a generic point of S^n over k, and if we put $\bar{x}_h = F_h(x)$ for $1 \leqq h \leqq n$, there is a linear k-isomorphism of S^n onto itself, mapping (x) onto $(\bar{x})$; let $\bar{V}$, $\bar{L}$ and $\bar{P}$ be the images of V, L and P, respectively, by this isomorphism. As we have seen that we may apply th. 10 of Chap. VI, §3, to the i'-symbol, we have $\mu' = i'(\bar{V}\cdot\bar{L}, \bar{P}; S^n)$; as $\bar{L}$ is a linear variety, we have, by prop. 4 of Chap. VI, §1, and by th. 10 of Chap. VI, §3, applied to the i-symbol, $\mu = j(\bar{V}\cdot\bar{L}, \bar{P})$. Put $M' = (v)$; then $\bar{L}$ is the subvariety $M' \times S^{n-r}$ of the space $S^n = S^r \times S^{n-r}$; and $\bar{P}$, being in $\bar{L}$, can be written $\bar{P} = M' \times N'$, with N' in S^{n-r}; we can therefore write $i'(\bar{V}\cdot\bar{L}, \bar{P}; S^n)$, i.e. μ', as

$$i'[\bar{V}\cdot(M' \times S^{n-r}), M' \times N'; S^r \times S^{n-r}];$$

to this we can apply our assumption (d); this shows that, if M is a generic point of S^r over k, $M \times N$ a point in $\bar{V} \cap (M \times S^{n-r})$, and $(N^{(1)}, \cdots, N^{(d)})$ a complete set of conjugates of N over $k(M)$, there is a specialization of the latter set over $M \to M'$ with reference to k, in which N' appears exactly μ' times. If now we apply th. 12 of Chap. VI, §3, to the i-symbol, we see that μ' must therefore be equal to

$$i[\bar{V}\cdot(M' \times S^{n-r}), M' \times N'; S^r \times S^{n-r}],$$

i.e. to $i(\bar{V}\cdot\bar{L}, \bar{P}; S^n)$, i.e. to $\mu = j(\bar{V}\cdot\bar{L}, \bar{P})$ by prop. 4 of Chap. VI, §1.

We shall now make no further use of our assumption (d), and use only (e) in addition to (a), (b), (c) and to the consequences of (a), (b), (c) which have been stated above. In the first place, we extend (e) to the intersection of a variety and of a linear variety of arbitrary dimension in S^n. Let W^{r-s} be a proper component of the intersection of a variety V^r and of a linear variety L^{n-s} in S^n; let k be a common field of definition for V and L; let M^{n-r+s} be a linear variety, defined in S^n by a generic set of $r - s$ linear equations over k; and let P be a point in $W \cap M$. Then, by th. 1 of Chap. V, §1, P is a proper point of intersection of W and M, and a generic point of W over $\bar{k}$. Moreover, P is not contained in any component of $V \cap L$ except W, since every component of $V \cap L$ is defined over $\bar{k}$ and cannot contain P without containing the locus W of P over $\bar{k}$. This implies that P is a component of $V \cap L \cap M$. If now we apply, as we may by assumption (a), th. 5 of Chap. VI, §2, to the proper component P of $V \cap L \cap M$, and to the i'-symbol, we get

$$i'(V\cdot L, W; S^n)\cdot i'(W\cdot M, P; S^n)$$
$$= i'[V\cdot(L \cap M), P; S^n]\cdot i'(L\cdot M, L \cap M; S^n).$$

In both sides of this relation, the second factor is 1, since the corresponding i-symbol has the value 1; as to the first factor in the right-hand side, it is equal to $j[V \cdot (L \cap M), P]$, by (e). By th. 4 of Chap. V, §2, and by the definition of the symbol $j(V \cdot L, W)$, this shows that $i'(V \cdot L, W; S^n) = j(V \cdot L, W)$.

Let now the assumptions and notations be the same as in th. 2 of Chap. VI, §1. By th. 9 of Chap. VI, §3, applied (as we have seen that we may do) to the i'-symbol, we have $i'(A \cdot B, C; U) = i'[(A \times B) \cdot \Delta_U, \Delta_C; U \times U]$. Apply now the same theorem to the intersection in $S^N \times S^N$ of the variety $A \times B$, which is contained in $U \times U$, and of the variety Λ; there is, by th. 1 of Chap. VI, §1, only one component of $(U \times U) \cap \Lambda$ which contains Δ_C, viz., the variety Δ_U; therefore th. 9 of Chap. VI, §3, applied to the i'-symbol as we have just said, shows that $i'[(A \times B) \cdot \Lambda, \Delta_C; S^N \times S^N]$, which, as has been shown above, is equal to $j[(A \times B) \cdot \Lambda, \Delta_C]$, i.e., by definition, to $i(A \cdot B, C; U)$, is equal to the product of the two integers

$$\alpha = i'[(U \times U) \cdot \Lambda, \Delta_U; S^N \times S^N], \quad \beta = i'[(A \times B) \cdot \Delta_U, \Delta_C; U \times U].$$

As we have shown that β is equal to $i'(A \cdot B, C; U)$, this result can be written as $i(A \cdot B, C; U) = \alpha \cdot i'(A \cdot B, C; U)$, where α does not depend upon A, B, C, but only upon U and Λ; applied to the case $A = B = C = U$, this gives $\alpha = 1$, which completes the proof of the identity of the i'-symbol with the i-symbol.

It will be observed that we have thus shown, not only that the i-symbol is uniquely determined by the properties (a), (b), (c) and (d), but also that it is so determined by the properties (a), (b), (c) and (e), or (in view of the definition of the j-symbol) by (a), (b), (c), and by the following property:

(e′) If P is a proper point of intersection of a variety V^r and of a linear variety L^{n-r} in S^n, there is a complete set of intersections of V and of L in which P appears exactly $i'(V \cdot L, P; S^n)$ times.

APPENDIX III

VARIETIES OVER TOPOLOGICAL FIELDS

If V is a variety, rational over a field k, one denotes by V_k the set of the points of V which are rational over k; similarly, if X is any subset of V, one writes $X_k = X \cap V_k$. We will now show that, if k is a topological field, one can derive canonically, from the given topology T on k, a topology on every set V_k, finer than that induced on V_k by the k-topology on V, which will be called the T-topology on V_k.

With the notation we have just explained, $(S^n)_k$ is nothing else than the n-dimensional coordinate space k^n over k; on this we define, as the T-topology, the usual product topology on k^n, derived from the topology T on k; in particular, the T-topology on $(S^1)_k = k$ is T. By the definition of a topological field, if F is any polynomial in $k[X]$, the mapping $(x) \rightarrow F(x)$ of $(S^n)_k$ into $(S^1)_k$, induced on $(S^n)_k$ by the polynomial function F on S^n, is T-continuous; by th. 1 of Chap. VII, §1, this implies that, if X is any k-closed subset of S^n, X_k is T-closed in $(S^n)_k$; we define the T-topology on X_k as that induced by the T-topology on $(S^n)_k$. In particular, if V is a variety in S^n, rational over k, this defines a T-topology on V_k, finer than the one induced by the k-topology on V.

Let now V, W be affine varieties and φ a mapping of V into W, all these being rational over k; if V' is the k-open subset of V where φ is defined, V'_k is a T-open subset of V_k, and φ induces on V'_k a mapping φ_k of V'_k into W_k; we will now show that φ_k is T-continuous. In fact, let (x) be a generic point of V over k, and put

$$\varphi(x) = (\varphi_1(x), \cdots, \varphi_m(x)),$$

where m is the dimension of the ambient space for W. If (x') is any point of V where φ is defined, we can write $\varphi_i(x) = F_i(x)/G(x)$ for $1 \leqq i \leqq m$, where the F_i and G are in $k[X]$ and $G(x') \neq 0$. Let V'' be the k-open subset of V where $G \neq 0$; then we have $\varphi_i(x'') = F_i(x'')/G(x'')$ for all i whenever (x'') is in V''. Therefore the mapping φ_k is continuous on V''_k, which is a T-neighborhood of (x') if we have taken (x') in V'_k. This proves our assertion.

In particular, if φ is a birational mapping of V into W, this shows that φ_k is T-bicontinuous at every point of V_k where φ is biregular. If at the same time φ is coherent, and if V', W' are the k-open subsets of V and W where φ and φ^{-1}, respectively, are defined (or, what amounts to the same if φ is coherent, where they are biregular), then φ_k is a T-homeomorphism of V'_k onto W'_k. From this, it follows at once that, if $V = [V_\alpha, f_{\beta\alpha}]_{\alpha,\beta \in A}$ is an abstract variety, rational over k, the equivalence relation between elements of the set-theoretical sum of the varieties V_α which has been used in Chap. VII, §3, in order to define the abstract variety V induces on the set-theoretic sum of the sets $(V_\alpha)_k$ an equivalence relation which is compatible with the T-topology; therefore the T-topology on the $(V_\alpha)_k$ determines a topology, called again the T-topology, on V_k; and, if P is a point of V_k, with a representative P_α on V_α, P has a T-neighborhood on V_k which is T-homeomorphic to $(V_\alpha)_k$. Let now V, W be abstract varieties and φ a mapping of V into W, all these being rational over k; let V' be the subset of V where φ is defined; the principle of localization, combined with what we have seen above, shows at once that φ determines a T-continuous mapping φ_k of V'_k into W_k; in particular, if V and W are k-isomorphic, V_k and W_k are T-homeomorphic. The principle of localization shows also immediately that the T-topology on $(V \times W)_k = V_k \times W_k$ is the product topology of those on V_k and on W_k. If k is a locally compact field and V is any variety, rational over k, the definitions show at once that V_k is locally compact for the T-topology. If at the same time k is not discrete and V is complete, V_k is compact; this will be proved by means of the following lemma:

LEMMA 1. *Let k be a non-discrete locally compact field, and P a monic polynomial in $k[X_1, \cdots, X_n]$. Then there is a compact subset B of k with the following property: if (x) is any set of quantities such that $P(x) = 0$, and (x') is a specialization of (x) over k such that $k(x') = k$, then at least one of the x'_i is in B.*

Let $M(X)$ be the dominating term in $P(X)$, and put

$$Q(Y) = M(Y)P(1/Y_1, \cdots, 1/Y_n);$$

then Q is in $k[Y]$, and we have $Q(0) = 1$; as Q defines a continuous polynomial function on k^n, there is a neighborhood U of 0 in k such that $Q(y) \neq 0$ if all the y_i are in U. Put $U_* = U - \{0\}$, and call B the closure of $k - U_*^{-1}$; it is known that B is compact; we will show that it has the property stated in the lemma. Let (x) and (x') be as above; as 0 is in B, our assertion is true if one of the x'_i is 0. Assume that none of the x'_i is 0; then none of the x_i is 0; we may put $y_i = 1/x_i$ for $1 \leqq i \leqq n$, and we have then $Q(y) = 0$. Put $y'_i = 0$ if $x'_i = \infty$, and $y'_i = 1/x'_i$ otherwise; then (y') is a finite specialization of (y) over k, so that we have $Q(y') = 0$; also, as $k(x') = k$, all the y'_i are in k. Therefore some y'_i must be in $k - U$; then x'_i is in $k - U_*^{-1}$, hence in B.

THEOREM 1. *Let V be a complete variety, rational over a non-discrete locally compact field k. Then V_k is compact for the T-topology defined on it by the given topology T on k.*

The proof will depend upon prop. 8 of Chap. VII, §3, and we shall use the same notations as there. Put $V = [V_\alpha, f_{\beta\alpha}]_{\alpha,\beta\in A}$; call S^{n_α} the ambient space for V_α; let M be a generic point of V over k, and let $(x_{\alpha 1}, \cdots, x_{\alpha n_\alpha})$ be its representative in V_α. By that proposition, there is, for every set $(i) = (i_\alpha)$ of integers such that $1 \leqq i_\alpha \leqq n_\alpha$ for all α, a monic polynomial $P_{(i)}$ in the indeterminates X_α, such that $P_{(i)}(x_{\alpha i_\alpha}) = 0$; to that polynomial, we can then attach a compact subset $B_{(i)}$ of k, with the property stated in lemma 1; let B be the union of all the sets $B_{(i)}$ corresponding to all choices of (i). Let now $\boldsymbol{M}'$ be a point in $\boldsymbol{V}_k$; let A' be the set of the elements α of A such that $\boldsymbol{M}'$ has a representative M'_α in V_α; then, if $(x'_{\alpha i})$ is a specialization over $\boldsymbol{M} \to \boldsymbol{M}'$, with reference to k, of the set $(x_{\alpha i})$ of all the coordinates of all the representatives of $\boldsymbol{M}$, we have, for every α in A', $M'_\alpha = (x'_{\alpha 1}, \cdots, x'_{\alpha n_\alpha})$; and, for every α not in A', at least one of the $x'_{\alpha i}$ is ∞, since otherwise $\boldsymbol{M}'$ would have a representative in V_α. We will now show that, for at least one α in A', all the $x'_{\alpha i}$ are in B. In fact, assume that this is not so; then, for each α in A', we can choose i_α so that $x'_{\alpha i_\alpha}$ is not in B; it is then in $k - B$, since $\boldsymbol{M}'$ and therefore M'_α are rational over k. Also, for each α not in A', we can choose i_α so that $x'_{\alpha i_\alpha} = \infty$. Then the set $(x'_{\alpha i_\alpha})$ is a specialization over k of the set $(x_{\alpha i_\alpha})$ for which we have $P_{(i)}(x_{\alpha i_\alpha}) = 0$; all the $x'_{\alpha i_\alpha}$ are either ∞ or in $k - B$; this contradicts the definition of B. We have thus shown that, if for every α we denote by $B_\alpha = V_\alpha \cap B^{n_\alpha}$ the set of the points of V_α whose coordinates are all in B, every point of $\boldsymbol{V}_k$ has a representative in at least one of the sets B_α. For the T-topology, every B_α is obviously compact, and is homeomorphic to the set of the points of $\boldsymbol{V}$ which have a representative in it. Thus $\boldsymbol{V}_k$ is the union of finitely many compact subsets.

Using prop. 12 of Chap. VII, §5, instead of prop. 8 of §3 of that chapter, one proves, in a quite similar manner, the following more general result: let $\boldsymbol{A}$ be a subvariety of $\boldsymbol{U} \times \boldsymbol{V}$ with the geometric projection $\boldsymbol{U}$ on $\boldsymbol{U}$; assume that $\boldsymbol{U}$, $\boldsymbol{V}$, $\boldsymbol{A}$ are rational over the non-discrete locally compact field k, and that $\boldsymbol{A}$ is everywhere complete over $\boldsymbol{U}$; then, if $\boldsymbol{X}$ is any compact subset of $\boldsymbol{U}_k$, the intersection of $\boldsymbol{A}_k$ with $\boldsymbol{X} \times \boldsymbol{V}_k$ is compact. In particular, if φ is a proper morphism of $\boldsymbol{U}$ into $\boldsymbol{V}$, all these being rational over k, φ_k is a proper mapping of $\boldsymbol{U}_k$ into $\boldsymbol{V}_k$ in the sense of the T-topologies.

We now want to show that, if k is a complete valued field, and $\boldsymbol{V}$ is a variety without multiple points, rational over k, one can derive canonically, from the given structure on $\boldsymbol{V}$, a structure of k-analytic variety on $\boldsymbol{V}_k$. This will be an immediate consequence of the following general result, which is valid over arbitrary fields:

PROPOSITION 1. *Let k be a field; let Z be the k-closed set determined in S^n by the equations $F_1 = \cdots = F_m = 0$, where the F_i are polynomials in $k[X]$; let (a) be a point of Z such that the matrix $\| \partial F_\mu / \partial a_i \|$ has the rank m. Then (a) is contained in one and only one component V of Z; V has the dimension $n - m$, is rational over a separably algebraic extension k' of k, and (a) is a simple point of V. Moreover, if K is a field containing k, and if a polynomial F in $K[X]$ is 0 on V, there are polynomials P_μ, Q in $K[X]$ such that $QF = \sum_\mu P_\mu F_\mu$ and that $Q(a) \neq 0$.*

Consider the polynomial functions $F_0 = 0, F_1, \cdots, F_m$ as mappings of S^n into S^1; let $\Gamma_0, \cdots, \Gamma_m$ be their graphs; Γ_μ is defined in S^{n+1} by the equation $X_{n+1} - F_\mu(X_1, \cdots, X_n) = 0$, so that $(a, 0)$ is a simple point of Γ_μ, the tangent linear variety T_μ to Γ_μ at $(a, 0)$ being given by the equation

$$X_{n+1} - \sum_{i=1}^{n} (\partial F_\mu / \partial a_i) \cdot (X_i - a_i) = 0.$$

Our assumption on the rank of the matrix $\| \partial F_\mu / \partial a_i \|$ amounts now to saying that the equations for $T_0, \cdots, T_m$ are linearly independent, so that these varieties have an intersection of dimension $n - m$. By the criterion of multiplicity 1 (th. 6 of Chap. VI, §2), it follows immediately from this, by induction on μ, that, for $0 \leqq \mu \leqq m$, the point $(a, 0)$ is contained in one and only one component of the intersection of the varieties $\Gamma_0, \cdots, \Gamma_\mu$ in S^{n+1}, that this variety has the dimension $n - \mu$, has a simple point at $(a, 0)$, and that it is a component of coefficient 1 in the S^{n+1}-cycle $\Gamma_0 \cdot \Gamma_1 \cdot \cdots \cdot \Gamma_\mu$; moreover, as it is contained in $\Gamma_0 = S^n \times (0)$, it can be written as $V_\mu \times (0)$. As the cycle $\Gamma_0 \cdot \Gamma_1 \cdot \cdots \cdot \Gamma_\mu$ is rational over k, any component of that cycle which has in it the coefficient 1 must have the order of inseparability 1 over k; by th. 8 of Chap. I, §8, and prop. 23 of Chap. I, §7, this is the same as to say that V_μ has a field of definition k_μ which is separably algebraic over k. As the subset

$$\Gamma_0 \cap \Gamma_1 \cap \cdots \cap \Gamma_m$$

of S^{n+1} is obviously the same as $Z \times (0)$, we have thus proved the first part of our proposition, with $V = V_m$ and $k' = k_m$. At the same time, we have shown that $V_{m-1} \times (0)$ and Γ_m are transversal to each other at $(a, 0)$ in S^{n+1} and that $V \times (0)$ is the unique component of their intersection which contains $(a, 0)$. Now we have, by th. 4(iv) and th. 5 of Chap. VIII, §3:

$$\begin{aligned}(V_{m-1} \times (0)) \cdot \Gamma_m &= [(V_{m-1} \times S^1) \cdot (S^n \times (0))] \cdot \Gamma_m \\ &= (V_{m-1} \times S^1) \cdot (\mathrm{div}(F_m) \times (0)) = (V_{m-1} \cdot \mathrm{div}(F_m)) \times (0).\end{aligned}$$

In view of what we have shown above, this proves that V is the only component of $V_{m-1} \cdot \mathrm{div}(F_m)$ containing (a), and that it has the coefficient 1 in that cycle. By th. 3 of Chap IX, §2, V must then be the only component containing (a) in the divisor $\mathrm{div}(f_m)$ of the function f_m induced by F_m on V_{m-1}, and it has the coefficient 1 in that divisor; in other words, (a) is not in the support of the divisor $\mathrm{div}(f_m) - V$ on V_{m-1}. Let j be the injection mapping of V_{m-1} into S^n, so that we have $f_m = F_m \circ j$; let K be a field containing k, and let F be a polynomial in $K[X]$ which is 0 on V and not on V_{m-1}; then the function $f = F \circ j$ induced by F on V_{m-1} is 0 on V and is not the constant 0, so that V is a component of $\mathrm{div}(f)$. In view of what we have proved about $\mathrm{div}(f_m)$, this implies that $v_W(f/f_m) \geqq 0$ for every subvariety W of V_{m-1} of codimension 1, containing (a); therefore, by th. 1 of Chap. IX, §2, f/f_m is defined and finite at (a) so that, if (x) is a generic point of V_{m-1} over $\bar{K}$, we can write the value of f/f_m at (x), which is $F(x)/F_m(x)$, in the form $A(x)/B(x)$, where A and B are in $\bar{K}[X]$ and $B(a) \neq 0$. Then the polynomial $BF - AF_m$ is 0 on V_{m-1}. The same is true if F is 0 on V_{m-1}, provided we take $B = 1$ and $A = 0$. Now we can prove the second part of our proposition by induction on m. For $m = 0$ there is nothing to prove; for $m \geqq 1$, we can apply the induction assumption to the polynomial $BF - AF_m$ which has just been constructed. This shows that there are polynomials P'_μ, Q' in $\bar{K}[X]$, such that $Q'F = \sum_\mu P'_\mu F_\mu$ and $Q'(a) \neq 0$.

Now let the c_λ be a maximal set of linearly independent elements over K among the coefficients of the polynomials P'_μ, Q'; then we can write

$$P'_\mu = \sum_\lambda c_\lambda P_{\lambda\mu}, \qquad Q' = \sum_\lambda c_\lambda Q_\lambda,$$

where the $P_{\lambda\mu}$, Q_λ are in $K[X]$; and we must have $Q_\lambda F = \sum_\mu P_{\lambda\mu} F_\mu$ for every λ. As the $Q_\lambda(a)$ cannot all be 0, this completes our proof. Incidentally, for $m = n$ and $0 \leqq \mu \leqq n - 1$, our proof shows that every function on V_μ which is 0 at (a) can be written, on V_μ, in the form $\sum_{\nu=\mu+1}^{n} f_\nu g_\nu$, where the f_ν, for $\mu + 1 \leqq \nu \leqq n$, are the functions induced on V_μ by the F_ν, and where the g_ν are functions on V_μ, defined and finite at (a). In the language of the theory of local rings, we have thus shown that the specialization-ring of a simple point on any variety is a "regular local ring".

COROLLARY. *Every variety without multiple points, rational over a field k, is k-isomorphic to a variety* $V = [V_\alpha, f_{\beta\alpha}]_{\alpha,\beta\in A}$ *such that every one of the* V_α *has the following properties: if n is the dimension of* V, *and* N_α *is the dimension of the ambient space for* V_α, *the ideal defining* V_α *over k is generated by* $N_\alpha - n$ *polynomials; and* $(X_{\alpha 1}, \cdots, X_{\alpha n})$ *is a uniformizing set of linear forms for* V_α *at all points of* V_α.

It is obviously enough to show that the set of the simple points on any affine variety W^n, rational over k, has a covering by k-open subsets, each of which is k-isomorphic to a variety V with the properties stated in our corollary, or in other words that each simple point (a) of W is contained in such a set. Let S^N be the ambient space for W; as (a) is simple on W, we can find, in the ideal defining W over k, $N - n$ polynomials $F_1, \cdots, F_{N-n}$ such that the matrix $\| \partial F_\nu/\partial a_i \|$ has the rank $N - n$; after reordering the coordinates if necessary, we may then assume that the determinant $\Delta(X)$ of the matrix $\| \partial F_\nu/\partial X_i \|$ for $1 \leqq \nu \leqq N - n$, $n + 1 \leqq i \leqq N$, is not 0 at (a). Let $\Phi_1, \cdots, \Phi_m$ be a basis for the ideal defining W over k; by prop. 1, we can find polynomials $P_{\mu\nu}$, Q in $k[X]$ such that $Q(a) \neq 0$ and $Q\Phi_\mu = \sum_\nu P_{\mu\nu} F_\nu$ for $1 \leqq \mu \leqq m$. Let Ω be the k-open subset of S^N where ΔQ is not 0; let (x) be a generic point of W over k, and let V be the locus of the point $(x, 1/\Delta(x)Q(x))$ over k in S^{N+1}; V is k-isomorphic to the k-open subset $W \cap \Omega$ of W, which contains (a); our proof will be complete if we show that V has the properties stated above. Denote by $(X_1, \cdots, X_N, Y)$ the indeterminates for S^{N+1}. The ideal defining V over k contains the polynomials $F_\nu(X)$ and the polynomial

$$F_0(X, Y) = \Delta(X)Q(X)Y - 1;$$

therefore, if (x', y') is any point of V, we have $\Delta(x') \neq 0$ and $Q(x') \neq 0$. As the determinant of the matrix

$$\| \partial F_\nu/\partial X_i \quad \partial F_\nu/\partial Y \|_{(0\leqq\nu\leqq N-n;\, n+1\leqq i\leqq N)}$$

is $\pm \Delta(X)^2 Q(X)$, we see that $X_1, \cdots, X_n$ is a uniformizing set of linear forms for V at every point of V. Now let G be a polynomial in $k[X, Y]$; write it as

$$G(X, Y) = A_0(X)Y^d + A_1(X)Y^{d-1} + \cdots + A_d(X),$$

where the A_h are in $k[X]$; and put

$$H(X) = \sum_{h=0}^{d} A_h\Delta^h Q^h.$$

As we have $\Delta(X)Q(X)Y \equiv 1 \bmod. F_0$, we have also $\Delta(X)^hQ(X)^hY^h \equiv 1 \bmod. F_0$ for every $h \geqq 0$, and therefore $(\Delta Q)^dG \equiv H$ and $G \equiv Y^dH \bmod. F_0$; this implies that G is 0 on V if and only if H is 0 on W. Assume now that this is so; then H can be expressed as a linear combination of the Φ_μ, with coefficients in $k[X]$; in view of the definition of Q, this implies that QH is in the ideal generated by $F_1, \cdots, F_{N-n}$. As we have

$$G \equiv (\Delta QY)Y^dH \equiv \Delta Y^{d+1}\cdot QH \quad \bmod. F_0,$$

we have thus shown that G is in the ideal generated by $F_0, F_1, \cdots, F_{N-n}$ in $k[X, Y]$. This completes our proof.

Now we come back to the case when k is a complete valued field. Let A be the given structure on k, and T the topology induced by A on k. Let V^n be a variety in S^N, rational over k; let $\mathfrak{P}$ be the ideal defining V over k; let (a) be a point of V_k, simple on V, and let $F_1, \cdots, F_{N-n}$ be polynomials in $\mathfrak{P}$, such that the matrix $\| \partial F_\nu/\partial a_i \|$ has the rank $N - n$. Just as in the proof of the corollary of prop. 1, and with the same notations as there, we may assume that the coordinates in S^N have been so reordered that $\Delta(a) \neq 0$; let Q and Ω be defined as in that proof. If all the F_ν are 0 at a point of Ω, then, since Q is not 0 there, all the Φ_μ must be 0 at that point, so that it is in V; this shows that $V \cap \Omega$ is the subset of Ω defined by the equations $F_1 = 0, \cdots, F_{N-n} = 0$. Now Ω_k is a T-open subset of the space $(S^N)_k = k^N$, hence a T-neighborhood of (a) in that space. It is now clear that, if we provide Ω_k with the k-analytic structure induced on it by the obvious one in k^N, the set $V_k \cap \Omega_k$ is a T-closed analytic subvariety of Ω_k, of analytic dimension n over k; this induces on $V_k \cap \Omega_k$ an analytic structure, called its A-structure. More precisely, if we write S^N as $S^n \times S^{N-n}$, our assumptions imply that the projection from S^N to S^n induces on V_k, in some neighborhood of every point of $V_k \cap \Omega_k$, an analytic isomorphism from that neighborhood to its projection on $(S^n)_k$.

This shows that, if V' is the set of the simple points on V, the k-analytic structure on k^N induces on V'_k a k-analytic structure of analytic dimension n which we call its A-structure. If φ is a mapping of V into a variety W, W and φ being also rational over k, then the same proof which has been used above to obtain the T-continuity of φ_k shows that φ_k is A-analytic in a neighborhood of every point (a) of V'_k such that $\varphi(a)$ is defined and simple on W. From this, one concludes at once that a k-isomorphism determines an A-isomorphism in the neighborhood of every simple point. By the principle of localization, one can then, in an obvious manner, define an A-structure on V_k if V is any abstract variety without multiple points, rational over k, or (what amounts to the same) on V'_k if V' is the set of simple points on any abstract variety V, rational over k; morphisms which are rational over k determine A-analytic mappings. Any reader interested in expressing these facts in the language of categories and functors will presumably be able to do so.

INDEX OF DEFINITIONS

N.B. All the definitions in the book are listed in this index, except for those in Chap. II, §6 and Chap. III, §§1–3 (which are not used anywhere else than in these §§), those in Chap. X, a few of those in the Appendices, and some of the definitions concerning abstract varieties which are direct consequences of the "principle of localization" of Chap. VII, §§4–5. For each definition, the index gives the Chapter, § and page, thus: IV_2, 75, i.e. Chap. IV, §2, p. 75; a.c. (= abstract case) indicates the definitions concerning abstract varieties; e.g. the entry "Subvariety, IV_1, 69, (a.c.) VII_3, 181" means that the definition of a subvariety of a variety in S^n will be found in Chap. IV, §1, p. 69, while the definition of a subvariety of an abstract variety is to be found in Chap. VII, §3, p. 181. Definitions have usually been italicized in the text (except again for some of those which are consequences of the principle of localization).